The J&P
Switchgear Book

J&P Books

General Editor: C. A. Worth

These two books, published originally by Johnson & Phillips Ltd, have for many years been accepted as standard works of reference by electrical engineers concerned with switchgear and transformers. They now appear under the Newnes-Butterworths imprint with the same team of contributors and editor.

The J&P Switchgear Book

The J&P Transformer Book

The J&P Switchgear Book

AN OUTLINE OF MODERN SWITCHGEAR PRACTICE
FOR THE NON-SPECIALIST USER

R. T. LYTHALL C.Eng.,F.I.E.E.

NEWNES-BUTTERWORTHS
LONDON   -   BOSTON
Sydney - Wellington - Durban - Toronto

The Butterworth Group

United Kingdom	**Butterworth & Co (Publishers) Ltd**	London: 88 Kingsway, WC2B 6AB
Australia	**Butterworths Pty Ltd**	Sydney: 586 Pacific Highway, Chatswood, NSW 2067 Also at Melbourne, Brisbane, Adelaide and Perth
Canada	**Butterworth & Co (Canada) Ltd**	Toronto: 2265 Midland Avenue, Scarborough, Ontario, M1P 4S1
New Zealand	**Butterworths of New Zealand Ltd**	Wellington: T & W Young Building, 77–85 Customhouse Quay, 1, CPO Box 472
South Africa	**Butterworth & Co (South Africa) (Pty) Ltd**	Durban: 152–164 Gale Street
USA	**Butterworth (Publishers) Inc**	Boston: 19 Cummings Park, Woburn, Mass. 01801

First published in 1927 by Johnston & Phillips Ltd
Sixth edition 1963
New impression of sixth edition 1969 by Iliffe Books Ltd
Seventh edition 1972 by Newnes-Butterworths
Revised reprint 1976
Reprinted 1979

© Butterworth & Co (Publishers) Ltd, 1972

All rights reserved. No part of this publication may be reproduced or transmitted in any form
or by any means, including photocopying and recording, without the written permission of
the copyright holder, application for which should be addressed to the Publishers. Such
written permission must also be obtained before any part of this publication is stored in a
retrieval system of any nature.

This book is sold subject to the Standard Conditions of Sale of Net Books and may not be
re-sold in the UK below the net price given by the Publishers in their current price list.

ISBN 0 408 00069 4

Filmset by Filmtype Services Limited, Scarborough, Yorkshire

Printed in England by Hazell Watson & Viney Ltd,
Aylesbury, Bucks

Editor's Foreword

Few technical books can claim so wide an international reputation as the J & P Switchgear Book which is regarded throughout the electrical world as a leading work of reference on modern switchgear practice and design, and an invaluable textbook for both the graduate and the student.

The material was first issued by Johnson & Phillips Ltd. with modest intent in 1925 as a series of pamphlets entitled *Switchgear Abstracts*. The immediate success of these led to the publication of the first edition of the *J & P Switchgear Book* in 1927, with a second edition in 1930, following many requests from engineers concerned with the selection and use of electrical switchgear for a wide variety of both supply and manufacturing industries.

In 1938, Mr. R. T. Lythall completely revised the material to produce the third edition, later adding a second volume to the work. In 1946 he revised both volumes to form the fourth edition which was published within one cover. Subsequent revisions in 1953 and 1963 for the fifth and sixth editions further enhanced the use and value of the book, which by now totalled over 800 pages of technical data and illustrations.

After the integration of J & P into the Delta Group, the switchgear interests of the company, together with those of several other switchgear manufacturers, were acquired by the English Electric Co. Ltd., which, in turn, became part of G.E.C. As the rationalisation of industry progressed, it was at first feared that the mass of valuable information contained in the book would be irretrievably lost. Fortunately, however, Iliffe Books (now a part of the Butterworth Group) were able to take over the copyright and published a revised impression in 1969 to satisfy the large demand for copies of the book that continued to arrive from all parts of the world. At the same time, a preparatory study was undertaken for the revision that was obviously necessary in the light of recent developments.

This, the seventh edition, is the outcome of a study extending over nearly three years, and parts of the work are based on the wealth of material placed at Mr. Lythall's disposal by his many friends in the switchgear manufacturing industry and on cable data made available by B.I.C.C. Ltd. The book contains a mass of up-to-date technical data together with some 750 pictorial illustrations and line drawings. Conversion to the applicable metric and SI units has been undertaken, and in consequence, the whole of the type matter has had to be reset and repaginated.

Every effort has been made to ensure that the information contained in the book is as up-to-date as possible at the time of going to press, and new information and data have been incorporated up to the last possible moment. It is hoped, therefore, that this new edition of the *J & P Switchgear Book* will prove as useful to the engineer as those that have preceded it.

C. A. WORTH,

Editor

Preface to the 7th edition

In the time which has elapsed since the appearance of the 6th edition many significant changes in both design and practice of switchgear have been noted, so much so that practically every chapter in this new edition has either been substantially revised, or in many cases, completely rewritten. Some part of the need for this has been due to the extensive restructuring of the British manufacturing industry, leading, among other things, to the elimination of many designs featured previously. This process has led to the disappearance of the original sponsors of the book, a sponsorship which is recognised by the retention of the original title by which it has become known in so many parts of the world.

Apart from the many descriptive changes found necessary, other factors have contributed to the need for extensive revision, notably the need to bring Chapters 3 and 8 in line with the S.I. system, various changes in switching practice, the growing use of new designs of circuit-breakers, i.e. small-oil-volume, SF_6 and vacuum, and of load breaking switches over a wide high-voltage range up to the highest at present in service.

While British designs and practice are naturally predominant in the text, those of continental Europe have been given notice in several chapters so that a wider picture of the scene has been presented. It must however be pointed out with some emphasis, that the scene can and does change with such rapidity that, in the period of time which must inevitably pass between composition and publication of a book of this size, some of the designs illustrated may well be modified or even superseded.

In the past, the book has been described as presenting an outline of switchgear practice to meet the needs of students and non-specialist users. In the former category young engineers would be included who are starting out on a career in the manufacturing or supply industries, or as works and service engineers. The present edition is similarly directed, but in addition much material of interest to those beyond these categories has now been more fully covered. This has been made possible by confining the contents to a.c. practice and by omitting the appendices which appeared in earlier editions, the subject matter of which is readily obtainable from other sources. In particular, the appendix on maintenance could only be regarded as containing general information, whereas much switchgear today requires more specialised attention and this is described in detail in manufacturers' manuals written specifically for a design.

It is now well over 50 years since the author was himself a beginner in the switchgear industry, and it is fascinating to look back to those early days to contemplate the 'state of the art' then (or even earlier) and to compare it with that of today. Some part of the latter is covered in this book, but access to historical records of the distant past are not readily available to the younger generation and it has therefore been considered appropriate to devote the first chapter to a brief look at the position before World War I, and between it and World War II. It can only be brief, using selected material from the author's personal collection of books, papers and articles of the period, but it is hoped that sufficient has been given to enable the reader to compare the designs, practices and facilities of today with those in existence (or non-existence) earlier in this century.

In preparing this material the author has sought and received permission to reproduce a number of illustrations from published works, acknowledgement to the publishers and others being given both at the place in the text where it is used and in a full list of acknowledgements. Where appropriate, a bibliography of works suitable for further study of the subject matter has been included at the end of a chapter.

Finally, it is important that the reader should recognise that the types and designs of switchgear selected to illustrate the text are indeed only a selection, and many others are available from numerous manufacturers but must be excluded because of space limitations.

R.T.L.

Author's Note

In the switchgear world, the 'state of the art' is always changing. Since 1972 many developments have been noted as will be evident by reference to the literature listed in the extended bibliographies (page 795) prepared for this reprint.

Especially the author would draw attention to the advances made in the manufacture and use of vacuum circuit-breakers, in particular for use on distribution systems up to 24 kV, with interrupting capacities of 25/35 kA. In parallel, the metal-clad housings to accommodate these breakers have been greatly simplified as compared with the established forms for bulk-oil or air-break breakers. Further extension of the voltage and breaking capacity range has already been noted, e.g. 45 kV 50 kA (*Electrical Review* 21/28 December, 1973, page 857).

The development and use of SF_6 metal-clad switchgear for high and extra-high voltages up to 765 kV, with an extension to 1100 kV on the horizon, has made rapid strides. It is now being produced by at least 13 manufacturers throughout the world.

Improved performance and higher interrupting capacities have been significant among developments related to high-voltage air-blast circuit-breakers. In 1972, references to generator breakers for large power stations could only hint as to the future. Today, normal current ratings up to 36 000 A with interrupting capacities of 150/200 kA at 36 kV have been achieved.

Of historical interest, we may note that the Reyrolle range of compound-filled metal-clad switchgear (see pp. 629–630) has, after some 66 years in production, been discontinued.

Similarly, the Brown Boveri air-break circuit-breakers described on pp. 448–451 and 462–464 are no longer in production. They have been superseded by equivalent designs by the Italian company SACE, now a member firm of the Brown Boveri Group.

It is hoped that the foregoing, coupled with the extended bibliography, will enable the reader to be brought as reasonably up-to-date as is possible.

R.T.L.

Acknowledgements

As with all previous editions with which the author has been associated (going back to 1938), valuable assistance has been received from many sources, without which some parts of this new edition could not have been written. To each and every one of these, which are listed below, the author acknowledges his indebtedness, and thanks them all. They are:

Alcan Industries Ltd
Aluminium Federation
Association of Short-circuit Testing Authorities
Benn, Ernest Ltd
Blackie & Son Ltd
British Aluminium Co. Ltd
British Insulated Callender's Cables Ltd
British Standards Institution
Brown Boveri & Co. Ltd
Brush Switchgear Ltd
Copper Development Association
Edgcumbe Peebles Ltd
Electrical Research Association
Ellison, George Ltd
EMP Electric Ltd
English Electric Fusegear Ltd
English Electric Power Transmission Ltd
Fluvent Electric Ltd
GEC Measurements Ltd
GEC Switchgear Ltd
Institution of Electrical Engineers
Long & Crawford Ltd
Lucy, W. and Co. Ltd
Merlin & Gerin Ltd
Nalder Bros. & Thompson Ltd
Permali Ltd
Pitman, Sir Isaac & Sons
Reyrolle, A. & Co. Ltd
Reyrolle Belmos Ltd
Siemens (United Kingdom) Ltd
South Wales Switchgear Ltd
Switchgear & Equipment Ltd
Yorkshire Switchgear and Engineering Ltd

The author's many friends in the switchgear and other manufacturing industries (included in the above tabulation) have, as in the past, provided much helpful data and advice concerning current designs and practices, along with many photographs and line drawings which illustrate the text.

In a number of chapters, references to, and, in some cases, extracts from, British Standards are given, these being:

*BS 88:1967.	Cartridge fuses for voltage ratings up to 660 V.
†BS 89:1954.	Electrical indicating instruments ‡.
*BS 116:1952.	Oil circuit-breakers for a.c. systems.
†BS 142:1966.	Electrical protective relays.
*BS 159:1957.	Busbars and busbar connections.
*†BS 923:1940.	Impulse voltage testing.
*BS 936:1960.	Oil circuit-breakers for medium-voltage a.c. systems.
*BS 2631:1955.	Oil switches for a.c. systems.
†BS 2692:1956.	Fuses for a.c. circuits above 660 V.
*†BS 2914:1957.	Surge diverters for a.c. high-voltage power circuits.
BS 3078:1959.	Isolators (including selectors) for a.c. systems.
*BS 3659:1963.	Heavy-duty air-break circuit-breakers for a.c. systems.
*BS 3938:1965.	Current transformers.
*BS 3941:1965.	Voltage transformers.
BS 3950:1965.	Electrical protective systems for a.c. plant.

Extracts are reproduced from those standards marked* by permission of the British Standards Institution, 2, Park Street, London W1Y 4AA, from whom copies of the complete standards containing the extracted data, or any other standard, can be obtained.

At the date of compiling the foregoing certain British Standards were in the course of revision. These are marked† but during the life of the 7th edition others will undoubtedly be revised or, in some cases, withdrawn when superseded by new Standards. Much of this work of revision is related to alignment with IEC standards or to metrication. When these revisions are published, the data given therein must be assumed to prevail over that noted in this book.

For permission to quote from ASTA No. 27 (interim rules for the application of synthetic testing methods to high-voltage circuit-breakers) in Chapter 5, the author is particularly grateful to The Association of Short-Circuit Testing Authorities.

In order to illustrate some part of the historical background to the present day state of the art, the source of suitable illustrations is mainly from old books and learned papers, published, in some cases, in the early part of this century. Those reproduced for this purpose in Chapter 1 are from such sources, by kind permission of the publishers (Ernest Benn Ltd, Blackie & Son Ltd and Sir Isaac Pitman & Sons Ltd), The Institution of Electrical Engineers and The Electrical Research Association.

‡ BS 89:Part1 : 1970 is now available.

Contents

Chapter 1

Introduction

Because of its vital importance in any switchgear installation, it is not surprising to find that the device used for making and breaking an electrical circuit has loomed large in the recorded history of the industry. Investigations into the problems involved are linked with fundamental research on power arcs, firstly the steady state form and later the transient phenomena. Such research is associated with such names as Sir Humphry Davy, Mrs. Ayrton, Dr. Slepian and many others.

A paper by Harvey[1] describes the works of some 20 or more people who were fascinated by the electric arc and whose work covers a period from about 1805 to the end of that century. Of more practical interest, Harvey records the invention by J. H. Holmes of the quick-break knife-switch[2]. This was perhaps the earliest form of circuit-breaker and Flurscheim[3] records that such switches were 'without any formal arc control other than that provided by the switch attendant who, armed with an insulated hatchet, was invited to chop the arc in two'.

Others have claimed that instead of a hatchet, the attendant used his cap to assist in extinguishing the arc. Be this as it may, the knife-switch had its limitations and Flurscheim goes on to record that 'an unknown inventor adopted the surprising, but as it proved, effective approach of immersing the whole contraption under inflammable transformer oil'. Thus was born the plain-break oil circuit-breaker.

At an early stage, and as the power increased, it was appreciated that a paramount requirement was an ability not only to interrupt load currents, but also those which occurred during a short-circuit when the current could reach a magnitude many times that of full load. Eminent engineers in both the manufacturing and supply industries were frequently drawing attention to this long before any real facilities were dreamed up to enable such ability to be proved. In passing it can be noted that while attention was directed to 'breaking capacity' (known for a long time as 'rupturing capacity') little was noted concerning the no less difficult problems of 'making capacity'.

In what was perhaps the first British book on electrical switchgear[4] carrying the dates 1916 (1st edition) and 1920 (2nd edition), we may note the late Dr. Charles G. Garrard pointing out that:

> 'Having determined what are the conditions of short-circuit or current rupturing to be met with in any particular case, the next point is to choose

a switch suitable for the duty. In the present state of the art, this is a matter of considerable difficulty owing to the lack of explicit information as to the precise maximum breaking capacity of the switches made by several manufacturers. The proper thing would be for each manufacturer to state, along with the voltage and amperage suitable for each switch, also the maximum breaking capacity. While some attempt has been made in this direction, the matter is, as yet, very far from satisfactory'.

He goes on to discuss how Germany had suggested certain standards which related breaking capacity to the size of the breaker, and to the head of oil above its contacts. In a table covering this suggestion, the related voltages were listed as 1 500 to 35 000 V and the breaking capacities ranging up to 6 000 A. This latter value may be remembered later when noting those of today.

In 1918 Dr. Garrard presented a paper to The Institution of Electrical Engineers under the title *Switchgear Standardisation* and in this he again expresses concern with regard to the problems, saying:

'The action of heavy-duty oil switches* is still really very little understood' and that:

'It must be confessed that many ratings of the switches* which are guaranteed by various manufacturers are merely intelligent guesses . . .'

From subsequent sections of this I.E.E. paper it is clear that in so far as European practice was concerned at that time, size was very largely the criterion of breaking capacity and a curve (reproduced here as Fig. 1.1) purports to show

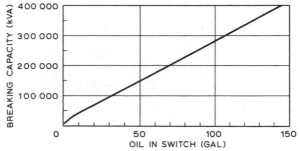

Figure 1.1. Curve relating quantity of oil to breaking capacity of oil circuit-breakers. Circa 1918 (courtesy The Institution of Electrical Engineers)

the connection between this and the quantity of oil. As will be noted later, this relationship was to be disproved by the success of the small-oil-volume circuit-breaker, a design used extensively for many years in countries outside Great Britain. Indeed it was not unknown when Dr. Garrard's book appeared in 1916/1920 because he included an illustration of just such a breaker as an example of American practice. Reproduced here as Fig. 1.2 it is of interest to note that baffle plates were used to cause the oil, under pressure generated by the arc, to flow into the arc, thereby lengthening it so that early interruption occurred.

If we now move on to 1924 it is noted in a book by Coates[5] that:

'The design of oil switches and circuit-breakers from the point of view of current-rupturing capacity is still, to some extent, an art based on experience rather than a precise science' and that:

* Dr. Garrard used the term *oil switches* where today we should say *oil circuit-breakers*.

2

'Empirical formulae have been devised to fix dimensions for switches of certain general types and the breaking capacity ratings determined in this way are closely borne out in tests with large capacity plants. They should be used with the greatest circumspection however by those not skilled in the art and practice of oil circuit-breaker design'.

A major problem in these early days was how a design could be tested to eliminate 'intelligent guesses' or to prove the 'empirical formulae'. In a limited way manufacturers of both alternators and switchgear could make some sort of a check by rigging up a short-circuit on a customer's alternator while on routine tests at the factory, and letting an appropriate circuit-breaker clear (or attempt to clear) the short-circuit. The author recalls witnessing one such test, but at best it was a 'Heath Robinson' affair with none of the essential measuring and oscillographic equipment available to record the performance. Both Dr. Garrard and W. A. Coates note the alternative possibility whereby a supply authority would allow controlled short-circuits to be applied to a suitable section of their network, but quite naturally this was not enthusiastically welcomed by many authorities whose aim was to avoid short-circuits rather than to produce them. Supply authorities were however just as much concerned

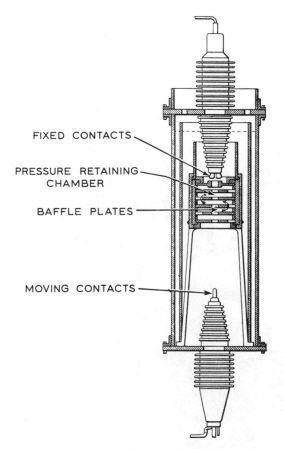

FIXED CONTACTS

PRESSURE RETAINING CHAMBER

BAFFLE PLATES

MOVING CONTACTS

Figure 1.2. Circuit-breaker of American design (courtesy Ernest Benn Ltd.)

as the manufacturers to get evidence of performance and there are records of some who did make plant available for the purpose.

In Dr. Garrard's I.E.E. paper he notes that the firm A.E.G. in Germany had built a special laboratory[6] for the specific purpose of testing oil switches. One senses a feeling of frustration when he goes on to point out that the British Government of that time had, through the then D.S.I.R., encouraged an investigation on the subject of 'switching and arcing' to the extent of a few hundred pounds, while the A.E.G. laboratory would have cost probably one hundred times as much.

What then were the breakers of those days like and about which so much concern was expressed? A typical example is the small breaker shown in Fig. 1.3 employing an extraordinarily flimsy moving contact system which made contact with fixed buttons at the lower ends of the insulators. The latter had corrugated surfaces on the outer ends, the purpose of which was (mistakenly) to give increased electrical clearance to earth. The oil tank of thin sheet metal (facetiously called a *biscuit tin*) was fixed to the flat top plate by four hinged studs with wing nuts.

The operating mechanism was of the simplest hand actuated type not remotely like any present day mechanism. No provision was made to vent the tank but in some designs the tank was spring suspended, so that under the pressure set up during fault clearance, the tank and top plate could part company slightly. No record exists of how much oil was spewed out on such occasions.

Figure 1.3. An early type of oil circuit-breaker

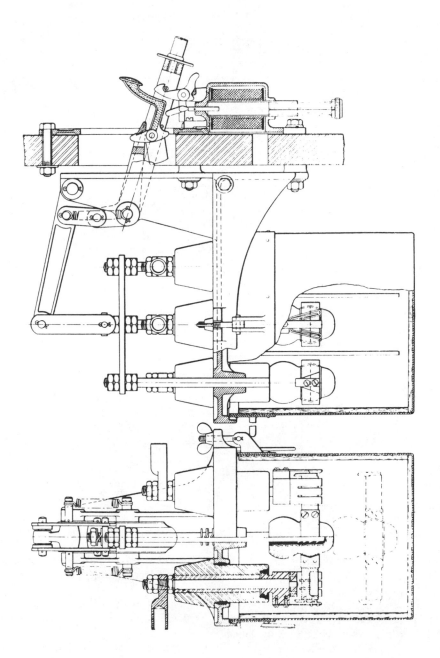

Figure 1.4. 3 300V oil-break switch for panel mounting (courtesy Ernest Benn Ltd.)

5

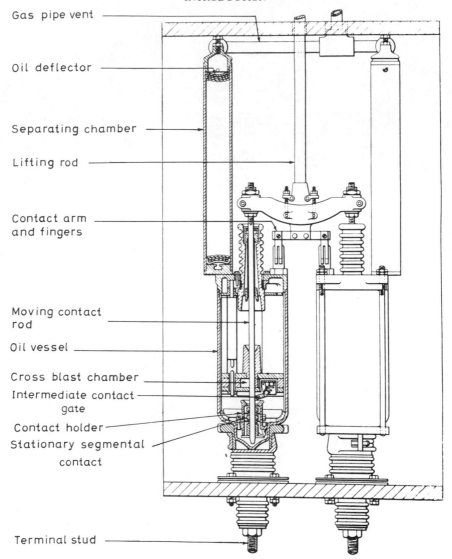

Gas pipe vent

Oil deflector

Separating chamber

Lifting rod

Contact arm
and fingers

Moving contact
rod

Oil vessel

Cross blast chamber

Intermediate contact
gate

Contact holder

Stationary segmental
contact

Terminal stud

Figure 1.5.   Type 'H' oil circuit-breaker by the B.T.H. Co. (courtesy Pitman Ltd.)

On this question of venting, Dr. Garrard records that in 1915 a Commission on High Tension Apparatus set up by the Swiss Electrotechnischer Verein (S.E.V.) reported[7] that:

'... it has been found necessary to have openings in the oil switch tanks to prevent their bursting when internal explosions take place'.

In other words, what we call today *vent pipes*.

From Fig. 1.3 little evidence is visible of any separate arcing contacts, nor is there any in other contemporary designs. Not that such contacts were unknown at this date because Dr. Garrard in his book shows a typical breaker of the period in which they are provided, as noted from Fig. 1.4.

It is of interest to note here a design of a 6 000 A circuit-breaker for service at 1 000 V as produced at that time by Ferranti Ltd.* and illustrated by Garrard[4] on page 55 of his book (1920). In this the main contacts and the arcing contacts are contained in separate oil tanks located one above the other, the lower tank being constructed of corrugated brass and containing the main contact system. In this arrangement the movement of the main contacts is described as relatively

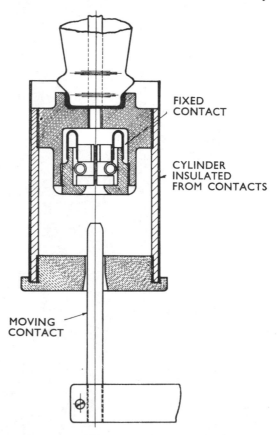

FIXED
CONTACT

CYLINDER
INSULATED
FROM CONTACTS

Figure 1.6.   Early form of explosion pot

MOVING
CONTACT

short and slow, and the arcing contacts, described as a *snapswitch*, have a quick action and a much longer travel. The description goes on to say:

'The breaking capacity is, of course, that of the snapswitch only, but the method adopted for dealing with the very difficult problem of breaking such large alternating currents has much to recommend it and reflects great credit on the designers thereof'.

An example of a small-oil-volume breaker has been given in Fig. 1.2. Another of this type is an early design by the General Electric Co. of America and which was produced in considerable quantity for power station application in Great Britain by the British Thomson-Houston Co. Ltd. (later to become a member firm of Associated Electrical Industries Ltd.). This design was noted by Coates

* In those days, Ferranti Ltd. were manufacturers of switchgear and associated protective apparatus and systems.

7

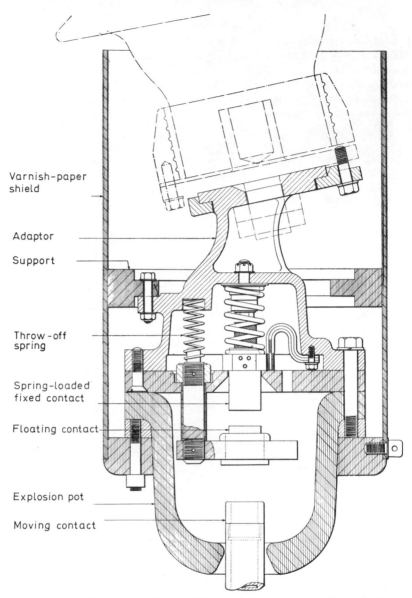

Varnish-paper shield

Adaptor

Support

Throw-off spring

Spring-loaded fixed contact

Floating contact

Explosion pot

Moving contact

Figure 1.7.   Cross-section through oil-blast explosion pot (courtesy Pitman Ltd.)

in his book previously referred to[5] and later (1938) in a book by Coates and Pearce[8] from which Fig. 1.5 is reproduced. This shows one phase only of a three-phase unit. The breaker is shown in the closed position so that to open, a vertical lift is necessary and the arc is drawn upwards as against the more usual reverse practice. Separate main contacts were employed outside the oil tank although later these were dispensed with. Two breaks per phase were used, but as we shall note later, small-oil-volume breakers of today are generally based on a single break, except at the highest voltages.

Apart from the designs noted in Figs. 1.2 and 1.5 developments in this country in the 1920s were largely concentrated on plain-break types of circuit-breaker, i.e. breakers without any special feature for controlling the arc. Within their limitations, designs reached a high level of reliability and it is of interest to note that in the medium voltage range (400 to 600 V), this type is still in use for relatively simple industrial applications where the prospective fault level and severity of duty is low. At higher voltages however, research was indicating that vastly improved performance, particularly consistent performance, could be achieved when devices to control the arc were fitted at each break.

An early form of such a device was known as an *explosion pot* shown typically in Fig. 1.6. The 'pot' comprised a strong shell which totally enclosed the arcing area at the contacts while the moving contact rod passed through a close-fitting throat at the lower end of the pot. The gas generated by the arc produced a very high pressure within the pot and this, combined with vapour turbulence flowing into the arc, greatly assisted extinction of the latter. If the process of extinction was not achieved before the moving contact left the pot, it occurred immediately

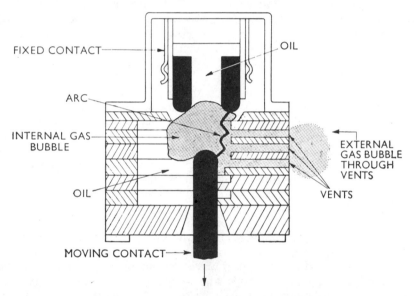

Figure 1.8. Basic design of side-blast arc-control device

after the rod left the throat due to the high-velocity axial blast now free to pass through the fully open throat. The drawback with this device lay in the fact that when interrupting small values of current, arcing times were rather long and erratic while with very high values the pressure set up within the pot was such as to introduce a tendency to burst it. Arising out of this, an improved form was developed and patented[9] and in this two breaks in series were obtained at each pole, as seen in Fig. 1.7. The upper break separating first, causes gas formation which drives the oil remaining in the pot across the lower gap and down the hollow contact when the second break occurs.

The main interest in controlled-arc oil circuit-breakers now centred on the work of the British Electrical and Allied Industries Research Association (E.R.A.) whose researches led to the original side-blast arc control device[10]. The historical details of this work are recorded in a two-part article by Dr. W. Bevan Whitney[11] and in a book entitled *Circuit Breaking*[12].

The basic principles of this device are shown typically in Fig. 1.8, which shows the box-like structure of plates which is fitted to enclose the arcing area at the contacts. Unlike the 'explosion pot' this device is side-vented so that when the oil within the box breaks down under the influence of the arc to form a gas, the pressure set up forces the gas and arc products through the side vents, displacing and lengthening the arc. At each current zero, the arc is extinguished and fresh oil enters the box, the process being repeated until at some point in the process the insulation level between the fixed and moving contacts is such as to prevent the arc restriking. It is seen that when the breaker is closed, all side vents are covered by the moving contact rod, but as soon as this has moved (on opening) to a point just beyond contact separation, the first (upper) vent is uncovered. If the area of this is such that it ensures sufficient pressure rise, the arc may be extinguished at this point. If not, the arc will restrike and the pressure will increase as the arc lengthens. By now however, the continuing movement of the contact rod will have uncovered a further vent and extinction of the arc should occur. Any further vents provided are usually as a safety precaution to prevent a dangerous pressure rise, should for any reason a particularly long arc be drawn before extinction. Multiple venting is fairly common in the devices in use today, but examples do exist where only a single vent is provided.

It can be claimed that the invention of the arc-control device provided a major break-through for the bulk-oil circuit-breaker, but as yet the means for proving it fully did not exist. The E.R.A. depended largely on facilities made available to them, firstly by the Newcastle Electric Supply Co. at their Carville Power Station and later by the London Power Co. at their Acton Lane Power Station in Willesden. It was becoming very essential that separate and much fuller facilities for high-power proving tests and research should become available, the plant being specially designed for the purpose in mind. This need was being vigorously pursued and urged in a number of quarters, not least by the E.R.A. who had in fact produced preliminary plans for a national proving station. Foremost among others who favoured such a station was the late H. W. Clothier (A. Reyrolle & Co. Ltd.) who campaigned tirelessly for it.

Unfortunately, insufficient support was forthcoming and this led to independent action being taken by Reyrolle who went ahead and built the first short-circuit test plant in Britain on a site adjacent to their works in Hebburn, Co. Durham. This station was commissioned in 1929 and through the help given by Mr. Clothier the E.R.A. had access to the station and were thus able to conduct a series of full-scale high-power tests on breakers fitted with their arc-control device. Such was the success of these and ensuing tests that licences to manufacture control devices based on the E.R.A. patent were actively sought by, and granted to, many British switchgear manufacturers.

Over the next decade, other large manufacturers built their own test stations, each being used mainly for research work and tests on their own products, although by agreement non-owners of such stations could have some access to the available facilities. The spate of short-circuit testing which followed proved still further the possible improvements in circuit-breaker performance when arc-control devices were fitted, and that in some cases higher ratings could be achieved without increase in bulk, or conversely, for a given breaking capacity, the size of a breaker could be reduced. The research work which could now be undertaken contributed considerably to a better appreciation of what took place in the process of interrupting an a.c. arc, as witness the host of learned papers and articles which appeared in the 1930s.

Given these new facilities, it became obvious that uniformity with regard to final proving tests was desirable, so that breakers tested at different plants were proved on the same basis and under defined conditions. Thus the need arose to write into British Standards the duty cycle tests and conditions now common-place. Out of this also came the call for an approval certificate of rating. The

Figure 1.9. Early experimental air-blast circuit-breaker (courtesy the Electrical Research Association)

first specification to appear including such data was a revised edition of the now universally known BS 116 covering oil circuit-breakers and this was followed by many others.

Thus the bulk-oil circuit-breaker achieved a high reputation which is, at this much later date, undiminished. It has been built for voltages up to 330 kV, and at 132 kV (the voltage adopted for the original national 'Grid' systems in the U.K.), many hundreds were installed. It can be noted in passing that the arc-control device was adopted in other countries in the small-oil-volume types of breaker which they favoured.

It is generally true to say that during the early days, short-circuit test plants were almost wholly concerned with research and tests on circuit-breaking devices. In later years they were to contribute to proving the ability of other apparatus to withstand the effects of short-circuit, e.g. busbars, connections, isolating switches or contacts, current transformers, cable boxes, h.r.c. fuses, etc., i.e. complete switchgear assemblies. Outside this, work on such things as power transformers, reactors, etc. could also be undertaken.

Meanwhile, what was happening in Britain with regard to the alternative form of circuit-breaker, i.e. the air-blast type? In answer, it must be noted that prior to the idea of the side-blast arc-control device, the E.R.A. were carrying out fundamental work on arc-rupture by gas blast (as in the air-blast type of breaker) and it was in the course of this work that the investigators had the idea for the side-blast arc-control device for oil breakers. Although work on the latter took temporary preference, patents were taken out in due course by the E.R.A. on gas-blast ideas and it was these which provided a basis for British designs of air-blast circuit-breakers when they ultimately appeared[11]. In a later chapter examples of these will be given, but here it is of interest to note early experimental breakers built by the E.R.A. research team in 1927 or thereabouts, these being shown in Figs. 1.9 and 1.10.

Concurrently, research into air-blast was being vigorously pursued on the continent, notably by the Brown Boveri Co. Ltd. in Switzerland and the A.E.G. in Germany. Some details regarding this work have been noted by B. Wood in his letter of Mar. 1968 to the Editor of *Electronics and Power* commenting on Dr. Whitney's historical survey. Because continental designers did not achieve the same degree of success with the bulk-oil breaker as their British counterparts, the air-blast breaker became a popular choice in the voltage range equivalent to our 3·3 kV to 11 kV with the alternative of small-oil-volume types. In this country, designs for these voltages were also made available[13], generally for indoor use and accommodated in enclosures of the types then in vogue, i.e. truck cubicles or stone cells, an illustration of the latter arrangement being shown in Fig. 1.11.

Such installations however cannot compete costwise with those using bulk-oil circuit-breakers, largely on account of the cost of the necessary compressed-air plants and associated pipe lines, although for certain applications, e.g. arc furnace switching, the air-blast breaker is the more suitable. By and large therefore, in this country the air-blast design found its biggest outlet on high-voltage systems, especially for outdoor use, although in recent years, numerous indoor installations at the highest voltages (up to 400 kV) have been made. The reasons for this will be noted later.

It is of interest at this point to note some of the types of switchgear assemblies which were used in the early days, particularly the indoor types for voltages up to 11 or 22 kV. For the simple oil circuit-breakers noted in Figs. 1.2 and 1.4, the so called *flat-back* switchboard was widely used. This comprised slabs of slate or white Sicilian marble supported on an angle or pipe framework, the circuit-breakers being behind the panel with its operating handle on the front, as Fig. 1.4 shows. Instruments (with large cast front bezels), relays and meters were displayed on the front face of the panel, and almost always swan-neck lamp fittings would be provided to illuminate the instruments on such panels. Also much favoured was a clock placed centrally above the switchboard and mounted in a highly ornamental wrought-iron scroll.

Figure 1.10.   Later form of experimental air-blast circuit-breaker (courtesy The Electrical Research Association)

13

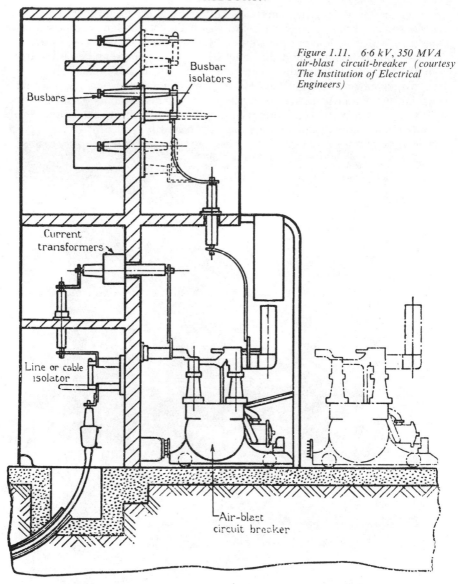

Figure 1.11. 6·6 kV, 350 MVA air-blast circuit-breaker (courtesy The Institution of Electrical Engineers)

Instrument transformers, busbars and connections, isolating switches, etc. were at the rear of each panel, all quite open and exposed to dust and vermin. Human access to the rear of the switchboard was safeguarded by expanded metal screens and locked gates at each end. Small wiring would be festooned on the rear faces of the panels with little sense of order and usually run at the discretion of the assembler. As opposed to the highly standardised unit constructions of today, it is recalled that in the days of the flat-back switchboard each individual panel on each contract had to be drawn out in detail by the draughtsman.

Problems of safety were a matter of concern to many users and designers and for a long time Clothier had been advocating a unit design which he originally designated *armourclad* or *ironclad*; today we call it *metalclad*. This construction was the subject of a patent as long ago as 1906 and reference to it is found in a paper read by Clothier in Newcastle in 1910. Figure 1.12 is reproduced from a Reyrolle reprint of that paper and shows how the individual components were separately enclosed in earthed metal casings with the busbars and connections surrounded by bitumastic compound or by oil. The circuit-breaker was carried on two cast-iron pedestals and it could be racked in to or out of contact with isolating plugs and sockets, i.e. horizontal isolation. Later in 1925 and again in 1932, Clothier presented papers to The Institution of Electrical Engineers in which he reviewed the progress made at those times in the development of his metalclad safety principles, which by now had been widely adopted by other switchgear manufacturers. In his 1932 paper it is noted that he included details of a series of short-circuit tests on circuit-breakers which had been carried out

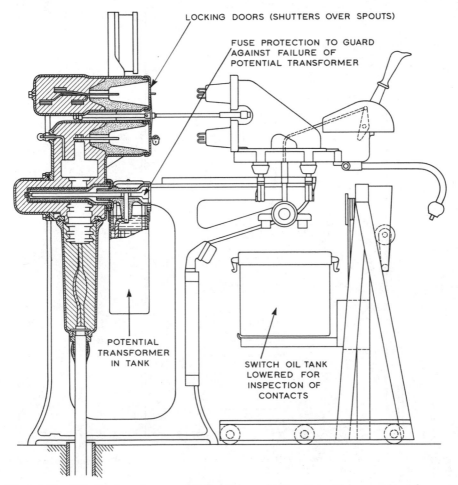

LOCKING DOORS (SHUTTERS OVER SPOUTS)

FUSE PROTECTION TO GUARD AGAINST FAILURE OF POTENTIAL TRANSFORMER

POTENTIAL TRANSFORMER IN TANK

SWITCH OIL TANK LOWERED FOR INSPECTION OF CONTACTS

Figure 1.12. Side elevation of armourclad oil-switch panel with switch withdrawn and tank lowered (courtesy A. Reyrolle & Co. Ltd.)

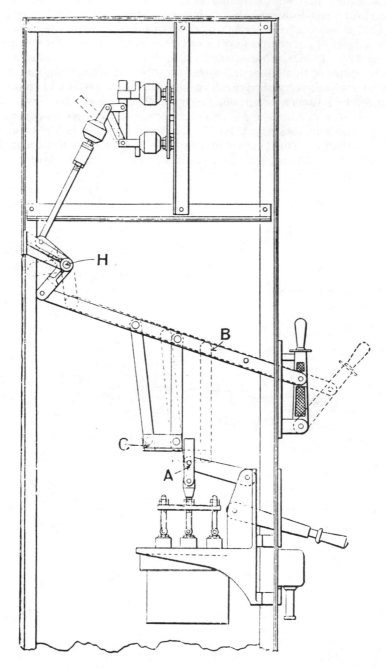

Figure 1.13. System of switchgear interlocking used by the General Electric Co. (courtesy Ernest Benn Ltd.)

on the relatively new Reyrolle test plant, the details including reproductions of the oscillographic records.

Garrard, in his book[4] described this same 'armourclad' unit and noted in addition a 22 kV unit built by Reyrolle on the same general principles. In other directions, greater safety was achieved by accommodating all the 'live' apparatus for each circuit in a totally-enclosed sheet-steel cubicle, the circuit-breaker being fixed so that separate isolating switches were essential. These were normally three-pole units with a ganged operating mechanism and were mechanically interlocked with the circuit-breaker to ensure that only the latter could break the load current. Figure 1.13 is an illustration from Garrard's book[4] showing an interlock arrangement as adopted by the General Electric Co. at

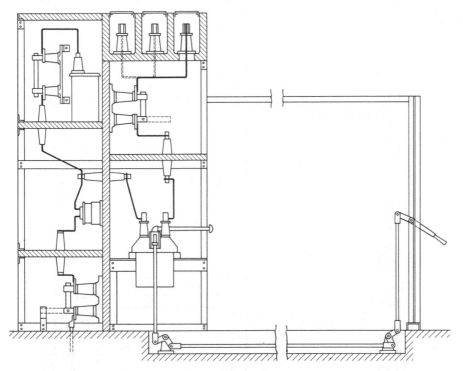

Figure 1.14.   Typical stone cellular switchgear with remote mechanical control from switchboard (courtesy Blackie & Son Ltd.)

that time. In this there happens to be only one set of isolating switches, i.e. on the busbar side. If, as is often essential, a further set was fitted on the cable side, the complications of the additional interlock can be imagined, particularly as full safety demanded that the various cubicle doors should also be interlocked in such a way that access to live apparatus was impossible.

It will be noted that sub-division within the cubicle provided separate compartments for the various components. This principle was also applied in the stone cellular cubicles which were in fashion. Built up from precast stone slabs (which had to comply with BS 268) with all holes for through bushings and for fixing bolts accurately located, it was a type which could not be assembled on the factory floor, such assembly being only possible on site. It involved very

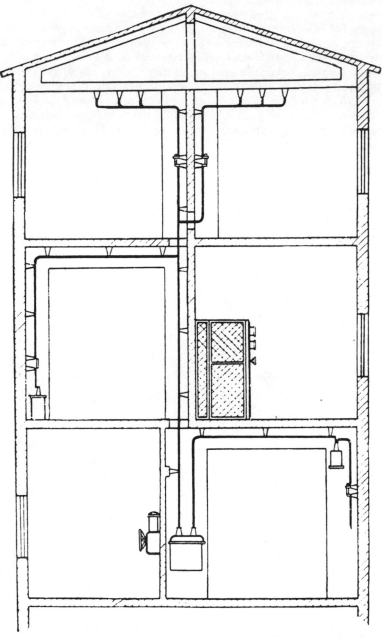

Figure 1.15.   Section through switchgear by one of the large continental manufacturers, for control of an 11 000V transformer (courtesy Blackie & Son Ltd.)

considerable drawing office work, in some cases the detailing of each individual slab to assist the specialist stonework firms who undertook this class of work. Nevertheless, there were many applications in power stations or major sub-stations, both industrial and electricity supply and Fig. 1.14 taken from Coates' book[5] is representative of the type. This illustration has, incidentally, been chosen because it also shows a method frequently employed to provide remote mechanical closing of the circuit-breaker. Behind this was the thought that it allowed the operator to be removed some distance away from the breaker should he be called upon to close it (or to attempt to) when a fault already existed on the circuit—an operation involving unpredictable consequences.

In stone cellular gear, phase separation was achieved by vertical stone slabs and this meant that the isolating switches had to be single-pole units, operated after opening the doors by means of a long insulated pole. In this gear, door

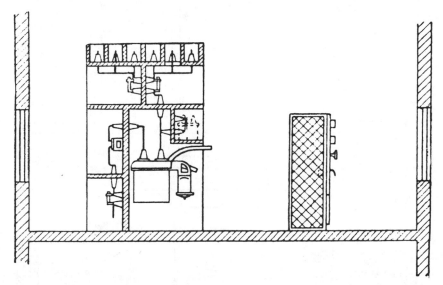

Figure 1.16. Typical British cubicle layout containing the same equipment as shown in Figure 1.15 (courtesy Blackie & Son Ltd.)

interlocks were also necessary—a complicated business bearing in mind the number of doors involved.

Stone cubicles are space consuming, but even so they were economical when compared with continental practice. The latter favoured an arrangement of open-type switchgear and Coates notes in his book[5] an article which appeared in the *BEAMA* Journal of October 1920, which cited proposals made by a British and a continental firm who were both tendering for the same project. The two proposals are shown in Figs. 1.15 and 1.16.

For the type of breaker shown in Fig. 1.15, stone cellular gear was generally used, the breaker on an upper floor with the busbars and isolating switches below, typically as shown in Fig. 1.17.

Last but not least, note must be taken of the popular draw-out type of unit which was known as the *truck* type. One such unit is shown in Fig. 1.18 and it shows a type which can be regarded as the forerunner of the many withdrawable types now in common use, although the majority today have vertical isolation

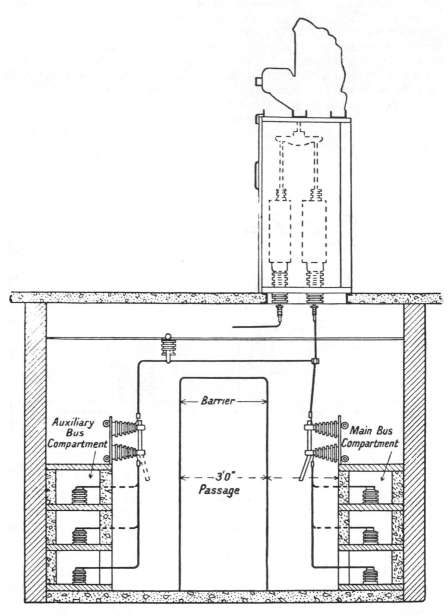

Figure 1.17.   *Typical cubicle with bottom-connected circuit-breaker as shown in Figure 1.5 (courtesy Blackie & Son Ltd.)*

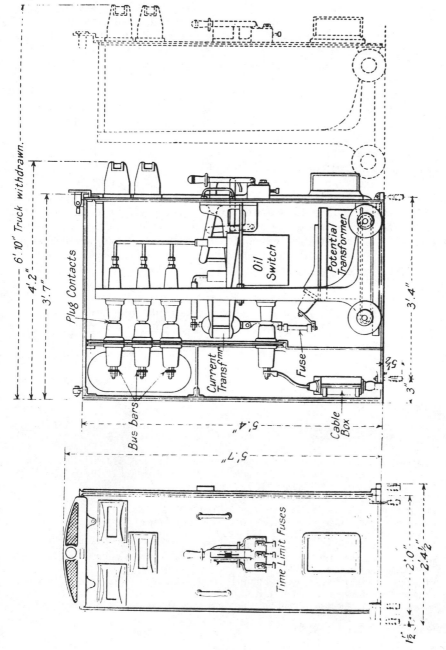

Figure 1.18. Draw-out cubicle, truck-type by B.T.H. Co. Ltd. (courtesy Ernest Benn Ltd.)

prior to withdrawal. It was popular because of the considerable accessibility for maintenance it afforded when the truck was withdrawn.

Interlocking was relatively easy when compared with the complexity of the fixed sheet-steel cubicle, and safety with the truck withdrawn was ensured by shutters which automatically covered the live isolating contacts in the fixed portion. It is interesting to note that a method of achieving this was patented by Ferguson Pailin Ltd. in 1917[14]. Not that such precautions were new because even in 1910 Clothier, discussing his 'armourclad' design (Fig. 1.11), mentions the provision of:

> '... a pair of doors, which are normally tucked away between the busbar and transformer chambers, automatically follow the switch carriage out and close over the orifices which contain the plug connections to the busbars and transformers respectively'.

Looking back at the works from which the foregoing has been largely derived, it is interesting to note that some forms of protection still in use today were current in the early years of the century. The paper read by Clothier in 1910 and the books by Garrard[4] and Coates[5] all show these, and a pamphlet published by Ferranti Ltd. in 1934 written by A. Hilton Higgs lists and describes the various systems in use. They include the familiar Merz-Price systems, self balance and busbar protection and core-balance earth fault protection. Systems rarely heard of today include those which require special cables with split cores for each phase and a special circuit-breaker with split contacts on the cable side.

As indicated in the preface, this story of the past is far from complete, but sufficient has perhaps been given to show some of the stages of development leading up to the ranges of switchgear to be noted later, so that the present can be compared with the past.

REFERENCES

1. HARVEY, A.P., *The Interruption of Alternating Current Circuits*. Paper read to the Students Section of the North Eastern Centre of the I.E.E., Newcastle-upon-Tyne (26.11.37)
2. HOLMES, J.E., U.K. Pat. 1 256 (14.2.1884)
3. FLURSCHEIM, C.H., 'Development in Power Engineering', *Proc. I.E.E.*, **112** No. 1, Jan. (1965)
4. GARRARD, C.G., *Electric Switch and Controlling Gear*, Ernest Benn Ltd. (1916 and 1920)
5. COATES, W.A., *Choice of Switchgear*, Blackie
6. Described in *The Electrician*, **79**, 884 (1917)
7. *Bulletin of the S.E.V.*, No. 8 (1915) and *The Electrician*, **77**, 8 (1916)
8. COATES, W.A. and PEARCE, H., *Switchgear Handbook*, vol. I, Pitman
9. BRITISH THOMSON-HOUSTON, U.K. Pat. 193 136 (1921)
10. WHITNEY, W.B. and WEDMORE, E.B., U.K. Pat. 366 998 (1930)
11. WHITNEY, W.B., 'The Early History of the High-Voltage Air-blast Circuit-breaker in the U.K.', *Electronics and Power*, Jan. and Sept. (1968)
12. TRENCHAM, W. (Ed.), *Circuit Breaking*, Butterworths (1953). A record of a series of lectures by six authors on the researches of the E.R.A.
13. BLANDFORD, A.R., 'Air-blast Circuit-breakers', *Journal of the Institution of Electrical Engineers*, Part 2, **90**, 180, 18 Dec. (1943)
14. PAILIN, F., U.K. Pat. 112 580 (1917)

Chapter 2

Circuit breaking

The vital importance of the device used for making and breaking an electrical circuit under conditions of varying severity has already been noted historically in Chapter 1. In many switchgear units, this device is a circuit-breaker either of the oil or air-break type, or one employing a gas blast principle. The adjective 'many' is introduced because in certain types of switchgear some of the functions expected of a circuit-breaker are assumed by an h.r.c. fuse, e.g. in fuse switches. In this chapter our concern will be with the circuit-breaker only, considering in some detail the problems involved in circuit interruption, noting first what the expected functions are:

1. It must be capable of closing on to, and carrying full load currents for long periods of time.
2. Under prescribed conditions, it must open automatically to disconnect the load or some small overload.
3. It must successfully and rapidly interrupt the heavy currents which flow when a short-circuit has to be cleared from the system.
4. With its contacts open, the gap must withstand the circuit voltage.
5. It must be capable of closing on to a circuit in which a fault exists and of immediately re-opening to clear the fault from the system.
6. It must be capable of carrying current of short-circuit magnitude until, and for such time as, the fault is cleared by another breaker (or fuse) nearer to the point of fault.
7. It must be capable of successfully interrupting quite small currents such as transformer magnetising currents (inductive) or line and cable charging currents (capacitive).
8. Last but not least, it must be capable of withstanding the effects of arcing at its contacts and the electro-magnetic forces and thermal conditions which arise due to the passage of currents of short-circuit magnitude.

Some of these requirements will be considered in later chapters dealing with particular types of circuit-breakers, and in the present discussion our concern will be with problems arising from points 3 and 7.

By way of introduction however, it is appropriate to note that under point 2 the normal or simple overload conditions involve currents to be interrupted which are equal to, or only slightly greater than, the rating of the circuit-breaker. These currents can range from something under 100 A up to a maximum of say

3 000–4 000 A*, and their interruption by modern circuit-breakers presents little or no difficulty. This is because interruption takes place under conditions of minimum severity, e.g. at the high power factor of the system. When a short-circuit occurs, however, not only is the current to be interrupted of much greater magnitude (as demonstrated in Chapters 3 and 4), but interruption takes place under conditions of much greater severity.

In the simplest terms, the problem of interrupting an a.c. arc can be stated as one of de-ionising (i.e. making non-conducting) the highly ionised (i.e. conductive) gaseous path between the contacts to an extent such that at an early current zero (on a 50 Hz system there are 100 zeros every second) the dielectric strength in the contact gap will withstand the rising voltage impressed across the gap tending to re-establish the arc after a current zero, i.e. to re-strike. Ideally this condition would be achieved at the first current zero after the arc is first established, but this is rarely achieved, and depending on the design and type of circuit-breaker, there will be several cycles of arcing prior to final extinction.

When the current to be interrupted is the normal load value, the power factor of the system will also be normal, e.g. 0·8 or better, so that at each current zero, the voltage will be almost in phase and will be almost zero (see Fig. 2.5 later). This makes for easy interruption but when a short-circuit occurs the power factor can be very low, so much so that when the fault is at locations near to the power source it can fall almost to zero. In this event, current and voltage will be out of phase such that at current zero the circuit voltage will be near its maximum and, as will be shown, this results in more difficult interruption.

All circuit-breakers consist essentially of pairs of mating contacts, each pair comprising a fixed and moving element. In normal service these elements are in contact to carry the load current, but on receipt of a tripping signal, which may be initiated by hand or via a protective device, the two elements will part company to interrupt the circuit. At the instant of separation an arc will be struck between them and will continue until interrupted. These elementary details are shown typically in Fig. 2.1 for three types of breaker in common use today; interruption of the arc depending on aid given either by high pressure, forced convection, turbulence or lengthening of the arc, or by two or more of these in combination.

In the oil circuit-breaker, the oil serves three purposes; firstly to insulate the live contacts from the earthed metal tank, secondly to provide an insulating barrier between the open contacts after the arc is extinguished and thirdly to produce hydrogen during the arcing period. In this latter respect it is seen in Fig. 2.1(a) that the arc is surrounded by a bubble of gas. This is caused by the heat of the arc breaking down the oil in the vicinity of the contacts and liberating a mixture of gases and vapours, with hydrogen representing about 70% of the whole. It is largely due to the hydrogen that successful interruption is achieved, as it recovers its dielectric strength rapidly at each current zero. Other factors aiding interruption are the turbulence of the oil in the neighbourhood of the arc and the closeness of cool oil to give a high-temperature gradient. In a plain-break design as illustrated, there is nothing to restrain the gas bubble in its

* There is a special case where higher normal currents arise, i.e. where the modern generator of large capacity is switched at generator voltage, a practice now returning to favour with the availability of special designs of air-blast circuit-breaker with normal current ratings up to 20 000 A and with higher possibilities on the horizon (see Chapter 15).

effort to push the oil away from the arc, so that the cooling action is diminished and the arc tends to lengthen. Such lengthening is not desirable, although it does increase the turbulence, which in turn assists the cooling process. Under these conditions, performance can be erratic and as we have noted in Chapter 1 consistent performance has been achieved by the addition of a device (Fig. 1.8) which encloses the contacts, arc, gas bubble and a quantity of oil. The device has side vents which allow the blast of hydrogen and oil vapour only one means of escape. The arc, as Fig. 1.8 shows, is forced by the blast of gas into the side vents and a means is provided whereby fresh-cool oil can refill the box-like enclosure.

In an air-break chute-type circuit-breaker shown in simple outline in Fig. 2.1(b) the arc exists in a mixture of nitrogen, oxygen and metallic vapours. Interruption is largely due to elongation of the arc which results in cooling and

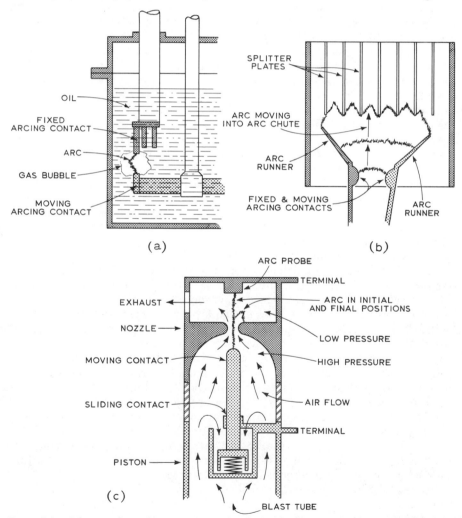

Figure 2.1. Schematic form of arcing in circuit-breakers. Part sections of (a) *a plain-break bulk-oil circuit-breaker,* (b) *a chute-type air-break circuit-breaker and* (c) *an air-blast circuit-breaker*

de-ionisation by diffusion. Owing to the high temperature of the arc relative to the surrounding air, the arc is subjected to strong convection currents which, coupled with the electromagnetic effect of the current loop, cause the arc to rise vertically. It is therefore driven into the arc chute where splitter plates assist the cooling and lengthening process so that its length is much greater than the direct distance between the fully open contacts. It would appear likely that the resistance of the long arc plays some part in successful interruption in that it brings the voltage more nearly into phase with the current, i.e. improves the power factor. In later chapters, descriptions of typical air-break designs will be given, from which it will be seen that considerable variations of this simple theme exist, in particular between the designs for medium and high voltages.

In an air-blast circuit-breaker, the interrupting process is aided by an axial blast of air at high pressure (from a compressed air installation) admitted to the arcing chamber, shown typically in Fig. 2.1(c). The air passes through a nozzle forming the main fixed contact and then to the atmosphere. On leaving the nozzle, the air expands so that its velocity through the nozzle reaches sonic level, centring the arc and transferring its upper root to a probe contact, as shown. In this position, the arc is subjected to high pressure and considerable heat loss by forced convection. In the design shown, movement of the moving contact is restricted, so that in the fully open position the contact gap is quite small. It is a feature of air-blast designs that there is a critical gap length for a given blast condition at which the interrupting capacity is a maximum, and when this critical gap is reached interruption should take place at the next current zero. If it does not, the subsequent zeros will occur at times of falling air pressure and interruption will be correspondingly more difficult. It is equally important that the moving contact reaches the critical gap as quickly as possible, as shown typically by travel curve No. 1 in Fig. 2.2(a) which shows that the gap is reached as the current passes through the first and second zeros. Curve No. 2 illustrates how, with a slower speed of opening, the critical gap (represented by the shaded area) is not reached until the seventh and eighth current zeros.

In this illustration, the moving contact has been assumed to travel on beyond the critical gap, so that in its final position full isolation has been achieved. This however is not normal practice, as in most practical designs travel of this contact is restricted so that it does not pass beyond the critical gap. As the air in the blast tube returns to atmospheric pressure after arc extinction, its dielectric strength in the small gap will be insufficient to withstand the normal system voltage, and therefore a separate isolating switch is provided to open automatically after current interruption. The moving contact, relieved of high pressure on its actuating piston, returns to its closed position, the circuit being restored by closing the external isolating switch. This sequence is illustrated in Fig. 2.2(c).

Although not simple to achieve, and for this reason rarely considered, it is possible to eliminate the separate isolating switch and yet retain the feature of restricted movement at the critical gap by arranging for the moving contact to pause for a short time at that gap and then to continue its stroke to a fully isolated position. This method is illustrated in Fig. 2.2(b).

In passing, it may be noted that Fig. 2.1(c) shows a moving contact arrangement which depends on the admission of high-pressure air to the blast tube for the opening movement, the air acting on a spring-loaded piston. In the circuit-breakers now in use at the higher transmission voltages, the whole of the blast

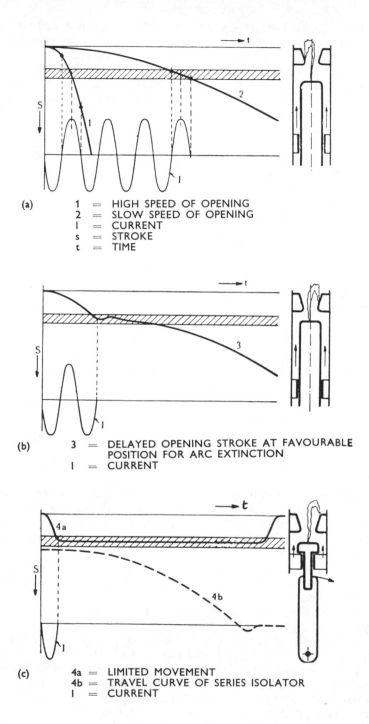

(a)
1 = HIGH SPEED OF OPENING
2 = SLOW SPEED OF OPENING
I = CURRENT
s = STROKE
t = TIME

(b)
3 = DELAYED OPENING STROKE AT FAVOURABLE
    POSITION FOR ARC EXTINCTION
I = CURRENT

(c)
4a = LIMITED MOVEMENT
4b = TRAVEL CURVE OF SERIES ISOLATOR
I = CURRENT

Figure 2.2. The interruption of an arc in an air-blast circuit-breaker at a critical gap (courtesy Brown Boveri & Co. Ltd.)

tube and interrupter chamber(s) is *permanently pressurised*, and the moving contact is mechanically activated. On receipt of a tripping impulse the contact opens, and simultaneously a blast valve opens to release the high pressure to the atmosphere. By this means, air at maximum pressure is available in the arcing area immediately, eliminating the pressure loss and the time delays inherent when the air has to travel the full length of the blast tube before reaching the arcing area. With air maintained at high pressure across the open gap after arc extinction, the need for a separate isolator disappears.

Bearing this in mind, let us now look at the conditions operating against and trying to prevent arc extinction, or rather, which try to restrike the arc after it has ceased naturally at each current zero.

The enemy in this respect is voltage, and Fig. 2.3 shows in oscillographic form the changing voltages through the extremely short period of time which elapses from the instant of short-circuit until final interruption. Reading from left to

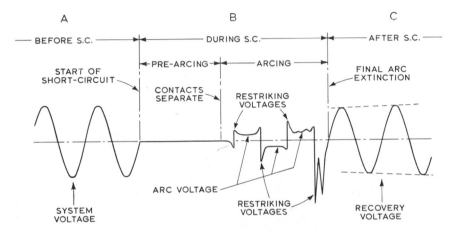

Figure 2.3. The voltage before, during and after a short-circuit

right it is seen that the normal system voltage existing prior to the short-circuit falls to zero when the fault occurs, and stays at zero during the pre-arcing period, i.e. until the contacts separate. At this point an arc is struck, with a voltage reappearing which is of low value and fairly constant; this voltage is known as the *arc* or *arc burning* voltage.

Just prior to the current reaching its natural zero, the effects of the de-ionisation and cooling of the arc gap predominate, causing the arc voltage to rise to a small peak above its average, forcing the current to zero. If at this point de-ionisation has not advanced sufficiently, the restriking voltage rising rapidly to a slightly higher peak in an opposite sense will restrike the arc, and fault current will flow again until the next natural zero, a process which may be repeated several times. In Fig. 2.3, interruption has been assumed to be finally successful at the fourth current zero in the arcing period, and now it is seen that the restriking voltage appears as a high frequency transient oscillating about the normal recovery voltage base at system frequency, but rapidly decaying down to the latter. It may be noted that Fig. 2.3 is a voltage record such as would appear on an electromagnetic oscillograph taken during a short-circuit test, being repeated for each phase. Such a record cannot show the true nature of the transient since the frequency is beyond the response limits of electro-magnetic oscilloscopes, and it is necessary therefore to study records taken on a cathode ray oscilloscope where the record is on a long time base and where, for example, one cycle of a 50 Hz test can be extended over 1 m or so. Typical of one such record is that shown in Fig. 2.4 where the frequency of oscillation is 8·65 kHz, the time scale showing that the oscillation is highly damped and decays to normal system power frequency within 0·002 s.

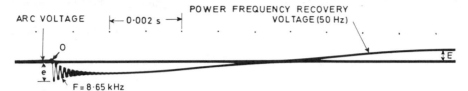

Figure 2.4. Cathode-ray oscillographic record of restriking voltage (courtesy A. Reyrolle & Co. Ltd.)

The voltage peaks impressed across the arc gap at current zeros will be dependent (in magnitude) on the power factor of the circuit up to the point of fault. This is demonstrated in Fig. 2.5(a) where it is seen that at unity power factor, the current zero coincides with the voltage zero. This is an unlikely condition even in normal healthy conditions and if we assume a power factor of say 0·85 or 0·9, as would be the case when interrupting normal load current, the voltage will still be very low at current zero. Under short-circuit conditions however, the circumstances are not so favourable, the power factor being very low. If, for example, the fault occurs at a point near to the power source (generators or power transformers) then the power factor will be very nearly zero, while for faults more remote it may be of the order 0·3. This slight improvement arises because of the resistance introduced in the circuit by cable feeders. These points will be noted again in Chapter 3 and demonstrated by an example.

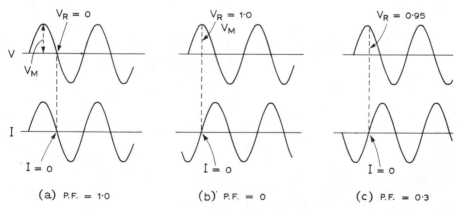

Figure 2.5. Variation of recovery voltage with power factor. (a) with p.f. = 1·0, (b) with p.f. = 0 and (c) with p.f. = 0·3
NOTE: Voltages at other lagging p.fs. can be obtained from the formula:
$$V_R = V_M \sin \theta$$
where V_R = Recovery voltage
and V_M = Max. voltage
Thus at p.f. 0·15, V_R = 0·989 with
$$V_M = 1·0$$

29

At this point it should be noted that if the power factor falls to zero as in Fig. 2.5(b) then the instantaneous recovery voltage at current zero is at its peak value, and from Fig. 2.5(c) it is seen that with a power factor of 0·3 the instantaneous recovery voltage is about 0·95 times the peak value. It is about these instantaneous values that the restriking transient oscillates.

In Fig. 2.6, the voltage conditions noted in Fig. 2.3 have been combined with the curve of arc current (assumed here to be symmetrical and completely out of phase, i.e. zero power factor) and from this it is seen that at current zeros A and B the restriking voltage breaks down the contact gap and the arc restrikes. At current zero C however, the de-ionisation process has sufficiently advanced

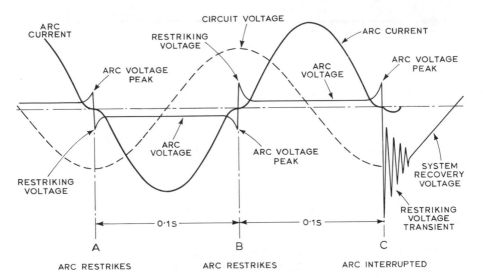

Figure 2.6. Typical oscillographic record of arcing through successive current zeros

such that the gap withstands the rapidly rising voltage and clearance is achieved. For clarity, the restriking voltage transient at C is diagrammatic only and would not appear with this definition on an electromagnetic oscillograph record (see Fig. 2.4 for cathode-ray record).

From the foregoing it would appear that at each current zero there is a race between the rapidly rising restriking voltage and the rising dielectric strength between the fixed and moving contacts. This dielectric race theory (advanced by Slepian in 1928) can be illustrated as shown in Fig. 2.7, where in (a) a curve representing the recovery of dielectric strength is shown to be less rapid than the rate of rise of voltage, and at the point of intersection the gap breaks down. This is the condition at current zeros A and B in Fig. 2.6. In (b) of Fig. 2.7 however, the opposite condition is reached and the current is finally interrupted, i.e. corresponding to current zero C in Fig. 2.6.

However this apparently simple theory offers no more than an introduction to the complex problems of what happens in the period of just before to just after current zero. It leaves unanswered the question as to how a curve representing dielectric recovery can be calculated for many different conditions, and various investigators from many countries have, over the years, offered other theories. One example, known as the energy balance theory, was advanced by

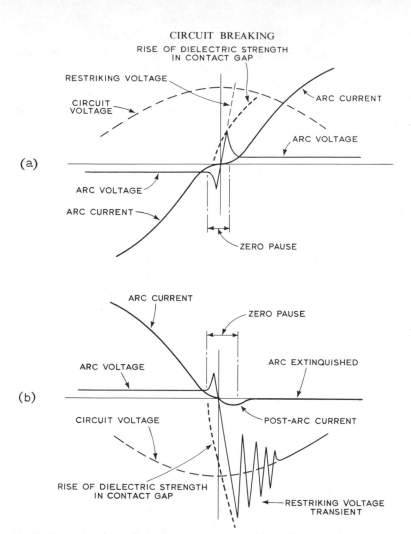

Figure 2.7. The dielectric race theory. (a) *shows the restrike as at* B *in Figure 2.6, and* (b) *shows the interruption as at* C *in Figure 2.6*

Cassie[1] following his researches at the E.R.A., and while this cannot be explained in detail here it is of interest to quote a rough description offered in a lecture given by Dr. W. Bevan Whitney[2] in 1952 at the Polytechnic, Regent Street, London and repeated later at the Armstrong College, Newcastle-upon-Tyne.

'At actual current zero, viz. when no current is flowing there is clearly no power input to the arc gap. If post arc conductivity continues for an instant in the gap and then ceases so that the current again becomes zero, the power input is again zero. Somewhere in between these two instants however, there is a flow of current and the power input will pass through a maximum. Clearly, if the maximum exceeds the power loss from the arc column by a sufficient amount, the column will heat up, its conductivity will increase and a full arc will form again and continue. According to this theory, the better the means for carrying away the energy given off by the path near zero, the better will be the chance of extinction'.

31

In the above extract, reference is made to post-arc conductivity and the current which flows due to this immediately after the actual current zero. This current, known as *post-arc* current, is noted in (*b*) of Fig. 2.7. In both parts of this illustration the vital period known as the *zero pause* is indicated. In terms of time it is a period of a few hundred microseconds only, and is the subject of continuous study by many investigators. Indeed, Garrard[3] has noted the existence of an informal group of international engineers interested in the subject and known as the *Zero Club*.

The restriking voltage transient at the instant of arc extinction, as discussed earlier in relation to Figs. 2.3 and 2.4, is important in respect of two quantities, i.e. the amplitude of the first peak (*e* in Fig. 2.4) and the frequency of oscillation, since upon these depends the initial rate at which the voltage builds up across the breaker contacts.

The amplitude, as we have noted in relation to Fig. 2.5, is affected by the magnitude of the normal frequency voltage at current zero, i.e. on the power factor. It is further affected by the nature of the fault, a typical case being that of a fault to earth on a system which is earthed at the supply neutral. Here it can be shown that, allowing for transient doubling, the peak voltage can reach $2 \times \sqrt{2}$ times the phase voltage. An even higher peak can be reached however, where, with the supply neutral earthed, a three-phase fault occurs, as represented in Fig. 2.8.

When interrupting a fault of this type, one phase will clear before the other two, and in this illustration the first phase to clear is assumed to be the blue

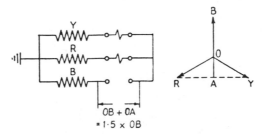

OB + OA
= 1·5 × OB

Figure 2.8. Recovery voltage across the first phase to clear with a three-phase fault

phase, with arcing maintained in the two other (red and yellow) phases. With this condition, the restriking voltage peak in the blue phase will be $1 \cdot 5 \times 2 \times \sqrt{2}$ times the phase voltage, i.e. on an 11 kV system a peak of 27 kV. Following successful interruption of blue phase current, the red and yellow phases form a series circuit and the current in these will have a common magnitude. Simultaneous interruption in the two phases will occur at the next current zero, and this will be achieved with relatively easy recovery voltage conditions.

Reference back to Fig. 2.5 will show that the current to be interrupted was assumed to be symmetrical, i.e. equal in magnitude in each half-cycle about zero. In most practical cases, the current in at least one phase will be asymmetrical to some degree and the current cycle will include major and minor loops as shown in Fig. 2.9. Assuming again a low power factor condition, it will be seen that the instantaneous recovery voltage will depend on whether interruption occurs at a current zero following a major or a minor loop. In either case however, it will be less than the peak associated with a symmetrical current, e.g. at *B* in Fig. 2.3. In passing, attention may be drawn to the fact that the peak current in a major loop is higher than that in a symmetrical loop and also that there is an increase in time between zeros of the major loop. The higher value of peak current must be taken into account in determining the electromagnetic forces which the breaker must withstand, and in particular, the mechanical strength of an arc-control device must be related to this condition as the pressures set up within the device are related to the current.

We have now seen that the instantaneous value of recovery voltage (normal frequency) is dependent on (a) the power factor, (b) the nature of the fault and (c) the degree of asymmetry. We have also noted the high-frequency restriking-voltage transient which is superimposed, but whose amplitude decays exponentially within a short period of time. The frequency of this transient will depend

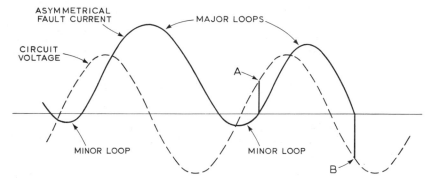

Figure 2.9.   *Instantaneous recovery voltages when fault current is asymmetrical.*
A.   *Instantaneous recovery voltage if interruption follows a minor loop*
B.   *Instantaneous recovery voltage if interruption follows a major loop*

on the inductance and capacitance on the supply and load sides of the circuit-breaker. Broadly speaking, when a fault occurs near to the power source, capacitance will be small and the frequency of oscillation will be of a high order, i.e. thousands of cycles per second. On the other hand, if the fault is at a remote point, the capacitance will be higher and in consequence the frequency will be of a lower order, i.e. hundreds of cycles per second. Here we may note that the natural frequency F_n of a system is given by:

$$F_n = \frac{1}{2\pi\sqrt{LC}}$$

where L is the inductance, largely determined by the plant and C is the capacitance, determined by the system length up to the point of fault. Resistance in the circuit tends to damp the oscillations, but where $R < 2\sqrt{L/C}$ the system will be oscillatory. It may be noted that the resistance introduced by cables or overhead lines to a remote fault has the two-fold effect of improving the power factor and dampening the oscillation of the restriking voltage transient, thus reducing the severity of duty during arc interruption. From this it follows that if resistance can be introduced into the system by an outside means, and if this added resistance is sufficient to make $R > 2\sqrt{L/C}$, then the high frequency oscillations can be entirely suppressed. This practice is adopted in practically all air-blast circuit-breakers and occasionally in extra high-voltage oil circuit-breakers, the resistance being connected in shunt across the contact gap. When so applied the resistance will normally only be inserted in the circuit during the

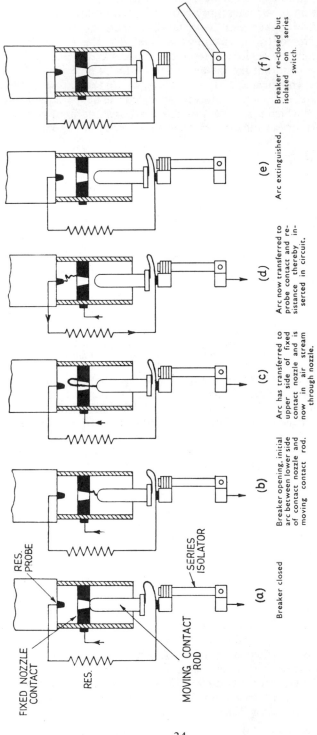

FIXED NOZZLE CONTACT

RES. PROBE

RES.

MOVING CONTACT ROD

SERIES ISOLATOR

(a) Breaker closed

(b) Breaker opening, initial arc between lower side of contact nozzle and moving contact rod.

(c) Arc has transferred to upper side of fixed contact nozzle and is now in air stream through nozzle.

(d) Arc now transferred to probe contact and resistance thereby inserted in circuit.

(e) Arc extinguished.

(f) Breaker re-closed but isolated on series switch.

Figure 2.10. Sequence diagram of resistance switching in an air-blast circuit-breaker

34

interrupting process, and Fig. 2.10(d) illustrates one method by which this is achieved. Interruption of the resistor current may be achieved by the normal air-blast as at (e) in Fig. 2.10, or alternatively, it can be interrupted on the series isolator when this opens automatically after the main arc has been extinguished, i.e. immediately after (d). These methods are satisfactory for relatively small resistor currents, noting that the power factor will be unity. For higher values of resistor current separate interrupters are employed, and in the case of air-blast circuit-breakers, these separate resistor interrupters may also be air-blast. When applied to oil circuit-breakers, the shunt resistors will be located outside the arc-control device along with suitable interrupting contacts.

The higher the frequency of the transient voltage, the steeper will be the average slope of the voltage rise from zero to its first peak. This is defined as the rate of rise of recovery voltage (dV/dt), which in technical literature and elsewhere is abbreviated to r.r.r.v., and is stated in volts or kilovolts per microsecond. For a single frequency transient oscillation (of which Fig. 2.4 is an example) r.r.r.v. is taken as the slope of a straight line passing through the origin (0 in Fig. 2.4) and the initial crest, as illustrated in Fig. 2.11. It is a measure

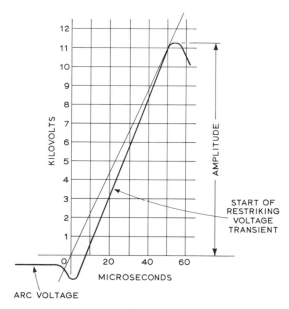

Figure 2.11. *How the r.r.r.v. is measured by the slope of a line passing through the point of current zero on the zero voltage axis and tangential to the transient wave. In this fictitious example the r.r.r.v. = 220V/μs.*
NOTE: The amplitude is measured in kV, from Figure 2.4.

of the severity of duty imposed on a circuit-breaker and to which some types, e.g. air-blast, are particularly sensitive. On the other hand, oil and air-blast types are relatively insensitive to r.r.r.v.

The method of determining the r.r.r.v. where the transient oscillation comprises more than one frequency is more complex than that shown in Fig. 2.11 for a single frequency. Double or multi-frequency oscillations can occur on systems when more than one oscillatory circuit is involved, and each frequency can have a different amplitude.

It is important to note that the circuit-breaker itself modifies the restriking transient, the degree of modification varying with the type of circuit-breaker. Thus it is usual to refer to the *inherent* r.r.r.v., which is the value obtained from the circuit parameters alone, so that for any one circuit we have the same inherent r.r.r.v. which is not dependent on the type of circuit-breaker being tested.

One of the results of increasing fault levels on extra high-voltage transmission systems (in the range 25–60 kA fault current) has been to reveal a phenomenon now known as a *short-line fault*, which produces conditions of extreme severity for air-blast circuit-breakers. This revelation arose out of a number of unexplained failures of otherwise fully proved circuit-breakers, and investigation showed that these failures were associated with faults occurring on a transmission line at points quite close to the line side terminal of the circuit-breaker, e.g. at a distance in the range of, say, 0·5 to 4 or 5 miles (1 km to 8 km). The investigations also showed that the restriking voltage transient across the circuit-breaker was of multiple frequency with a very steep r.r.r.v. to the initial peak, and that this

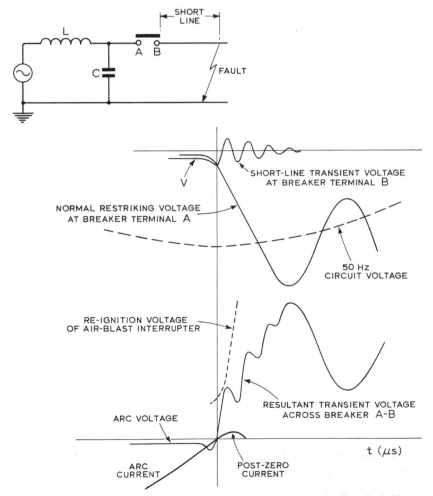

Figure 2.12. Short-line fault restriking voltages (courtesy A. Reyrolle & Co. Ltd.)

transient was the summation of two voltages, one at the supply side terminal of the breaker and the other at the line side terminal. That at the supply terminal is the normal restriking voltage transient as previously discussed, while that at the line terminal is a high frequency saw-toothed transient, the maximum amplitude of which is at the terminal and decays to zero at the fault point.

These conditions are shown typically in Fig. 2.12 from which it is seen that the first peak of the resultant restriking voltage transient is very close to the dielectric-recovery curve and produces post-zero current which is much greater than that which could be produced by the supply side transient alone. There is therefore an appreciable power input to the post-zero arc, and air-blast circuit-breakers are particularly sensitive to this kind of fault because of their inability to absorb a large power input into the post-zero arc. Hence failure to interrupt occurs before the interrupting device has experienced any appreciable recovery voltage.

The amplitude of the saw-toothed transient at the line side terminal will be dependent on the fault current, which will naturally be at its maximum value at points near the power source. Beyond, say, 4 to 5 miles (6·5–8 km), the impedance of the transmission line reduces the fault current sufficiently to ease the nature of the transient and the duty on the breaker. The frequency of the saw-toothed transient is inversely proportional to the distance between the breaker and the fault, while the r.r.v. is proportional to the current. In a paper presented to a conference at The Institution of Electrical Engineers, Amer and Lightly[4] noted that a 60 kA source fault level produces line side r.r.v. of the order of 12 000 V/μs. Since the problems of short-line faults have been recognised, facilities have been introduced in test plants whereby the conditions can be simulated and tests made to prove the ability of circuit-breakers to deal with such faults.

Discussion up to this point has been concerned with problems met when the value of current to be interrupted is very high, i.e. short-circuit currents. The need for powerful de-ionisation action at the zero pause in the current cycle has been noted, but to have equally powerful aid available at other periods in the cycle can lead to other problems. This is the case when the current to be interrupted is small and inductive, such as the magnetising current of a power transformer.

In an air-blast circuit-breaker, the de-ionising force does not differ whether the current is large or small, i.e. the high-pressure air-blast is constant. This leads to a tendency to force a small value of current to zero *before* the natural pause in the cycle, a condition which is known as *current chopping*. In an oil circuit-breaker on the other hand, the de-ionising forces, i.e. gas generation and pressure, are dependent on the value of current, so that in this type current chopping is unlikely. Figure 2.13 is included here to illustrate the phenomenon, this illustration being used by Cox and Wilcox[5] in relation to the following extract from their I.E.E. paper:

'As the 50 Hz current being interrupted approaches zero, a value is reached at which de-ionisation of the arc in the contact gap is so rapid that the current is forcibly suppressed before the natural zero point. If the total reactance of the circuit is such that the current to be interrupted is of the order of 150A r.m.s. or above, this forcible suppression occurs when the current has nearly reached zero. With higher values of circuit reactance giving lower values of 50 Hz current, the total amount of ionisation of the contact gap is less and suppression of the current occurs earlier before the current zero at a higher instantaneous value, thereby inducing a higher voltage in the increased circuit inductance. With a correctly designed breaker, this voltage is prevented from rising to a dangerous level by breaking down the contact gap and re-establishing the normal arc. The arc current which flows is again forcibly suppressed and the process is repeated until the current almost reaches its normal zero'.

The overvoltages caused by these sudden current interruptions before a natural zero can be as high as 2·5 to 3 times normal voltage, depending on the type of circuit-breaker. The transient overvoltages arising out of interrupting transformer magnetising currents can also be the cause of what is known as an *evolved fault*. This arises out of the fact that the overvoltage causes the protective

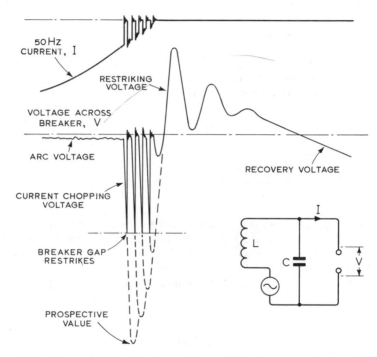

Figure 2.13. Current chopping when interrupting small inductive currents (courtesy J.I.E.E.)

rod-gap on the power transformer bushing to flash-over, and simultaneously a restrike may occur in the circuit-breaker which may result in power current flowing through the circuit-breaker and the rod-gap which are effectively in series. The mechanism of an evolved fault on oil-break circuit-breakers is demonstrated in Fig. 2.14, an illustration which together with the following extracted description, is due to Morton[6]:

The chopped current, as we have noted, produces a transient overvoltage which is impressed across the transformer causing the rod-gap to spark over. In Fig. 2.14 this is the voltage x and is the sum of the instantaneous 50 Hz voltage and the transient voltage marked y. The voltage across the rod-gap falls to zero, but because of its short distance away from the transformer the potential of circuit-breaker terminal B follows this collapse in voltage as a

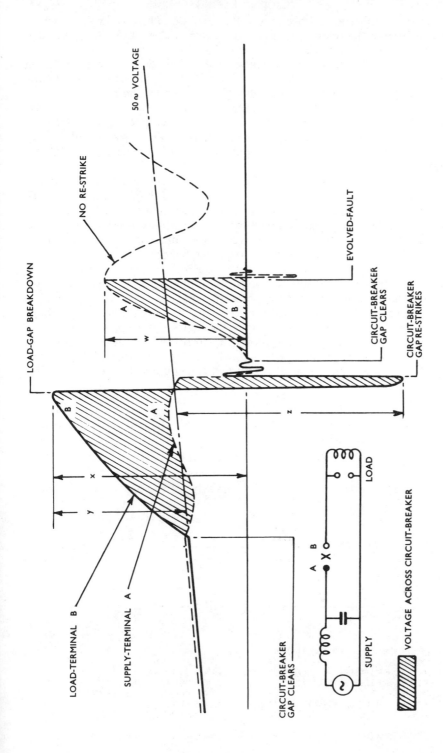

Figure 2.14. *Mechanism of an evolved fault on an oil circuit-breaker* (courtesy A. Reyrolle & Co. Ltd.)

high-frequency transient and overshoots the earth potential. The voltage across the circuit-breaker therefore increases from y to z, and the circuit-breaker gap may restrike if the ratio z/y is greater than unity.

When the circuit-breaker gap restrikes, the breaker clears its own restriking current and is then subjected to recovery voltage. If the latter restrikes the circuit-breaker gap again, it produces an evolving fault because the rod-gap will not have de-ionised by this time. For this fault to occur, the ratio w/y must also be greater than unity. Because of inherent damping in the circuit, the value of w cannot be more than 1·8 times the 50 Hz voltage peak and it is assumed that the dielectric strength of the residual arc-path has hardly increased in this time interval.

Morton also shows that for an evolved fault to occur the flashover value of the rod-gap (x in Fig. 2.14) must be set to a value less than 2·8 times the peak value of the system voltage, but notes that in practice a setting of this order is low and is more usually about four times, which cannot produce an evolved fault. Heavily polluted insulation however, can reduce the insulation level to such an extent that the transformer bushing may flashover.

Where an evolved fault does occur, it is severe in its effects on an oil circuit-breaker whether of the bulk-oil or small-oil-volume types. The reason for this is that at the instant of restrike the contacts may have separated an appreciable distance, and if the current is of a value close to the rating of the breaker, damage to the arc-control device is possible due to the high-impulse pressure set up by restriking a heavy current in relatively low-pressure oil. The chances of an evolved fault occurring with an air-blast circuit-breaker are remote because the rod-gap setting has to be extremely small (nearly half that quoted for oil-break). This

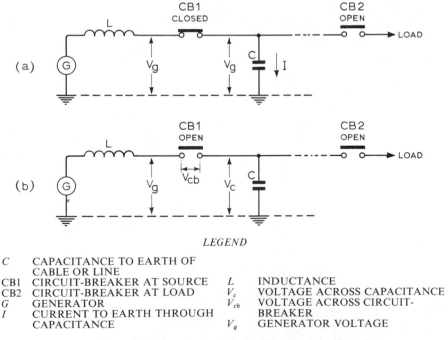

LEGEND

C	CAPACITANCE TO EARTH OF CABLE OR LINE		
CB1	CIRCUIT-BREAKER AT SOURCE	L	INDUCTANCE
CB2	CIRCUIT-BREAKER AT LOAD	V_c	VOLTAGE ACROSS CAPACITANCE
G	GENERATOR	V_{cb}	VOLTAGE ACROSS CIRCUIT-
I	CURRENT TO EARTH THROUGH		BREAKER
	CAPACITANCE	V_g	GENERATOR VOLTAGE

Figure 2.15. Equivalent circuits when switching unloaded cables or lines

lower setting is necessary because the high rate-of-rise of dielectric-recovery of the air-blast circuit-breaker requires a larger ratio of z/y.

A further problem related to the interruption of relatively small currents and giving rise to overvoltages, is that which arises when a circuit-breaker is opened to disconnect an *unloaded* cable or line. In this operation, the breaker is called upon to interrupt the current flowing to earth via the capacitances of the cable or line. The assumed conditions before and after this operation are shown diagrammatically in Fig. 2.15 (a) and (b), *CB2* being open at the load end and *CB1* being the breaker to be opened. In a circuit of this nature, the current I will lead the voltage V_g by 90°, so that when the current is interrupted at a natural zero the voltage will be at its peak, V_{gp}. This is shown in Fig. 2.16 and the cable or line will remain charged to this value (subject to diminution due to leakage), i.e. V_c is equal to V_{gp}, while the supply voltage continues its 50 Hz oscillation. This means that the voltage across the contact gap in the circuit-breaker is now the algebraic difference between V_g and V_c, giving a resultant V_{cb}. At its peak this is seen to be equal to twice the peak value of the circuit voltage, but as the

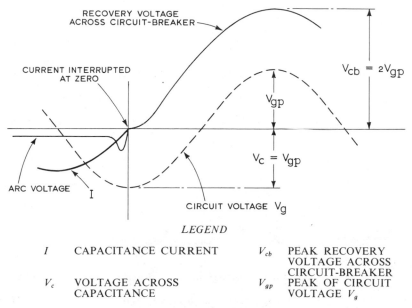

RECOVERY VOLTAGE ACROSS CIRCUIT-BREAKER

CURRENT INTERRUPTED AT ZERO

$V_{cb} = 2V_{gp}$

V_{gp}

$V_c = V_{gp}$

ARC VOLTAGE

I

CIRCUIT VOLTAGE V_g

LEGEND

I	CAPACITANCE CURRENT	V_{cb}	PEAK RECOVERY VOLTAGE ACROSS CIRCUIT-BREAKER
V_c	VOLTAGE ACROSS CAPACITANCE	V_{gp}	PEAK OF CIRCUIT VOLTAGE V_g

Figure 2.16.   Recovery voltage across CB1 in Figure 2.15 after interrupting capacitance current from cable or line to earth

rate of rise to V_{cb} is relatively slow there is reasonable time for de-ionisation of the arc-gap before the peak is reached. The conditions are easily withstood in air-blast circuit-breakers, as here the full de-ionising force will be available, but in an oil circuit-breaker where the contacts may have parted only a short distance by the time the peak voltage V_{cb} is reached and the de-ionising forces will be minimal, a restrike may occur.

If this happens, the restrike current will be a high-frequency oscillation with high initial peak magnitude, the frequency of the oscillation being dependent on the capacitance C (plus any capacitance on the supply side) and the inductance L in accordance with the formula on page 33. Its first zero is reached quickly, and if it is interrupted at this point the voltage across the capacitance is now three times V_{gp} and the capacitance remains charged at this value. On the supply side the voltage continues its 50 Hz oscillation so that a point is reached when the voltage V_{cb} across the breaker becomes four times V_{gp}. If this results in a further restrike, the build-up of voltage becomes progressively greater and theoretically could go on indefinitely. Fortunately practical factors make for easement, not the least of these being the leakage which inevitably occurs so that the voltage on the cable or line falls sensibly from its maximum. Even so, in the book edited by Trencham[7], Gosland notes that voltages of 2·5 times the normal peak have been observed on the line and 3·5 times across the circuit-breaker.

The conditions noted for cable or line capacitance switching are also those involved with the switching of capacitors, such as those in wide use for power factor improvement. When such switching is achieved by an oil circuit-breaker, the latter may be in some difficulty.

REFERENCES

1. CASSIE, A.M., 'A New Theory of Arc Rupture and Circuit-breaking', *C.I.G.R.É.*, **10**, paper 102 (1939)
2. TRENCHAM, H. (EDITOR), *Circuit Breaking* (a series of six lectures by different authors), 1–45, Butterworths (1953)
3. GARRARD, C.J.O., 'High-voltage Switchgear—a Review of Progress', *Proc. I.E.E.*, **113** No. 9, Sept. (1966)
4. AMER, D.F. and LIGHTLY, D., 'Permanently Pressurised Heavy-duty Air-blast Circuit-breakers for 400 kV and Above', a paper included in 'Design Criterion and Equipment for Transmission at 400 kV and Higher Voltages', *I.E.E. Conf. Pub.*, No. 15, 178 (1965)
5. COX, H.E. and WILCOX, T.W., 'The Performance of High-voltage Oil Circuit-breakers Incorporating Resistance Switching', *J.I.E.E.*, **94**, Part 2, Aug. (1947)
6. MORTON, J.S., 'Modern High-voltage Circuit-breaking and Arc-control', *Reyrolle Review*, No. 181, Dec. (1962). Reprint No. RR107
7. TRENCHAM, H. (EDITOR), *Circuit Breaking* (a series of six lectures by different authors). Lecture No. 3, 'Circuit Constants in Relation to Circuit Breaking', Butterworths (1953)

BIBLIOGRAPHY

ALLAN, A. and AMER, D.F., 'The Extinction of Arcs in Air-blast Circuit-breakers', *J.I.E.E.*, **94**, Part 2, Aug. (1947)
BALTENSPERGER, P., 'Solving Problems in High-voltage Switchgear', *Brown Boveri Rev.*, **57**, Dec. (1970)
BICKFORD, J.P., 'Switching Overvoltages on Transmission Lines', *Elect. Rev.*, 1 Sept. (1967)
BOLTON, E. *et al*, 'Short-line Fault Tests on the C.E.G.B. 275 kV System', *Proc. I.E.E.*, **117** No. 4, April (1970)
COX, H.E. and WILCOX, T.W., 'The Influence of Resistance Switching in the Design of High-voltage Air-blast Circuit-breakers, *J.I.E.E.*, **91** No. 24, Part 2, Dec. (1944)
COX, H.E. and WILCOX, T.W., 'The Performance of High-voltage Oil Circuit-breakers Incorporating Resistance Switching', *J.I.E.E.*, **94**, Part 2, Aug. (1947)
CRANE, P.H.G., '*Switchgear Principles*', Macmillan (1957)
EIDINGER, A. and JUSILA, J. 'Transients During Three-phase Short-line Faults', *Brown Boveri Review*, **51** No. 5, May (1964)
GRAY, W. and AMER, D.F., 'Some Recent Developments in Switchgear', *Reyrolle Review*, No. 190, summer (1967). Reprint No. RR 122
HARLE, J.A. and WILD, R.W., 'Restriking Voltage as a Factor in the Performance, Rating and Selection of Circuit-breakers', *J.I.E.E.*, **91** No. 24, Part 2, Dec. (1944)

CIRCUIT BREAKING

KÖPPL, G. and RUOSSE, E., 'Switching Overvoltages in E.H.V. and U.H.V. Networks', *Brown Boveri Rev.*, **57**, Dec. (1970)

MORTLAKE, J.R., 'The Evaluation of Restriking Voltages', *J.I.E.E.*, **92** No. 30, Part 2, Dec. (1945)

RUOSSE, E., 'Test Methods and Facilities in the High-power Testing Station', *Brown Boveri Review*, **55** No. 12, Dec. (1968)

SWIFT-HOOK, D.T., 'Circuit-breaker Reliability', *Elect. Rev.*, 5 Jan. (1968)

WILLIAMS, W.P., 'Switchgear for Extra-high-voltage Systems', *J. of Sci. & Tech.*, **37** No. 2 (1970)

Chapter 3

Short-circuit calculations for
symmetrical faults

The importance of determining the fault level at any point on an electrical system where switchgear is to be installed or for check purposes when plant extensions are contemplated, is well known. This knowledge is essential for the purchase of circuit-interrupting devices (circuit-breakers, fuses, fuse-switches, load-breaking switches) of proved rating, and to enable the switch-gear manufacturer to supply associated apparatus such as busbars, connections, current transformers, cable-end boxes, etc. designed to withstand the electro-magnetic and thermal conditions which arise due to the passage of the fault current until it is interrupted. These latter problems will be noted in some detail in Chapters 8 and 23.

For high and extra-high-voltage transmission systems where there is often considerable interconnection between power sources with highly concentrated load conditions (the British 'grid' systems are typical) the relatively simple 'do-it-yourself' calculations to be demonstrated here are not applicable. For such systems, many factors and operating conditions beyond those that we shall note here have to be known and taken into account, the complexity of the calculations being such as to demand the aid of machines, e.g. network analysers, computers, etc.

In this chapter, our purpose is to concentrate on calculations which can be made by simple methods and which give results sufficiently accurate for the situation under consideration. These situations are, in general, related to relatively small (usually privately owned) generating stations and cable distribution systems up to 33 kV, but with the emphasis on calculations for medium-voltage networks such as those that occur in industrial and service installations.

For the purposes noted earlier, calculations can normally be made on the assumption of a three-phase fault as represented in Fig. 3.1, i.e. a symmetrical or balanced fault condition. Other types of fault such as those between two phases or between one phase and earth resulting in unsymmetrical (unbalanced) conditions will be considered in Chapter 4 where the more complicated method of calculation using symmetrical component theory will be introduced.

The basic information necessary for any calculation is threefold; firstly that relating to all the sources from which fault power can originate, secondly that

44

of factors which control the magnitude of the fault, and thirdly a system schematic showing how the sources of power and the limiting factors are connected
or interconnected.

The sources of fault power reside very largely in generating plant, but it is
important not to overlook the fact that significant contributions to the fault
current can be made by large induction motors, such as those which because of
their size, operate in the voltage range 3·3 to 11 kV, typical examples occurring
in power station practice for auxiliary services and in heavy industries such as
steel works, paper and board mills and chemical plants. Elsewhere in industry,
much smaller motors operating at say 415 V may, in the aggregate, total many
thousand horsepower, and in these circumstances again the contribution to
the fault current may be such that it cannot be ignored.

Operating for a short period as generators for which the source of excitation
is the stored magnetic energy, these large motors or concentrations of smaller
motors, or a combination of both, can feed current of some magnitude into a

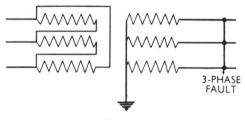

3-PHASE
FAULT

Figure 3.1

faulted system in the first half-cycle of short-circuit, reaching ten or more
times the aggregate-normal full-load current. The source of excitation however
is rapidly consumed, so that the fault current decays from its peak value in the
first half-cycle until, after say 5 cycles or so, it is relatively insignificant. This at
once suggests that if the operating time (from instant of short-circuit to contacts
part) of the circuit-breaker whose duty it is to isolate the fault, extends to 5
cycles or more, fault current contributions from motors can be ignored in
assessing the fault level for a 'break' duty. Much faster operating times are
however now common, and are essential to system stability, so that at the time
the breaker contacts part, the fault feed from the motors will have decayed only
slightly below its peak and will need to be added to that from other sources.

In some cases it is reasonable to assume that motor contributions will be
taken care of in the margin of difference between the *calculated* fault level based
on system parameters, and the rating of the nearest (higher) *standard* circuit-
breaker which must be chosen. Thus, for a calculated fault level of say 190 MVA
at 11 kV, the nearest standard circuit-breaker is one rated 250 MVA, or for
a calculated fault level of say 27 MVA at 415 V, the chosen circuit-breaker will
be one rated 31 MVA, and margins of this order may be sufficient to cover the
motor contribution. It is also reasonable to assume that these margins will in
themselves include a small factor of safety in that the calculated fault levels
will take no account of details which further limit the fault current, e.g. the
impedance of busbars, connections, series coils and current transformers.

The importance of the motor contribution to the fault current is of equal
and possibly greater concern, in so far as it affects the duty of a circuit-breaker
where the latter is called upon to 'make' on to a fault. The current involved in

this duty is always the high initial peak in the first half-cycle of short-circuit and therefore includes the highest contribution from the motors, and it is important therefore to ensure that the making capacity of the chosen circuit-breaker is at least equal to the total peak current from *all* sources.

Motor contributions to the fault current are influenced by various factors and the problem of assessing what they may be for a given installation is beyond the simplified approach of this chapter. It suffices to note that *large* motor loads can contribute significantly, as has been shown in two recent I.E.E. papers[1,2] both based on test results and giving practical guidance in the matter.

The magnitude of a fault, ignoring the foregoing, is controlled by the combined impedances of all machines, transformers, cables or overhead lines and, if employed, series reactors. It is essential therefore in any calculation to have knowledge of all impedances between the source(s) of power and the point of fault, and in particular, how they are connected, i.e. in series or parallel or a combination of both, or as we shall note later, forming a star or delta network. It may be noted here that impedance Z is the value obtained by the vectorial addition of resistance R and reactance X, as in Fig. 3.2. In some cases resistance is so small in comparison with reactance that it is of little significance, and can therefore be assumed to be zero.

This condition is generally true for generators, transformers, synchronous motors and reactors, while on the other hand resistance in cables and overhead

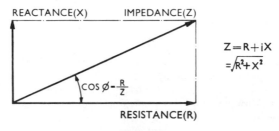

$$Z = R + iX$$
$$= \sqrt{R^2 + X^2}$$

$$\cos \phi = \frac{R}{Z}$$

Figure 3.2

lines can be considerable and cannot be ignored in the calculations, as will be noted in the examples to be demonstrated later, more particularly those relating to medium-voltage systems, i.e. in the range 400–600 V. In general, it can be assumed that when the resistance is less than one-third of the reactance value, a calculation which ignores resistance will not be in error by more than 5%, 'error' in this sense meaning that the calculated fault level will be higher than the true value.

Resistance, reactance and impedance may be expressed either in percentage or ohmic terms, manufacturers normally quoting the former for generators, transformers, reactors, etc. and the latter for cables or overhead lines. While short-circuit calculations can be made using either percentage or ohmic values, they cannot be made using a mixture, so that if, as in this chapter, calculations are to be made using percentages, any item for which ohmic values are given must first be converted to an equivalent value, using the formula:

$$\frac{\% \text{ value on given kVA base}} = \frac{\text{kVA base} \times \text{value in ohms} \times 10^5}{V^2}$$

Where V is the voltage between lines, in volts.

The term *kVA base* in the foregoing points to the fact that a proper evaluation can only be made when *all* percentage values are related to a common base kVA. It is not important what value is chosen as a base, and it may well be unrelated to the kVA rating of any part of the system. In what follows, calculations will be made using percentage values on a 100 000 kVA base, and while this may appear to be unduly high in relation to many actual system ratings, it has the advantage of producing decimal values which are reasonably manageable in the calculations.

This conversion from ohmic to percentage values is almost wholly concerned with cables or overhead lines. Manufacturers tables for these however normally give values in ohms per kilometre, but as many cable lengths, particularly in medium-voltage installations, and those at the lower end of the high-voltage range (3·3 to 11 kV) are more conveniently measured in metres, the appropriate tables given later will be on the basis of percentage per metre, thus permitting a simple multiplication by the number of metres in a given example. The value given in any manufacturers tables in ohms per kilometre can be converted to percentage values on a 100 000 kVA base per metre by the simple process of multiplying the ohmic value by one of the following factors:

System voltage (V)	Multiplying factor
400	62·5
415	58·0
440	51·5
500	40·0
550	33·0
600	28·0
3 300	0·918
6 600	0·229
11 000	0·0826
15 000	0·0444
22 000	0·0207
33 000	0·0090

Tables for machines and transformers whose percentage values are normally quoted by manufacturers at the normal kVA rating must be prepared on our chosen 100 000 kVA base using the formula:

$$\frac{\% \text{ value on}}{\text{kVA base}} = \frac{\text{kVA base} \times \text{normal percentage}}{\text{machine or transformer kVA}}$$

Thus, a transformer rated 400 kVA with a reactance of 4·75 %, will, on our base kVA, have a reactance of

$$\frac{100\,000 \times 4·75}{400} = 1187·5\%$$

HIGH-VOLTAGE CALCULATIONS

For the purpose of demonstrating how calculations may be made for high-voltage systems (up to 33 kV and assuming cable networks) Tables 3.1 to 3.5

have been compiled based on the foregoing discussion. In Table 3.1 it should be noted that the typical normal reactances are only representative, while in Table 3.2 they are based on the average reactance values for typical power transformers. In both cases, actual values should, whenever possible, be ascertained and converted to reactance values on the kVA base as previously discussed.

Tables 3.3, 3.4 and 3.5 give values for both resistance and reactance for a range of paper-insulated cables to the new metric standard BS 6480: Part 1 (1969), the resistance values being given alternatively for copper and aluminium conductors. With these tables available, short-circuit calculations are very much simplified as will be demonstrated in the following worked examples, starting with the simple system shown in Fig. 3.3. Here, a single generator feeds a busbar at 6·6 kV from which a number of feeder circuits are taken. It is assumed that a fault occurs at F_1 at a point close-up to the circuit-breaker on a feeder,

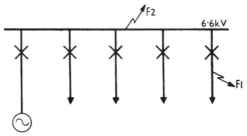

Figure 3.3.   5 000 kVA generator 240% on 100 000 kVA from Table 3.1

or, alternatively on the busbars at F_2. For the first condition, the breaker in the faulty feeder will open to isolate the fault, while for the second condition, the circuit-breaker in the generator circuit must trip open. In this example, the only impedance to either fault is that of the generator. As noted earlier, the resistance R for the generator may be assumed to be zero, while the reactance X on our 100 000 kVA base, taken from Table 3.1 is seen to be 240 %. The impedance Z is therefore:

$$Z = R + jX$$

i.e. $$Z = \sqrt{R^2 + X^2}$$

$$= \sqrt{0^2 + 240^2}$$

$$= 240\%$$

The formula to obtain the fault value is:

$$\text{s.c. MVA} = \frac{\text{kVA base} \times 100}{Z \times 1\,000}$$

and as all our calculations will be on a 100 000 kVA base, this simplifies to:

$$\text{s.c. MVA} = \frac{100\,000 \times 100}{Z \times 1\,000} = \frac{10\,000}{Z}$$

so that for the example in Fig. 3.3 we get:

$$\text{s.c. MVA} = \frac{10\,000}{240} = 41\cdot66$$

Table 3.1

HIGH-SPEED GENERATORS

Rating (kVA)	Typical normal reactance (%)	Voltage (kV)	% Reactance on 100 000 kVA base
1 000	12·0		1 200
2 000			600
5 000		up to 11	240
7 500			160
10 000			120
15 000			80
20 000	13·5	up to 11	67·5
25 000			54·0
30 000	15	up to 11	50·0
30 000	20·0	22/33	66·6

Table 3.2

POWER TRANSFORMERS

Rating (kVA)	% Reactance on 100 000 kVA base			
	H.V. Winding kV			
	3·3/6·6	11·0	15·0	22/33
100	4 750	4 750	5 000	5 000
150	3 166	3 166	3 333	3 333
200	2 375	2 375	2 500	2 500
250	1 900	1 900	2 000	2 000
300	1 583	1 583	1 666	1 666
400	1 187	1 187	1 250	1 250
500	950	950	1 000	1 000
600	791	791	833	833
750	633	633	666	666
1 000	475	475	500	500
1 250	400 ·	400	440	440
1 500	366	366	400	400
2 000	300	300	300	300
2 500	240	240	240	240
3 000	—	200	217	233
4 000	—	150	157	175
5 000	—	120	130	140
6 000	—	117	117	125
7 500	—	93	100	107
10 000	—	—	—	90
12 500	—	—	—	80
15 000	—	—	—	70
20 000	—	—	—	50
25 000	—	—	—	40
30 000	—	—	—	35

This simple example can be used, in passing, to demonstrate that the choice of kVA base does not affect the result. If we assume that a base equal to the generator rating is used, i.e. 5 000 kVA, then the impedance value will be the normal value which is shown in Table 3.1 as 12% and we now get:

$$\text{s.c. MVA} = \frac{5\,000 \times 100}{12 \times 1\,000} = 41.66$$

As a network becomes more complicated, the system of impedances is more readily visualised if drawn in the form of an impedance diagram. A diagram for the simple example is shown in Fig. 3.4.

As an extension to the foregoing, we may assume a larger station in which there are three generators in parallel and that each has a different rating, as shown in Fig. 3.5. Again it is assumed that a fault occurs on a feeder as at F close-up to the circuit-breaker, and that all generators are in service. The impedance diagram for this system can be drawn in the form shown in Fig. 3.6 which shows the parallel connection of the three impedances. Before the calculation can proceed however, these must be converted to a single equivalent impedance based on the reciprocal of the sum of the reciprocals, as follows:

$$Z = \frac{1}{\dfrac{1}{0+\text{j}240} + \dfrac{1}{0+\text{j}120} + \dfrac{1}{0+\text{j}160}}$$

$$= \frac{1}{0 - \text{j}0.01875}$$

$$= 0 + \text{j}53.33\%$$

Table 3.3

THREE-CORE PAPER-INSULATED CABLES WITH COPPER AND ALUMINIUM CONDUCTORS, MANUFACTURED IN ACCORDANCE WITH BS 6480:PART 1 (1969)

Nominal area of conductor mm^2	*Percentage resistance (R) and reactance (X) per metre on a 100 000 kVA base*								
	3 300 V (belted)			*6 600 V (belted)*			*11 000 V (belted)[1]*		
	$R^{[2]}$		$X^{[4]}$	$R^{[2]}$		$X^{[4]}$	$R^{[3]}$		$X^{[4]}$
	Cu	*Al*	*Cu & Al*	*Cu*	*Al*	*Cu & Al*	*Cu*	*Al*	*Cu & Al*
10	2·060	3·43	0·087	0·513	0·855	0·026·	—	—	—
16	1·310	2·18	0·084	0·325	0·543	0·024	0·112	0·187	0·0092
25	0·825	1·37	0·076	0·206	0·341	0·022	0·071	0·117	0·0087
35	0·595	0·99	0·074	0·149	0·247	0·0211	0·051	0·085	0·0081
50	0·440	0·73	0·073	0·110	0·180	0·0204	0·038	0·063	0·0077
70	0·305	0·506	0·072	0·076	0·126	0·0195	0·026	0·043	0·0074
95	0·220	0·366	0·067	0·055	0·092	0·0186	0·019	0·033	0·0071
120	0·175	0·290	0·066	0·044	0·072	0·0181	0·015	0·025	0·0068
150	0·143	0·236	0·065	0·035	0·059	0·0179	0·012	0·021	0·0067
185	0·114	0·188	0·064	0·029	0·047	0·0174	0·010	0·016	0·0064
240	0·088	0·144	0·063	0·022	0·036	0·0170	0·0075	0·012	0·0064
300	0·071	0·171	0·062	0·018	0·029	0·0167	0·0060	0·010	0·0063
400	0·057	0·091	0·062	0·014	0·023	0·0165	0·0048	0·008	0·0062

Notes (1) See Table 3.4 for screened type 11 kV cables.
(2) At maximum conductor temperature 80°C.
(3) At maximum conductor temperature 65°C.
(4) At a frequency of 50 Hz.
Cables of 10 mm² area have circular solid conductors, all others stranded [see BS 6480: Part 1 (1969) for details of shapes, etc.]
Based on data provided by British Insulated Callender's Cables Ltd.

Table 3.4
THREE-CORE PAPER-INSULATED CABLES WITH COPPER AND ALUMINIUM CONDUCTORS, MANUFACTURED IN ACCORDANCE WITH BS 6480:PART 1 (1969)

Nominal area of conductor mm²	*11 000 V (screened)*			*15 000 V (screened)*			*22 000 V (screened)*[1]		
	$R^{(2)}$		$X^{(4)}$	$R^{(2)}$		$X^{(4)}$	$R^{(3)}$		$X^{(4)}$
	Cu	*Al*	*Cu & Al*	*Cu*	*Al*	*Cu & Al*	*Cu*	*Al*	*Cu & Al*
16	0·114	0·189	0·0093	—	—	—	—	—	—
25	0·072	0·119	0·0088	0·038	0·064	0·0050	0·0177	0·0293	0·0025
35	0·051	0·086	0·0082	0·028	0·046	0·0047	0·0127	0·0213	0·0024
50	0·038	0·064	0·0078	0·021	0·034	0·0045	0·0094	0·0156	0·0023
70	0·027	0·044	0·0075	0·014	0·024	0·0042	0·0065	0·0108	0·0022
95	0·019	0·032	0·0072	0·010	0·016	0·0041	0·0047	0·0078	0·0021
120	0·015	0·026	0·0069	0·008	0·013	0·0039	0·0037	0·0062	0·0020
150	0·012	0·021	0·0068	0·0066	0·011	0·0038	0·0031	0·0050	0·00197
185	0·010	0·016	0·0067	0·0053	0·0088	0·0037	0·0024	0·0041	0·00188
240	0·0076	0·013	0·0065	0·0041	0·0067	0·0036	0·0018	0·0031	0·00182
300	0·0062	0·010	0·0064	0·0033	0·0054	0·0035	0·0015	0·0025	0·00178
400	0·0050	0·008	0·0062	0·0026	0·0042	0·0034	0·0012	0·0019	0·00172

Percentage resistance (R) and reactance (X) per metre on a 100 000 kVA base

Notes (1) See Table 3.5 for SL type 22 kV cables.
(2) At maximum conductor temperature 70°C.
(3) At maximum conductor temperature 65°C.
(4) At a frequency of 50 Hz.
Stranded conductors—see BS 6480:Part 1 (1969) for details of shapes, etc.
Based on data provided by British Insulated Callender's Cables Ltd.

Table 3.5
THREE-CORE PAPER-INSULATED CABLES WITH COPPER AND ALUMINIUM CONDUCTORS, MANUFACTURED IN ACCORDANCE WITH BS 6480:PART 1 (1969)

Percentage resistance (R) and reactance (X) per metre on a 100 000 kVA base

Nominal area of conductor mm²	*22 000 V (SL)*[1]			*33 000 V (screened)*			*33 000 V (SL)*		
	$R^{(2)}$		$X^{(3)}$	$R^{(2)}$		$X^{(3)}$	$R^{(2)}$		$X^{(3)}$
	Cu	*Al*	*Cu & Al*	*Cu*	*Al*	*Cu & Al*	*Cu*	*Al*	*Cu & Al*
25	0·0177	0·0298	0·0028	—	—	—	—	—	—
35	0·0127	0·0213	0·0027	—	—	—	—	—	—
50	0·0094	0·0156	0·0026	0·0041	0·0068	0·00112	0·0042	0·0068	0·00124
70	0·0065	0·0108	0·0024	0·0028	0·0047	0·00110	0·0028	0·0047	0·00117
95	0·0047	0·0078	0·0023	0·0021	0·0034	0·00100	0·0021	0·0034	0·00110
120	0·0037	0·0062	0·0022	0·00163	0·0027	0·00096	0·00163	0·0027	0·00106
150	0·0031	0·0050	0·00219	0·00132	0·0022	0·00092	0·00132	0·0022	0·00102
185	0·0024	0·0041	0·00211	0·00106	0·0017	0·00089	0·00106	0·00174	0·00098
240	0·0018	0·0031	0·00204	0·00087	0·0013	0·00085	0·00082	0·00134	0·00095
300	0·0015	0·0025	0·00196	0·00065	0·0011	0·00083	0·00065	0·00110	0·00092
400	0·0012	0·0019	0·00192	0·00052	0·0008	0·00081	0·00052	0·00084	0·00087

Notes (1) See Table 3.4 for screened type 22 kV cables.
(2) At maximum conductor temperature 65°C.
(3) At a frequency of 50 Hz.
Stranded conductors—see BS 6480:Part 1 (1969) for shapes, etc.
Based on data provided by British Insulated Callender's Cables Ltd.

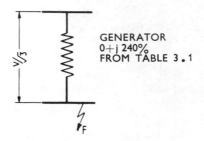

GENERATOR
0+j 240%
FROM TABLE 3.1

Figure 3.4

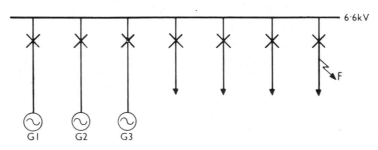

6·6kV

F

Figure 3.5. Three generators, each with different ratings. From Table 3.1: G1 is 5000 kVA (0+j240%), G2 is 10000 kVA (0+j120%) and G3 is 7500 kVA (0+j160%)

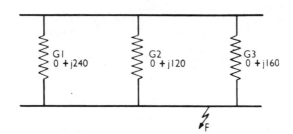

G1
0 +j240

G2
0 +j120

G3
0 +j160

F

Figure 3.6

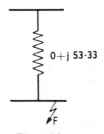

0+j 53·33

F

Figure 3.7

52

The impedance diagram therefore reduces to that shown in Fig. 3.7 and the short-circuit value will be:

$$\text{s.c. MVA} = \frac{10\,000}{53 \cdot 33} = 187 \cdot 5$$

Developing a stage further, let us assume that one of the feeders gives supply to a substation as shown in Fig. 3.8, the essential particulars for the cable between the two points being as indicated. It is now required to determine the fault level at the substation when a fault occurs at F close-up to the substation

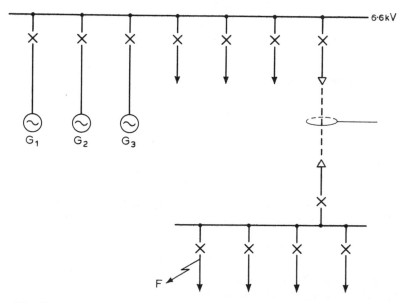

Figure 3.8. Generator ratings as Figure 3.5. 6·6 kV 3-core cable with copper conductors. Nominal area = 240 mm², length = 1 500m, R = 0·022% per metre and X = 0·017% per metre, from Table 3.3

circuit-breaker. Redrawn as an impedance diagram, the condition is as shown in Fig. 3.9 which indicates that we have three impedances (generators) in parallel and one (the feeder cable) in series with them. Using the data previously obtained from Figs. 3.6 and 3.7, the network can at once be reduced to give Fig. 3.10, which shows two impedances in series, which are added arithmetically to result in a single equivalent impedance, as shown in Fig. 3.11.

This example is one in which account must be taken of both the resistance and reactance factors relating to the cable, and in the impedance diagrams the values shown are derived from the per metre figures given in Table 3.3 multiplied by the cable length, i.e. 1 500 m.

From Fig. 3.11 the impedance to the fault is given by:

$$Z = 33 + j78 \cdot 83$$

$$= \sqrt{33^2 + 78 \cdot 83^2}$$

$$= \sqrt{7\,303} = 85 \cdot 45\%$$

53

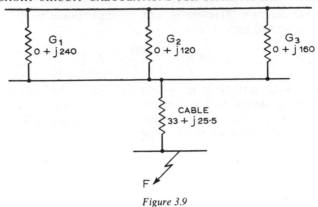

Figure 3.9

and the fault level will be:

$$\text{s.c. MVA} = \frac{10\,000}{85\cdot45} = 117$$

The approximate power factor (p.f.) at the fault may be calculated from:

$$\text{p.f.} = \frac{R}{Z} = \frac{33}{85\cdot45} = 0\cdot38$$

To emphasise the effect of taking the cable resistance into account, we may note that if this had been ignored, the fault level would have been calculated as:

$$\text{s.c. MVA} = \frac{10\,000}{78\cdot83} = 127 \text{ (approx.)}$$

If it is now assumed that the substation is fed by two cables, as in Fig. 3.12, each having the same data, the impedance diagram will appear as in Fig. 3.13, which shows two groups of parallel impedances in series. The single equivalent impedance for the three generators will be as determined previously. For the two cables, which have *equal* resistance and reactance values, the equivalent impedance will be half of the individual value of one cable, so that the impedance diagram reduces to Fig. 3.14, and adding the series impedances arithmetically this in turn is further reduced to Fig. 3.15. From this, the calculation to arrive at the substation fault level proceeds thus:

$$Z = 16\cdot5 + j66\cdot08$$

$$= \sqrt{16\cdot5^2 + 66\cdot08^2}$$

$$= \sqrt{4\,639} = 68\cdot1\%$$

$$\text{s.c. MVA} = \frac{10\,000}{68\cdot1} = 146\cdot8$$

This demonstrates that with the two parallel cables, the fault level at the substation is *higher* than when only one cable is used. It should also be noted that if the two cables had had different characteristics (resistance and/or reactance values) the determination of the equivalent single values is more

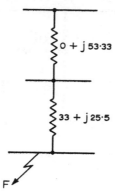

Figure 3.10.   Reduction of Figure 3.9 (using data obtained in Figures 3.6 and 3.7)
to two impedances in series

Figure 3.11

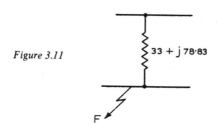

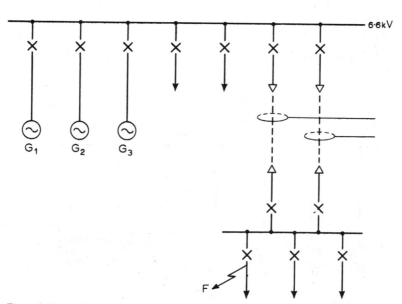

Figure 3.12.   Substation fed by two cables. Ratings as Figure 3.5, cables as Figure 3.8

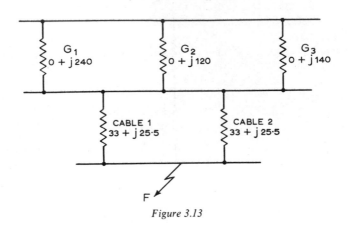

Figure 3.13

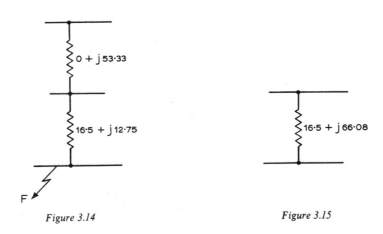

Figure 3.14

Figure 3.15

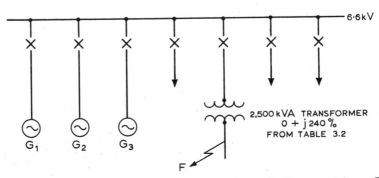

Figure 3.16. Power transformer controlled by one of the feeder circuits. Generator ratings as Figure 3.5

56

complicated and will be demonstrated later in one of the examples relating to calculations for medium-voltage systems.

One further extension of the system may be considered, i.e. where one of the feeder circuits controls a power transformer as shown in Fig. 3.16, and it is required to determine the fault level at a point just beyond the transformer, for the purpose of selecting a circuit-breaker for installation at this point. The impedance diagram for this condition is given in Fig. 3.17, which reduces to Fig. 3.18 by adding series impedances arithmetically, and the fault level will be:

$$\text{s.c. MVA} = \frac{10\,000}{293\cdot33} = 34\cdot1$$

The value of reducing an electrical diagram to an impedance diagram and the subsequent reduction to a single equivalent impedance is well demonstrated

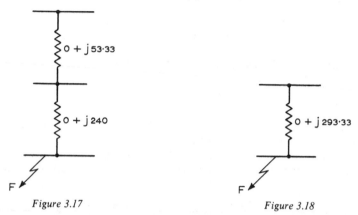

Figure 3.17   *Figure 3.18*

by a study of a system in which busbar reactors are introduced (Fig. 3.19) for the purpose of limiting the fault MVA, noting that without the reactors and with all three machines in operation, a calculation as previously demonstrated would show the fault level to be of the order of 600 MVA. With reactors installed, three conditions need to be studied, i.e. for faults at the points F_A, F_B and F_C respectively. For these, three impedance diagrams are required, as shown in Fig. 3.20 (a), (b) and (c).

For a fault at F_A (Fig. 3.20 a) the first step is to resolve the parallel values 50 and (50+16·66) to busbar B, as follows:

$$Z = \frac{1}{\dfrac{1}{50} + \dfrac{1}{50+16\cdot66}}$$

$$= \frac{1}{0\cdot02+0\cdot015} = 28\cdot6\%$$

The new impedance diagram is now as shown in Fig. 3.21, a study of which reveals a further parallel network resolved as follows:

$$Z = \frac{1}{\dfrac{1}{50} + \dfrac{1}{28\cdot6+16\cdot66}}$$

$$= \frac{1}{0 \cdot 02 + 0 \cdot 022} = 23 \cdot 8 \%$$

Thus the final impedance diagram becomes Fig. 3.22 and the fault level at F_A is:

$$\text{s.c. MVA} = \frac{10\,000}{23 \cdot 8} = 420$$

For a fault at F_B (Fig. 3.20b) we have a simple case of parallel values which can be reduced in one step as follows:

$$Z = \frac{1}{\dfrac{1}{50 + 16 \cdot 66} + \dfrac{1}{50} + \dfrac{1}{50 + 16 \cdot 66}}$$

$$= \frac{1}{0 \cdot 015 + 0 \cdot 02 + 0 \cdot 015} = 20 \%$$

This is shown in Fig. 3.23 and the fault at F_B will be:

$$\text{s.c. MVA} = \frac{10\,000}{20} = 500$$

For a fault at F_C, the fault level will be the same as at F_A, i.e. 420 MVA, as the system of impedances is the same.

This example serves to illustrate that the introduction of busbar reactors can result in the use of switchgear rated at 500 MVA instead of 750 MVA (the

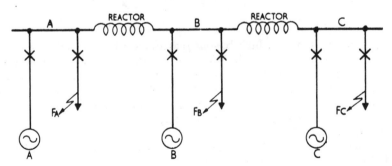

Figure 3.19.   Introduction of busbar reactors to limit fault MVA. From Table 3.1 generators A, B and C = 30 000 kVA, 0+j50%. Reactors 5% on 30 000 kVA = 16·66% on 100 000 kVA

next nearest standard), if reactors are absent. While included here to demonstrate network reduction by impedance diagrams, the use of such reactors involves other problems such as their effect on regulation, as will be noted later.

So far, the examples considered have dealt with impedances forming series and/or parallel branches, but in other cases they may be found to be connected either in star or delta groups. In this event, network reduction proceeds by the use of two three-terminal transformations, by means of which three impedances connected in star can be replaced by an equivalent delta connected group, and vice versa.

The delta/star transformation is perhaps the easiest to manipulate. Given, as

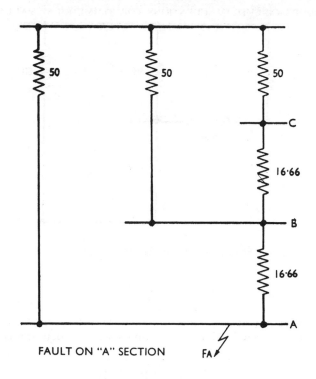

FAULT ON "A" SECTION

Figure 3.20(a)

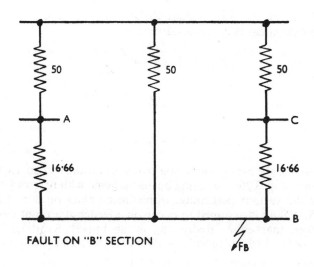

FAULT ON "B" SECTION

Figure 3.20(b)

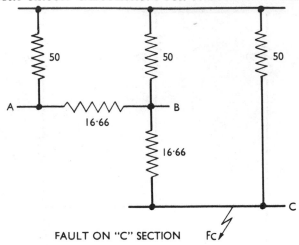

Figure 3.20(c)

in Fig. 3.24, three impedance values Z_{12}, Z_{23} and Z_{31} connected in delta, the equivalent star connected values Z_1, Z_2 and Z_3 can be determined from:

$$Z_1 = \frac{Z_{12} \times Z_{31}}{Z_{12} + Z_{23} + Z_{31}}$$

$$Z_2 = \frac{Z_{23} \times Z_{12}}{Z_{12} + Z_{23} + Z_{31}}$$

$$Z_3 = \frac{Z_{31} \times Z_{23}}{Z_{12} + Z_{23} + Z_{31}}$$

Alternatively, given the three values Z_1, Z_2 and Z_3, connected in star as in Fig. 3.25 the equivalent delta values are:

$$Z_{12} = Z_1 + Z_2 + \frac{Z_1 \times Z_2}{Z_3}$$

$$Z_{23} = Z_2 + Z_3 + \frac{Z_2 \times Z_3}{Z_1}$$

$$Z_{31} = Z_3 + Z_1 + \frac{Z_3 \times Z_1}{Z_2}$$

To demonstrate the use of a delta/star transformation, we can use the electrical layout shown in Fig. 3.26*, i.e. a ring busbar scheme with reactors, the numerals representing the various percentage impedance values on our chosen base of 100 000 kVA. A fault is assumed to occur on a feeder at a point close-up to the circuit-breaker, marked F. Redrawing as an impedance diagram results in Fig. 3.27, a study of which reveals two delta-connected groups comprising the

---

* This example and the subsequent diagrams shown in Figs. 3.27 to 3.35 were first used by the author in his book *The Calculation of Fault Currents in Electrical Networks*, and are used here by courtesy of the publishers, Sir Isaac Pitman & Sons, London.

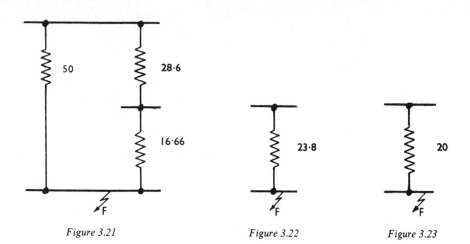

Figure 3.21   *Figure 3.22*   *Figure 3.23*

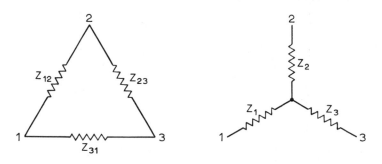

Figure 3.24

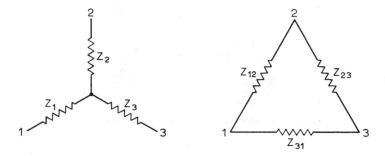

Figure 3.25

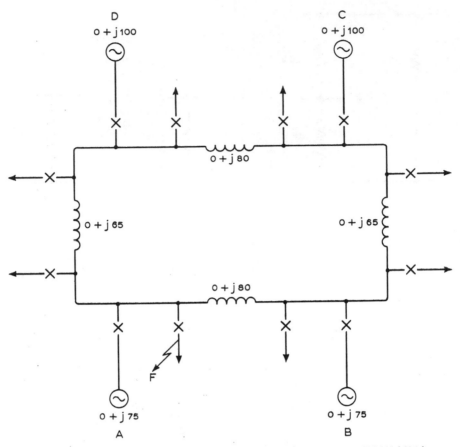

Figure 3.26.   11kV ring-busbar scheme with reactors. Impedances are on a 100 000 kVA base

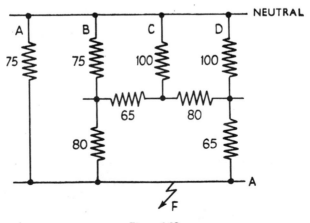

Figure 3.27

62

impedances 75, 65, 100, and 100, 80, 100, respectively. The first step will be to convert one of these groups to a star formation, then introducing it into a revised impedance diagram to see its effect. For this purpose, we may take the delta group with values 75, 65, 100, and using the formula noted, determine the star values to be:

$$Z_1 = \frac{75 \times 65}{75 + 65 + 100} = 20 \cdot 3$$

$$Z_2 = \frac{100 \times 75}{75 + 65 + 100} = 31 \cdot 25$$

$$Z_3 = \frac{65 \times 100}{75 + 65 + 100} = 27 \cdot 08$$

this result being noted in Fig. 3.28.

Figure 3.28

Introducing the star formation into the impedance diagram results in Fig. 3.29 and a study of this shows there are impedances in series, i.e. 20·3, 80 and 27·08, 80, which can be added arithmetically to further simplify the diagram to that shown in Fig. 3.30. This reveals that a new delta group is formed comprising the impedances 31·25, 107·08, 100, and calculating as before the equivalent star

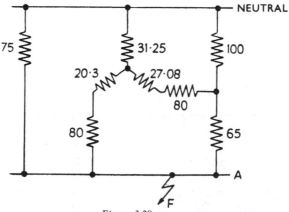

Figure 3.29

group will be as shown in Fig. 3.31. This star group is now introduced into the impedance diagram (Fig. 3.32) which reduces at once to Fig. 3.33 by adding values in series. The two impedances in parallel (114·34 and 109·9) are now resolved to a resultant single impedance thus:

$$\frac{1}{\dfrac{1}{114 \cdot 34} + \dfrac{1}{109 \cdot 9}} = 56$$

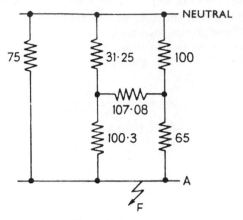

Figure 3.30

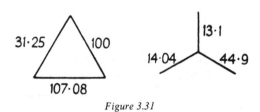

Figure 3.31

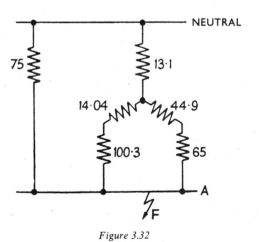

Figure 3.32

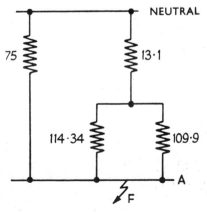

Figure 3.33

64

leaving the network as shown in Fig. 3.34. The parallel values shown can now be resolved thus:

$$\frac{1}{\dfrac{1}{75} + \dfrac{1}{13 \cdot 1 + 56}} = 35 \cdot 96\%$$

leaving a final impedance diagram as in Fig. 3.35, from which the short-circuit MVA for a fault at F in Fig. 3.26 is determined as:

$$\text{s.c. MVA} = \frac{10\,000}{35 \cdot 96} = 278$$

From the examples studied, we have seen that the fault level at a given point in a network and the resultant fault current which flows through that network, is limited by the impedances in the circuit between the source(s) of power and

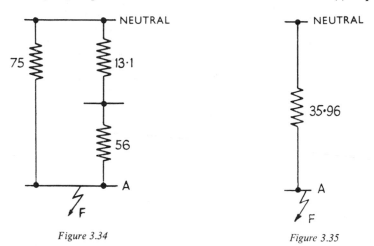

Figure 3.34   Figure 3.35

the point of fault. Normally these impedances are internal, i.e. in generators, transformers and cables, but it is possible as we have seen in two examples, to increase the impedance artificially by incorporating reactors, of which two types are in general use, viz. iron-cored and air-cored. Unfortunately the addition of such apparatus brings with it some disadvantages, e.g. increased regulation, voltage drops and system losses and a lowering of the power factor, so that when studying the possible use of reactors, these problems must be taken into account. Some indication of the increase in regulation for example, is given in Table 3.6, noting particularly the effect with loads of poor power factor. How added reactance affects the power factor is noted in Fig. 3.36.

Reactors are normally rated in percentage terms, e.g. a 10% reactor is one which, with full load current flowing, will cause a voltage drop across it of 10% of line to neutral voltage. On a 6 600 V three-phase system, the voltage drop would therefore be 381·5 V.

When used, reactors should be located at points in the network where they can be most effective. It is rarely necessary or desirable to include them in generator circuits, although instances arise where modern machines are to operate in parallel with older ones and there may be a case here for adding

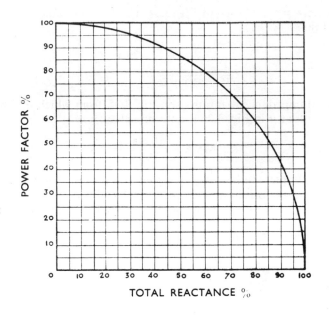

Figure 3.36. Effect of added reactance on power factor

Table 3.6

INCREASE IN REGULATION DUE TO ADDED REACTANCE

Added reactance (%)	Load power factor			
	1·0	0·9	0·8	0·5
1	—	0·4	0·5	0·75
2	—	0·75	1·15	1·5
3	—	1·25	1·75	2·4
4	0·1	1·6	2·4	3·25
5	0·15	2·2	3·0	4·1
6	0·2	2·7	3·75	5·0
7	0·25	3·2	4·5	6·0
8	0·3	3·75	5·15	7·0
9	0·4	4·3	5·8	8·0
10	0·5	5·0	6·6	9·0

artificial reactance in the circuits of the older machines to give them roughly the same characteristics as the new machines.

Reactors installed in feeder circuits are a costly expedient when there are a large number of such circuits involved, but when they are so placed, the added value of reactance is usually of the order 3 to 5%. A good case can however be made for a reactor in a group feeder (see Fig. 9.10 in Chapter 9) where the added reactance may be essential to reduce the fault level at the group of smaller circuit-breakers controlled by the main feeder. This same condition can arise in large industrial systems where groups of high-voltage motors of sizable h.p. are fed through one or two feeders from the public supply, where it is desirable to reduce the fault level at the motor control gear for economic or technical reasons.

The alternative and probably the most usual location is in the busbar system, typically as indicated in Figs. 3.19 and 3.26 and in other illustrations in Chapter 9. Their use in the busbars is particularly valuable where, as so often happens, the loads on the supply increase to such an extent that additional power infeeds become necessary. The degree of security required may necessitate that the old

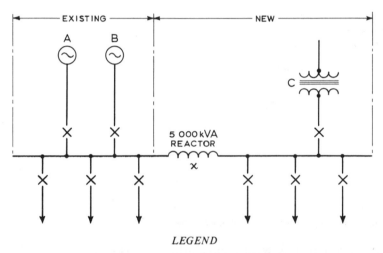

LEGEND

A and B   5 000 kVA GENERATORS (FROM TABLE 3.1 240% EACH)
C   10 000 kVA TRANSFORMER (FROM TABLE 3.2 33/11 kV 90%)
x   REACTOR VALUE TO BE DETERMINED

Figure 3.37.   Original electrical system (left) and new electrical system (right)

and new sources of supply be paralleled at a common bus, but if this interconnection is made directly, i.e. the old and new busbars are solidly linked, then the breaking capacity of the original switchgear may be quite inadequate for the higher fault level attributable to the new power source. One solution is to replace the old switchgear, but a more economical solution is to tie the two busbar systems through a reactor.

To demonstrate this, we may consider the electrical system in Fig. 3.37 where, to the left, the original system is shown, comprising two 5 000 kVA generators with appropriate outgoing feeders. A calculation on the basis of this chapter will show that under the original circumstances the fault level would be 83·3 MVA, and for this, switchgear rated 100 MVA could be installed.

To cater for increased loads, it is proposed to take bulk supply from the electricity authority via a 10 000 kVA power transformer, and this source can now contribute a further 111 MVA to a fault, so that the switchgear rating, both old and new, should normally be 250 MVA.

The addition of a reactor in the busbars as shown however, will safeguard the old switchgear and its value can be calculated as follows, again using our chosen base of 100 000 kVA:

$$\text{Total reactance necessary to safeguard existing switchgear} = \frac{100 \times \text{kVA base}}{\text{MVA rating of existing switchgear} \times 1\,000}$$

$$= \frac{100 \times 100\,000}{100 \times 1\,000} = 100\%$$

$$\text{Reactance of existing machines in parallel on a 100 000 kVA base} = \frac{240}{2} = 120\%$$

$$\text{Reactance of new transformer on a 100 000 kVA base} = 90\%$$

The value x for the reactor is calculated from:

$$\frac{1}{120} + \frac{1}{90+x} = \frac{1}{100}$$

$$\therefore \quad \frac{1}{90+x} = \frac{1}{100} - \frac{1}{120}$$

$$= \frac{6}{600} - \frac{5}{600} = \frac{1}{600}$$

so that $\qquad\qquad\qquad 90 + x = 600$
and $x = 510\%$ on a 100 000 kVA base

If it is assumed that the reactor has a rating of 5 000 kVA, then x at this rating will be:

$$\frac{5\,000}{100\,000} \times 510 = 25 \cdot 5\%$$

Note has already been taken of some of the disadvantages arising out of the use of series reactors, and it is of interest therefore to note here a new development by A.E.I.[3], marketed by English Electric Power Transmission Ltd., which eliminates these and which is described as a short-circuit limiting coupling (SLC). This is a static resonance-link which can be installed in the busbars or in individual feeders, typically as we have noted earlier for reactors. Shown schematically in Fig. 3.38, the SLC is a resonance-link which, under healthy conditions, offers a low impedance and a low loss to normal load currents but automatically changes to a high impedance when a fault occurs and can be designed to limit the through-fault contribution to a desired limit, e.g. twice normal load or events just above normal load. After the fault has been cleared the link automatically recovers to the low impedance condition, the changes in both directions being accomplished without moving parts, electronic circuits, relay operation or switching action.

Referring to Fig. 3.38, and assuming healthy conditions, the series reactor and series capacitor are in series tune, presenting low impedance to normal through-current and with no effect on power factor. When a fault occurs, the increased current causes the voltage across the capacitor to rise. Due to the relative values of components, the higher voltage is sufficient to cause saturation in both the main and auxiliary saturating reactors. The action detunes the series circuit and causes the capacitor and saturating network to assume partial parallel tune, thus forming a low impedance network not including the series reactor which now presents its full value of impedance to the fault current.

At the time of fault removal, i.e. when the fault is removed by tripping the appropriate circuit-breaker, the coupling very rapidly returns to normal. This

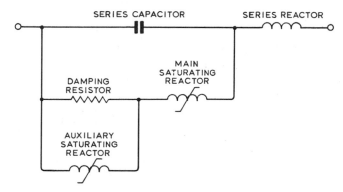

Figure 3.38. Schematic diagram of A.E.I. short-circuit limiting coupling (S.L.C.) (courtesy English Electric Power Transmission Ltd.)

reversion must take into account the possibility of the system being out of synchronism, and the coupling must be capable of passing the required amount of reactive power to enable any induction motors to attain working speed. To this end, the coupling is designed so that the auxiliary saturating reactor desaturates first, effectively inserting the resistor in series with the main saturating reactor, and causing rapid detuning of the parallel circuit. When system recovery is complete, the main saturating reactor desaturates and the series reactor once more assumes series tune with the capacitor. To assist further in the damping of oscillatory transients during machine synchronising or running-up periods, a small damping filter is sometimes added to the capacitor by-pass circuit.

When included in a distribution system at the design stage, the SLC can result in the rating of certain components such as switchgear and cables being lower than would be necessary without the link. Added to existing systems it can provide higher security or increased utilisation of existing equipment. It can be used at all voltage levels, both in industrial or power supply applications. Published data (see bibliography) have noted various industrial applications at 6·6 and 11 kV, in particular one at the Stanlow Oil Refinery of Shell U.K. Ltd., which will permit about 60 MW of extra site generation to be accommodated without the need to uprate the associated switchgear and without permitting the fault backfeed into the Area Board to exceed about 40 MVA. At the higher voltages, design studies for a 200 MVA link at 132 kV and a 750 MVA link at 275 kV have been made. In the case of the 132 kV study, it is noted that the link limits an inherent through-fault contribution of 2 500 MVA to less than 375 MVA.

It has also been noted that in some cases where conventional series reactors are in use, the SLC method may be used by installing capacitor and by-pass circuit equipment designed to operate in series with the existing reactors, thus giving a more effective method of limiting the fault level.

Correct application of SLC requires that it be designed for the particular circumstances of the system and possible future conditions. It involves considerable power system engineering and analytical experience, and the designers of the apparatus use full information of the system including protection operating times, generator reactances, cable impedances, load details including induction motor reactances, etc.

MEDIUM-VOLTAGE CALCULATIONS

Short-circuit calculations for medium-voltage systems (400–600 V) follow the methods noted for high-voltage systems, but here it is important that every factor tending to limit the fault current is taken into account. Too often it may be assumed that a sufficiently accurate fault level can be determined from the transformer rating(s), reactance or impedance and calculating from the formula:

$$\text{s.c. MVA} = \frac{\text{transformer rating (kVA)} \times 100}{\% \text{ reactance or impedance} \times 1\,000}$$

Fault values arrived at in this way however can only represent the condition of a fault at the transformer secondary terminals, and only then if a solidly bolted short-circuit at those terminals is envisaged, a condition which is improbable in service. If there are two or more transformers operating in parallel, the condition is obviously impossible. However, it is of interest to note the order of MVA values calculated in this way, and these are shown in Table 3.7 for a range of transformers normally used in medium-voltage industrial or service applications where the primary voltage does not exceed 11 kV.

Table 3.7

MVA FAULT VALUES AT TRANSFORMER SECONDARY TERMINALS

Single transformer		Two transformers in parallel		Three transformers in parallel		Four transformers in parallel	
kVA	s.c. MVA	kVA	s.c. MVA	kVA	s.c. MVA	kVA	s.c. MVA
400	8·42	—	—	—	—	—	—
500	10·5	—	—	—	—	—	—
750	15·8	2 × 400	16·8	—	—	—	—
1 000	21·0	2 × 500	21·0	3 × 400	25·26	—	—
1 250	25·0	2 × 750	31·4	3 × 400	25·26	4 × 400	33·7
1 500	27·3	2 × 750	31·4	3 × 500	31·5	4 × 400	33·7
2 000	33·33	2 × 1 000	42·0	3 × 750	47·4	4 × 500	42·0

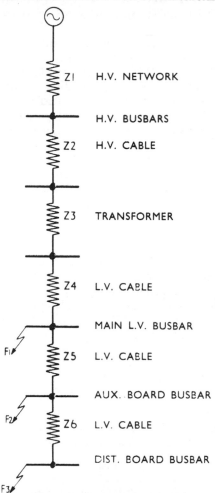

FAULT AT F1 LIMITED BY IMPEDANCES Z1 Z2 Z3 Z4
FAULT AT F2 LIMITED BY IMPEDANCES Z1 Z2 Z3 Z4 Z5
FAULT AT F3 LIMITED BY IMPEDANCES Z1 Z2 Z3 Z4 Z5 Z6

Figure 3.39

Because the loss of one transformer out of a bank is not so wide ranging in its effect as is the loss of a single large unit, because of the greater operational flexibility and the lower normal-currents to be carried by both switchgear and cables, many engineers prefer to use several transformers in parallel, often with one acting as a standby. It is of passing interest in this connection to note that in some instances the resultant short-circuit MVA will be higher for an equal total kVA capacity. This is shown by Table 3.7, where for example, one 2 000 kVA transformer results in 33·33 MVA whereas four 500 kVA units in parallel give 42 MVA. It is for reasons such as this that sectionalised busbars are adopted, effectively dividing the system into two or more normally segregated parts. In an example later, the reduced fault levels achieved by sectionalising will be demonstrated.

Based on Table 3.7 it is seen that if calculations are limited to transformer reactance alone, then a single 1 000 kVA transformer would dictate the use of switchgear rated 26 MVA at 415 V (nearest standard) while a single 2 000 kVA transformer would call for switchgear rated say 35 MVA (non-standard). In what follows it will be shown that the estimated values in Table 3.7 are high because other impedances play an important part in limiting the fault level, Fig. 3.39 serving to illustrate these from a high-voltage source through to a sub-distribution point.

With the foregoing in mind, we can proceed to tabulate these various sources of impedance in the manner adopted for high-voltage calculations, the tables again being on our chosen kVA base, i.e. 100 000 kVA.

H.V. network

How the reactance or impedance of the high-voltage network is deduced and then used to determine the fault level at the busbars has been demonstrated earlier. The reactance or impedance values as deduced may be used in medium-voltage calculations but such values are not always known or obtainable. What is usually known however is the MVA rating of the high-voltage switchgear, and this can be used in a formula as follows:

$$\text{Equivalent percentage reactance of high-voltage network} = \frac{\text{kVA base} \times 100}{\dfrac{\text{MVA rating}}{\text{of switchgear}} \times 1\ 000}$$

From this, Table 3.8 can be prepared for use in later worked examples. In this table it is noted that column 1 suggests alternatively the MVA rating of the switchgear or the calculated MVA at the high-voltage busbars. The significance

Table 3.8

MVA rating of high-voltage switchgear or calculated MVA at busbars	Equivalent percentage reactance of high-voltage network on a 100 000 kVA base
50*	200
75*	133·3
100*	100·0
125	80·0
150*	66·6
175	57·0
200	50·0
250*	40·0
300	33·33
350*	28·6
400	25·0
450	22·22
500*	20
750*	13·33
1 000*	10

* Standard switchgear ratings

72

of this is that the latter will always be *lower* than the rating of the switchgear, and if this lower value is used in the formula instead of the switchgear rating, it results in a higher equivalent reactance with greater effect on the calculations. Use of the switchgear MVA rating, on the other hand, provides a small factor of safety.

Transformers

Table 3.2, prepared for high-voltage calculations can be used for our purpose here.

Cables

If, in any calculation, the high-voltage system is being worked out in detail in preparation for use in subsequent medium-voltage calculations, the resistance and reactance values for any high-voltage cables involved will be taken from Tables 3.3, 3.4 or 3.5, as appropriate.

Table 3.9 has been prepared to cover a range of multicore medium-voltage cables in the new metric sizes to BS 6480:1969:Part 1, using the formula noted earlier for converting ohmic values of resistance and reactance to percentage

Table 3.9
THREE AND FOUR-CORE PAPER-INSULATED CABLES WITH COPPER AND ALUMINIUM CONDUCTORS

Percentage resistance (R) and reactance (X) per metre on a 100 000 kVA base*								
	400 V			415 V			440 V		
Nominal area of conductor (mm²)	$R^{(1)}$		$X^{(2)}$	$R^{(1)}$		$X^{(2)}$	$R^{(1)}$		$X^{(2)}$
	Cu	Al	Cu & Al	Cu	Al	Cu & Al	Cu	Al	Cu & Al
4[3]	356	597	5·81	330	554	5·40	292	492	4·79
6[3]	238	395	5·50	221	366	5·05	196	325	4·53
10[3]	141	234	5·25	121	207	4·87	117	193	4·33
16	88	148	5·00	83	137	4·64	73	122	4·12
·25	56	93	4·75	52	86	4·43	46	77	3·91
35	40·5	67·5	4·63	37·5	62·6	4·30	33	57	3·81
50	30·0	49·8	4·56	27·8	46·2	4·23	24·7	41	3·76
70	20·8	34·4	4·44	19·25	32·0	4·12	17·0	28·4	3·65
95	15·0	24·9	4·31	13·86	23·0	4·00	12·3	20·5	3·55
120	11·25	19·7	4·25	10·44	18·3	3·95	9·3	16·2	3·50
150	9·70	16·0	4·25	9·00	14·9	3·95	8·0	13·2	3·50
185	7·75	12·8	4·25	7·20	11·9	3·95	6·4	10·6	3·50
240	5·96	9·8	4·25	5·53	9·1	3·95	4·8	8·1	3·50
300	4·82	7·87	4·19	4·47	7·3	3·88	4·4	6·5	3·45
400	3·86	6·17	4·19	3·58	5·7	3·88	3·2	5·1	3·45

Notes (1) At maximum conductor temperature of 80°C.
(2) At a frequency of 50 Hz.
(3) Circular-stranded conductors. All others shaped stranded.
* Manufactured in accordance with BS 6480:Part 1 (1969), and based on data provided by British Insulated Callender's Cables Ltd.

Table 3.9 (CONTINUED)

Nominal area of conductor (mm^2)	Percentage resistance (R) and reactance (X) per metre on a 100 000 k V A base								
	500 V			550 V			600 V		
	$R^{(1)}$		$X^{(2)}$	$R^{(1)}$		$X^{(2)}$	$R^{(1)}$		$X^{(2)}$
	Cu	Al	Cu & Al	Cu	Al	Cu & Al	Cu	Al	Cu & Al
4[3]	228	382	3·72	188	315	3·07	160	267	2·64
6[3]	152	252	3·52	125	208	2·9	107	177	2·46
10[3]	90	150	3·36	74·5	124	2·77	63·3	105	2·35
16	57	95	3·20	46·2	78	2·64	39·7	66·4	2·24
25	36	59	3·04	29·6	49	2·51	25·1	41·7	2·13
35	26	43·2	2·96	21·4	35·6	2·44	18·1	30·24	2·07
50	19	31·8	2·92	15·8	26·2	2·41	13·4	22·29	2·04
70	13·2	22·0	2·84	10·9	18·2	2·34	9·3	15·43	1·99
95	9·6	15·8	2·76	7·9	13·1	2·27	6·7	11·14	1·93
120	7·2	12·6	2·72	5·9	10·4	2·24	5·1	8·82	1·90
150	6·2	10·3	2·72	5·1	8·48	2·24	4·42	7·20	1·90
185	4·96	8·2	2·72	4·1	6·76	2·24	3·43	5·74	1·90
240	3·81	6·28	2·72	3·15	5·18	2·24	2·67	4·40	1·90
300	3·10	5·05	2·68	2·54	4·16	2·21	2·16	3·53	1·87
400	2·46	3·95	2·68	2·03	3·26	2·21	1·73	2·77	1·87

Notes (1) At maximum conductor temperature of 80°C.
(2) At a frequency of 50 Hz.
(3) Circular-stranded conductors. All others shaped stranded.

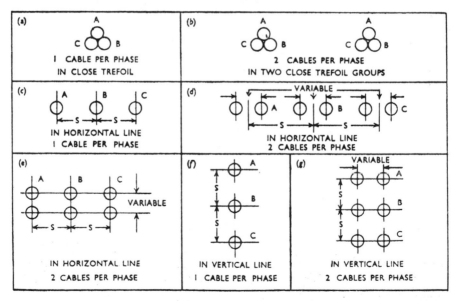

Figure 3.40. A few of the possible formations for single-core cables. Heavy currents may demand three such cables per phase

values on our 100 000 kVA base, these latter values again being given in terms per metre.

When transformers of relatively large rating are employed, the normal currents on the secondary side will be comparatively high, and it is often preferable to use single-core cables rather than a large three-core cable. When the current rating is very high, several single-core cables in parallel per phase may be necessary.

To determine the reactance of such cables is a matter of some complication, the calculations necessary requiring a knowledge of spacing, sheath currents, how laid (i.e. in magnetic or non-magnetic ducts or in free air), together with other factors. The variables are therefore many, particularly in the matter of spacing and formation where the possibilities are almost unlimited. Some of the possible formations are noted in Fig. 3.40, and assuming space is available it will be clear that the spacing S can be varied at will, and indeed as the reactance increases as the spacing is increased, this offers a means whereby additional reactance is obtained to assist in MVA reduction.

The problem is further complicated where, as at (d), (e) and (g) in Fig. 3.40, there is more than one cable per phase which again may be on variable centres. In such cases a complex calculation is involved in which the multiple conductors

Table 3.10

SINGLE-CORE MEDIUM-VOLTAGE PAPER-LEAD
CABLES UP TO 600 V, 50 Hz LAID IN CLOSE
TREFOIL WITH CABLES TOUCHING AND ONE
CABLE PER PHASE

Cable size (mm²)	Percentage reactance per metre on a 100 000 kVA base*					
	400 V	415 V	440 V	500 V	550 V	600 V
240	5·25	4·88	4·34	3·36	2·78	2·33
300	5·18	4·82	4·29	3·32	2·74	2·31
400	5·06	4·70	4·18	3·24	2·68	2·25
500	5·00	4·65	4·13	3·20	2·65	2·22
630	4·94	4·59	4·08	3·16	2·61	2·19
800	4·81	4·47	3·98	3·08	2·55	2·14
1 000	4·75	4·41	3·93	3·04	2·51	2·11

*All data computed and supplied by British Insulated Callender's Cables Ltd.

per phase are first of all reduced to a single cable equivalent. It is for reasons such as these that reference books rarely give reactance tables for single-core cables in the manner given for multicore types, as it is manifestly impossible to do so for all possible variations. The simplest arrangements are those in Fig. 3.40 at (a), (c) and (f), i.e. one cable per phase, and Tables 3.10 and 3.11 have been compiled to cover these within narrow limits. The tables, for example, cover only the largest cable sizes as they are the ones used most regularly in practice. No values of resistance have been given, as these are so much smaller than the reactance values that they can be ignored in fault calculations and regarded as a small factor of safety.

Should the need arise to include the reactance value for other formations or spacings in any calculation or where more than one single-core cable is used per phase, it is recommended that the appropriate data be sought from the cable supplier.

Table 3.11

SINGLE-CORE MEDIUM-VOLTAGE PAPER-LEAD CABLES
UP TO 600 V, 50 Hz, ONE CABLE PER PHASE RUN IN
SINGLE LINE HORIZONTALLY OR VERTICALLY AS
SHOWN

Phase spacing S (mm)	Cable size (mm²)	Percentage reactance per metre on a 100 000 kVA base*					
		400 V	415 V	440 V	500 V	550 V	600 V
50		8·19	7·61	6·77	5·24	4·33	3·64
75		9·81	9·12	8·11	6·28	5·19	4·36
90		10·50	9·76	8·68	6·72	5·55	4·67
100	240	10·94	10·16	9·04	7·00	5·79	4·86
125		11·81	10·97	9·76	7·56	6·35	5·25
150		12·50	11·61	10·33	8·00	6·61	5·56
50		7·75	7·20	6·41	4·96	4·10	3·44
75		9·83	8·71	7·75	6·00	4·96	4·17
90		10·06	9·35	8·32	6·44	5·32	4·47
100	300	10·50	9·76	8·68	6·72	5·55	4·67
125		11·38	10·57	9·40	7·28	6·02	5·06
150		12·06	11·21	9·97	7·72	6·38	5·36
50		7·31	6·79	6·04	4·68	3·87	3·25
75		8·88	8·25	7·34	5·68	4·69	3·94
90		9·56	8·88	7·90	6·12	5·06	4·25
100	400	10·00	9·29	8·26	6·40	5·29	4·44
125		10·88	10·10	8·99	6·96	5·75	4·83
150		11·63	10·80	9·61	7·44	6·15	5·17
50		6·81	6·33	5·63	4·36	3·60	3·03
75		8·44	7·84	6·97	5·40	4·46	3·75
90		9·13	8·48	7·54	5·84	4·83	4·06
100	500	9·56	8·88	7·90	6·12	5·06	4·25
125		10·44	9·70	8·63	6·68	5·52	4·64
150		11·13	10·34	9·19	7·12	5·88	4·94
50		6·31	5·86	5·22	4·04	3·34	2·81
75		7·88	7·32	6·51	5·04	4·17	3·50
90		8·63	8·41	7·13	5·52	4·56	3·83
100	630	9·00	8·36	7·44	5·76	4·76	4·00
125		9·88	9·17	8·16	6·32	5·22	4·39
150		10·63	9·87	8·78	6·80	5·62	4·72
50		5·81	5·40	4·80	3·72	3·07	2·58
75		7·44	6·91	6·15	4·76	3·93	3·31
90		8·13	7·55	6·72	5·20	4·20	3·61
100	800	8·56	7·96	7·08	5·48	4·53	3·81
125		9·44	8·77	7·80	6·04	4·99	4·19
150		10·19	9·46	8·42	6·52	5·39	4·53
75		6·94	6·45	5·73	4·44	3·67	3·08
90		7·69	7·14	6·35	4·92	4·07	3·42
100	1 000	8·06	7·49	6·66	5·16	4·26	3·58
125		8·94	8·30	7·39	5·72	4·73	3·97
150		9·69	9·00	8·01	6·20	5·12	4·31

*All data computed and supplied by British Insulated Callender's Cables Ltd.

Bare conductors

As an alternative to the use of single-core cables in heavy current applications, and particularly where the transformer is immediately adjacent to the medium-voltage switchgear with perhaps only a fire wall intervening, it is often convenient to do away with cables and all the joints they involve and use bare conductors in the form of busbars to join the transformer to the switchgear. As with single-core cables, here the values of reactance depend on spacing and formation, and in addition on the cross-section and number of bars per phase. The detailed calculations are laborious and are outside the scope of this book but the interested readers requiring detailed information should consult References 4 and 5.

Table 3.12 has been included to give percentage reactance per metre run on our selected base for various busbar sections at a number of phase spacings. Assumptions have been made for simplification, but the errors which the assumptions introduce are such as to be on the safe side for the purpose of

Table 3.12

PERCENTAGE REACTANCE PER METRE ON A 100 000 kVA BASE FOR A SELECTION OF 3-PHASE 50 Hz RECTANGULAR CONDUCTORS (Cu or Al) IN HORIZONTAL FORMATION AS IN SKETCH. SPACING BETWEEN LAMINATIONS EQUAL TO BAR THICKNESS

No. of bars per phase	Size of each bar (mm)	Phase centres S (mm)	400 V	415 V	440 V	500 V	550 V	600 V
3	50 × 6·3	102	7·81	7·10	6·27	4·84	3·63	3·41
		127	8·58	7·70	7·10	5·28	4·10	3·74
		153	9·35	8·60	7·60	5·94	4·40	4·10
		178	10·00	9·13	8·14	6·27	4·83	4·40
		204	10·56	9·57	8·58	6·60	4·95	4·62
		229	11·00	10·00	8·90	6·93	5·17	4·84
2	80 × 6·3	77	6·10	5·61	4·95	3·85	2·97	2·64
		102	7·15	6·49	5·83	4·51	3·41	3·19
		127	8·10	7·37	6·71	5·10	3·85	3·52
		153	8·80	8·10	7·15	5·50	4·18	3·85
		178	9·46	8·58	7·70	5·94	4·51	4·07
		204	9·90	9·13	8·14	6·27	4·73	4·29
3	80 × 6·3	102	6·71	6·10	5·39	4·18	3·19	2·97
		127	7·59	6·82	6·16	4·73	3·52	3·30
		153	8·25	7·59	6·82	5·28	3·96	3·63
		175	8·91	8·14	7·26	5·61	4·29	3·96
		204	9·46	8·58	7·70	5·94	4·51	4·07
		229	9·90	9·13	8·00	6·27	4·73	4·29
4	80 × 6·3	127	7·10	6·50	5·72	4·51	3·30	3·10
		153	7·81	7·15	6·38	4·95	3·74	3·41
		178	8·47	7·81	6·93	5·39	4·10	3·74
		204	9·10	8·25	7·37	5·72	4·29	3·96
		229	9·46	8·58	7·70	5·94	4·51	4·18
		254	9·90	9·13	8·10	6·27	4·73	4·40

Table 3.12 (CONTINUED)

No. of Bars per phase	Size of each bar (mm)	Phase centres S (mm)	400 V	415 V	440 V	500 V	550 V	600 V
1	100 × 6·3	77	5·72	5·28	4·73	3·63	2·86	2·53
		102	6·71	6·10	5·39	4·18	3·19	2·97
		127	7·59	6·82	6·16	4·73	3·52	3·30
		153	8·25	7·59	6·82	5·28	3·96	3·63
		178	8·91.	8·14	7·26	5·61	4·29	3·96
		204	9·46	8·58	7·70	5·94	4·51	4·07
		229	9·90	9·13	8·10	6·27	4·73	4·29
2	100 × 6·3	77	5·34	4·95	4·40	3·41	2·53	2·31
		102	6·27	5·72	5·10	3·93	2·97	2·75
		127	7·10	6·49	5·72	4·51	3·30	3·10
		153	7·81	7·15	6·38	4·95	3·74	3·41
		178	8·47	7·81	6·93	5·39	4·10	3·74
		204	9·10	8·25	7·37	5·72	4·29	3·96
		229	9·46	8·47	7·70	5·99	4·51	4·18
3	100 × 6·3	127	6·82	6·27	5·61	4·29	3·30	2·97
		153	7·48	6·93	6·10	4·73	3·52	3·30
		178	8·14	7·37	6·71	5·10	3·74	3·52
		204	8·58	7·81	7·10	5·39	3·96	3·74
		229	9·10	8·25	7·37	5·72	4·29	3·96
		254	9·79	8·80	7·70	6·10	4·51	4·18
		280	9·90	9·13	8·14	6·27	4·73	4·40
		305	10·23	9·35	8·36	6·49	4·95	4·51
4	100 × 6·3	153	6·93	6·49	5·72	4·51	3·30	3·08
		178	7·70	7·10	6·27	4·84	3·63	3·41
		204	8·25	7·48	6·71	5·17	3·96	3·63
		229	8·69	7·81	7·15	5·39	4·18	3·85
		254	9·13	8·25	7·48	5·72	4·40	4·07
		305	9·79	9·13	8·10	6·27	4·62	4·29
		381	10·67	9·90	8·80	6·82	5·10	4·73

short-circuit calculations. As with single-core cables, resistance values can be ignored as they are small compared with reactance.

Typical calculations

A few calculations will demonstrate the use of these tables. Consider the simple system shown in Fig. 3.41. This can be redrawn as an impedance diagram, shown in Fig. 3.42. It should be noted that in this (and in subsequent examples) the impedance values have been set against each element with an indication of the table from which they have been taken. In the case of cables, the multiplier represents the length in metres, and in the case of the medium-voltage cables, is divided by 3 since we have this number of cables in parallel per phase, each of the same impedance. Thus the single equivalent impedance for these is

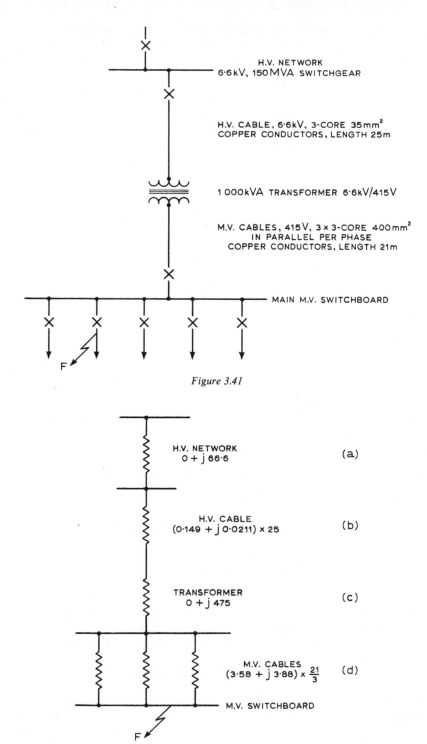

H.V. NETWORK
6·6kV, 150 MVA SWITCHGEAR

H.V. CABLE, 6·6kV, 3-CORE 35mm²
COPPER CONDUCTORS, LENGTH 25m

1 000kVA TRANSFORMER 6·6kV/415V

M.V. CABLES, 415V, 3 x 3-CORE 400mm²
IN PARALLEL PER PHASE
COPPER CONDUCTORS, LENGTH 21m

MAIN M.V. SWITCHBOARD

F

Figure 3.41

H.V. NETWORK
0 + j 66·6   (a)

H.V. CABLE
(0·149 + j 0·0211) × 25   (b)

TRANSFORMER
0 + j 475   (c)

M.V. CABLES
$(3·58 + j\, 3·88) \times \frac{21}{3}$ (d)

M.V. SWITCHBOARD

F

*Figure 3.42.   Calculations are derived as follows: (a) from Table 3.8, (b) from Table 3.3, (c) from
Table 3.2 and (d) from Table 3.9*

79

$(3\cdot58+j3\cdot88)\times7$, i.e. $25\cdot06+j27\cdot16$. This leaves a series arrangement of impedances which can be added arithmetically:

$$
\begin{aligned}
\text{h.v. network} &= 0 &&+ j66\cdot6 \\
\text{h.v. cable} &= 3\cdot75+ &&j0\cdot5275 \\
\text{transformer} &= 0 &&+j475\cdot0 \\
\text{m.v. cable} &= 25\cdot06+ &&j27\cdot16 \\
\hline
Z\ \text{(total)} &= 28\cdot81+ &&j569\cdot2875
\end{aligned}
$$

These figures can be conveniently rounded-off without significant error so that:

$$
\begin{aligned}
Z\ \text{(total)} &= \sqrt{29^2 + 570^2} \\
&= 570\cdot73\%
\end{aligned}
$$

and the fault level at the main m.v. switchboard will be:

$$
\text{s.c. MVA} = \frac{10\,000}{570\cdot73} = 17\cdot52
$$

and the power factor at the fault will be:

$$
\frac{R}{Z} = \frac{29}{570\cdot73} = 0\cdot05
$$

This calculation shows that instead of a fault level of 21 MVA as indicated in Table 3.7 for a calculation based on the transformer impedance alone, we now have the lower value of 17·52 MVA.

As a second example, we may assume that it is required to ascertain the fault level at a distribution board fed from the main m.v. switchboard shown in Fig. 3.41, typically as shown in Fig. 3.43. The impedance diagram for Fig. 3.43 is shown in Fig. 3.44 which in turn reduces to Fig. 3.45 by adding impedances in series. The fault level at the distribution board is then resolved from:

$$
Z = 3\,349+j755\cdot6
$$

$$
= \sqrt{3\,349^2 + 755\cdot6^2} \equiv 3\,433\%
$$

$$
\text{s.c. MVA} = \frac{10\,000}{3\,433} = 2\cdot9
$$

A study of this example illustrates the importance of the cable between the main and distribution boards in limiting the fault level at the latter, and how resistance plays an important part, being more than four times the reactance. This will also result in a high power factor for faults at this point:

$$
\text{p.f.} = \frac{R}{Z} = \frac{3\,349}{3\,433} = 0\cdot97 \text{ approx.}
$$

Figure 3.46 shows the electrical connections for a larger system and here it is required to determine the fault levels at each of the three m.v. switchboards, e.g. for faults at F_A, F_B and F_C. Translating to an impedance diagram we get Fig. 3.47, and the first calculation will be for a fault at F_A, the initial step being to convert the impedances of the parallel cables between each transformer and

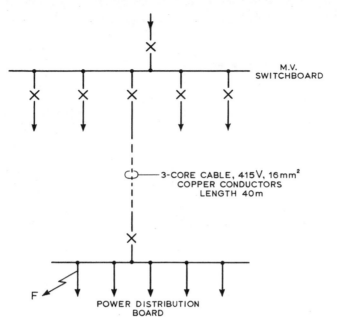

Figure 3.43

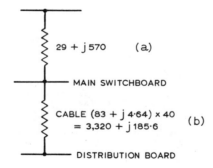

Figure 3.44. Calculations are derived as follows: (a) from Figure 3.41 and (b) from Table 3.9

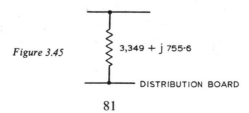

Figure 3.45

81

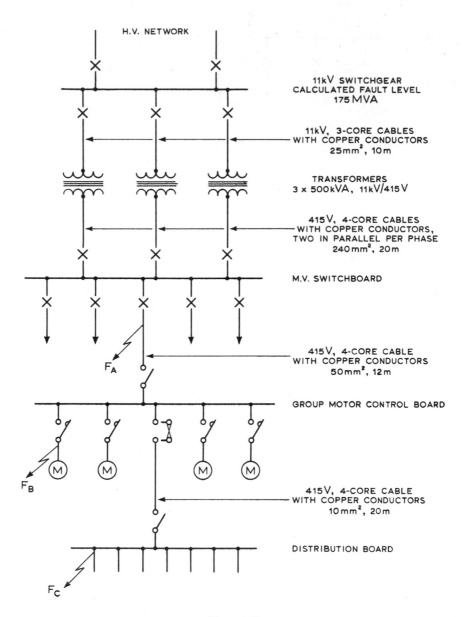

H.V. NETWORK

11kV SWITCHGEAR
CALCULATED FAULT LEVEL
175 MVA

11kV, 3-CORE CABLES
WITH COPPER CONDUCTORS
25mm², 10m

TRANSFORMERS
3 × 500kVA, 11kV/415V

415V, 4-CORE CABLES
WITH COPPER CONDUCTORS,
TWO IN PARALLEL PER PHASE
240mm², 20m

M.V. SWITCHBOARD

F_A

415V, 4-CORE CABLE
WITH COPPER CONDUCTORS
50mm², 12m

GROUP MOTOR CONTROL BOARD

F_B

415V, 4-CORE CABLE
WITH COPPER CONDUCTORS
10mm², 20m

DISTRIBUTION BOARD

F_C

Figure 3.46

82

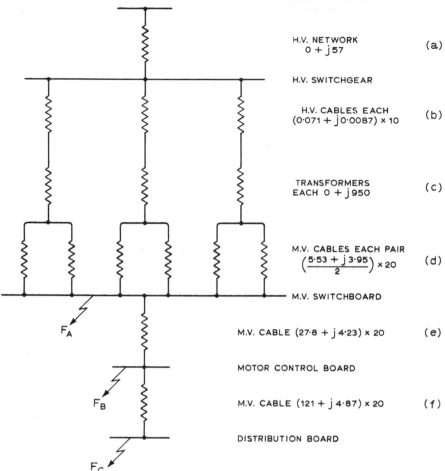

Figure 3.47. Calculations are derived as follows: (a) from Table 3.8, (b) from Table 3.3, (c) from Table 3.2, (d), (e) and (f) from Table 3.9

the main m.v. switchboard to single equivalent impedances, a step which enables the impedance diagram to be redrawn as in Fig. 3.48 (this, for convenience, omits the switchboards further on in the system). The three parallel circuits between the h.v. and m.v. switchboards can now be resolved into a single equivalent by dividing the impedances of one circuit by 3 (each being equal), so that the diagram now reduces to Fig. 3.49.

We now have a simple set of impedances in series which can be added arithmetically:

$$
\begin{aligned}
\text{h.v. network} &= 0 \quad\;\; + \text{j}57 \\
\text{h.v. cables} &= 0 \cdot 236 + \quad \text{j}0 \cdot 029 \\
\text{transformers} &= 0 \quad\;\; + \text{j}316 \cdot 0 \\
\text{m.v. cables} &= \underline{18 \cdot 44 \; + \; \text{j}13 \cdot 16} \\
Z \text{ (total)} &= \overline{18.676 + \text{j}386 \cdot 189}
\end{aligned}
$$

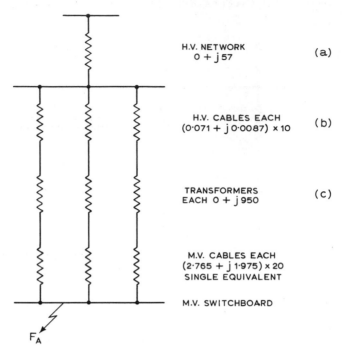

H.V. NETWORK
0 + j 57   (a)

H.V. CABLES EACH
(0·071 + j 0·0087) × 10   (b)

TRANSFORMERS
EACH 0 + j 950   (c)

M.V. CABLES EACH
(2·765 + j 1·975) × 20
SINGLE EQUIVALENT

M.V. SWITCHBOARD

F_A

Figure 3.48. Calculations are derived as follows: (a) from Table 3.8, (b) from Table 3.3 and (c) from Table 3.2

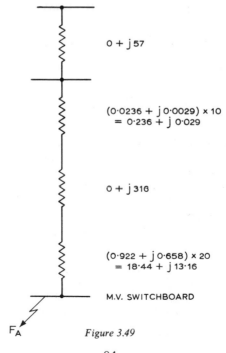

0 · + j 57

(0·0236 + j 0·0029) × 10
= 0·236 + j 0·029

0 + j 316

(0·922 + j 0·658) × 20
= 18·44 + j 13·16

M.V. SWITCHBOARD

F_A *Figure 3.49*

84

It is at once obvious that the reactance is so large compared with resistance that for all practical purposes the latter can be ignored, using the reactance value only to obtain the fault level at F_A:

$$\text{s.c. MVA} = \frac{10\,000}{386 \cdot 189} = 26 \text{ approx.}$$

Looking back at Table 3.7 we find that a calculation based on the impedance due to the three transformers in parallel would show a fault level of 31·5 MVA,

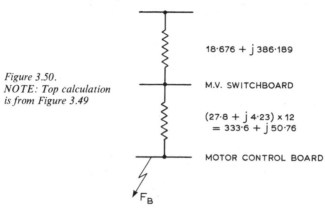

Figure 3.50.
NOTE: Top calculation is from Figure 3.49

18·676 + j 386·189

M.V. SWITCHBOARD

$(27 \cdot 8 + j\,4 \cdot 23) \times 12$
$= 333 \cdot 6 + j\,50 \cdot 76$

MOTOR CONTROL BOARD

F_B

whereas a true level is 26 MVA. To continue the calculation to obtain the fault level at the group motor control board, the impedance diagram can be drawn as in Fig. 3.50, and adding for the series circuit the following:

Impedance as calculated to main m.v. board =	$18 \cdot 676 + j386 \cdot 189$
Cables to motor control board	$= 333 \cdot 6 \quad + \quad j50 \cdot 76$
Z (total)	$352 \cdot 276 + j436 \cdot 949$

It is now seen that resistance is a significant part of the impedance, and must be taken into account. Rounding-off the figures, we get:

$$Z \text{ (total)} = \sqrt{352^2 + 437^2}$$
$$= 561\% \text{ approx.}$$
$$\text{s.c. MVA} = \frac{10\,000}{561} = 17 \cdot 8$$
$$\text{p.f. at fault} = \frac{352}{561} = 0 \cdot 63 \text{ approx.}$$

To complete the calculation for the fault level at the sub-distribution board, the new impedance diagram appears as in Fig. 3.51, and again adding for a series circuit we get:

Impedance as calculated to group motor control board =	$352 + j437$
Cable to sub-distribution board	$= 2\,420 + \quad j97 \cdot 4$
Z (total)	$= 2\,772 + j534 \cdot 4$
	$= 2\,823\% \text{ approx.}$
s.c. MVA	$= \frac{10\,000}{2\,823} = 3 \cdot 54$

85

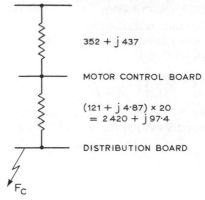

$352 + j\,437$

MOTOR CONTROL BOARD

$(121 + j\,4\cdot87) \times 20$
$= 2\,420 + j\,97\cdot4$

DISTRIBUTION BOARD

F_C

Figure 3.51. NOTE: Top calculation is from Figure 3.50

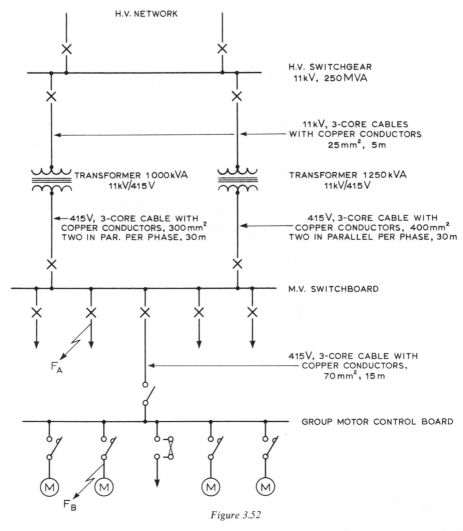

H.V. NETWORK

H.V. SWITCHGEAR
11kV, 250MVA

11kV, 3-CORE CABLES
WITH COPPER CONDUCTORS
25mm^2, 5m

TRANSFORMER 1000kVA   TRANSFORMER 1250kVA
11kV/415V   11kV/415V

415V, 3-CORE CABLE WITH   415V, 3-CORE CABLE WITH
COPPER CONDUCTORS, 300mm^2 COPPER CONDUCTORS, 400mm^2
TWO IN PAR. PER PHASE, 30m   TWO IN PARALLEL PER PHASE, 30m

M.V. SWITCHBOARD

F_A

415V, 3-CORE CABLE WITH
COPPER CONDUCTORS,
70mm^2, 15m

GROUP MOTOR CONTROL BOARD

F_B

Figure 3.52

86

The examples so far considered have been relatively simple by reason of the fact that parallel circuits have each been of equal rating and impedance, so that the conversion of the impedances to a single equivalent required only a division by the number of impedances in parallel. When parallel circuits differ in the foregoing respects, the calculation to obtain the resultant impedance is slightly more complex, and to study this calculations will be made for the system shown in Fig. 3.52, firstly to find the fault level at the main m.v. switchboard, and secondly the level at the group motor control board (this could equally well be a power-distribution board).

The impedance diagram for the system is given in Fig. 3.53, and in making our calculations we shall ignore the very short lengths of h.v. cable to the transformers, as it is clear that the small values of impedance attributable to these cables will have extremely little effect. As a first step, the equivalent impedance of the two power transformers in parallel can be determined as follows:

$$Z = \frac{1}{\dfrac{1}{475} + \dfrac{1}{400}} = \frac{1}{0 \cdot 0021 + 0 \cdot 0025}$$

$$= \frac{1}{0 \cdot 0046} = 217\%$$

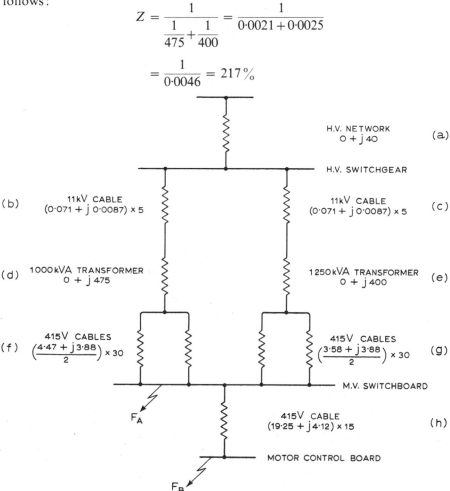

H.V. NETWORK
0 + j 40   (a)

H.V. SWITCHGEAR

(b)   11kV CABLE
(0·071 + j 0·0087) x 5

11kV CABLE
(0·071 + j 0·0087) x 5   (c)

(d)   1000 kVA TRANSFORMER
0 + j 475

1250 kVA TRANSFORMER
0 + j 400   (e)

(f)   415V CABLES
$\left(\dfrac{4 \cdot 47 + j 3 \cdot 88}{2}\right)$ x 30

415V CABLES
$\left(\dfrac{3 \cdot 58 + j 3 \cdot 88}{2}\right)$ x 30   (g)

M.V. SWITCHBOARD

F_A

415V CABLE
(19·25 + j 4·12) x 15   (h)

MOTOR CONTROL BOARD

F_B

Figure 3.53. Calculations are derived as follows: (a) from Table 3.8, (b) and (c) from Table 3.3, (d) and (e) from Table 3.2 and (f), (g) and (h) from Table 3.9

and this enables us to reduce the impedance diagram (up to the main m.v. switchboard) to Fig. 3.54, in which the parallel impedances of the cables to the switchboard have also been shown as single equivalents.

There are several methods which may be used to determine the single equivalent impedance for the two branches in parallel now left in Fig. 3.54. These have *unlike* values to be resolved, and to maintain the simplicity of approach the calculation which follows is made on the basis of admittances, where:

$$\text{Admittance} = \frac{1}{\text{Impedance}} = \frac{1}{R+jX}$$

The two parallel branches for this purpose are therefore redrawn as in Fig. 3.55 and the calculation proceeds as below:

Branch No. 1

$$\text{Admittance} = \frac{1}{R_1+jX_1}$$

$$= \frac{1}{67 \cdot 05 + j58 \cdot 2}$$

$$= \frac{67 \cdot 05 - j58 \cdot 2}{67 \cdot 05^2 + 58 \cdot 2^2}$$

$$= \frac{67 \cdot 05 - j58 \cdot 2}{7\,883}$$

$$= 0 \cdot 0085 - j0 \cdot 0074$$

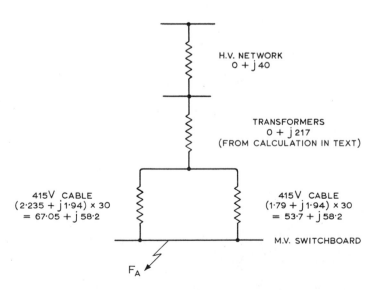

H.V. NETWORK
0 + j40

TRANSFORMERS
0 + j217
(FROM CALCULATION IN TEXT)

415V CABLE
(2·235 + j1·94) × 30
= 67·05 + j58·2

415V CABLE
(1·79 + j1·94) × 30
= 53·7 + j58·2

M.V. SWITCHBOARD

F$_A$

Figure 3.54

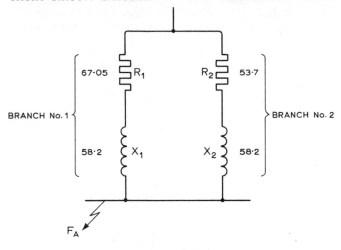

Figure 3.55

Branch No. 2

$$\text{Admittance} = \frac{1}{R_2 + jX_2}$$

$$= \frac{1}{53\cdot7 + j58\cdot2}$$

$$= \frac{53\cdot7 - j58\cdot2}{53\cdot7^2 + 58\cdot2^2}$$

$$= \frac{53\cdot7 - j58\cdot2}{6\ 271}$$

$$= 0\cdot0086 - j0\cdot0094$$

To arrive at a total admittance these values are added arithmetically:

Branch No. 1 $\quad = \quad 0\cdot0085 - j0\cdot0074$
Branch No. 2 $\quad = \quad 0\cdot0086 - j0\cdot0094$
Total admittance $\quad = \quad \overline{0\cdot0171 - j0\cdot0168}$

$$\therefore \text{Total impedance} = \frac{1}{0\cdot0171 - j0\cdot0168}$$

$$= \frac{0\cdot0171 + j0\cdot0168}{0\cdot0171^2 + 0\cdot0168^2}$$

$$= \frac{0\cdot0171 + j0\cdot0168}{0\cdot00058}$$

$$= \quad 29\cdot6 + j29$$

The impedance diagram can now be redrawn to show these impedances in series (Fig. 3.56), and from the total impedance shown thereon, the fault level at F_A is found to be:

$$Z \text{ (total)} = \sqrt{29 \cdot 6^2 + 286^2}$$

$$= 287 \cdot 5\%$$

$$\text{s.c. MVA} = \frac{10\,000}{287 \cdot 5} = 34 \cdot 8$$

To ascertain the fault level at F_B, it is only necessary to add the series impedance of the cable to the motor control board to the total calculated for a fault at F_A, so that:

$$
\begin{aligned}
\text{Impedance to fault at } F_A &= 29 \cdot 6 + j286 \\
\text{Impedance of cable} &= 288 \cdot 75 + j61 \cdot 8 \\
\therefore Z \text{ (to fault } F_B) &= \overline{318 \cdot 35 + j347 \cdot 8} \\
&= \sqrt{318 \cdot 35^2 + 347 \cdot 8^2} \\
&= 471\% \\
\text{s.c. MVA} \qquad &= \frac{10\,000}{471} = 21 \cdot 25
\end{aligned}
$$

To illustrate the reduction in fault level achieved by sectionalising the busbars, we may consider the system previously calculated, i.e. Fig. 3.52, but now arranged for the main medium-voltage switchboard to be sectionalised as shown in Fig. 3.57. The section switch (or circuit-breaker) and the two transformer circuit-breakers will be interlocked so that at any one time only two of the three can be closed. A disadvantage of the scheme is that should the 1 250 kVA transformer be lost for any reason, there will be a complete shut-down of the motor control board until such time as the section switch can be closed. This situation could be mitigated by using, say, two 600 kVA transformers instead of one 1 250 kVA, and then the loss of one unit would leave the other to maintain supply, although some load shedding might be necessary.

To investigate the possible reduction in fault level at both the main and motor control boards, the impedance diagram is now drawn as in Fig. 3.58, and again ignoring the impedance of the h.v. cable, the impedance to a fault at F_A can be summed up as follows:

$$
\begin{aligned}
\text{h.v. network} &= 0 + j40 \\
\text{transformer} &= 0 + j400 \\
\text{cables} &= 53 \cdot 7 + j58 \cdot 2 \\
\therefore Z \text{ (total)} &= \overline{53 \cdot 7 + j498 \cdot 2} \\
&= \sqrt{53 \cdot 7^2 + 498 \cdot 2^2} \\
&= 501 \cdot 6\% \\
\text{s.c. MVA} \qquad &= \frac{10\,000}{501 \cdot 6} = 19 \cdot 9
\end{aligned}
$$

90

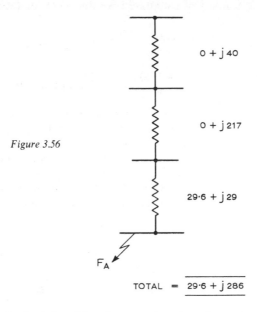

Figure 3.56

$0 + j\,40$

$0 + j\,217$

$29\cdot6 + j\,29$

F_A

TOTAL $=$ $29\cdot6 + j\,286$

This shows that the fault level has been reduced at the main m.v. switchboard from 34·8 MVA to say 20 MVA.

For a fault at F_B on the motor control board we sum up as follows:

Impedance to fault F_A $\quad= \quad 53\cdot7 \;+j498\cdot2$
Impedance of cable to motor control board $= 288\cdot75+ \;\; j61\cdot8$
Z (total to F_B) $\quad= \quad 342\cdot45+j560\cdot0$

$$= \sqrt{342\cdot45^2 + 560^2}$$

$$= 656\cdot4\%$$

s.c. MVA $\qquad\qquad\qquad = \dfrac{10\,000}{656\cdot4} = 15\cdot23$

This compares with 21·25 MVA worked out earlier for the two transformers in parallel.

Having demonstrated the simple methods of arriving at a fault level in MVA so that switchgear of an appropriate rating may be chosen, it is necessary for other purposes to translate into current values as it is only in terms of the latter that, for example, cables having an adequate short-time rating may be selected or the electromagnetic stresses on bus structures and the thermal conditions in conductors can be calculated.

From the MVA value therefore, the three-phase short-circuit current is determined from:

$$\text{kA r.m.s. symmetrical} = \frac{\text{MVA} \times 1\,000}{\text{voltage} \times 1\cdot73}$$

where the voltage is in volts.

91

Thus, taking the example just calculated we find that for faults at F_A and F_B the currents involved are:

$$\text{At } F_A = \frac{20 \times 1000}{415 \times 1 \cdot 73} = 27 \cdot 8 \text{ kA r.m.s. sym.}$$

$$\text{At } F_B = \frac{15 \cdot 23 \times 1000}{415 \times 1 \cdot 73} = 21 \cdot 2 \text{ kA r.m.s. sym.}$$

As we shall note in Chapter 5, the current in the first half-cycle of short-circuit can rise to a high peak, its value being dependent largely on the power factor at the fault. When the latter occurs at points relatively close to a power source, e.g. generators or transformers, the power factor will be low as the fault current is mainly limited by the *reactance* of such plant only. When the fault is at some distance from the power source, the power factor will be relatively high due to the fact that, in addition to reactance, resistance in the circuit can

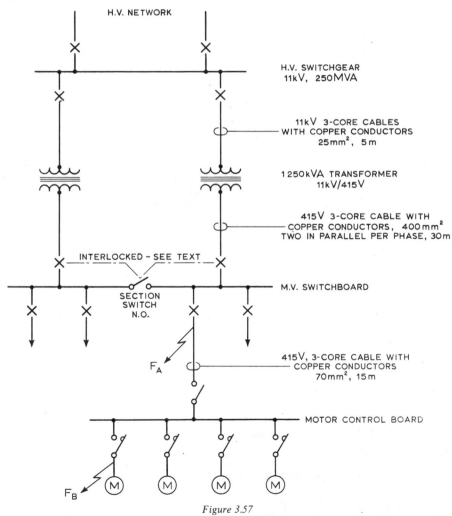

Figure 3.57

92

be significantly high by reason of the connecting cables. The power factor is determined from:

$$\text{p.f.} = \frac{\text{Resistance}}{\text{Impedance}} = \frac{R}{Z}$$

We can note that for the faults at F_A and F_B under consideration, the power factor will be:

$$\text{At } F_A = \frac{53 \cdot 7}{501 \cdot 6} = 0 \cdot 17$$

$$\text{At } F_B = \frac{342 \cdot 5}{656 \cdot 4} = 0 \cdot 52$$

It is generally accepted that for power factors of the order of 0·15 or less, the peak current in the first half-cycle may reach a value of 2·55 times the r.m.s. symmetrical value, while for power factors of 0·3 or higher, the multiplying factor is 2·0. Using this convention we can assume the worst condition applies for a fault at F_A so that the peak current will be:

$$27 \cdot 8 \times 2 \cdot 55 = 70 \cdot 2 \text{ kA } (70\,200 \text{ A})$$

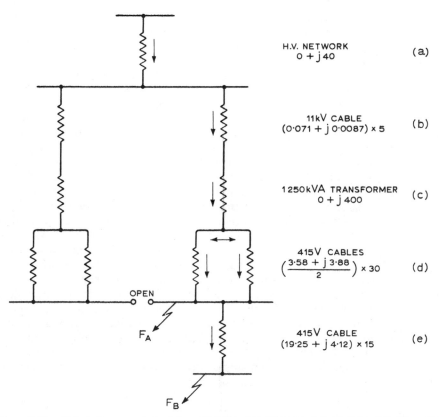

H.V. NETWORK
0 + j 40   (a)

11kV CABLE
(0·071 + j 0·0087) x 5   (b)

1250kVA TRANSFORMER
0 + j 400   (c)

415V CABLES
$\left(\dfrac{3 \cdot 58 + j\,3 \cdot 88}{2}\right)$ x 30   (d)

OPEN

F_A

415V CABLE
(19·25 + j 4·12) x 15   (e)

F_B

Figure 3.58.   Calculations are derived from (a) Table 3.8, (b) Table 3.3, (c) Table 3.2, (d) and (e) Table 3.9. NOTE: arrows denote fault path

while for a fault at F_B, the condition will be less severe, the peak current being:

$$21 \cdot 2 \times 2 \cdot 0 = 42 \cdot 4 \text{ kA (42 400 A)}$$

These then are the currents which decide the required 'making' capacity of the chosen circuit-breakers and which must be used in calculations to determine the maximum electromagnetic stresses on busbars and other conductors, the structures supporting them, and other apparatus.

SHORT-TIME RATING OF CABLES

Although this book is primarily concerned with switchgear, and the calculations in this chapter are those necessary to determine the fault levels at points where switchgear is installed, it is not inappropriate to include a brief reference to some of the considerations which have to be taken into account when selecting a cable size to match the fault level. This is necessary because, firstly, the cables have to carry the fault current for a time corresponding to the clearance time of the circuit-breaker or fuse. Secondly, because cables, like all other conductors, experience electromagnetic stresses and thermal conditions when carrying currents of high magnitude. Thirdly, because the impedance of the cables has an important bearing on the prospective fault level. This latter point is significant because instances can arise where it is necessary, in order to meet the fault current to be carried, to use a larger cable than normal load conditions would dictate, so that the cable impedance is less and the fault level is increased.

What current a cable will carry safely for short periods of time (0·2–3·0 s) depends on many factors, among them being the type of conductor (copper or aluminium), whether the conductors are stranded or solid, the type of insulation (paper or p.v.c.), the safe final temperature of the conductor or lead sheath, the risk of bursting a multicore cable due to electromagnetic stresses, how the cables are laid (in air or buried), in some cables on the pre-fault loading, whether armoured or not and if armoured whether by single wires or steel tape, and last but by no means least, the length of time the current has to be carried.

From the foregoing, it will be appreciated that to determine a safe short-time rating for a particular type and size of cable is a complex problem and is one which has been (and continues to be) the subject of research and investigation by the Electrical Research Association (E.R.A.) and cable manufacturers. Based on recent work, the E.R.A. have published several reports[6,7,8,9], and arising out of these, but subject to variations which other factors introduce (e.g. the risk of bursting the lead sheath) the fault current which a cable conductor can carry for a specified time is based on it reaching a temperature not exceeding 160°C where the insulation is paper and 130°C for p.v.c. insulation. The general formula to give the short-time current on this basis for multi-core paper-insulated lead-covered and single-wire armoured cables, and single and multicore armoured p.v.c. insulated cables, is:

$$I_F = \frac{K \times A}{\sqrt{t}}$$

where I_F = fault current, in A

A = cross sectional area, in in^2 or mm^2

K = a constant depending on the metal, on the initial and final temperatures, and whether A is in Imperial or metric terms

t = duration of short-circuit, in s

Values of K are given in Tables 3.13 and 3.14.

Table 3.13

CONSTANT K FOR PAPER-INSULATED CABLES

Voltage (kV)	Maximum continuous conductor temperature (°C)	K					
		Copper		Aluminium			
				Stranded		Solid	
		When A in formula is in:					
		in^2	mm^2	in^2	mm^2	in^2	mm^2
0·66/1·1	80						
1·9/3·3	80	70 000	108	44 500	69	36 000	56
3·8/6·6	80						
6·35/11							
single core	70	74 500	115·5	48 000	74·4	—	—
3-core belted	65	76 500	118·6	49 000	76·0	—	—
3-core screened	70	74 500	115·5	48 000	74·4	—	—
12·7/22	65	76 500	118·6	49 000	76	—	—
19/33	65	76 500	118·6	49 000	76	—	—

Table 3.14

CONSTANT K FOR P.V.C. INSULATED CABLES

Voltage (kV)	Maximum continuous conductor temperature (°C)	K			
		Copper		Aluminium (stranded or solid)	
		When A in formula is in:			
		in^2	mm^2	in^2	mm^2
0·25/0·44	70				
0·66/1·1	70	62 000	96	40 000	62
1·9/3·3	70				

Single-core cables used on a.c. systems are generally unarmoured so that in the event of an earth fault the lead sheath has to carry the return fault current. An acceptable safe temperature for the lead sheath is 250°C, a temperature which would be exceeded if the cables were rated on the short-circuit capacity of the conductor. For this reason, single-core medium-voltage cables (660/1 100 V) are generally rated on the sheath rather than the conductor, resulting in lower short-time ratings, the general formula being:

$$I_F = \frac{K \times A_S}{\sqrt{t}}$$

where A_s = cross-sectional area of sheath in Imperial or metric terms
$\quad K$ = 19 100 when A is in in^2
$\qquad$ = 30 when A is in mm^2
$\quad t$ = duration of short-circuit, in s

For high voltages, the short-time rating of single-core cables will depend on whether or not means of limiting the earth fault current, i.e. resistance in the earthed neutral, is incorporated in the system. Where this is included, short-time ratings based on the conductor can be used, but if not then the rating may need to take into account the lead sheath. For a more detailed consideration of this and other factors which determine the short-time ratings of cables, a brochure published by A.E.I. Cables Ltd.[10] will be found invaluable.

It may be noted that some increase in the short-time rating of p.v.c. cables is possible where these are fractionally loaded, i.e. if it carries a continuous or intermittent load such that the maximum permissible continuous-conductor temperature is not attained. Table 3.15, attributable to A.E.I. Cables Ltd., gives an indication of the possible increase against the pre-loading condition.

Table 3.15
POSSIBLE INCREASE AGAINST THE PRE-LOADING
CONDITION

% of full load current prior to fault	Short-circuit rating factor
90	1·09
80	1·17
70	1·24
60	1·30
50	1·34
40	1·38
30	1·41

It is generally accepted that in using the formulae noted earlier, t should not be less than 0·2 s. When the circuit interrupting device is an h.r.c. fuse in particular or a fast acting circuit-breaker, the total break-time (i.e. the time during which the cable has to carry the fault current) is much less than 0·2 s and this would appear to suggest that such shorter times be used in the formulae, resulting in higher short-time ratings for the cables. This however is not practicable as these higher currents would lead to the bursting of the lead sheath as the electromagnetic forces would be extremely high. Indeed, even using 0·2 s in the formulae for some larger cables, currents beyond the safe limit with respect to bursting are obtained and so they have to be restricted. As an example, published literature for cables in Imperial sizes shows that a cable in the 660/ 1 100 V grade of 0·25 in^2 section should, by the formula for copper conductors, be able to carry about 39 900 A for 0·2 s, but because of the danger of bursting this is restricted to about 30 000 A, while for a cable 0·5 in^2 section, the nominal short-time rating would be nearly 80 000 A but is restricted to about 50% of this value. In metric sizes, these cables approximate to 150 mm^2 and 300 mm^2 respectively. Indiscriminate use of the formulae therefore should not be made and the advice of the cable manufacturer sought, the purpose of this short discussion being to draw attention to the fact that cables should be chosen in the knowledge that they, like switchgear, are concerned with system fault levels.

REFERENCES
1. WAGNER, W.P., 'Short-circuit Contributions of Large Induction Motors', *Proc. I.E.E.*, **116** No. 6, June (1969)
2. COOPER, C.B., MACLEAN, D.M. and WILLIAMS, K.G., 'Application of Test Results to the Calculation of Short-circuit Levels in Large Industrial Systems with Concentrated Induction Motor Loads', *Proc. I.E.E.*, **116** No. 11, Nov. (1969)
3. THANAWALA, H.L., U.K. Pat. 1 108 608 (1968)
4. THOMAS, A.G. and RATA, P.J.H., *Aluminium Busbar*, Hutchinson (1960)
5. LAURIE, J.B., *Copper for Busbars*, Copper Development Association, Jan. (1954)
6. GOSLAND, L. and PARR, R.G., *A Basis for Short-circuit Ratings for Paper-insulated Lead-sheathed Cables up to 11 kV*, E.R.A., Report F/T195 (1960)
7. PARR, R.G., *Bursting Currents of 11 kV Three-core Screened Cables—Lead-sheathed, Paper-Insulated*, E.R.A., Report F/T202 (1962)
8. PARR, R.G., *Short-circuit Ratings for 11 kV Three-core Paper-insulated Screened Cables*, E.R.A., Report No. 5057 (1964)
9. PARR, R.G. and YAP, J.S., *Short-circuit Ratings for p.v.c. Insulated Cables (600/1100 V grade)* E.R.A., Report No. 5056 (1965)
10. *Short-circuit Current Ratings*, A.E.I. Cables Ltd. (Power Cables Division), Publication No. 5250–51, March (1968)

BIBLIOGRAPHY
*JOHN, M.N., 'S.L.C.—An Automatic Resonance Link', *Electrical Times*, 29 Aug. (1968)
KALSI, S.S. *et al.*, 'Calculation of System Fault Currents Due to Induction Motors', *Proc. I.E.E.*, **118** No. 1, Jan. (1971)
Short-circuit Current Ratings, A.E.I. Cables Ltd. (Power Cable Div.), Pub. 5950–51 (m), First Metric edn. (1971). Reference 10 above is to the 1968 edn. which covers symmetrical (3-phase) fault conditions in relation to cables to Imperial standards. This new edition covers the same range but relative to metric standards. It also provides a wealth of data relating to earth fault conditions which involves, in addition to the conductors, the lead sheath and/or the armour.
THOMAS, A.G., 'Short-circuit Ratings of Aluminium Cables', *Electrical Review*, 10 Nov. (1961)
*ANON., 'Limiting Short-circuit Current', *Works Engineering & Factory Services*, Aug. (1968)
*ANON., 'Short-circuit Limiters for Shell Oil Refinery Pass Tests', *Electrical Review*, 11 July (1969)

---

* Available as reprints from English Electric Power Transmission Ltd., Stafford.

Chapter 4

Short-circuit calculations for unsymmetrical faults

It has been shown in Chapter 3 how calculations are made for the condition of a symmetrical fault, this being the accepted method for the selection of suitably rated circuit-breakers or fuses and for the stresses set up in busbar and connection structures under short-circuit conditions. Such calculations are also adequate for determining the overcurrent factors for current transformers and protective gear stability on through faults.

Fault conditions however, are not confined to the three-phase condition, and indeed the majority of faults are those which involve only one line and in some cases two. Such faults are thus unsymmetrical in nature and it becomes necessary for engineers to calculate the fault currents which can occur under each of the three conditions shown in Fig. 4.1. The information obtained is necessary for the determination of protective gear relay settings and in studies of transient stability in an interconnected power system. Not only is it essential to know the current at the point of fault but also how it is distributed (and in what magnitude) throughout the network behind the fault. A full study of this subject also involves the unsymmetrical voltages which arise, a knowledge of which is essential particularly in protective systems of the directional type where the voltage element is important. Here we shall concern ourselves only with the current aspect but a number of books and papers noted in the bibliography include a full study of the voltage condition.

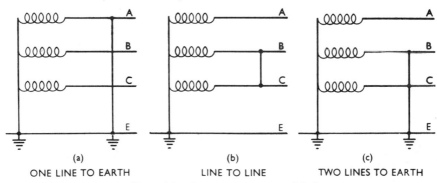

| (a) | (b) | (c) |
| ONE LINE TO EARTH | LINE TO LINE | TWO LINES TO EARTH |

Figure 4.1.   Types of unsymmetrical fault

98

In order to calculate the values of current for unsymmetrical faults, use has to be made of the theory of symmetrical components, the principles of which were originally stated by Stovkis and were enunciated in practical form later (1918) by Fortescue[1]. It is beyond the scope of this book to study the theoretical basis of symmetrical components, instead we will accept the theory and demonstrate its practical use.

This then is the purpose of this chapter, but firstly it is necessary to state the facts established by the theory. They are:

1. In any three-phase system the occurrence of faults of the type shown in Fig. 4.1 causes unbalance, the currents and voltages becoming unequal in magnitude, while the phasors* representing them are no longer spaced 120° or equal.

2. In any unbalanced system, it is possible to analyse that system into two or three balanced systems known as positive, negative and zero-phase sequences.

3. The positive-phase sequence system is that system in which the phase or line currents or voltages reach a maximum in the same cyclic order as those in a normal supply, e.g., assuming the conventional counter-clockwise rotation, then the positive-phase sequence phasors are those shown at (a) in Fig. 4.2. A

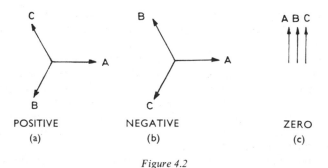

POSITIVE	NEGATIVE	ZERO
(a)	(b)	(c)

Figure 4.2

balanced system corresponding to normal conditions contains a positive-phase sequence only. It is also the condition for a three-phase fault as calculated in Chapter 3.

4. The negative-phase sequence system is that system in which the phasors still rotate anti-clockwise but reach a maximum in a reverse order, i.e., ACB as indicated at (b) Fig. 4.2. This sequence only arises under conditions of unbalance as when faults of the type shown in Fig. 4.1 occur, such faults contain also the positive sequence system as (3) above and, in the case of faults to earth, a zero-phase sequence system as noted in (5) below.

5. The zero-phase sequence system is a single-phase phasor system combining three equal phasors in phase, as shown at (c) Fig. 4.2, and represents the residual current or voltage present under fault conditions on a three-phase system with a fourth wire or earth return present. Clearly the zero-phase sequence therefore embraces the ground, in addition to the three line wires and represents a fault condition to earth or to a fourth conductor, if present. Its presence arises only where fault to earth currents can return to the system via the star point of that

* The term 'phasor' is now used to represent a time-varying sinusoidal quantity (such as voltage or current), which in the past has been incorrectly referred to as a 'vector'.

system or via an artificial neutral point provided to earth a delta system. In an earth fault, positive and negative-phase sequences are also present.

This is the basis of the theory from which it is possible to calculate the fault current under any condition. As the three-phase fault has been dealt with in Chapter 3, our concern here will be with:

(a) Single-phase line to line faults involving the positive and negative-phase sequences, and

(b) Single-phase line to earth faults involving the positive, negative and zero-phase sequences.

The impedances to these phase-sequence currents are important to the calculations and as differences arise between types of plant, cables and transmission lines, some idea of the values must be noted before proceeding to typical calculations. For easy reference, particularly in the worked examples, the three impedances will be given the following notation:

$$Z_1 = \text{Positive-phase sequence impedance}$$
$$Z_2 = \text{Negative-phase sequence impedance}$$
$$Z_0 = \text{Zero-phase sequence impedance}$$

In all *static* plant (and this includes cables and overhead lines) $Z_1 = Z_2$ but may differ from Z_0. On *rotating* plant, however, all three are different. In power transformers, Z_1 and Z_2 are equal and are the normal impedances quoted by the manufacturer, but Z_0 will depend on the transformer connections. For those with delta/star (star neutral earthed) star/star (both neutrals earthed) and star or delta/interstar (interstar neutral earthed) connections, Z_0 is equal to Z_1 and Z_2. For star/star connected transformers where the primary is three-wire and providing the core is of the three-limb type, Z_0 will be approximately 0·66 times Z_1. In the case of a three-phase shell-type or a group of three single-phase transformers, Z_0 may be as high as 4 or 5 times Z_1. For all other connections, it may be assumed that there is an open circuit to zero-phase sequence currents.

In cables and overhead transmission lines, Z_1 and Z_2 are equal and are the ohmic values given in manufacturers tables. On the other hand, Z_0 is only determined by calculations of some complexity, involving in the case of cables a knowledge of sheath resistances, conductor spacing, how laid and whether earthed or not, while for overhead lines the value varies with regard to single or double circuit lines, with or without earth wires and whether the latter are magnetic or non-magnetic.

Because of these complications, Z_0 can only be accurately determined for a specific case, but a number of authors have given approximations which can be used for general calculations, these approximations being as follows:

Cables
    Three core $Z_0 = 3Z_1$ to $5Z_1$
    Single core $Z_0 = 1 \cdot 25Z_1$
Overhead lines, single circuit
    No ground wire $Z_0 = 3 \cdot 5Z_1$
    Steel ground wire $Z_0 = 3 \cdot 5Z_1$
    Non-magnetic ground wire $Z_0 = 2Z_1$

Overhead lines, double circuit

No ground wire	$Z_0 = 5{\cdot}5Z_1$
Steel ground wire	$Z_0 = 5Z_1$
Non-magnetic ground wire	$Z_0 = 3Z_1$

A large part of the zero-sequence impedance for cables is resistive and it is here that many variations occur, dependent on the earthing conditions. In a paper by Wagner and Evans[2], for example, the detailed calculations are given for a three-core cable 450 000 circular mils 13·2 kV, the cable being buried in damp earth. These authors show that for this case:

$$Z_1 = 0{\cdot}146 + j0{\cdot}169 \ \Omega \ \text{per phase}$$
$$Z_0 = 1{\cdot}42 \ + j0{\cdot}78 \ \Omega \ \text{per phase}$$

so that zero sequence resistance is nearly ten times the positive sequence resistance, while the zero-sequence reactance is only 4·6 times the positive-sequence reactance, and it is stated that these multiples may be used for approximations.

In the case of rotating plant where all three values differ, Z_1 is the normal value quoted by the manufacturer, i.e. the values used in three-phase short-circuit calculations as in Chapter 3. In certain circumstances, as for example where a long time delay may be applied to a protective system, it will be necessary to use the synchronous or steady state impedance, as, after several seconds, the initial short-circuit current will have fallen to the much lower steady state value. Alternatively, standard decrement curves can be applied to the calculated initial values.

Z_2 for rotating machines is generally somewhat less than Z_1 and varies with the type of winding, type of machine, number of poles, etc. and it is important in any particular calculation to ascertain the value from the machine designer. As we are only concerned here with demonstrating the use of symmetrical components it will suffice if we assume that $Z_2 = 0{\cdot}73Z_1$. Similar factors concern the value of Z_0 for rotating machines and here again various authors give average values for use if actual figures are not available. These average values indicate that at 11 kV, Z_0 is equal to about $0{\cdot}33Z_1$, while at 22 and 33 kV it is about $0{\cdot}5Z_1$.

In calculations for line to earth faults, one further impedance may be present and considered, namely that which may be purposely introduced in the neutral connection to earth (see Chapter 7) and which may be either a resistance or a reactor. The value of this impedance must be multiplied by three as it is in series with each line.

For the sake of simplicity, the typical calculations which follow will be on the basis that the various impedances are purely reactive, i.e. that Z will be $R+jX$ where R is zero. It has, however, been shown in Chapter 3 that where cables or overhead lines are included in any calculation, resistance often plays a most important part in reducing the value of fault current. It will be remembered too that all calculations in Chapter 3 were on a percentage impedance basis and that normal values were converted to others on a chosen kVA base. Examples included in that chapter could have been calculated with equal ease using ohmic values, and as an exercise these will be used in the first example to be given. But here it must be noted that when working with ohmic values, it is necessary to use a base voltage instead of kVA. Where only one voltage is involved this can be used as the base, but where step-up or step-down transformers are included, then all calculations must be on a chosen voltage.

Using the ohmic method and a base voltage requires formulae for conversion, and those essential to the calculations are:

1. Given the percentage reactance (or impedance) of a machine or transformer of known kVA rating:

$$\text{Ohmic value} = \frac{\% \text{ value} . 10 . (\text{kV})^2}{\text{kVA}}$$

where kV = kilovolts between lines

2. Given the ohmic value of reactance (or impedance) of a cable or overhead line at working (normal) voltage:

$$\text{Ohmic value at base voltage} = \text{Ohmic value at normal voltage} . \left(\frac{V_2}{V_1}\right)^2$$

where V_1 = normal voltage in volts
and V_2 = base voltage in volts

As a first example, assume a simple network as in Fig. 4.3 where it is required to ascertain the fault currents for a fault at F under two conditions, i.e. line to line and one line to earth. Here two voltages are concerned (6·6 and 11 kV) and as the fault is assumed to be on the 6·6 kV system, it is convenient to use this

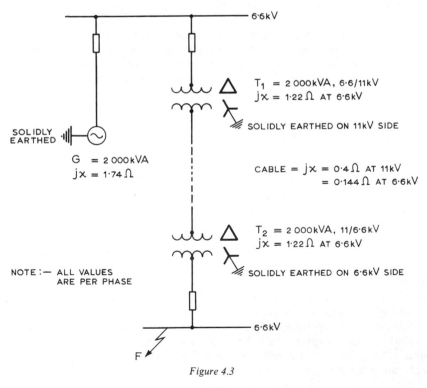

Figure 4.3

102

voltage as a base. The generator of 2 000 kVA has a reactance of 8% and from the formula just given we find:

$$\text{Ohmic reactance} = \frac{8.10.6\cdot6^2}{2\,000} = 1\cdot74\,\Omega$$

The transformers each of 2 000 kVA with a reactance of 5·6% are converted to:

$$\text{Ohmic reactance of each transformer} = \frac{5\cdot6.10.6\cdot6^2}{2\,000} = 1\cdot22\,\Omega$$

(Note that this value is at our chosen base of 6·6 kV)

The cable between the two transformers has a reactance of 0·4 Ω at 11 kV and converting this to a value on a 6·6 kV base, we get:

$$0\cdot4\left(\frac{6\,600}{11\,000}\right)^2 = 0\cdot144\,\Omega$$

Bearing in mind previous notes concerning the relative values of Z_1, Z_2 and Z_0, the figures relating to Fig. 4.3 may be summarised thus:

Z_1 Generator—Positive-phase sequence impedance $= 0+j1\cdot74\,\Omega$
Z_2 „ —Negative „ „ „ $= (0+j1\cdot74)0\cdot73\,\Omega$
$\qquad\qquad\qquad\qquad\qquad\qquad\qquad\qquad\qquad\qquad\qquad = 0+j1\cdot27\,\Omega$
Transformer T_1
$\quad Z_1$ „ —Positive-phase sequence impedance $= 0+j1\cdot22\,\Omega$
$\quad Z_2$ „ —Negative „ „ „ $= 0+j1\cdot22\,\Omega$
$\quad Z_1$ Cable —Positive-phase sequence impedance $= 0+j0\cdot144\,\Omega$
$\quad Z_2$ „ —Negative „ „ „ $= 0+j0\cdot144\,\Omega$
Transformer T_2
$\quad Z_1$ „ —Positive-phase sequence impedance $= 0+j1\cdot22\,\Omega$
$\quad Z_2$ „ —Negative „ „ „ $= 0+j1\cdot22\,\Omega$
$\quad Z_0$ „ —Zero „ „ „ $= 0+j1\cdot22\,\Omega$

It will be noted that the only area where zero-phase sequence current can appear is at Transformer T_2, i.e., a line fault to earth at F back to the 6·6 kV neutral of this transformer via the ground.

The three sequences can now be set down as indicated in Fig. 4.4 and adding the various impedances in series arithmetically, obtain:

	Z_1	Z_2	Z_0
Generator	$0+j1\cdot74$	$0+j1\cdot27$	—
Transformer T_1	$0+j1\cdot22$	$0+j1\cdot22$	—
Cable	$0+j0\cdot144$	$0+j0\cdot144$	—
Transformer T_2	$0+j1\cdot22$	$0+j1\cdot22$	$0+j1\cdot22$
	$0+j4\cdot324$	$0+j3\cdot854$	$0+j1\cdot22$

With these values, we can proceed to calculate for the two fault conditions as follows.

103

Line to earth fault

As explained earlier, faults to earth embrace the three sequence components and therefore the total impedance to the fault will be:

$$Z_t = Z_1 + Z_2 + Z_0$$
$$= 0 + j4\cdot324 + 0 + j3\cdot854 + 0 + j1\cdot22$$
$$= 0 + j9\cdot398 \ \Omega$$

The earth fault current will be:

$$I_f = \frac{3E}{Z_t}$$

where E = Normal line to neutral voltage of the selected base voltage.

$$\therefore \ I_f = \frac{3 \times 3\,810}{9\cdot398} = 1\,217 \text{ A}.$$

The condition at the fault can be shown as in Fig. 4.5.

Line to line fault

In this case, only the positive and negative-phase sequence impedances will limit the fault, and:

$$Z_t = Z_1 + Z_2$$
$$= 0 + j4\cdot324 + 0 + j3\cdot854$$
$$= 0 + j8\cdot178 \ \Omega$$

$$\text{and } I_f = \frac{\sqrt{3}E}{Z_t}$$

$$= \frac{\sqrt{3} \times 3\,810}{8\cdot178} = 806 \text{ A}$$

The condition at the fault can be shown as in Fig. 4.6.

We have seen, therefore, that there is a considerable difference in fault current between line to earth and line to line faults, and any protective gear installed must be sensitive to these different values. By a calculation similar to those undertaken in Chapter 3 it can be shown that the three-phase fault current at F would be 880 A, so that there are three different values for different fault conditions. Alternatively, the three-phase value could be determined from:

$$I_f = \frac{E}{Z_1} = \frac{3\,810}{4\cdot324} = 880 \text{ A}$$

In the calculation for a line to earth fault, the earth resistance has been assumed zero. This is a condition which is unlikely, as apart from any resistance which may be purposely installed in the neutral connection to limit the earth fault current, e.g. to twice full-load current with line to neutral voltage impressed, there is the resistance of the return path to the neutral. Let us assume that this is 2 Ω and this has to be multiplied by three as noted earlier.

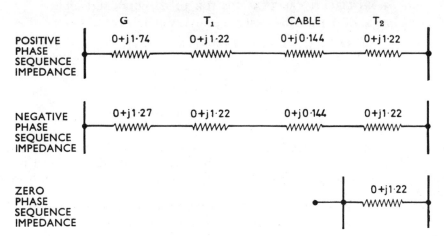

Figure 4.4

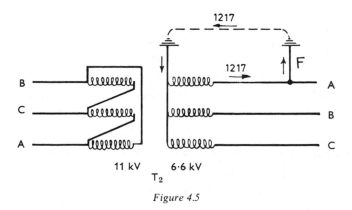

Figure 4.5

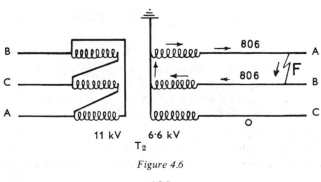

Figure 4.6

105

For a line to earth fault, the total impedance will now be:

$$Z_t = 0 + j4\cdot324 + 0 + j3\cdot854 + 6 + j1\cdot22$$
$$= 6 + j9\cdot398$$
$$= \sqrt{6^2 + 9\cdot398^2} = 11\cdot15\,\Omega$$

$$\text{and } I_f = \frac{3 \times 3\,810}{11\cdot15} = 1\,025\text{ A}$$

compared with 1 217 A previously calculated with zero resistance. In addition, the cable which joins transformer T_2 to its 6·6 kV switchgear will have some value of Z_1, Z_2 and Z_0 which will tend to further reduce the value of earth fault current.

We have now determined the fault currents which arise at the point of fault. It now remains to determine the distribution back to the source, proceeding as follows.

Line to earth fault

The positive, negative and zero-phase sequence currents in the fault are equal and each are one-third of I_f, so that:

$$I_{f_1} = I_{f_2} = I_{f_0} = I_f/3,$$

where I_{f_1} = positive-phase sequence current
I_{f_2} = negative-phase sequence current
I_{f_0} = zero-phase sequence current

and in the faulty phase A, the total fault current I_{f_A} is the sum of the three sequence currents I_1, I_2 and I_0 and

$$I_{f_1} + I_{f_2} + I_{f_0} = I_f = I_{f_A}.$$

The total fault current in the phases B and C is given by:

$$I_{f_B} = I_0 + a^2 I_1 + a I_2$$
$$I_{f_C} = I_0 + a I_1 + a^2 I_2$$

where the operators a and a^2 are:

$$a = -\tfrac{1}{2} + j\frac{\sqrt{3}}{2} = -0\cdot5 + j0\cdot866$$

$$a^2 = -\tfrac{1}{2} - j\frac{\sqrt{3}}{2} = -0\cdot5 - j0\cdot866$$

so that:

$$I_{f_B} = I_0 + I_1(-0\cdot5 - j0\cdot866) + I_2(-0\cdot5 + j0\cdot866)$$
$$= I_0 - 0\cdot5(I_1 + I_2) - j0\cdot866(I_1 - I_2)$$
$$I_{f_C} = I_0 + I_1(-0\cdot5 + j0\cdot866) + I_2(-0\cdot5 - j0\cdot866)$$
$$= I_0 - 0\cdot5(I_1 + I_2) + j0\cdot866(I_1 - I_2)$$

In the example, a 6·6 kV star base has been used. To obtain the true currents at 11 kV, i.e. in the secondary of T_1 and the primary of T_2, account must be taken of the phase displacement which occurs in respect of the 6·6 kV star base. The

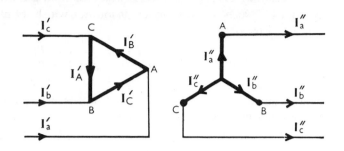

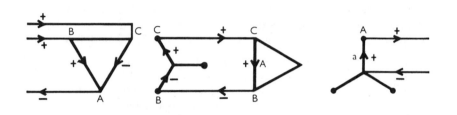

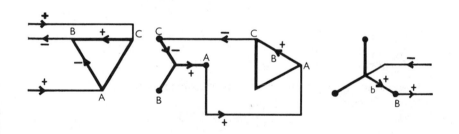

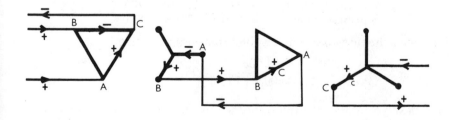

Figure 4.7

equations for such conversions are as follows, which should be read in conjunction with Fig. 4.7:

$$I'_a = n(I''_b - I''_c) = I'_B - I'_C$$
$$I'_b = n(I''_c - I''_a) = I'_C - I'_A$$
$$I'_c = n(I''_a - I''_b) = I'_A - I'_B$$

where n equals the turns per phase ratio of transformation in the direction of transformation being considered, and

$$I'_a I'_b I'_c = \text{Converted line currents being sought,}$$
$$I''_a I''_b I''_c = \text{Line currents on star base.}$$

With this essential data, the calculations are as follows, using the total value to earth of 1 217 A:

$$I_{f_1} = \text{Positive-sequence network current} = 1\,217/3 = 406\,\text{A}$$
$$I_{f_2} = \text{Negative-sequence network current} = 1\,217/3 = 406\,\text{A}$$
$$I_{f_0} = \text{Zero-sequence network current} = 1\,217/3 = 406\,\text{A}$$

I_{f_A} in secondary line $T_2 = I_{f_1} + I_{f_2} + I_{f_0} = 1\,217\,\text{A}$

$$
\begin{aligned}
I_{f_B} \text{ in secondary line } T_2 &= I_0 + a^2 I_1 + a I_2 \\
&= I_0 - 0.5(I_1 + I_2) - j0.866(I_1 - I_2) \\
&= 406 - 0.5(812) - j0.866(0) \\
&= 406 - 406 = 0\,\text{A}
\end{aligned}
$$

$$
\begin{aligned}
I_{f_C} \text{ in secondary line } T_2 &= I_0 + a I_1 + a^2 I_2 \\
&= I_0 - 0.5(I_1 + I_2) + j0.866(I_1 - I_2) \\
&= 406 - 0.5(812) + j0.866(0) \\
&= 406 - 406 = 0\,\text{A}
\end{aligned}
$$

$$
\begin{aligned}
I_{f_A} \text{ in primary line } T_2 &= -0.346(0 - 0) = 0\,\text{A} \\
I_{f_B} \text{ in primary line } T_2 &= -0.346(0 - 1\,217) = 422\,\text{A} \\
I_{f_C} \text{ in primary line } T_2 &= 0.346(1\,217 - 0) = -422\,\text{A}.
\end{aligned}
$$

Note: 0.346 is the turns per phase ratio of transformation, i.e.

$$\frac{6\,600}{11\,000 \times 1.73} = 0.346$$

The minus sign before the turns ratio indicates a reversal of line currents brought about by the cascade delta/star transformations.

$$
\begin{aligned}
I_{f_A} \text{ in primary line } T_1 &= -0.96(422 - (-422)) = -810\,\text{A} \\
I_{f_B} \text{ in primary line } T_1 &= -0.96(-422 - 0) = 405\,\text{A} \\
I_{f_C} \text{ in primary line } T_1 &= -0.96(0 - 422) = 405\,\text{A}
\end{aligned}
$$

Note: 0.96 is the turns per phase ratio of transformation, i.e.

$$\frac{11\,000}{6\,600 \times 1.73} = 0.96$$

Where positive values of current appear, this indicates flow in the direction of the fault. Negative values indicate flow in the opposite direction. The values of current have now been calculated in each line for the complete network up to the fault and are conveniently shown diagrammatically in Fig. 4.8.

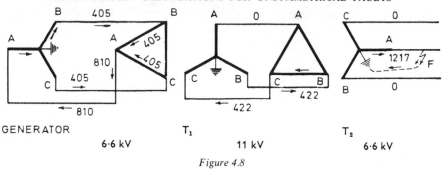

Figure 4.8

Line to line fault

It has been shown that a fault between lines A and B has a current value of 806 A. There will be no current in line C. For the line to line condition, the positive and negative-phase sequences only are involved, and the sequence currents I_1 (positive) and I_2 (negative) are:

$$
\begin{aligned}
I_1 &= \tfrac{1}{3}(I_A + aI_B + a^2 I_C) \\
&= \tfrac{1}{3}[I_A + I_B(-0\cdot5 + j0\cdot866) + I_C(-0\cdot5 - j0\cdot866)] \\
&= \frac{806 - 806(-0\cdot5 + j0\cdot866) + 0}{3} \\
&= \frac{806 + 403 - j697}{3} = 403 - j232\cdot3
\end{aligned}
$$

$$
\begin{aligned}
I_2 &= \tfrac{1}{3}(I_A + a^2 I_B + aI_C) \\
&= \tfrac{1}{3}[I_A + I_B(-0\cdot5 - j0\cdot866) + I_C(-0\cdot5 + j0\cdot866)] \\
&= \frac{806 - 806(-0\cdot5 - j0\cdot866) + 0}{3} \\
&= \frac{806 + 403 + j697}{3} = 403 + j232\cdot3
\end{aligned}
$$

The total fault current is the sum of the two sequence-network currents thus:

$$
\begin{aligned}
I_1 &= 403 - j232\cdot3 \\
I_2 &= 403 + j232\cdot3 \\
\hline
I_f &= 806 \text{ A.}
\end{aligned}
$$

The currents in the line throughout the complete circuit can be solved as follows:

$$
\begin{aligned}
I_A \text{ in secondary line } T_2 &= 806 \text{ A} \\
I_B \text{ in secondary line } T_2 &= -806 \text{ A} \\
I_C \text{ in secondary line } T_2 &= 0 \text{ A} \\
I_A \text{ in primary line } T_2 &= -0\cdot346(-806 - 0) &= 279 \text{ A} \\
I_B \text{ in primary line } T_2 &= -0\cdot346(0 - 806) &= 279 \text{ A} \\
I_C \text{ in primary line } T_2 &= -0\cdot346(806 - (-806)) &= -558 \text{ A}
\end{aligned}
$$

109

I_A in primary line T_1 $= -0.96(279-(-558)) = -806$ A
I_B in primary line T_1 $= -0.96(-558-279) = 806$ A
I_C in primary line T_1 $= -0.96(279-279) = 0$ A

The values can now be included in a diagram of the network, as shown in Fig. 4.9. The purpose of calculations such as the foregoing, for line to earth and line to line faults, may be seen by an inspection of the two diagrams shown in Figs. 4.8 and 4.9. In these we see the currents at each point in the network for faults at a remote point.

It is clear that unless some form of discriminating protection be applied, there is every indication that, for a fault at the point chosen for our example,

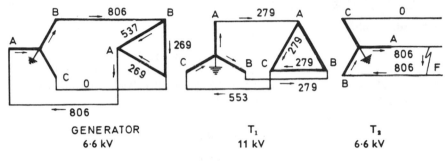

GENERATOR	T_1	T_2
6·6 kV	11 kV	6·6 kV

Figure 4.9

the generator and the transformers will all be disconnected by the through fault current. For example, the normal current of the generator is 175 A, and for both types of fault, currents considerably in excess of normal are experienced. If simple overcurrent be fitted, high settings would be essential to avoid operation.

A second example may be worked using the percentage reactance method and a common kVA base. For this purpose, a system is shown in Fig. 4.10 and it will be our task to ascertain the fault current at a point close up to the 400 V busbars at substation C, on the occurrence of an earth fault between phase A and ground. The reactances indicated in the diagram are those to the positive-phase sequence currents. The first task, as in three-phase fault calculations, is to convert all reactances to a common base, e.g., 100 000 kVA as follows using the formulae noted in Chapter 3:

$$\text{Generators } G_1 \text{ and } G_2 = \frac{100\,000 \times 20}{10\,000} = 200\% \text{ each}$$

$$\text{Transformers } T_1 \text{ and } T_2 = \frac{100\,000 \times 6\cdot8}{5\,000} = 136\% \text{ each}$$

$$\text{Overhead line} = \frac{100\,000 \times 100\,000 \times 3\cdot6}{(33\,000)^2} = 33\%$$

$$\text{Generator } G_3 = \frac{100\,000 \times 12}{2\,000} = 600\%$$

$$\text{Transformer } T_3 = \frac{100\,000 \times 5\cdot3}{1\,500} = 353\%$$

The positive, negative and zero-phase sequence reactances are shown in Table 4.1.

Following the procedure when calculating three-phase symmetrical faults, a series of network reduction diagrams are deduced in order that a single reactance to the fault may be ascertained. In this case, however, separate

Table 4.1
POSITIVE, NEGATIVE AND ZERO-PHASE
SEQUENCE REACTANCES

	Z_1	Z_2	Z_0
Generators G_1, G_2	200%	146%	—
Transformers T_1, T_2	136%	136%	—
Overhead line	33%	33%	—
Generator G_3	600%	438%	—
Transformer T_3	353%	353%	353%

Note. In the table above, the blanks under Z_0 for generators G_1, G_2 and G_3 and transformers T_1 and T_2 do not imply that these have no zero-phase sequence impedance, but simply that no path exists at these neutrals for the return of earth fault current originating on the 400 V system beyond T_3.

diagrams are required for each of the phase sequences, and Fig. 4.11 is a set of reactance diagrams for the original network. These can be reduced at once, by combining parallel values, and adding series values, to Figs. 4.12 and 4.13.

Values in parallel in Fig. 4.13 are evaluated as follows:

$$\text{Positive network} \quad \frac{1}{\dfrac{1}{405} + \dfrac{1}{600}} = 241\%$$

$$\text{Negative network} \quad \frac{1}{\dfrac{1}{378} + \dfrac{1}{438}} = 203\%$$

and the network diagrams now become Fig. 4.14. From this we determine that:

$$Z_1 = 594\%$$
$$Z_2 = 556\%$$
$$Z_0 = 353\%$$

and the total reactance Z_t to the fault is:

$$Z_t = Z_1 + Z_2 + Z_0 = 1\,503\%$$

and the fault current to earth is:

$$I_f = \frac{3I \times 100}{Z_t}$$

where I is the current due to 100 000 kVA at 400 V, i.e. 144 000 A, and

$$I_f = \frac{3 \times 144\,000 \times 100}{1\,503} = 28\,800 \text{ A}$$

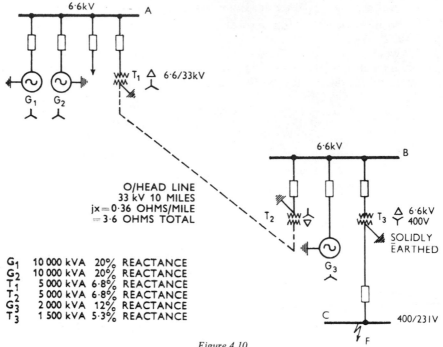

O/HEAD LINE
33 kV 10 MILES
jx = 0·36 OHMS/MILE
= 3·6 OHMS TOTAL

G₁	10 000 kVA	20%	REACTANCE
G₂	10 000 kVA	20%	REACTANCE
T₁	5 000 kVA	6·8%	REACTANCE
T₂	5 000 kVA	6·8%	REACTANCE
G₃	2 000 kVA	12%	REACTANCE
T₃	1 500 kVA	5·3%	REACTANCE

Figure 4.10

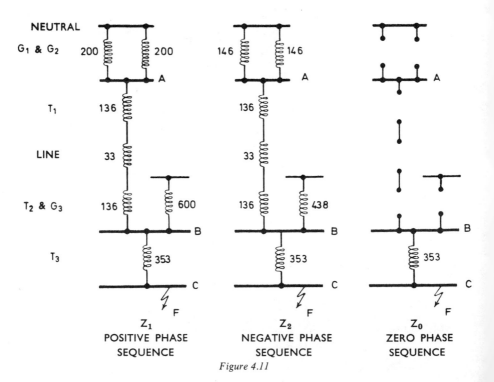

Figure 4.11

112

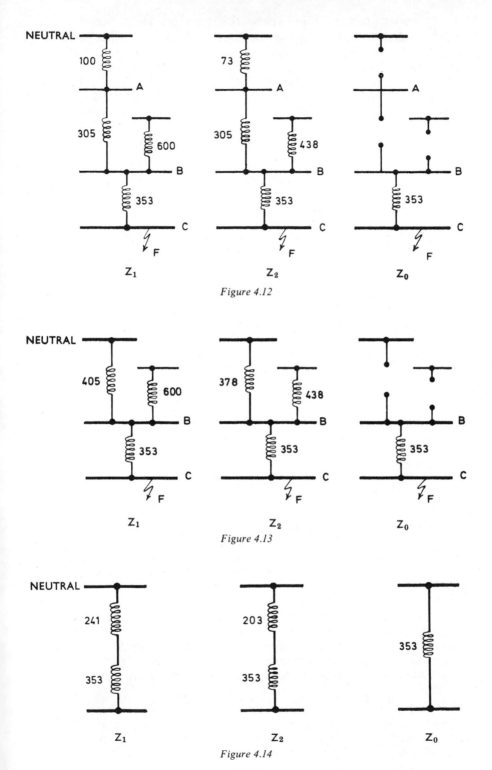

Figure 4.12

Figure 4.13

Figure 4.14

113

Thus for a fault to earth at a point close up to the 400 V busbar we have the condition shown in Fig. 4.15. This condition again ignores any earth resistance either at the ground plate or in the earth path, and further it does not take account of the sequence impedances of the 400 V cable between the transformer and the switchgear. If this is of any length, the reduction due to this cable might be appreciable, and as in the calculations for three-phase faults at the lower

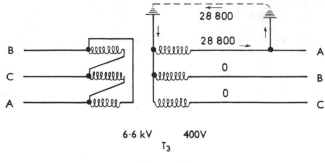

Figure 4.15

voltages demonstrated in Chapter 3, the inclusion on this cable should be considered.

In passing it can be noted that had we been seeking the current for a line to line fault, the result would have been:

$$I_f = \frac{\sqrt{3} \times I \times 100}{Z_1 + Z_2} = \frac{\sqrt{3} \times 144\,000 \times 100}{594 + 556}$$

$$= 21\,700 \text{ A}$$

or for a three-phase fault:

$$I_f = \frac{I \times 100}{Z_1} = \frac{144\,000 \times 100}{594} = 24\,200 \text{ A}$$

In order to determine the distribution of current throughout the complete network it is convenient to adopt a method suggested by Wagner and Evans where the reactance diagrams (Figs. 4.11 to 4.14) are worked through in a reverse order, and assuming a figure of 1 A at the fault determine the proportions of this in other branches of the network in inverse proportion to the reactances. The three sequences are placed side by side and Fig. 4.16 shows the stages of calculation. Figures in brackets are reactance values; the other figures are current values in terms of 1 A at the fault. At this stage, it will be noted that all values of current are in terms of the 400 V star base voltage. Correction for voltage and star/delta transformation will be made later. We have seen that the total fault current I_f can be split into its sequence values as follows:

$$I_{f_1} = I_{f_2} = I_{f_0} = I_f/3 = 28\,800/3 = 9\,600 \text{ A}$$

This value is then equal to our 1 A in Fig. 4.16(c), and by using the factors throughout the remainder of the network we obtain the current distribution on the 400 V base. This will be clear from Fig. 4.17, where, on the left are shown

114

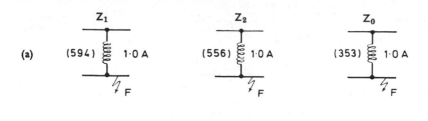

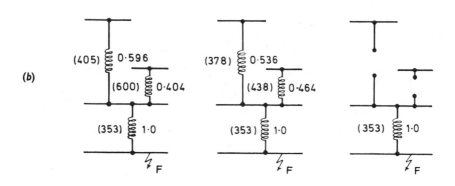

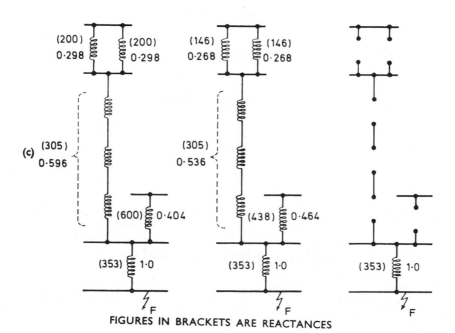

FIGURES IN BRACKETS ARE REACTANCES

Figure 4.16

115

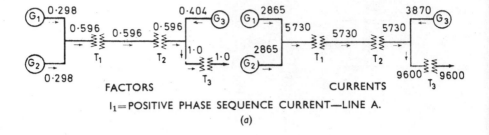

FACTORS   CURRENTS

I_1=POSITIVE PHASE SEQUENCE CURRENT—LINE A.

(a)

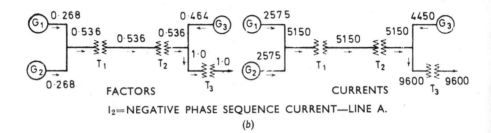

FACTORS   CURRENTS

I_2=NEGATIVE PHASE SEQUENCE CURRENT—LINE A.

(b)

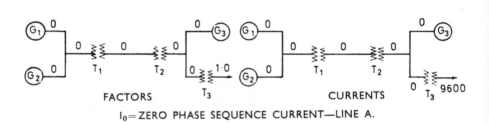

FACTORS   CURRENTS

I_0=ZERO PHASE SEQUENCE CURRENT—LINE A.

(c)

Figure 4.17

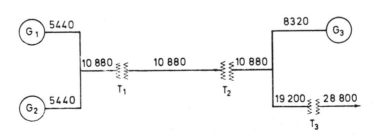

Figure 4.18.   Total fault currents in line A on 400V star base, being the sum of the values $I_1 + I_2 + I_0$
in Figure 4.17

116

the factors (taken from Fig. 4.16(c)) and on the right the current values obtained by using these factors applied to the total current in each phase sequence, i.e. 9 600 A. These values are, of course, those in line A, the faulted line. Adding the values given in Fig. 4.17 for I_1, I_2 and I_0, we get the total currents in line A throughout the network, the result being Fig. 4.18. It remains now to determine values for lines B and C, and using the formulae previously given we get:

Lines B and C (generators G_1 and G_2)

$$\begin{aligned}
I_B &= I_0 + a^2 I_1 + a I_2 \\
&= I_0 + I_1(-0 \cdot 5 - j0 \cdot 866) + I_2(-0 \cdot 5 + j0 \cdot 866) \\
&= I_0 - 0 \cdot 5(I_1 + I_2) - j0 \cdot 866(I_1 - I_2) \\
&= 0 - 0 \cdot 5(2\,865 + 2\,575) - j0 \cdot 866(2\,865 - 2\,575) \\
&= -2\,720 - j251 \cdot 5 \\
I_C &= I_0 + a I_1 + a^2 I_2 \\
&= -2\,720 + j251 \cdot 5
\end{aligned}$$

These are the values for *each* generator.

Lines B and C (primary transformer T_1)

I_B and I_C here will be the addition of the values for the two generators G_1 and G_2.

Lines B and C (secondary transformer T_1 and secondary transformer T_2)

As we are still working on our common base, these values will be the same as for the primary of T_1.

Lines B and C (generator G_3)

$$\begin{aligned}
I_B &= I_0 + a^2 I_1 + a I_2 \\
&= -4\,160 + j503 \\
I_C &= I_0 + a I_1 + a^2 I_2 \\
&= -4\,160 - j503
\end{aligned}$$

Lines B and C (primary transformer T_3)

The values here will be the addition of the secondary currents from T_2 and the current from G_3.

The values so obtained can now be set down as in Figs. 4.19 and 4.20 for lines B and C respectively. It remains only to ascertain the currents at the normal voltages, taking into account star/delta transformation, using the equations on page 108. Starting from the fault, and working backwards:

Primary lines T_3

$$\text{Line } A = -\frac{231}{6\,600} \times (0 - 0) = 0 \text{ A}$$

$$\text{Line } B = -\frac{231}{6\,600} \times (0 - 28\,800) = 1\,010 \text{ A}$$

$$\text{Line } C = -\frac{231}{6\,600} \times (28\,800 - 0) = -1\,010 \text{ A}$$

Secondary lines T_2 and lines G_3

The current in these lines is at the same voltage as the primary lines of T_3. Therefore the values for the latter will be divided in the proportion 8 320/19 200 for the generator G_3 and 10 880/19 200 for T_3. Thus:

$$\text{Line } A \quad G_3 = \frac{8\,320 \times 0}{19\,200} = 0 \text{ A}$$

$$\text{Line } B \quad G_3 = \frac{8\,320 \times 1\,010}{19\,200} = 438 \text{ A}$$

$$\text{Line } C \quad G_3 = \frac{8\,320 \times (-1\,010)}{19\,200} = -438 \text{ A}$$

and by subtraction (G_3 from T_3) we get:

Secondary lines T_2

$$\text{Line } A = 0 \text{ A}$$
$$\text{Line } B = 1\,010 - 438 = 572 \text{ A}$$
$$\text{Line } C = -1\,010 - (-438) = -572 \text{ A}$$

Primary lines T_2, converting from secondary currents T_2

$$\text{Line } A = -\frac{3\,810}{33\,000}[572 - (-572)] = -132 \text{ A}$$

$$\text{Line } B = -\frac{3\,810}{33\,000}(-572 - 0) = 66 \text{ A}$$

$$\text{Line } C = -\frac{3\,810}{33\,000}(0 - 572) = 66 \text{ A}$$

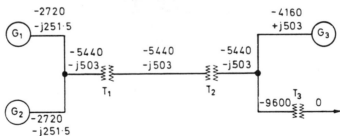

Figure 4.19.   *Total fault currents in line B on 400V star base*

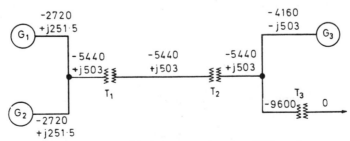

Figure 4.20.   *Total fault currents in line C on 400V star base*

Primary lines T_1, converting from primary currents T_2

$$\text{Line } A = -\frac{19\,050}{6\,600}(66-66) = 0\text{ A}$$

$$\text{Line } B = -\frac{19\,050}{6\,600}[66-(-132)] = -572\text{ A}$$

$$\text{Line } C = -\frac{19\,050}{6\,600}(-132-66) = 572\text{ A}$$

Generators G_1 and G_2

The currents here will be one-half of those in the primary lines of T_1:

$$\text{Line } A = 0\text{ A}$$
$$\text{Line } B = -286\text{ A}$$
$$\text{Line } C = 286\text{ A}$$

We are now able to construct a diagram of the complete network to show the magnitude and direction of current at each point due to an earth fault at a point just beyond the transformer T_3. The diagram is shown in Fig. 4.21.

The calculations could, with equal facility, be carried out using ohmic values instead of percentage. In this case (and as previously indicated) a voltage base is chosen instead of a kVA base. Taking the example in Fig. 4.10, it is convenient to take as a base the voltage at the fault, i.e. 400 V and the following will indicate the procedure for calculating the fault current to earth.

G_1 or G_2 (10 000 kVA 6·6 kV 20% reactance)

Full load normal current = 876 A

$$\text{Reactance to neutral} = j\frac{20}{100} \times \frac{3\,810}{876} = j0\!\cdot\!87\ \Omega$$

Referred to 400 V star base

$$\text{Reactance to neutral} = j0\!\cdot\!87\left(\frac{231}{3\,810}\right)^2 = j0\!\cdot\!0032\ \Omega$$

Thus, $Z_1 = j0\!\cdot\!0032\ \Omega$
$Z_2 = 0\!\cdot\!73Z_1 = j0\!\cdot\!002335\ \Omega$

T_1 or T_2 (5 000 kVA 6·8% reactance, T_1 at 6·6 kV, T_2 at 33 kV)

Full load normal current T_1 = 438 A at 6·6 kV
Full load normal current T_2 = 87·5 A at 33 kV

$$\text{Reactance to neutral } T_1 = j\frac{6\!\cdot\!8}{100}\!\cdot\!\frac{3\,810}{438}$$

$$= j0\!\cdot\!592\ \Omega$$

$$\text{Reactance to neutral } T_2 = j\frac{6\!\cdot\!8}{100}\!\cdot\!\frac{19\,050}{87\!\cdot\!5}$$

$$= j14\!\cdot\!8\ \Omega$$

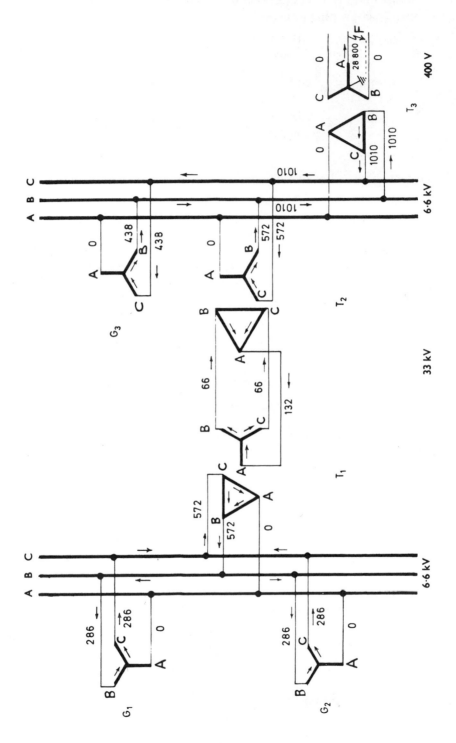

Figure 4.21

120

Referred to 400 V star base

$$T_1 = j0\cdot592\left(\frac{231}{3\,810}\right)^2 = j0\cdot00218\,\Omega$$

$$T_2 = j14\cdot8\left(\frac{231}{19\,050}\right)^2 = j0\cdot00218\,\Omega$$

Thus, $Z_1 = Z_2 = j0\cdot00218\,\Omega$ for T_1 or T_2.

G_3 (2 000 kVA 6·6 kV 12% reactance)

Full load normal current = 175 A

Reactance to neutral $= j\dfrac{12}{100}\cdot\dfrac{3\,810}{175} = j2\cdot61\,\Omega$

Referred to 400 V star base

Reactance to neutral $= j2\cdot61\left(\dfrac{231}{3\,810}\right)^2 = j0\cdot0096\,\Omega$

Thus, $Z_1 = j0\cdot0096\,\Omega$
$Z_2 = 0\cdot73Z_1 = j0\cdot007\,\Omega$

T_3 (1 500 kVA 6·6 kV 5·3% reactance)

Full load normal current = 131·3 A

Reactance to neutral $= j\dfrac{5\cdot3}{100}\cdot\dfrac{3\,810}{131\cdot3} = j1\cdot535\,\Omega$

Referred to 400 V star base

Reactance to neutral $= j1\cdot535\left(\dfrac{231}{3\,810}\right)^2 = j0\cdot00565\,\Omega$

Thus $Z_1 = Z_2 = Z_0 = j0\cdot00565\,\Omega$

Overhead line (33 kV)

Reactance to neutral $= j3\cdot6\,\Omega$
Referred to 400 V star base

Reactance to neutral $= j3\cdot6\left(\dfrac{231}{19\,050}\right)^2 = j0\cdot00053\,\Omega$

Thus $Z_1 = Z_2 = j0\cdot00053\,\Omega$

Proceeding now as described earlier, a series of network reduction diagrams (Figs. 4.22, 4.23 and 4.24) will result in the ascertainment of a single equivalent reactance for each of the phase sequences.

We now have:

$$\begin{aligned}Z_t &= Z_1+Z_2+Z_0 \\ &= j0\cdot00952+j0\cdot0089+j0\cdot00565 \\ &= j0\cdot02407\,\Omega\end{aligned}$$

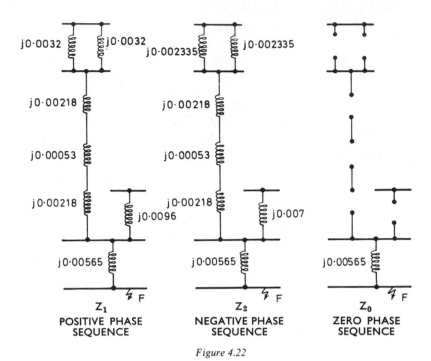

Z_1
POSITIVE PHASE
SEQUENCE

Z_2
NEGATIVE PHASE
SEQUENCE

Z_0
ZERO PHASE
SEQUENCE

Figure 4.22

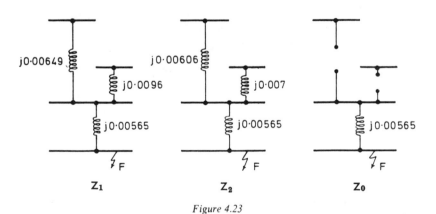

Z_1

Z_2

Z_0

Figure 4.23

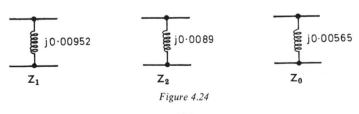

Z_1

Z_2

Z_0

Figure 4.24

122

The total earth fault current is then:

$$I_f = \frac{3E}{Z_t} = \frac{3 \times 231}{0 \cdot 02407} = 28\,800 \text{ A}$$

exactly as calculated by the percentage reactance method. Current distribution calculation will be as before.

It is of interest to note that where there are two reactances in parallel, current distribution is determined as follows:

$$I_A = \frac{Z_Y}{Z_X + Z_Y} \cdot I_t$$

$$I_B = \frac{Z_X}{Z_X + Z_Y} \cdot I_t$$

where Fig. 4.25 represents the conditions.

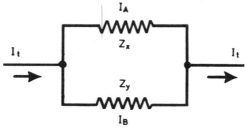

Figure 4.25

Where, as previously demonstrated, a delta/star conversion is undertaken, it is necessary when determining current distribution in the network to work backwards. For example, the reactance reduction procedure might be as shown at Fig. 4.26 where a delta/star conversion occurs from (*a*) to (*b*).

Working backwards for current distribution we have Fig. 4.27, working from (*e*) to (*a*) and at (*b*) we have currents in a star to be converted to distribution in the delta network at (*a*). This conversion is carried out by making use of the fact that the voltage difference between any two terminals of the delta group is the voltage difference between the two corresponding terminals of the star group. These voltage differences may be determined from the current distribution and

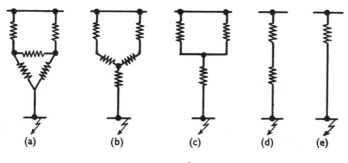

(a)   (b)   (c)   (d)   (e)

CIRCUIT IMPEDANCE REDUCTION

Figure 4.26

123

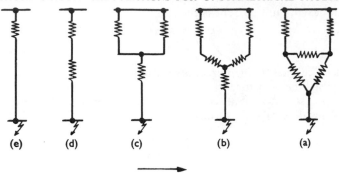

UNIT CURRENT DISTRIBUTION

Figure 4.27

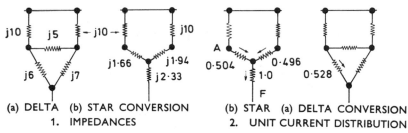

(a) DELTA (b) STAR CONVERSION	(b) STAR (a) DELTA CONVERSION
1. IMPEDANCES	2. UNIT CURRENT DISTRIBUTION

Figure 4.28

reactances of the star group. Having found the voltage difference it is divided by the corresponding delta impedance, giving the current distribution in the equivalent branch of the delta group. Fig. 4.28 illustrates this where at (1) we have the delta/star conversion of reactances and at (2) the star/delta conversion for current distribution, the latter determined as follows:

$$\text{Voltage difference } A \text{ to } F \text{ (Fig. 4.28)} = (1{\cdot}0 \times j2{\cdot}33) + (0{\cdot}504 \times j1{\cdot}66) = j3{\cdot}167 \text{ V}$$

$$\text{Current distribution} = \frac{j3{\cdot}167}{j6} = 0{\cdot}528 \text{ A}$$

The other two branches of the delta may be similarly calculated.

REFERENCES

1. FORTESCUE, C. le G., 'The Method of Symmetrical Components Applied to the Solution of Polyphase Networks', *Trans. A.I.E.E.*, **37** (1918)
2. WAGNER, C.F. and EVANS, R.D., *Symmetrical Components as Applied to the Analysis of Unbalanced Electrical Circuits*, McGraw-Hill (1933)

BIBLIOGRAPHY

CASSON, W. and BIRCH, F.H., 'The Management of Protective Gear on Power Supply Systems', *J.I.E.E.*, **89** No. 10, Part 2, Aug. (1942)
CLARKE, E., *Circuit Analysis of A.C. Power Systems*, Vol. 1, Wiley
MONSETH, I.T. and ROBINSON, P.H., *Relay Systems*, McGraw-Hill
MYATT, L.J., *Symmetrical Components*, Pergamon (1968)
STIGANT, S.A. and FRANKLIN, A.C., *The J & P Transformer Book*, Butterworths (1961)
STUBBINGS, G.W., *Elements of Symmetrical Components Theory*, Pitman

Chapter 5

Short-circuit testing

Having noted some of the phenomena associated with the interruption of alternating currents under conditions of short-circuit or when switching small inductive or capacitive currents, and having shown how the magnitude of short-circuit currents can be calculated, we must now look at the facilities and the procedures necessary to prove the ability of circuit-breakers and associated apparatus to perform as they were intended to under the most severe conditions possible.

The historical background to this subject was discussed in Chapter 1, and it will be recalled that in the early days the most urgent need was the provision of facilities for research, development, and high-power short-circuit testing on circuit-breakers (in particular those fitted with the newly invented side-blast arc-control device).

However, when a short-circuit occurs on an electrical network, it is not only the circuit-breaker which is involved; it has to be remembered that the high value of fault current has to be carried for a short time (until interrupted by a circuit-breaker or fuse) by other elements of the primary circuit, e.g. busbars, connectors, isolating switches or contacts, current transformer primaries, series overload coils, cable terminations, etc. It is essential that all or any of these associated with the circuit-breaker need to be capable of withstanding the electromagnetic stresses and the thermal conditions which arise due to the passage of fault current. It follows therefore that such proof can best be obtained, when physically possible, by including them in the circuit-breaker test, i.e. by carrying out short-circuit tests on complete units of switchgear. When not physically possible or when conditions not applicable to circuit-breaker testing prevail, part or sub-assembly proof testing will be made which nevertheless requires the full or partial facilities of the short-circuit test plant with its ability to produce high fault currents under prescribed conditions, closely controlled and fully recorded on special measuring instruments.

Apart from this, other apparatus such as contactors, motor starters, distribution boards, medium and high-voltage fuses, fuse-switches, miniature and moulded-case circuit-breakers, busbar trunking, etc. must all, in one way or another and in varying degrees, be suitable for installation on systems of a known fault level. They must therefore be proved, and over the past decade or so standard specifications for a wide variety of apparatus have been revised to include rules for the tests required, most of which require the services of a short-circuit test plant of a type suited to the work involved.

In 1938 the Association of Short-circuit Testing Authorities (A.S.T.A.) was formed in the U.K., its membership initially comprising seven manufacturing companies operating four major high-power short-circuit testing stations. Its main purpose was to co-ordinate tests and testing methods and procedures, to publish rules for the testing of apparatus not covered in the current standards (or where they did exist to provide agreed interpretations if necessary), to provide reports of performance and to issue certificates of rating which would be nationally recognised. In 1970, membership of A.S.T.A. comprised six companies operating five testing stations, but outside this organisation many firms had built and were operating smaller test plants. These were specifically designed and laid out for research into and the testing of equipment (up to 3·3 kV) outside the high-power field, generally as noted earlier. Thirteen such firms operating twelve testing stations have now (1970) become associate members of A.S.T.A., and are able to issue reports of performance and certificates of rating for equipment and apparatus within their range of test facilities. Concurrently, A.S.T.A. can now issue two additional forms of certificate, one a certificate of type tests covering in addition to short-circuit tests, those numerous other type tests that are specified in British Standards, and another, known as a certificate of supplementary tests, which enables a manufacturer to claim wider performance for a particular apparatus without the expense of repeating full scale tests[1].

Throughout Europe and in America, many short-circuit test plants are in operation and bearing in mind the differences between the various national standards and the progress towards wider acceptance of I.E.C. rules (to which national standards will be adjusted in time), co-operation in testing techniques and an interchange of technical experience are desirable objectives. To this end, A.S.T.A. has already established links with its German counterpart Prufung Electrischer Hochleistungs Apparate (P.E.H.L.A.) and with Keuring van Electrotechnische Materialen (K.E.M.A.) in Holland. This has led to the position where, for example, a circuit-breaker to be tested to BS 116, can be tested at P.E.H.L.A. stations or at K.E.M.A. in accordance with the A.S.T.A.

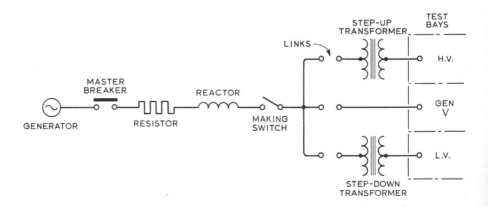

Figure 5.1. Basic single-line diagram for short-circuit test plant

rules applying to that specification, and a British manufacturer can obtain a certificaté of rating from any of these sources which has equal validity. Conversely, British equipment can be certified by A.S.T.A. to foreign standards, or foreign manufacturers can obtain certificates at A.S.T.A. stations to their own or other standards.

In its very simplest form, a short-circuit test plant would be as shown in Fig. 5.1; the smaller test plants follow this basic pattern but are more elaborate in order to cover particular requirements. However, in the large high-power plants this would form only one element of the whole, and there would be several generators, transformer banks, etc. with complicated arrangements whereby one or all can be used as a particular test demands. These larger stations will also have other associated facilities for special tests, e.g. short-line faults, capacitor switching, etc.

Power for the short-circuit tests is derived from a generator, which externally will look much like any normal machine, but as it is going to be short-circuited repeatedly, it will have specially braced windings and the stator will have a low reactance in order to give the maximum short-circuit output in the first half-cycle. The stator windings will be arranged so that they can be connected in star or delta to provide two nominal voltages, or alternatively double stator windings may be used with a terminal arrangement permitting the windings to be connected in parallel delta or star, and series delta or star, thus providing four nominal voltages, viz. 6·6, 11, 12·7 or 22 kV. To minimise the mechanical shock transmitted to the foundation due to the short-circuit oscillating torque, the machine will be mounted on a resilient base.

In the majority of test plants, the generator is motor-driven, the motor being connected to the service supply mains. Just before the short-circuit is initiated the motor is disconnected from the mains, since reflection of the short-circuit load on to the mains would be excessive and so the energy for the short-circuit comes from the kinetic energy of the generator rotor. An alternative is to use a slip-ring motor, and with this the external rotor resistances that are normally used for starting can be re-inserted automatically in the rotor circuit at the instant of short-circuit. This limits the current drawn from the mains, and after the test sequence is complete the rotor resistance can be shorted out so that the motor resumes its normal running. These procedures result in the diminishing speed of the generator and consequently a decrement in voltage, which has to be compensated for by boosting the generator field excitation during the period of the test.

Beyond the generator is the master or back-up circuit-breaker. The possibility of failure of the apparatus on test is something which cannot be ignored, and indeed during research testing it is often required to test until failure occurs, as for example, by raising the fault current level by increments when testing a circuit-breaker. Failure must therefore be cleared and this is the duty of the master breaker which is set to open at a predetermined time after the initiation of the short-circuit. This breaker must have an interrupting capacity in excess of the short-circuit MVA of the generator.

Next in line, resistors and reactors are installed. Resistors are used for the control of the power factor so that it is in accordance with the specified limits, and the reactors are used for control of the test current magnitude. Tapping points enable the required reactance to be chosen to suit the test requirement.

The making switch is a particularly vital item in the circuit and is always a

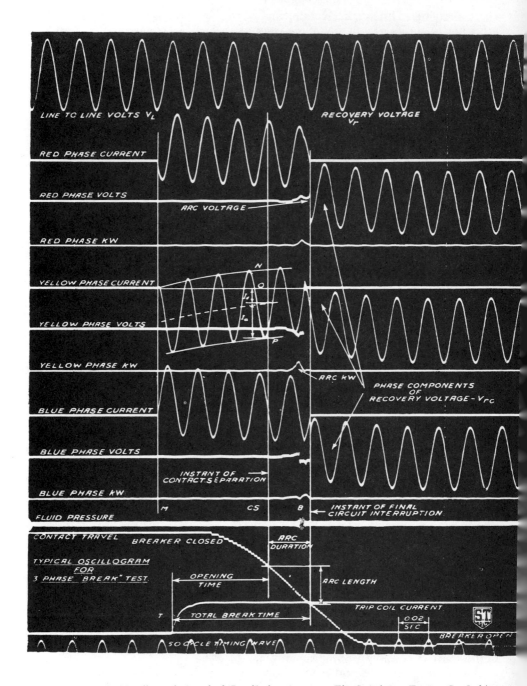

Figure 5.2. Oscillograph record of 'Break' shot (courtesy The Switchgear Testing Co. Ltd.)

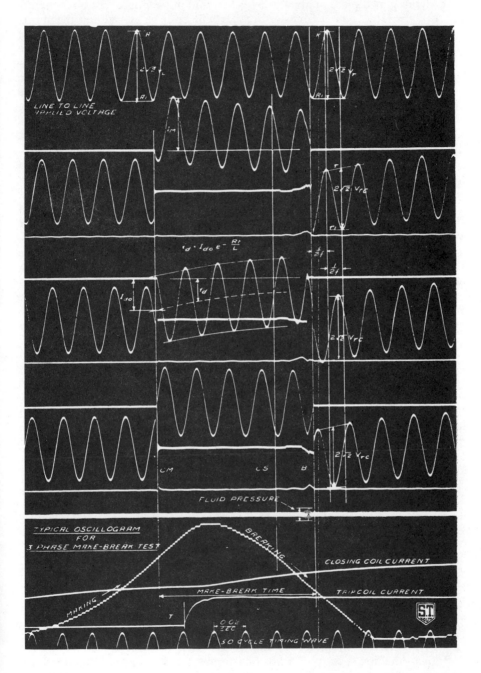

Figure 5.3.   Oscillograph record of 'Make-Break' shot (courtesy The Switchgear Testing Co. Ltd.)

specially designed piece of apparatus. When making a 'break' test on a circuit-breaker, the latter and the master breaker will both be closed and the short-circuit will be established by closing the making switch. It is now the duty of the breaker on test to clear the short-circuit. The making switch has therefore to be capable of closing repeatedly at high-speed on to fault currents of high-peak magnitude without pre-arcing as the contacts approach the 'touch' position. Accurate control of its closing instant is necessary so that it can be closed at any selected point on the supply voltage wave, thereby controlling the degree of asymmetry in the short-circuit current at fault inception. This is known as *point-on-wave* control and is established through electronic devices. The making switch is not called upon to break current, and when a circuit-breaker on test is to be proved for making capacity, i.e. to be closed on to a fault, the master breaker and the making switch are both closed first, leaving the breaker on test to be closed to establish the short-circuit and then clear it.

From the outgoing terminals of the making switch, connections are taken to the test bays either directly for testing at the available generator voltages or via step-down or step-up transformers for tests at lower or higher voltages. These transformers will be specially designed for the duties involved and the repeated short-circuits to which they will be subjected. While the step-down transformer may be a three-phase unit, those for stepping-up to very high voltages will usually be single-phase units having multiple primary and secondary windings. In these, the primary windings will be able to accept more than one generator voltage while the secondary windings may be connected in series-parallel arrangements to give multiple output voltages, single or three phase.

At the point where all this plant is controlled, three items of particular importance will be available, viz. (*a*) an electromagnetic oscillograph (EMO) for recording power frequency quantities, (*b*) a cathode-ray oscillograph (CRO) for recording voltages of a transient nature, e.g. restriking voltages whose frequency of oscillation is beyond the response of the EMO (see Fig. 2.4), and (*c*) a time-sequence controller. The data recorded on the EMO will include the following:
1. The short-circuit current in each phase.
2. The voltage across each pole of the test piece before, during and after the short-circuit.
3. In oil circuit-breakers, the oil pressure.
4. The travel of the moving contacts.
5. The current in the closing and/or trip-coil circuits.
6. The generator voltage.
7. A timing mark.
Two typical EMO records relating to a circuit-breaker test are reproduced in Fig. 5.2 and 5.3. The former covers a 'break' test in which the breaker on test has to interrupt the short-circuit when applied by the making switch. The latter is a 'make-break' test in which, with the making switch already closed, the breaker on test has to close to complete the short-circuit and then immediately open to interrupt the short-circuit.

Prior to making such tests, a no-load timing test will have been made from which it will be possible to determine the exact point on a travel curve at which the contacts 'break' when opening or 'make' when closing. This record will also show how these occurrences are related to either the energising of the trip coil on breaking or the closing coil on making. A typical timing oscillogram for a breaker opening operation is shown in Fig. 5.4. To obtain the trace which shows the instant of contact separation, direct current is passed through the closed contacts of the circuit-breaker. This is recorded on an EMO element, which while current flows has its spot deflected above zero and which assumes the zero position at contact separation.

The trace which records the travel of the contacts is obtained by passing direct current through a variable resistance, the slide being connected to the moving contact system. As contact is made with successive points on the resistance so will the latter be cut out and the trace will be recorded as a stepped curve. From the two traces it can now be determined at which step contact separation occurs (or in a closing operation at which step contact make occurs) so that the corresponding steps can be located on the short-circuit test oscillogram. The trace showing trip-coil current (or conversely, closing-coil current) in conjunction with the other traces enable the circuit-breaker opening time, total-break time, make time and make-break time to be determined.

The time-sequence controller may be of the drum-type designed to actuate, in a pre-arranged sequence, a number of auxiliary contacts at predetermined

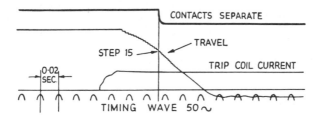

Figure 5.4. Typical timing oscillogram for breaker opening

intervals of time, e.g. the making switch closing coil, the test-breaker trip coil and the master-breaker trip coil, this being the order of operations for a break test. An alternative is a pendulum-type controller on which the auxiliary contacts are operated on the first strokes of the pendulum. This is a more accurate method, but unless the stroke of the pendulum is large, the number of contacts is limited. Most test plants have developed their own controllers incorporating the advantages of both types.

With the foregoing in mind, a detailed study of Figs. 5.2 and 5.3 can be made showing how oscillograms of this type are interpreted. In so doing, it should be remembered that both oscillograms have been specially marked-up for the purpose, and that similar markings would not appear on actual test records.

Studying first the oscillogram of a 'break' test (Fig. 5.2) it will be noted that three vertical lines are drawn marked *M*, *CS* and *B*, respectively. The line *M* is drawn at the point at which short-circuit occurs (initiated by closing of the making switch), a point easily discernible as that at which current wave traces begin. The line *CS* is drawn at the point of contact separation determined from the timing wave after reference to the timing oscillogram, i.e. in Fig. 5.4, the point of contact separation is noted as being at step 15, and by counting this number of steps on Fig. 5.2 the point *CS* is determined. The line at *B* indicates the point at which final interruption of the short-circuit is made and is determined by reference to the traces of current where the last phase to clear becomes zero.

131

From the information so far noted, coupled with reference to the 50 Hz timing wave and the trip coil current curve, it is possible to determine the following:

(a) The opening time of the circuit-breaker, measured horizontally from point T (trip coil energised) to point CS.
(b) The arcing time, measured horizontally from point CS to point B.
(c) The total break time, measured horizontally from point T to point B.
(d) The arc length, measured vertically between points CS and B as indicated.

The record of Fig. 5.3 is not very different from Fig. 5.2 but here the short-circuit is made by closing the circuit-breaker under test to complete the short-circuit and the breaker 'makes' and then 'breaks'. Hence, the travel curve in this illustration shows the movement of the contact bar in two directions. Three lines are drawn as in the earlier description, that at CM being the point at which the contacts touch on the closing stroke, i.e. at step 15. Other points (CS and B) are determined as previously, while the distance measured horizontally between CM and B is the total make-break time of the circuit-breaker. This illustration has one additional trace, i.e. that of closing coil current.

We may now consider in some detail the other records which these oscillograms show. Right at the top is a trace V_L giving the line to line voltage. Initially, this records the open-circuit voltage at the generator terminals. Close examination of this trace will show that at the point M (or CM) there is a reduction in the voltage. The value of this reduction is equal to the inductive drop in the generator windings, and it is a progressive reduction as the generator field is demagnetised.

At the point B, the short-circuit is cleared and the generator-terminal voltage builds up slowly to its original open-circuit value.

Three current traces are now noted, for the red, yellow and blue phases respectively. Up to the point of short-circuit (M or CM), this trace is a zero reading. Thereafter, it follows a sine-wave form until clearance is made at B. It should be particularly noted that these traces are, with one exception (i.e. that for the blue-phase current in Fig. 5.3), all offset to some degree about zero, thus illustrating the asymmetry of which note has been made earlier.

The current broken is measured at the instant of contact separation CS, and in certain duty cycles, it is symmetrical values of current which are used, whilst in one duty cycle it is the asymmetrical value of current which is used. The current in the first case is not considered to be symmetrical if the d.c. component in any phase exceeds 20%. In the second case, to be asymmetrical, the current in one of the phases must have a d.c. component of 50% or more.

In Figs. 5.2 and 5.3 the d.c. component is shown by I_d and the peak a.c. component by I_a, and it follows that the

$$\text{a.c. component} \quad = I_a = \frac{OP + ON}{2}$$

$$\text{d.c. component} \quad = I_d = \frac{OP - ON}{2}$$

$$\% \text{ d.c. component} = \frac{I_d}{I_a} \times 100$$

For symmetrical breaking current, the r.m.s. symmetrical value is:

$$\frac{I_a}{\sqrt{2}}$$

For asymmetrical breaking current, the r.m.s. asymmetrical value is:

$$\sqrt{\left(\frac{I_a}{\sqrt{2}}\right)^2 + I_d{}^2}$$

In a 'make-break' shot, the breaker contacts have to close on to a peak current as we have previously noted. The value of this peak current is that of the first *major* loop of the current wave after the instant of short-circuit CM (Fig. 5.3) and is marked I_m, measured between the current zero line and the peak of the wave. It is of interest to note that the current wave of red-phase current shows a *minor* loop immediately after CM and this is ignored, the making current in that phase being that of the major loop which immediately follows.

We can now consider the three traces which record the phase voltages, red, yellow and blue. It is best to consider first the record of these voltages for the make-break test, see Fig. 5.3. Initially, the full phase-volts are across the open circuit-breaker contacts. At the point CM where current starts due to closing of the contacts, the voltage falls to zero, being absorbed in the generator windings and the series reactors. At the point CS where the contacts separate, an arc is struck which continues until final extinction at point B. Between these two points it is noted that voltage appears, first above, and then below the zero line in succession as the current alternates above and below zero. This voltage is the arc voltage (see Chapter 2) and, since the arc path is almost pure resistance of a value proportional to the arc length for a given current, the arc voltage is in phase with the current and its value progressively increases as the arc lengthens due to the contacts separating.

Close examination of the oscillograms will show that the arc is extinguished in one phase before the other two. This is because the current in an a.c. circuit can be extinguished only at a normal zero or very near to it. Since current zero occurs at different instants in the three phases, one phase must be interrupted first. When this occurs, the currents in the other two phases are equal and opposite and the circuit becomes single phase. Both of these currents will be interrupted at the subsequent zero since one phase acts as a return path for the other.

At the instant when the arc is extinguished in the first phase, the voltage across the arc path rises to a value which may reach 1·5 times the open circuit value as discussed in Chapter 2. Furthermore, it is at point B that transient voltages appear (as described earlier) and these can be studied only by means of a cathode-ray oscillogram. Subsequently, the voltage assumes a normal sine-wave form and this is known as the *recovery* voltage (not to be mistaken for or confused with the transient *restriking* voltage). This recovery voltage must reach a prescribed value as set down in British or other standards and it is measured between lines during the second complete half-cycle after final interruption (point B). This is shown at RR_1 in Fig. 5.3 and if V_r is the recovery voltage (line/line) then:

$$V_r = \frac{RR_1}{2\sqrt{2}}$$

Alternatively, the line to line recovery voltage may be derived from the average value of the phase components (V_{ph}) measured in each phase during the second complete half-cycle after B thus:

$$V_r = \sqrt{3}V_{ph} \text{ for a three-phase test}$$

$$\text{where } V_{ph} = \tfrac{1}{3}\left(\frac{V_a}{2\sqrt{2}} + \frac{V_b}{2\sqrt{2}} + \frac{V_c}{2\sqrt{2}}\right)$$

and where V_a, V_b and V_c are the red, yellow and blue-phase voltages respectively, indicated in Fig. 5.3 as $2\sqrt{2}V_{rc}$ in each voltage trace. The phase-voltage traces in a 'break' test, Fig. 5.2, differ from those in a 'make-break' test in that no voltage is recorded prior to the commencement of current flow because the circuit-breaker under test is isolated from the power source by the open condition of the making-switch.

Examination of the traces of phase voltage between the points M and CS or CM and CS show that they undulate slightly. In some heavy current tests this is much more pronounced and is due to the resistive and inductive drops across the circuit-breaker and its connections prior to contact separation.

Three further traces on the oscillograms represent the power absorbed in the arc in each phase. These are noted as red, yellow and blue-phase kW respectively and the deflection at any point is proportional to the instantaneous values of arc-current and voltage across the arc. Note that the deflection is always in the same direction, i.e. above the zero line, because the arc power factor is unity. By determining the area of the trace above the zero line, the energy consumed can be obtained with the aid of appropriate kilowatt and time scales. This value is stated in kW seconds.

For circuit-breakers which employ oil as the insulating medium it is usual to record the pressure attained within the tank and is shown in Figs. 5.2 and 5.3 recorded in lb/in^2 by measurement against a pressure scale. In oil circuit-breakers having arc-control devices, most of the pressure will be contained within the devices, showing only relatively low values in the tank. By special arrangements it is possible to record the pressure within the arc-control device. The measuring circuits to obtain these oscillographic records will be those shown in Fig. 5.5.

To prove a design at the research stage, many unrelated and perhaps only partial tests will be carried out. To prove the final production unit, and to obtain a certificate of rating, a series of tests under prescribed conditions must be carried out. The nature and extent of the series will depend on the type of apparatus and the British or other standard with which it claims to comply. While a circuit-breaker must be capable of breaking, making and carrying short-circuit current, a fuse on the other hand is largely only concerned with interrupting such current. Oil switches and load-breaking switches are not required to interrupt a short-circuit but they must be capable of closing (making) on to a fault at its peak value and of carrying the short-circuit current for a short time until it is interrupted elsewhere.

The number and type of test duties which must be performed satisfactorily to obtain a certificate of rating are normally included in national and international standards. In the U.K. where a British Standard does not as yet include such data, or where for the time being there is no British Standard, rules governing the testing of such equipment are issued by A.S.T.A. In accordance with

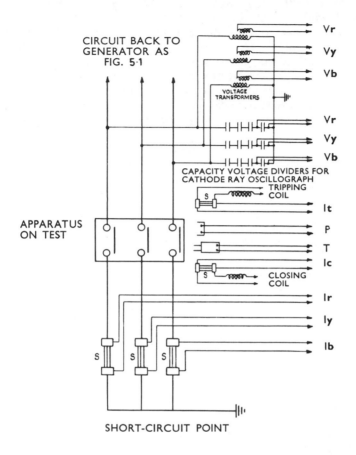

CIRCUIT BACK TO
GENERATOR AS
FIG. 5·1

→ Vr
→ Vy
→ Vb

VOLTAGE
TRANSFORMERS

→ Vr
→ Vy
→ Vb

CAPACITY VOLTAGE DIVIDERS FOR
CATHODE RAY OSCILLOGRAPH

TRIPPING
COIL

→ It

APPARATUS
ON TEST

→ P
→ T
→ Ic

CLOSING
COIL

→ Ir
→ Iy
→ Ib

S   S   S

SHORT-CIRCUIT POINT

LEGEND

Vr	RED PHASE VOLTAGE
Vy	YELLOW PHASE VOLTAGE
Vb	BLUE PHASE VOLTAGE
It	TRIP COIL CURRENT
P	FLUID PRESSURE
T	TRAVEL RECORDER
Ic	CLOSING COIL CURRENT
Ir	RED PHASE CURRENT
Iy	YELLOW PHASE CURRENT
Ib	BLUE PHASE CURRENT
S	SHUNT

Figure 5.5.   Test plant measurement circuits. NOTE: the generator voltage will be measured at a point between the generator and the master-breaker

135

this, Table 5.1 gives the recognised standards or A.S.T.A. rules for apparatus of the type with which this book is concerned.

It is not possible here to relate all the tests involved or the test procedures and conditions which are covered in these documents. It is possible however, to take brief note of the major series of tests which have to be carried out to obtain certification for a circuit-breaker.

Basically, the series of tests is designed to cover the known variable performance of different circuit-breakers under the worst conditions anticipated in service. Thus, a circuit-breaker may be capable of interrupting with relative

Table 5.1

RECOGNISED STANDARDS OR A.S.T.A. RULES FOR VARIOUS TYPES OF EQUIPMENT

Type of equipment	Recognised standard or A.S.T.A. rule
Unit testing of circuit-breakers for making and breaking capacity	A.S.T.A. No. 15
Supplementary proving tests and auto-reclosing duties for circuit-breakers	A.S.T.A. No. 18
Interim rules for the application of synthetic testing methods to high-voltage a.c. circuit-breakers	A.S.T.A. No. 27
High-voltage switches	I.E.C. Pub. No. 265*
Oil circuit-breakers	BS 116 or BS 936
Oil switches	BS 2631
Air-break circuit-breakers	BS 3659
Fuses up to 660 V	BS 88
Fuses above 660 V	BS 2692
Isolators for alternating currents	BS 3078
Circuit-breakers and automatic switches in combination with fuse-links	A.S.T.A. No. 22
Air-blast circuit-breakers	A.S.T.A. No. 17

*Applies to all types of load-breaking fault-making switches based on liquid or gas interruption for voltages of 1 kV to 765 kV.

ease the symmetrical current equal to its full rating, e.g. 350 MVA at 11 kV equivalent to 18·4 kA r.m.s. symmetrical, and yet be in considerable difficulty when called upon to interrupt some value of current less than 100%. This is the case in oil circuit-breakers where, as noted in Chapter 2, the de-ionising forces are dependent on the magnitude of the current. On the other hand the de-ionising forces in an air-blast circuit-breaker are constant regardless of current magnitude, and current chopping can occur at low values of current. It has also been noted in Chapter 2 how when the current is asymmetrical there will be major and minor loops. The former may be of such magnitude as to produce very-high gas pressure in an arc-control device in an oil circuit-breaker. British Standards and/or A.S.T.A. rules (and international and other national specifications) therefore require that proving tests be carried out at 10, 30, 60 and 100% values of symmetrical breaking capacity and at 100% asymmetrical breaking capacity, the 100% symmetrical test to include making capacity duties.

For oil circuit-breakers to BS 116, air-break circuit-breakers to BS 3659 and air-blast circuit-breakers to A.S.T.A. 17, the 10, 30 and 60% tests must *each* comprise three break (*B*) operations with three-minute intervals between them, these duties being designated *B-3-B-3-B*. For the 100% symmetrical test, make (*M*) operations are introduced so that the duty cycle is now *B-3-MB-3-MB*. For the 100% asymmetrical test, the circuit-breaker must interrupt an asymmetrical current whose symmetrical component is the rated symmetrical current.

For circuit-breakers to BS 936, the tests required are confined to the symmetrical condition only and involve duty cycles of *B-3-MB* at 30 and 100% of the rated breaking and making capacity. This easement is possible because circuit-breakers to this specification are intended for use in those parts of an

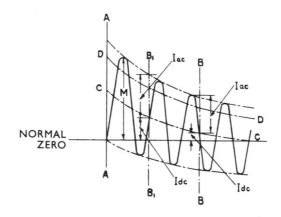

AA = START OF SHORT-CIRCUIT

BB & B_1B_1 = INSTANTS OF CONTACT SEPARATION

Iac = PEAK VALUE OF AC COMPONENT OF CURRENT AT CONTACT SEPARATION

Idc = DC COMPONENT OF CURRENT AT CONTACT SEPARATION

$\dfrac{\text{Idc.100}}{\text{Iac}}$ = PERCENTAGE DC COMPONENT AT CONTACT SEPARATION

CC = DISPLACED ZERO-LINE OF CURRENT WAVE

DD = RMS VALUE OF SYMMETRICAL CURRENT AT ANY INSTANT MEASURED FROM CC

$\dfrac{\text{Iac}}{\sqrt{2}}$ = RMS SYMMETRICAL BREAKING CURRENT

$\sqrt{\left(\dfrac{\text{Iac}}{\sqrt{2}}\right)^2 + \text{Idc}^2}$ = RMS ASYMMETRICAL BREAKING CURRENT

M = MAKING CURRENT (PEAK VALUE)

Figure 5.6. Symmetrical and asymmetrical values of short-circuit current and peak making-current

electrical system remote from a power source where marked asymmetry does not occur, where the power factor will be relatively high and restriking voltages will be less severe.

If we revert to those cases which require asymmetrical tests, it has to be noted that the degree of asymmetry *in one phase* must be such that the d.c. component in the current wave at contact separation is *not less* than 50% of the peak value of the symmetrical component. Thus, for the example mentioned earlier where the r.m.s. symmetrical current was noted as 18·4 kA, this will have a *peak value*

137

$\sqrt{2}$ times greater, i.e. 27 kA and 50% of this is 13·5 kA so that the asymmetrical breaking current at contact separation in the test must be not less than:

$$\sqrt{18\cdot4^2 + 13\cdot5^2} = 22\cdot8 \text{ kA r.m.s.}$$

which is approximately 1·23 times the symmetrical breaking current.

Figure 5.6 serves to illustrate these values, the wave of short-circuit current being assumed to be completely asymmetrical in the first half-cycle of short-circuit. This illustration shows how the degree of asymmetry is progressively reduced with time until at some point the wave will become symmetrical, i.e. reach the steady short-circuit state. In the majority of circuit-breakers, contact separation will occur before the steady state is reached, and if, in the asymmetrical test, the d.c. component must be not less than 50% of the a.c. component it may be necessary to energise the circuit-breaker trip-coil slightly in advance of the closing of the making switch to apply the short-circuit to ensure that the breaker contacts will separate at an early point in the current wave, e.g. at $B_1 B_1$ in Fig. 5.6. If tripped too late, the contacts may not separate until the d.c. component has fallen below the stipulated 50% value, e.g. at BB in Fig. 5.6.

It may be noted here that in the symmetrical tests, the d.c. component *must not* exceed 20% of the a.c. component at contact separation so that the timing of trip coil energisation coupled with the previously measured curve of contact travel (Fig. 5.4) must be determined accordingly, i.e. to ensure contact separation at BB.

The making capacity is, as we have noted, checked in the 100% symmetrical duty cycle and the magnitude of the current at contact touch will always be the peak value M in Fig. 5.6. This assumes that the first loop of short-circuit current is a major loop. If, as can be the case, the first loop is minor, as for example the red-phase current wave at CM in Fig. 5.3, then the second will be a major loop and is taken as the making current. With complete asymmetry, the peak value of this loop may be as high as 2·55 times the r.m.s. symmetrical value, e.g. in the example used earlier 2·55 times 18·4 kA which is equal to 46·9 kA. The severity of duty imposed on a circuit-breaker in these circumstances is largely due to the magnitude of the electromagnetic forces caused by the high peak value of current, which will be noted in a later chapter. There is also a danger of an arc striking just before the contacts touch, a condition which can set up high impulse pressures. For circuit-breakers to BS 936, the peak making current will be less than the 2·55 times mentioned before, as the power factor condition will be improved, i.e. 0·3 as against 0·15, and for these the recognised making capacity is twice the r.m.s. symmetrical breaking current.

Standard specifications recognise two classes of circuit-breaker in relation to the make-break (MB) operation. The first is described as a *closed circuit-breaker* (or *fixed-trip* type) which when closing on to the short-circuit must latch in the *fully closed* position before reopening to break the short-circuit. The second has a *trip-free operation* in which the tripping impulse will be initiated immediately current is established by the contacts touching on the make operation. With the latter type, the time interval between contact make and contact break may be very short, with the result that at contact break the d.c. component may be considerably greater than the maximum 20% stipulated during symmetrical tests. In these circumstances a test authority can segregate the *B-3-MB-3-MB* test and carry out two separate duties, i.e. *M-3-M* and *B-3-B-3-B*.

Circuit-breakers are available which act much as an h.r.c. fuse does, i.e. they reduce the short-circuit current to be actually interrupted to a value below that which would appear had the circuit-breaker not been present. In such cases, the circuit-breaker will be credited with interrupting or making the prospective values determined by a test with the circuit-breaker absent, giving an oscillo-gram much as shown in Fig. 5.6. In h.r.c. fuse terminology, the reduced current is known as the *cut-off* value and will be discussed in Chapter 10.

While the foregoing covers the major proving tests of a circuit-breaker, there are other factors which have to be proved. For example, it is recognised that in certain types of circuit-breaker there may be a critical current below the 10% value at which the arc duration is markedly high. In the case of oil circuit-breakers to BS 116, the yardstick is a comparison of arcing times on the 10 and 30% tests, and where the former is greater than the latter an additional test duty at 5% will be called for when the full rating of the circuit-breaker exceeds 10 kA r.m.s. symmetrical breaking capacity. In some cases, manufac-turers may go even further and test down to 2·5 or even 1%. Similar checks may be required on air-break and air-blast circuit-breakers, but using a different yardstick.

Beyond this, where a circuit-breaker has all three poles within a common enclosure, e.g. in an oil tank, it is necessary to ensure that the circuit-breaker can interrupt 100% symmetrical breaking current on *one pole*, usually an outer pole. This test is carried out at phase to neutral voltage and proves the ability of the breaker to withstand the unbalanced forces produced under such con-ditions. In service, this requirement can arise in the case of a fault between one line and earth where the impedance of the earth circuit is very low resulting in a high value of earth fault current.

There now remains to be satisfied the question of the ability of the circuit-breaker to withstand the effects of carrying through-fault current while the fault is being cleared elsewhere. In the short-circuit tests noted earlier, the major effect has been electromagnetic, but when a circuit-breaker (and other apparatus) has to carry fault current for an appreciable time, it has to withstand both electromagnetic and thermal effects, with the latter predominating because of the time factor. Two time-ratings are generally recognised, viz. 3 s or 1 s. For circuit-breakers to BS 116, BS 3659 or to A.S.T.A. 17 the 3 s rating is chosen when the ratio of the symmetrical breaking current to the rated normal current is 40 or less. When this ratio is over 40, then the 1 s rating is acceptable. Thus, for the 350 MVA/11 kV breaker used in earlier examples, a normal current rating of 1 200 A would give a ratio of 18 400/1 200, i.e. 15·3, and would have a 3 s short-time rating, whereas if its normal current rating is only 400 A, the ratio would be 46, and a 1 s short-time rating would suffice. In practice, current literature would tend to indicate that in both these cases the manufacturer can give the 3 s rating, but it is important to note that circuit-breakers of much lower rating would have inadequate copper sections to withstand the thermal effects for more than 1 s. It is equally important to remember that any associated current transformers must have comparable short-time ratings, particularly those with wound primary-windings and low primary-current ratings.

The test for short-time current ratings requires a current to be carried for the appropriate time which has an r.m.s. value not less than the rated symmetrical breaking current. With the breaker closed and latched in, the short-circuit is made and maintained for one or three seconds (or some other appropriate time) and it is a requirement that the highest peak value of the first major loop in the current wave must not be less than the rated making capacity. Because of the decrement of current value over the test duration the value is determined from the oscillogram as an equivalent r.m.s. value using Simpson's rule. The test duration of current (1 or 3 s) is divided into 10 equal parts* and the r.m.s. values of the a.c. component of the current measured at these instants are designated I_0, I_1, I_2 ... I_{10}, where I_0 is the value at the instant of short-circuit. The r.m.s. short-time current is then given by the expression:

$$\sqrt{\left[\tfrac{1}{30}\{I_0^2 + 4(I_1^2 + I_3^2 + I_5^2 + I_7^2 + I_9^2) + 2(I_2^2 + I_4^2 + I_6^2 + I_8^2) + I_{10}^2\}\right]}$$

This test may be made at any voltage (see Fig. 5.10 for example), provided it is above the minimum necessary to give the required current for the test duration.

What has been discussed up to this point is known as *direct* testing and requires that the generators be capable of giving an output equal to the rating of the *complete* three-phase circuit-breaker. With the ever increasing fault levels of present day power systems however, the provision of generator and other test plant would, in terms of capital cost, be quite prohibitive, and it is essential to resort to other methods. In passing it may be noted that in the 1920s the fault level on the original British Grid System required circuit-breakers with a breaking capacity of 1 500 MVA at 132 kV. Today, the 400 kV network demands a breaking capacity of 35 000 MVA and to meet the requirements of future networks at even high voltages, higher fault levels are envisaged.

One method of assessing the breaking capacity of a three-phase circuit-breaker where plant limitations prevail is that of single-phase testing on one pole of that breaker, e.g. a high-voltage oil circuit-breaker with each pole in a separate tank. When testing by this method it is important that the phase recovery voltage be such that the conditions experienced on three-phase testing are obtained. In Chapter 2 we have seen how, on the first phase to interrupt the short-circuit current, the phase recovery voltage is 1·5 times the phase voltage. In a single-phase test this condition can only be ensured by raising the test voltage so that it includes this multiplying factor so that a single-phase test on one pole of a 275 kV circuit-breaker for example, requires the single-phase test voltage to be $1\cdot5 \times 275/\sqrt{3}$, i.e. 238 kV. Some doubts as to the complete acceptance of single-phase testing have been raised however, because (a) it does not reveal how the operation of the single pole is affected when coupled through the common drive mechanism to the other two poles, and (b) how the electromagnetic conditions are affected due to the absence of the other two poles. Making allowance for this however, single-phase testing demands a total plant MVA only 50% of that required for three-phase testing for the same breaking capacity.

The second method of testing is one which can be applied to the many high and extra-high-voltage circuit-breakers which use a number of *identical* interrupter heads operating in series per pole, e.g. the air-blast type. For designs of this type what is known as *unit* testing is employed in which one interrupter head is tested at full current and at a voltage equal to the full voltage reduced in proportion to the number of interrupter heads used in a complete pole of

---

* See for example Fig. 6 in BS 3659 or equivalent in other specifications.

the breaker. From such unit tests, coupled with supplementary part tests on a complete breaker pole (a) at full voltage with reduced current and (b) with full current at reduced voltage, the breaking capacity of a circuit-breaker as a whole can be determined and proved. The validity of this method rests in the proof that in service there is equal voltage distribution between the multiple breaks, usually taken care of in the design by the employment of shunt resistors across each break.

The present day high-power test plants have power sources of 3 000–5 000 MVA, and if unit testing is relied on, circuit-breaker designers must take this into account. For example, a multiple-break design for a rating of 35 000 MVA at 400 kV would, with a 3 000 MVA power source available require 12 interrupter heads each capable of interrupting 3 000 MVA. With 5 000 MVA available, the number of heads could be reduced to seven, each able to interrupt 5 000 MVA (in a practical design, probably eight heads would be employed). If the test sources could be further increased, say to 10 000 MVA, only four interrupter heads would be required, but a substantial increase in the size of a test plant of this order is generally agreed to be impracticable, and as noted earlier, prohibitive in cost. However, the future envisages circuit-breakers having much higher breaking capacities (figures such as 50 000–100 000 MVA* are talked of) and if unit testing must be relied on and there is no increase in plant capacity, a very large number of interrupter heads in series per pole would be necessary, leading to considerable design complications.

The need therefore is to reduce (or at least not increase) the number of interrupter heads per pole. Development has already resulted in interrupter heads with breaking capacities in excess of the available test plant power sources, with the result that if these are to be usefully employed, an alternative method of testing becomes essential. This alternative is found in the method known as synthetic (or compound) testing, a method which uses two sources of power, one to supply the short-circuit current at reduced voltage, i.e. the conventional generating plant, and the other a low-power source comprising a large capacitor bank to inject a high voltage across the breaker contacts to simulate the full restriking voltage.

The synthetic method of testing is not new and a variety of circuits have been used for many years for research and development. Its application as a means of proving circuit-breakers has in recent years been the subject of investigation, in particular a co-ordinated series of investigations on a collaborative basis by representatives of British Industry, the C.E.G.B. and the E.R.A., whose findings have been reported fully[2,3].

Interim rules for the application of synthetic testing methods to high-voltage a.c. circuit-breakers, in particular air-blast or other gas-blast types, have been published by A.S.T.A.[4] and will be amplified in due course when investigations into the validity of the method as applied to all types of oil circuit-breaker have reached a conclusive stage.

The subject of synthetic testing is far too extensive to be covered here in any detail and reference to the aforementioned documentations should be made. It must therefore suffice to note that two methods are covered in the A.S.T.A. rules. The first is the parallel current-injection method, in which by definition the voltage circuit is effectively connected in parallel with the current circuit

* In modern parlance these would be described as 50–100 GVA.

and the test breaker before main current zero. The other is the series current-injection method in which the voltage circuit is effectively connected in series with the current circuit and the test breaker before main current zero. The former method has been the one used for most of the validity testing performed in the U.K., and is the preferred method. It is suitable for testing with transient recovery voltages whose frequences are 1·0 kHz and above. For frequencies below this, several factors may cause the validity of the method to be in doubt and for these the series current-injection method may be used.

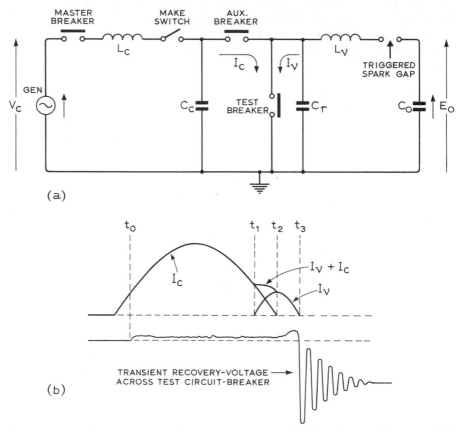

Figure 5.7. *Synthetic testing—parallel current-injection method.* (a) *schematic diagram and* (b) *current and voltage waveforms (courtesy The Association of Short-circuit Testing Authorities)*

Figure 5.7(a)* shows the circuit used in the parallel current-injection method and that the current circuit comprises a generator (or generator-transformer combination), a master-breaker and making switch in series with an inductance L_c to control the short-circuit current, an auxiliary breaker and the test breaker. Capacitor C_c eases the duty on the auxiliary breaker.

The voltage circuit comprises a source capacitor C_o charged from a separate d.c. source in series with a triggered spark gap and an inductance L_v, the whole being connected across the test circuit-breaker in parallel with capacitor C_r

*Figs. 5.7 and 5.8 and the text discussing them are based on ASTA No. 27, which is quoted by permission of The Association of Short-Circuit Testing Authorities.

which controls the frequency of the transient recovery voltage. A damping resistor may when necessary be connected either in parallel or in series with C_r. The source capacitor C_o is of such value that it resonates with the series inductance at some frequency higher than that of the power frequency current. C_r, and its damping resistance if required, are chosen together with L_v and the voltage to which C_o is charged so that the required frequency, form and magnitude of the transient recovery voltage is obtained.

Operation of the circuit is as follows, read in conjunction with the current and voltage waveforms shown in Fig. 5.7(b). The current circuit is set to give the required power frequency current, the make switch being open and the auxiliary and test breakers both closed. The source capacitor C_o is charged to a value appropriate to the required test voltage. If the make switch is closed at a voltage peak, the symmetrical test current I_c will flow through the auxiliary and test breakers in series. At a predetermined time t_o the auxiliary and test breakers open and arcing commences in both. At time t_1 the triggered spark gap is fired and a current I_v flows from the voltage source through the test breaker, adding to the power-frequency current I_c. When the power-frequency current reaches zero at time t_2 the auxiliary breaker interrupts, leaving current I_v from the voltage circuit flowing alone through the test circuit-breaker. At time t_3, I_v reaches zero and the test circuit-breaker will attempt to interrupt. Should interruption occur, capacitor C_r will be charged from C_o through L_v causing the transient recovery voltage to appear across the test breaker. If the test breaker re-ignites, the current from the high-voltage circuit will be re-established through the test breaker.

If the voltage E_o to which C_o is charged is equal to the peak value of the power-frequency component of the test recovery voltage, and the components of the voltage circuit (C_r and L_v) have the same values as those which would be used in an equivalent direct test, both the rate-of-change of current I_v at its zero and the transient recovery voltage will approximate closely to the conditions of the direct test. In practice, the actual values of the voltage circuit parameters and the voltage E_o differ somewhat from those indicated, mainly for two reasons: (a) The reactance in the voltage circuit will have different characteristics from those of a generator or generator-transformer combination, and (b) C_o in the voltage circuit will lose some charge in the cycle of operation and consequently the voltage to which it is charged will have to exceed the peak value of the power frequency component of the recovery voltage.

Figure 5.8(a) shows the series current-injection circuit from which it is seen that the voltage circuit is connected across the auxiliary breaker instead of across the test circuit-breaker. Operation of this circuit is similar to that of the parallel current-injection circuit, but C_o is charged to the opposite polarity. The current and voltage waveforms are shown in (b) and when the triggered spark gap is fired at time t_1, the current I_v from the voltage circuit flows in opposition to the power frequency current I_c. The result of this is that the current in the auxiliary breaker comes to zero at time t_2 prior to the normal zero of the power-frequency current which occurs at t_2'. At time t_2 the auxiliary breaker clears leaving the current and voltage circuits in series to drive a current I_v' through the test breaker. This current results from the combination of the voltages and inductances of both circuits. At time t_3, I_v' comes to zero and if the test circuit-breaker interrupts, a transient recovery voltage resulting from the combination of the voltages in the two circuits appears across its terminals.

143

Reference in the foregoing to an 'auxiliary breaker' indicates a breaker used to disconnect the current circuit from direct connection with the test circuit-breaker. When using synthetic testing methods, it is not possible to conduct making duties or duties involving make-break tests in precisely the same way as in direct testing. A.S.T.A. Pub. No. 27 includes alternative methods by which such tests can be made, either at a reduced voltage or at the full-rated voltage. Additionally, tests to simulate short-line fault conditions are noted, the elements comprising the artificial line being connected in the voltage circuits of Figs. 5.7 and 5.8.

Synthetic testing is now an established procedure available in most, if not all, high-power short-circuit test plants. By its use, the output of the available conventional power source is augmented considerably, figures of 5 to 10 times being noted in the literature on the subject.

Reference has just been made to tests which simulate short-line faults. The problem of these has been noted in Chapter 2 and to prove the ability of a circuit-breaker to interrupt such faults involves the construction of a suitable artificial line, the surge impedance of which must be adjustable to give fractional

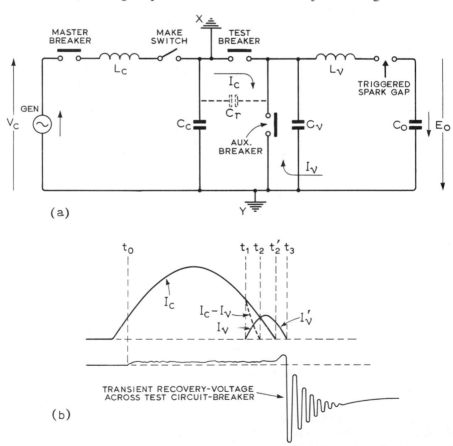

Figure 5.8. Synthetic testing—series current-injection method. (a) schematic diagram and (b) current and voltage waveforms. Note that X and Y are alternative earthing points (see ASTA pub. No. 27, appendix D, clause D5) (courtesy The Association of Short-circuit Testing Authorities)

values. Such an artificial line can be an actual length of overhead line but the more usual construction is a ladder network comprising inductances and capacitors in the form shown in Fig. 5.9. Constructions of this type usually represent an equivalent length of line (maximum) of 6·5–8 km (4–5 miles), the values of the inductances and capacitances corresponding to those of the actual line, but noting that in the latter, capacitance and inductance are distributed infinitesimally.

As we have seen in Chapter 2, short-circuits are not the only interrupting duty of a circuit-breaker. It must also be capable of interrupting small inductive currents such as transformer magnetising, etc. and capacitive currents such as

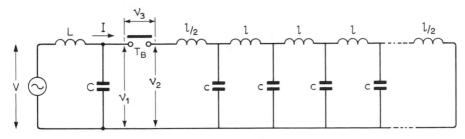

LEGEND

V	SUPPLY VOLTAGE	I	SHORT-CIRCUIT CURRENT
L	INDUCTANCE ON THE SUPPLY SIDE	v_1	VOLTAGE ON SUPPLY SIDE
C	CAPACITANCE ON THE SUPPLY SIDE	v_2	VOLTAGE ON LINE SIDE
l	INDUCTANCES	v_3	VOLTAGE ACROSS THE BREAKER (T_B) ON TEST
c	CAPACITANCES OF SYNTHETIC LINES		

Figure 5.9. Synthetic line for short-line fault tests (ladder network). Master-breaker, make switch, etc. omitted for clarity (courtesy Brown Boveri & Co. Ltd.)

those that occur when switching an unloaded line. These capabilities must also form a part of the work in a test plant, and facilities for simulating the conditions are available. Inductive conditions are provided by a transformer and possibly reactors, while capacitive conditions are provided by a bank of capacitors.

The rules for short-circuit testing of circuit-breakers include a variety of departures and alternatives acceptable under certain prescribed conditions in addition to data as to what is and what is not permitted in the course of testing. The extent of this material is such as to preclude mention here and the reader must therefore be referred to the British Standards or A.S.T.A. rules for details.

Extensive use is made today of oil switches on distribution systems at 3·3 to 33 kV. These switches are primarily intended for isolating and earthing ring-main circuits by hand without protective devices, and therefore are not called upon to break short-circuit current. They are, however, subject to (a) being closed on to a fault and therefore must have a rated making-capacity and (b) carrying a through fault for a period of time, e.g. 3 s, and must have a short-time rating. The requirements for the testing of this apparatus have been included in BS 2631:1955 and show that the following should be complied with:

1. The main switch must be capable of breaking normal load and charging currents and test duty cycles *B-3-B-3'-B* at 130% and 30% of normal current rating, and are specified at a power factor of 0·7 lag.

2. The main switch *and* the earthing switch must both be capable of making on to the peak current in the first half-cycle of short-circuit and a test duty cycle *M-3'-M* at 100% of making capacity is specified, and on 'making' must be held for at least 10 half-cycles. BS 2631 schedules a range of standard sizes which indicates that at each voltage a preferred upper limit of making capacity is 33·4 kA peak and a through short-time rating of 13·1 kA for 3 s.

There are in use today a number of circuit-breakers and automatic switches which, in themselves, have only a limited breaking and making capacity but when backed up by h.r.c. fuses or fuse-links can be regarded as being adequate for use on systems whose fault values are within the rating of the fuses or fuse-links. Tests to prove such combinations have been enumerated in A.S.T.A. Pub. No. 22 and include tests under circumstances where the fuse-link has or has not been separately tested, tests to prove the ability of the circuit-breaker or switch to make and break fault current within its own ability, i.e. fuse-links replaced by links, and tests at five times the normal current rating or twice the take-over current (i.e. the current at which the fuse-links take over the current-breaking duty from the circuit-breaker or switch) whichever value is the higher, again with the fuse-links replaced by links. Tests made with the fuses or fuse-links present must be at power factors applicable to the type of fuse-link and the British Standard appropriate to the type, i.e. BS 88 or BS 2692. Tests made with the fuse-links removed may be at a power factor not exceeding 0·7 lagging.

High-voltage fuses, usually pole-mounted, are an economical form of protection for rural distribution networks. Such types are covered in BS 2692 for a wide range of voltages and breaking capacities and this specification recognises the existence of various types, i.e. liquid, powder-filled and oil tank, in addition to those used in the primary circuit of voltage transformers. The short-circuit proving tests for the various types are comprehensively covered in this British Standard.

To conclude this chapter, it is appropriate to take a brief look at two typical test plants. The first is a plant of limited capacity which would entitle the operator to associate membership of A.S.T.A. The second is a high-power plant capable of testing up to and beyond the highest present-day voltages and interrupting capacities, entitling the operator to full membership of A.S.T.A. The two classes of membership are as discussed in the preamble to this chapter.

Figure 5.10 shows the three-phase diagram for the first of these stations, primarily designed for short-circuit tests on medium and high-voltage contactors, isolating switches, fuse-switches, miniature and moulded circuit-breakers and busbars, and for short-time current tests. The generator is induction-motor driven and the set can, in an emergency, be brought to rest in 3 min by a battery operated braking system. The generator can be connected in star or delta and is separately excited with provision for field forcing to compensate for the demagnetising effect of the high stator currents on the field system. The generator with its driving motor and exciter are seen in Fig. 5.11.

Beyond the generator, the diagram shows the basic apparatus as discussed in relation to Fig. 5.1, i.e. the master breaker, transformers, make switch, reactors and resistances, noting that whereas in Fig. 5.1 the reactors and resistances are shown between the master breaker and the make switch, in this plant they are located beyond the make switch, i.e. on the load side of the device under test.

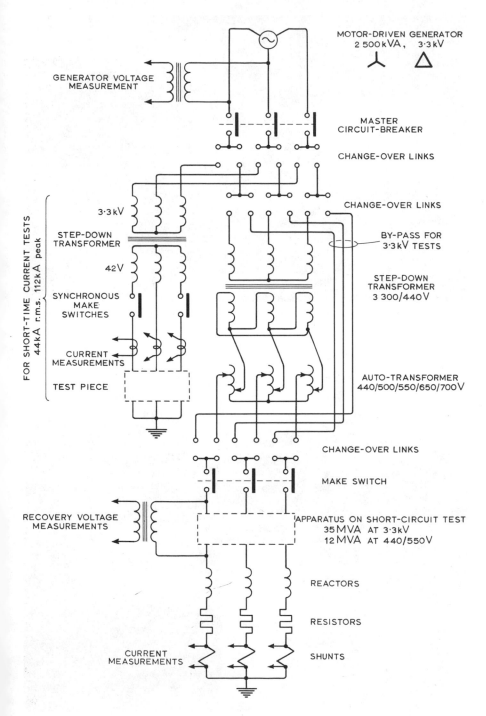

GENERATOR VOLTAGE MEASUREMENT

MOTOR-DRIVEN GENERATOR
2 500 kVA, 3·3 kV

MASTER CIRCUIT-BREAKER

CHANGE-OVER LINKS

CHANGE-OVER LINKS

3·3 kV

STEP-DOWN TRANSFORMER

42 V

SYNCHRONOUS MAKE SWITCHES

CURRENT MEASUREMENTS

TEST PIECE

FOR SHORT-TIME CURRENT TESTS
44 kA r.m.s. 112 kA peak

BY-PASS FOR 3·3 kV TESTS

STEP-DOWN TRANSFORMER 3 300/440 V

AUTO-TRANSFORMER 440/500/550/650/700 V

CHANGE-OVER LINKS

MAKE SWITCH

RECOVERY VOLTAGE MEASUREMENTS

APPARATUS ON SHORT-CIRCUIT TEST
35 MVA AT 3·3 kV
12 MVA AT 440/550 V

REACTORS

RESISTORS

CURRENT MEASUREMENTS

SHUNTS

Figure 5.10. Connection diagram of short-circuit and heavy-current test plant (courtesy A. Reyrolle & Co. Ltd.)

147

Figure 5.11. The short-circuit generator with driving motor and exciter (courtesy A. Reyrolle & Co. Ltd.)

Figure 5.12. Short-circuit test plant showing generator, transformers, reactors, resistors, etc. (courtesy A. Reyrolle & Co. Ltd.)

This arrangement is now preferred for apparatus such as contactors, fuse-switches, etc. and in particular for load-switching tests such as eight times full-load current for contactors or three times for fuse-switches. The main equipment shown in this diagram is seen in Fig. 5.12.

For short-time heavy-current tests a further three-phase step-down transformer is available, with provision to connect this directly to the generator through the master breaker. The secondary output of this transformer is 44 kA r.m.s. at 42 V, with a peak current in the first half-cycle of 112 kA.

The synchronous make switches (in the outer phases only) are separate units not coupled mechanically. Each is closed and held closed by a d.c. magnet and a safety switch ensures that the coils are not de-energised until the master breaker has opened at the end of the test duration. Synchronising is achieved by an adjustable-rotating spark gap on the generator shaft, the discharge current in the spark being used to trigger a thyratron which in turn fires an ignitron which applies the direct current to the two magnet coils. By this means 'point-on-wave' switching is achieved with an accuracy of ± 0.2 ms and both switches will be fully closed before the peak in the first half-cycle of short-circuit is reached. These switches form part of the assembly shown in Fig. 5.13 which

Figure 5.13.   Two in-line synchronous make switches and special measuring current transformers for short-time heavy-current test (courtesy A. Reyrolle & Co. Ltd.)

also shows the current measuring transformers, specially designed to handle the high d.c. component of the test current.

The schematic diagram shown in Fig. 5.14 shows the electrical layout of an extremely large high-power short-circuit testing station. The original station (marked 1929) comprised generator G_1 only and is the station noted historically in Chapter 1. The output at that time was 500 MVA single-phase at voltages up to 22 kV. In 1934 the output was doubled by the addition of a second generator G_2 and by the addition of further transformers the available test voltage was raised to 76 kV. The extensions (marked 1954) included further generator and transformer capacity such that by using the three generators and 15 single-phase transformers, tests could be made on units of rating up to 3 200 MVA with a maximum available voltage of 304 kV. The addition of a fourth generator and three further transformers in 1968 made it possible to carry out direct tests up to at least 5 000 MVA rating and synthetic tests up to

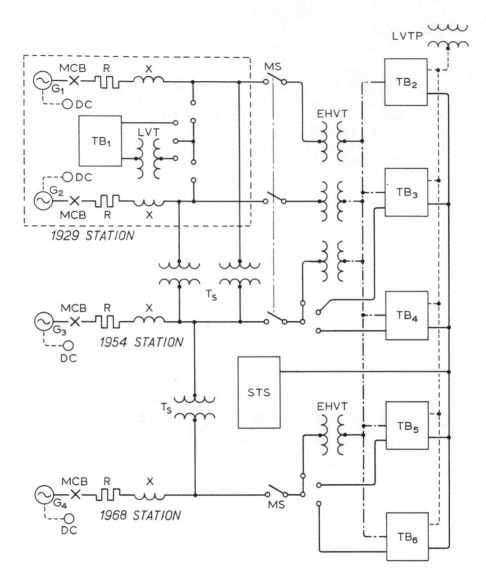

LEGEND

DC	D.C. EXCITERS	MS	MAKING SWITCHES
EHVT	EXTRA-HIGH-VOLTAGE	R	RESISTORS
	TRANSFORMERS	T_S	SYNCHRONISING
G_1-G_4	GENERATORS 1 TO 4		TRANSFORMERS
LVT	LOW-VOLTAGE	STS	SYNTHETIC TEST SOURCE
	TRANSFORMER	TB_1-TB_6	TEST BAYS 1 TO 6
LVTP	PORTABLE LOW-VOLTAGE	X	REACTORS
	TRANSFORMER		
MCB	MASTER CIRCUIT-BREAKER		

Figure 5.14. Simplified single-line schematic diagram of short-circuit test stations (courtesy A. Reyrolle & Co. Ltd.)

150

about 20 000 MVA rating, while the maximum voltage available is now 608 kV.

Each of the three elements of the complete station can operate independently using only a part of the power plant, or the full plant can be used as a single unit when testing at the highest ratings. Because of the magnitude of the current which might flow in the event of a fault in a generator circuit, direct paralleling is undesirable and paralleling on the high-voltage side of the power transformers is adopted, using synchronising transformers as shown, to ensure synchronism prior to the application of the short-circuit.

Generators G_1, G_2 and G_3 each have two stator windings per phase which can be connected in series or parallel, star or delta, to give four basic three-phase voltages of 6·35, 11, 12·7 and 22 kV, intermediate voltages being arranged by excitation control. Generator G_4 has two permanently-paralleled windings

Figure 5.15.   Extra-high-voltage transformer bank (courtesy A. Reyrolle & Co. Ltd.)

per phase for connection in star or delta for either 12·7 or 22 kV. To obtain a high current with high recovery voltage and thereby virtually to increase the available output, over-excitation is employed to boost the field current *before* the short-circuit is applied, raising the initial voltage of the generator to a value higher than normal. The high-voltage transformer-bank comprises in all some 18 single-phase units, a part view being shown in Fig. 5.15. Six of these units are provided with two primary windings and four secondary windings, the latter for 38 kV. They can be connected in four series-parallel arrangements to give 38, 76, 114 or 152 kV. Four of these transformers are mounted on insulated supports so that they can be cascaded to produce a maximum voltage between terminals of 608 kV.

For each generator there are three single-pole making switches. Each three-pole assembly is capable of separate operation. Alternatively, the nine single-poles associated with generators G_1, G_2 and G_3 can be ganged mechanically

Figure 5.16.   General view of making switches (courtesy A. Reyrolle & Co. Ltd.)

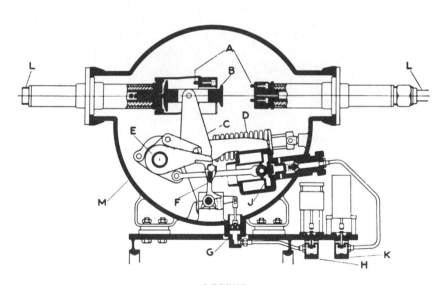

LEGEND

A	FIXED CONTACTS	H	TRIP-VALVE AND MAGNET
B	MOVING CONTACTS	J	PISTON FOR CHARGING
C	CONTACT LEVER		OPERATING-SPRING
D	OPERATING SPRING	K	CHARGING-VALVE AND
E	MAIN SHAFT		MAGNET
F	TRIPPING LATCH	L	TERMINALS
G	TRIPPING-RELAY CYLINDER	M	PRESSURE TANK

Figure 5.17.   Interior of making-switch (courtesy A. Reyrolle & Co. Ltd.)

152

by means of clutches while the three switches for generator G_4 can be closed in synchronism with the other nine by an electrical means.

Figure 5.16 shows a general view of the nine single-pole switches, while Fig. 5.17 illustrates the interior design. To control the degree of asymmetry in break tests (as discussed earlier), point-on-wave closing of the making switches is provided, the desired point on the voltage wave being detected by a small constant-voltage a.c. generator, mechanically coupled to one of the main generators, which feeds a voltage through a phase-shifter and peaking circuit

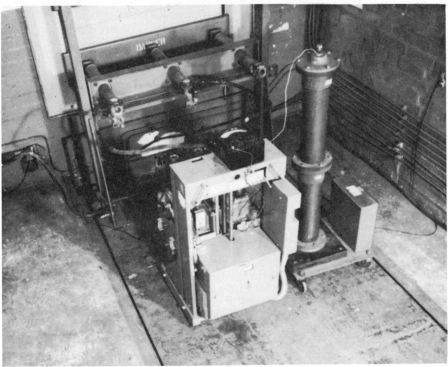

Figure 5.18. Interior of one of eight test cells in the switchgear research laboratory (courtesy A. Reyrolle & Co. Ltd.)

to a thyratron grid. Firing of the thyratron occurs at the selected point of the voltage wave, being initiated by the voltage pulse from the peaking circuit after the appropriate contact on the test-sequence controller has closed. This point-on-wave switching operates with a tolerance (overall) of ± 10 electrical degrees. In order to reduce the effect of pre-arcing when closing, i.e. just before the contacts of the making switch touch, each pole operates in compressed air. High-speed closing is obtained through a spring mechanism, the springs being charged by compressed air.

Synthetic testing by the parallel-current injection method is available (see Fig. 5.7) the voltage-source capacitor bank being in a separate building (see Fig. 5.14). The bank is arranged in six towers each of which has four trays of 18 capacitors connected in a series-parallel arrangement with a total capacitance of $20\,\mu F$ at a voltage of 50 kV. The four trays in each tower can be connected in series, series-parallel or parallel, to give 200, 100 or 50 kV respectively, and connections between towers enable voltages of 150, 300 and 400 kV to be obtained.

Apart from the main test plant, a small testing station is used for research work. This has a single generator with a three-phase output of 80 MVA which provides a range of outputs from 13 kA at 3·3 kV to 3 kA at 11 kV, with corresponding currents at 5·5 or 6·6 kV, while synthetic testing equipment extends the test capability to cater for 250 MVA gear. Figure 5.18 shows one of the test cells associated with this research station. A heavy-current cell is fitted with a three-phase transformer having an output of 40 kA at 120 V and proportionally lower currents at voltages up to 760 V. Two outdoor test cells are connected to two single-phase heavy-current transformers by separate busbar systems enabling 80 kA to be obtained at 80 V. For higher-voltage tests, two single-phase transformers each with six 3·3 kV windings can be connected as required.

Other facilities in this research station include a transient analyser, by means of which complete electrical circuits can be set up and their response to various electrical disturbances shown visually as a repetition trace on oscilloscopes; a steady-state network analyser which enables investigations to be made into problems of load-flow, fault studies and stability states on mimic power-systems; and the application of digital computation to network analysis problems.

REFERENCES

1. ANON., *Supplementary Proving Tests and Auto-reclosing Duties for Circuit-breakers*, A.S.T.A., publication No. 18, Feb. (1969)
2. ANDERSON, J.G.P., *et al*, 'Synthetic Testing of a.c. Circuit-breakers, Part 1: Methods of Testing and Relative Severity', *Proc. I.E.E.*, **113** No. 4, April (1966)
3. ANDERSON, J.G.P., *et al*, 'Synthetic Testing of a.c. Circuit-breakers, Part 2: Requirements for Circuit-breaker Proving', *Proc. I.E.E.*, **115** No. 7, July (1968)
4. ANON., *Interim Rules for the Application of Synthetic Testing Methods to High-voltage Circuit-breakers*, A.S.T.A., publication No. 27, Jan. (1969)

BIBLIOGRAPHY

BALTENSPERGER, P., 'Solving Problems in High-voltage Switchgear', *Brown Boveri Rev.*, **57**, Dec. (1970)

CRANE, P.H.G., *Switchgear Principles*, Macmillan (1957)

EHRENBERG, A.C. *et al*, 'The Synthetic Testing of Air-blast Circuit-breakers', *A.E.I. Engng.*, May/ June (1966)

GARRARD, C.J.O., 'High-voltage Switchgear—A Review of Progress', *Proc. I.E.E.*, **113** No. 9, Sept. (1966)

LUGTON, W.T., 'Short-circuit Testing of Circuit-breakers with Particular Reference to the Interpretation of Oscillograms', *Reyrolle Rev.*, No. 174, Christmas (1959). Reprint No. RR95

STEEL, J.G. and SWIFT-HOOK, D.T., 'Statistics of Circuit-breaker Performance', *Proc. I.E.E.*, **117** No. 7, July (1970)

WASS, C.A.A. and LORD, H., 'A New Plant for Research and Testing Equipment for Flammable Atmospheres', *Elect. Rev.*, June 12 (1970)

WILKINSON, J.R., 'A.S.T.A.—Progress and Plans', *Elec. Times*, 31 Oct. (1968)

ANON., 'C.E.S.I. Serves the World', *Elec. Rev.*, 7 June (1968)

ANON., 'E.R.A. Synthetic Testing Techniques Under Thorough Investigation', *Elect. Rev.*, 23 Oct. (1964)

ANON., 'Extension of Reyrolle Laboratories', *Reyrolle Rev.*, Spring (1968). Reprint No. RR 124

VARIOUS, 'The High-power Testing Station', *Brown Boveri Rev.*, **55** No. 12, Dec. (1968). This special issue includes seven articles by various authors on the Brown Boveri testing station, its equipment, test methods and facilities, measuring techniques and equipment and network analysis.

Chapter 6

Surge protection and impulse levels

Overvoltages which appear on electrical systems can be broadly described as internal or external. In more detail they are as follows:

Internal overvoltages. These originate in the system itself and may be transient, dynamic or stationary. Those of a transient nature will have a frequency unrelated to the normal system frequency and will persist for a few cycles only. They can be caused by the operation of circuit-breakers when switching inductive or capacitive loads, 'current chopping' when interrupting very small currents (see Chapter 2) or by the sudden earthing of one phase of a system operating with an insulated neutral.

Dynamic overvoltages occur at normal system frequency and persist only for a few seconds. They may be caused, for example, by the disconnection of a generator which overspeeds, or when a large part of the load is suddenly removed.

Stationary overvoltages also occur at system frequency but they may persist for some time, perhaps hours. Such a condition can arise when an earth-fault on one line is sustained, as indeed it may be when the neutral is earthed through an arc-suppression coil as described in Chapter 7, thereby leading to overvoltages on the sound phases.

Overvoltages as described above rarely exceed three to five times the normal phase to neutral *peak* voltage of the system, and subject to apparatus having an adequate insulation level they should be relatively harmless.

External overvoltages. These overvoltages are produced by atmospheric discharges such as static charges or lightning strokes and are therefore not related to the system. They are often of such magnitude as to cause considerable stress on the insulation, and, in the case of lightning, will vary in intensity depending on how directly the line is struck, i.e. directly by the main discharge, directly by a branch or streamer, or by induction due to a flash passing near to but not touching the line.

Switchgear specifications describe two classifications for an installation. One is 'electrically exposed' resulting in the apparatus being subject to overvoltages of atmospheric origin, and another which is 'electrically non-exposed' and therefore not subject to this type of overvoltage. The first of these is generally recognised as an installation connected directly to overhead transmission lines, e.g. outdoor switchgear or transformers, but it can apply to indoor gear connected to overhead lines via outdoor to indoor through bushings or by a short length of cable. The second classification is one usually associated with underground cable networks and the switchgear will normally be of the indoor type.

The need to avoid a breakdown of primary insulation due to overvoltages on the system, if at all possible, requires that circuit-breakers, transformers, post and tension insulators, isolators and other apparatus should have a 'withstand' voltage level greater than the protective level of devices provided to give overvoltage protection, e.g. surge diverters. Thus it is found in present day practice that high-voltage switchgear is designed to an impulse 'withstand' level quoted in terms of peak kV. Any surge protection applied to the system on which the switchgear is used will be chosen such that any surge reaching terminal insulation will not exceed the given 'withstand' level of that insulation, i.e. the surge diverter will discharge at a voltage below that of the insulation level.

In the past, surge protection against overvoltages of atmospheric origin has been accepted practice in many countries where lightning is prevalent and particularly when the apparatus to be protected is associated with overhead line transmission. More recently, attention has been focused on similar protection against surges of internal origin, i.e. switching surges, more particularly those arising on extra-high-voltage transmission systems.

In this chapter it will be our purpose to consider first the nature of surges due to lightning, and then briefly the design and functioning of protective surge diverters. This will be followed by discussion on impulse 'withstand' levels and impulse testing, and finally some reference to protection against switching surges will be made.

A surge due to lightning is the movement of a charge that is suddenly released in a conductor and which travels along that conductor in the form of a wave. The potential of a conductor being a measure of charge density, it follows that the potential wave must be accompanied by a current wave. The shape of the voltage wave is affected by a number of factors, such as inductance and capacitance. Thus, on a line where the impedance is purely inductive, the front of the wave would be almost vertical, while if the impedance is purely capacitive then the wave front would slope steeply away from the vertical. From this it is clear that the wave shape is affected by the relation between the L and C values, this relationship being expressed as the surge impedance:

$$Z = \sqrt{L/C}$$

where Z = Surge impedance in ohms
L = Inductance in henries
C = Capacitance in farads

As the wave travels along the line its front is modified by the inductance of the line and the distributed capacitances to earth. It may be further modified by the capacitances of bushings, insulators, etc., which the wave encounters on its journey, thus reducing the steepness of the wave front.

A further point has also to be considered, namely that when the travelling wave reaches a point where there is a change in surge impedance of the line, reflection of the wave will occur, reflection being whole or partial depending on the amount of change in surge impedance. In the case, for example, of an open-ended feeder, the change in surge impedance is infinite and a travelling wave would be totally reflected, with the result that the pressure would be practically doubled at the point of reflection due to the front of the wave being reversed and adding itself to the remainder of the wave still travelling forward; the duration of doubled value will depend on the length of the wave tail. In other cases, such as one where an overhead line is joined to an underground cable, the change in surge impedance is not infinite and the reflection will depend on the relative values of the impedances of the overhead line and the cable.

It is clear that when travelling along a line the surge will reach terminal apparatus such as cable boxes, transformers or switchgear, and, unless some means is provided to release the surge, there is a danger of a breakdown of the insulation at the terminal apparatus, unless the insulation level of the latter is high enough to be invulnerable.

SURGE DIVERTERS (LIGHTNING ARRESTERS)

At one time, the usual practice was to put choke coils in the line, coupled with horn gaps connected between line and earth. This apparatus provides some protection, but in fact could add to the dangerous conditions by reflecting the surge wave and permitting considerable power current to flow to earth following discharge. To be really effective a surge diverter should reduce the surge voltage crest and at the same time absorb the transient energy to an extent sufficient to prevent reflection. Two characteristics are essential:
1. The impulse sparkover voltage of the diverter must safeguard the insulation of the terminal apparatus.
2. The diverter must, after discharge, cease to carry current, i.e. it must become an insulator again.

Diverters of this type may be correctly described as *valve arresters*, the characteristics being those of a 'safety valve', which is normally closed but opens in the event of dangerous overvoltages, and, after relieving the system of these voltages, closes again. After operation, the diverter must be in a condition to accept and deal with ensuing surges, i.e. there must be no failure of the diverter itself.

In practice, diverters which provide these features comprise one or more air gaps mounted in series with non-linear resistors, the function of the air gaps being to keep the circuit through the arrester to earth open under all normal power frequency conditions, but to flash over and close the circuit when abnormal voltages appear at the diverter terminals.

The non-linear resistances must absorb surge energy, and in conjunction with the air gaps suppress the flow of power current. These resistances have the important characteristic that the resistance value decreases very rapidly as the current through the material increases. It follows that they can carry very large currents without the voltage drop across them rising to an excessive value. The residual voltage across the diverter therefore remains low, thus limiting the voltage on the line to a value which will not damage the system insulation. As soon as the surge has been discharged the voltage across the diverter tends to fall and the current therefore to decrease. The resistance of the resistor then begins to increase, and the flow of power current due to the system voltage is then reduced, and within a short time (usually less than one half-cycle of system frequency), is sufficiently reduced to be interrupted by the spark gaps as the

157

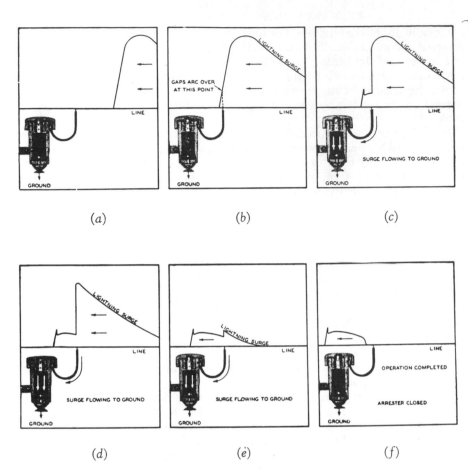

Figure 6.1.   Stages of surge diverter operation

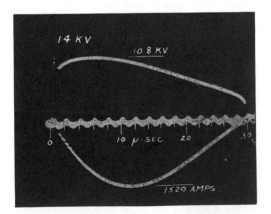

Figure 6.2.   Typical oscillogram of surge diverter operation

system voltage passes through zero. At this point, the diverter resumes its normal non-conducting condition and is ready for further operation.

The successive stages of diverter operation are shown diagrammatically in Fig. 6.1. At (a) we note the front of a surge wave approaching the diverter which may be assumed to be protecting terminal apparatus not shown, but connected to the line to the left of the diverter. At (b) the surge has reached the diverter and, in about 0·25 μs, the voltage has reached a value sufficient to break down the spark gaps and, as shown at (c), surge current flows to earth. As the crest of the surge approaches the point of the line at which the diverter is connected, so the voltage applied increases, and just as rapidly, the resistance of the element decreases, thus permitting further surge energy to discharge and so limiting the voltage impressed on the terminal apparatus to a safe value—as indicated by the lower value of voltage beyond the diverter line connection. At (d) the crest of the wave is shown passing the terminal point, and at (e) the tail of the wave is shown approaching. At this stage the voltage is decreasing, and in consequence the current to earth decreases while the resistance increases, reaching a stage when the current flow is interrupted by the spark gaps thus 'sealing' the diverter as shown at (f). The whole of this operation takes place in a matter of microseconds, as for example in a typical case shown in Fig. 6.2, in 30 μs.

This oscillogram depicts the operation of a 3 kV diverter with an average rate of voltage rise at the beginning of arrester discharge of 50 kV/μs and the average rate of current rise, after the beginning of the discharge, of 150 A/μs to a crest of 1 520 A. This steepness of wave-front is typical of lightning surges and in the wave-front impulse sparkover test in BS 2914:1957 (Surge Diverters) it is laid down that the steepness must comply with values listed in that specification and which vary according to the rated diverter voltage. This standard specification provides for a number of type tests which must be made as follows:

Test No. 1. 1/50 impulse sparkover test.
  ,,   ,, 2. Wave-front impulse sparkover test (mentioned above).
  ,,   ,, 3. Peak discharge residual voltage at low current.
  ,,   ,, 4. Peak discharge residual voltage at rated diverter current.
  ,,   ,, 5. Operating duty test.
  ,,   ,, 6. Impulse current withstand test.

For test No. 1 it is noted that this is described as '1/50 impulse sparkover test'. The significance of the term '1/50' is that it denotes both the steepness of the wave-front and the decline of the wave-tail to a value equal to one-half the peak value, and both figures are in microseconds. This is perhaps better understood by studying Fig. 6.3 which shows how, in the left hand wave-form the front reaches its peak voltage (100 kV) in 1 μs and the tail has fallen to 50 kV, i.e. one-half of the peak value in 50 μs. In the right hand curve the tail falls to 50 kV in 20 μs and is therefore designated a '1/20' wave.

For tests Nos. 4 and 5 a current wave of 8/20 μs has to be passed, indicating a tail of just over twice the duration of the front. In test No. 6, rectangular current impulses* of a magnitude dependent on the rated diverter current must be passed 20 times and the maximum current has to be maintained for a period of time which is again related to the rated diverter current. Full details of all

---

*BS 2914 defines a rectangular impulse wave as a unidirectional wave of voltage or current which rises rapidly to a maximum value, remains substantially constant for a specified period and then falls rapidly to zero.

the tests are given in BS 2914:1957, and examples of oscillographic records on representative surge diverters will be noted later.

Surge diverters are rated in terms of voltage and current, the rated diverter voltage being the highest r.m.s. value of power frequency voltage, measured between the line and earth terminals of the diverter, at which the diverter is designed to work continuously, while the rated diverter current is that value of impulse current used in test Nos. 4 and 5 and can be one of four standard ratings.

To select a surge diverter of suitable voltage rating for a given system voltage will require a knowledge of the system earthing condition, i.e. whether 'effectively earthed' or 'non-effectively earthed' as defined in many British Standards. To be 'effectively earthed' all transformer star-connected windings should have their neutrals solidly earthed directly, i.e. a multiple earthed system, and for

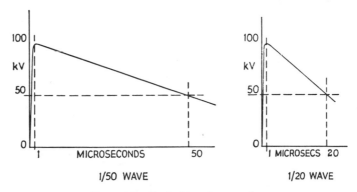

Figure 6.3. Typical impulse wave-forms

this condition the line to earth voltage will not exceed 80% of the highest system voltage. A 'non-effectively earthed' system, on the other hand, includes those with a limited number of solidly earthed neutrals and those earthed through a resistor or reactor of low impedance or an arc-suppression coil, and here the line to earth voltage under fault conditions will be greater than 80% but will not exceed 100% of the highest system voltage (110% of nominal).

On unearthed systems it is possible for line to earth voltages higher than 100% of the highest system voltage to appear, but it is usual practice to assume that this is an abnormal condition and select a diverter on the 100% basis. It is a choice between risking a diverter failure or going to the next higher rating with a substantially reduced degree of protection.

From the foregoing it follows that the line to earth r.m.s. voltage rating of a chosen surge diverter will be lower for a given system voltage when the system is effectively earthed than for the same system non-effectively earthed. Thus, for a 33 kV effectively-earthed system, a diverter rating of 30 kV line to earth can be chosen, but if non-effectively earthed, the diverter rating would be 37 kV—see Table 6.1.

There are four standard diverter current ratings, viz. 10 000, 5 000, 2 500 and 1 500 A, and these represent the values of impulse current used in tests 4 and 5. These alternative current ratings are used as follows:
1. 10 000 A rating (station type) for the protection of major power stations and substations in which the frequency of occurrence of lightning strokes to earth is known to be high.

160

Table 6.1

RECOMMENDED RATED DIVERTER VOLTAGES FOR USE ON NORMAL THREE-PHASE SYSTEMS

Rated system voltage (kV)	Highest line/line voltage (kV)	Rated diverter voltage	
		Non-effectively earthed neutral systems (kV)	Effectively earthed neutral systems (kV)
3·3	3·7	3·7	3
6·6	7·3	7·3	5·9
11	12·5	12·5	10
15·9	17·5	17·5	14
22	25	25	20
33	37	37	30
66	73	73	61
88	100	100	80
110	123	123	100
132	145	145	116
220	245	245	196
275	300	—	245

Note. Based on Table 9 of BS 2914:1957.

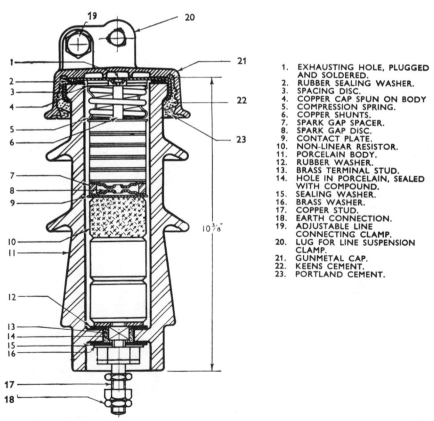

1. EXHAUSTING HOLE, PLUGGED AND SOLDERED.
2. RUBBER SEALING WASHER.
3. SPACING DISC.
4. COPPER CAP SPUN ON BODY
5. COMPRESSION SPRING.
6. COPPER SHUNTS.
7. SPARK GAP SPACER.
8. SPARK GAP DISC.
9. CONTACT PLATE.
10. NON-LINEAR RESISTOR.
11. PORCELAIN BODY.
12. RUBBER WASHER.
13. BRASS TERMINAL STUD.
14. HOLE IN PORCELAIN, SEALED WITH COMPOUND.
15. SEALING WASHER.
16. BRASS WASHER.
17. COPPER STUD.
18. EARTH CONNECTION.
19. ADJUSTABLE LINE CONNECTING CLAMP.
20. LUG FOR LINE SUSPENSION CLAMP.
21. GUNMETAL CAP.
22. KEENS CEMENT.
23. PORTLAND CEMENT.

Figure 6.4. Sectional view of surge diverter, 1 500A rating, for system voltages up to 33 kV

161

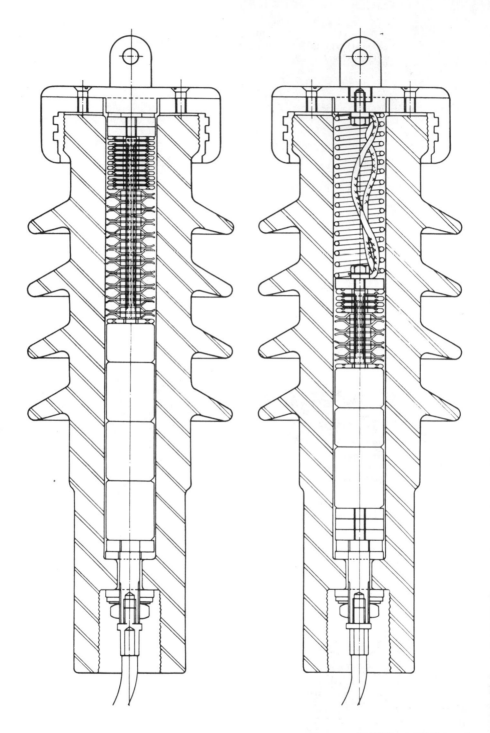

Figure 6.5. Sectional views of typical design for 2 500A surge diverters of 5·9 kV and 10 kV (rated diverter voltages)

162

2. 5 000 A rating (line or intermediate type) for the protection of other power stations and large substations.

3. 2 500 A rating (rural or secondary type) for the protection of small substations where higher current ratings are not economically justified.

4. 1 500 A rating (rural or secondary type) for the protection of rural distribution systems where diverters are installed at frequent intervals to protect small transformers.

These values of current are those required by test No. 5 to be applied 30 times in succession without damage to the diverter, whilst subjected to its rated voltage. For a limited number of operations however, most diverters will pass, without

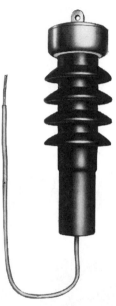

Figure 6.6. External view of a typical 10 kV, 2 500A surge diverter

damage, currents considerably in excess of the rated value and in the published literature of manufacturers withstand currents of 65 000 to 100 000 peak amperes (5/10 μs wave) are noted, usually for two successive applications. A typical diverter in the 1 500 A (rated discharge current) class available for system voltages up to 33 kV is shown in Fig. 6.4.

Designs for diverters rated at 2 500 A for rated diverter voltages of 5·9 kV and 10 kV respectively, would be typically as shown in Fig. 6.5. In this illustration the spark-gap components and the non-linear resistors forming the series circuit between the line and earth are all maintained in contact under pressure by the relatively large compression spring. The external appearance of the 10 kV diverter is indicated in Fig. 6.6.

On page 159 reference has been made to the tests with which surge diverters must comply. Oscillographic records of some of these tests are reproduced in Figs. 6.7 to 6.12, these being facsimile reproductions from K.E.M.A. Report No. 2642-60 for research tests on diverters similar to the designs shown in Fig. 6.5.

For system voltages up to about 30/33 kV if effectively earthed, or 20/22 kV if non-effectively earthed, diverters in the 5 000/10 000 A duty classes are commonly (but not always) designed for bracket mounting on cross-arms of steel

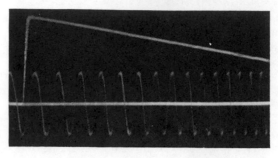

Figure 6.7.   1/60 µs impulse sparkover test. Time calibration 250 kHz

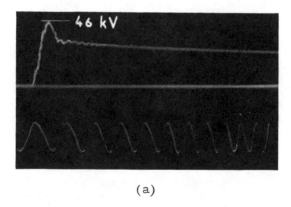

(a)

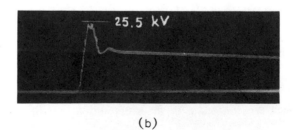

(b)

Figure 6.8.   Wave-front impulse sparkover tests. (a) *oscillogram of 10 kV r.m.s. diverter, nominal steepness 83 kV/µs, time calibration 1 000 kHz and* (b) *oscillogram of 5·9 kV r.m.s. diverter, nominal steepness 49 kV/µs*

164

or wood, a unit of this type being shown in Fig. 6.13. For higher system voltages, pedestal mounting has to be employed, and examples will be noted, but in all designs some form of pressure relief has to be provided to ensure the safety of the diverter and adjacent equipment should the diverter be subjected to duties beyond its designed maximum. Such excess duty can arise from several causes, such as an incorrect selection of diverter voltage which can result in a failure to re-seal, so that the follow current after the discharge which

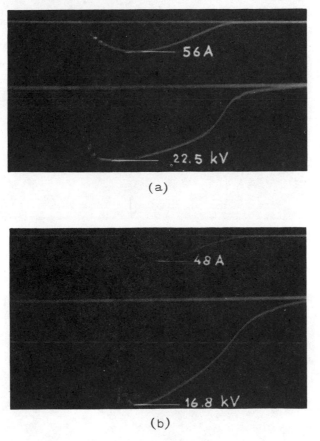

Figure 6.9.   Peak discharge residual voltage tests at low current. (a) of the 10 kV r.m.s. diverter and (b) of the 5·9 kV diverter

is caused by the power-frequency voltage is not interrupted. This results in overheating of the gap electrodes and resistors, the production of ionised gas and a flash-over across the diverter. The rapidly increasing internal pressures can in these circumstances cause the insulator to disintegrate before a circuit-breaker can interrupt the earth-fault current.

When the diverter is bracket mounted, protection can be provided by the fitting of an automatic earth-disconnect device at the lower (earthed) end of the diverter. A device of this type is seen in Fig. 6.13 and in section in Fig. 6.14, the action being such that if the follow current is not interrupted after the half-cycle on which the surge occurred, the earth lead is ejected, thus isolating the

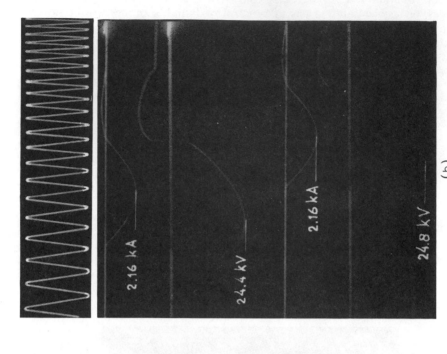

(b)

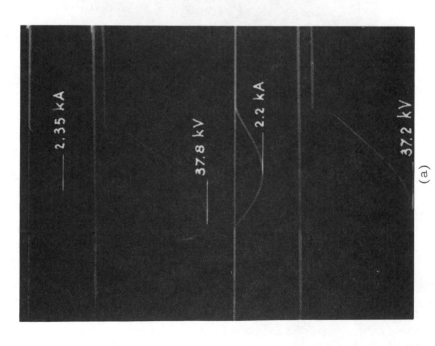

(a)

Figure 6.10. Peak discharge residual voltage tests at rated diverter currents. (a) of 10 kV r.m.s. before and after operating duty test and (b) of 5·9 kV r.m.s. before and after operating duty test with time calibration of 250 kHz

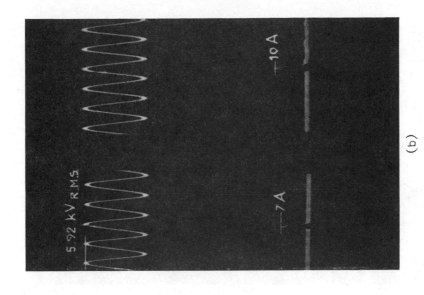

(b)

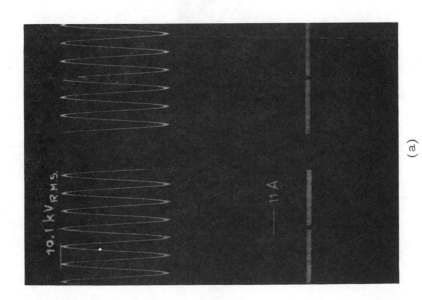

(a)

Figure 6.11. Operating duty tests. (a) 30th impulse on 10 kV r.m.s. diverter and (b) 25th impulse on 5·9 kV r.m.s. diverter

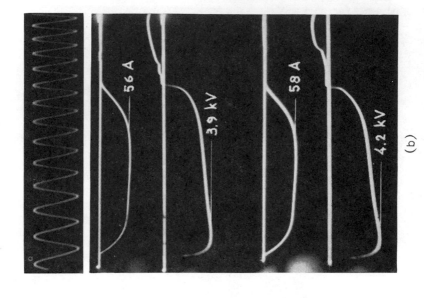

(b)

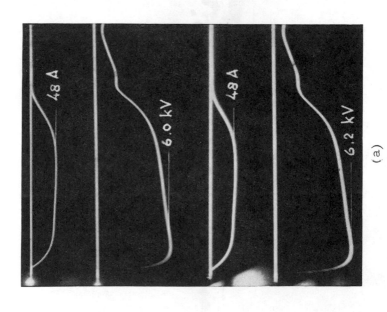

(a)

Figure 6.12. Impulse current-withstand tests. (a) 4th and 20th oscillogram of the current-withstand test on a 1·5in resistor and (b) 2nd and 20th oscillogram of current-withstand test on a 5/16in resistor

diverter. Such a device after operation gives a visual indication that the diverter is faulty.

With a pedestal-mounted diverter, other means must be sought and here it is usual to provide pressure diaphragms at each end of the unit (see Fig. 6.17).

In most modern heavy-duty diverters, magnetically-blown spark gaps and non-linear resistors of low ohmic value are used. In the diverter shown in Fig. 6.13, a gap construction as shown in Fig. 6.15 is employed comprising a series of spark gaps in ceramic arc-quenching chambers interleaved with ferrite magnets. Voltage distribution through the gap assembly is maintained at the

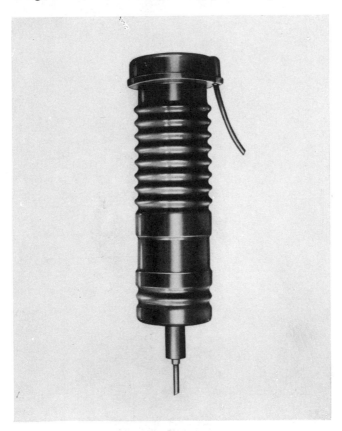

Figure 6.13.   Heavy-duty bracket-mounted diverter with earth disconnect (courtesy EMP Electric Ltd.)

designed gradient by a shunt circuit of grading resistors of the non-linear type, while a capacitor connected in parallel determines the voltage distribution under surge conditions.

The magnetic method used to move the arc in the gap results in a sequence illustrated in Fig. 6.16, rapidly increasing its length and the arc voltage. Movement of the arc away from the tip of the electrodes ensures that they are kept in a clean condition to preserve the sparkover characteristics of the gap.

Figure 6.17 illustrates in cross-section a pedestal-type diverter with, shown inset, the arc-control system used in the spark gap. Again a magnetic system

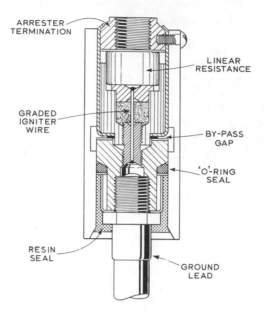

Figure 6.14. Earth disconnect device graded to discriminate with 10A quick-acting expulsion fuses (courtesy EMP Electric Ltd.)

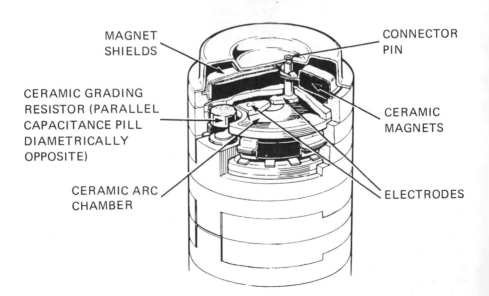

Figure 6.15. Spark gap construction in heavy-duty diverter (courtesy EMP Electric Ltd.)

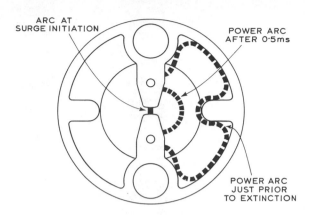

Figure 6.16. *Sequence of arc quenching in the current-limiting gap chamber of Fig. 6.15 (courtesy EMP Electric Ltd.)*

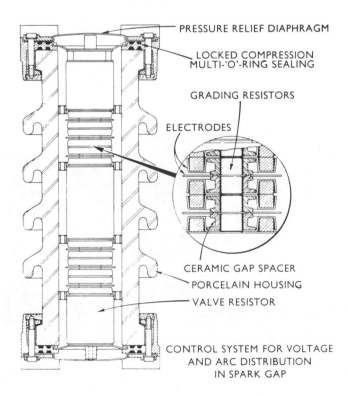

Figure 6.17. *Cross-section of unit in a 10 000A pedestal-type surge diverter (courtesy EMP Electric Ltd.)*

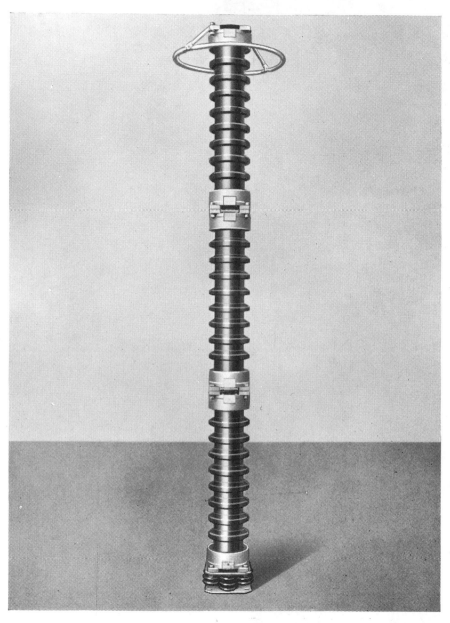

Figure 6.18. Multi-unit station-type surge diverter, pedestal-type, 145 kV rating (courtesy EMP Electric Ltd.)

is used to achieve high-speed arc rotation thus ensuring uniform distribution of arc energy over the full spark-gap surface, and avoiding deterioration of that surface. In this assembly, as in that shown in Fig. 6.15 ceramic magnets are used in preference to coil-operated magnetic systems on the grounds that by this means the diverter performance remains independent of the system short-circuit capacity.

For the higher system voltages, two or more units will be mounted in a vertical column and connected in series, a typical multi-mist diverter being shown in Fig. 6.18. In a design of diverter for use on a 750 kV system, Brown Boveri use five units each rated at 133 kV, to give an overall rated diverter voltage of 665 kV.

Surge counters

It is not easy to assess the functioning of surge diverters as there is nothing to indicate operation or otherwise. There are however devices available known as *surge counters* which, when inserted in the earth lead of the diverter, will record each operation on a counter or on a paper disc.

In one such device a paper disc is revolved, after the manner of a chart recorder, in a spark gap which is in the earth lead of the surge diverter. The construction is shown in Fig. 6.19 from which it will be seen that the paper disc is driven by a small synchronous motor which is connected to any convenient l.v., a.c. supply. The disc has an appropriately divided scale of days and hours and makes one revolution per week.

When the surge diverter operates, the spark gap flashes over and a hole is punctured in the paper disc. The size of the hole will be approximately related

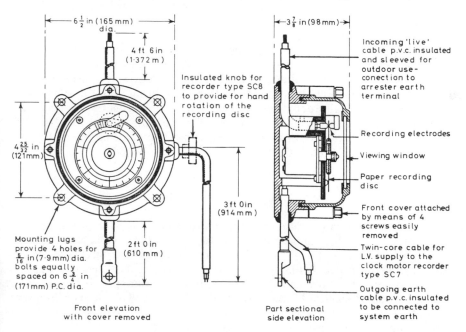

Figure 6.19. Surge counter with recording paper disc (courtesy EMP Electric Ltd.)

173

to the magnitude of the surge and its position will indicate the time and on what day it occurred.

Application of surge diverters

When considering the application of surge diverters, it is necessary to have a full knowledge of the impulse voltage level of the apparatus to be protected and the protective characteristics of the surge diverter. For high-voltage systems, the use of apparatus of a high insulation level which has been impulse tested is now practically standard practice. This is costly if applied at lower voltages, and the use of diverters can provide an economical alternative method of protection. As indicated, however, co-ordination of insulation levels is very necessary as obviously that of the apparatus must be above that of the breakdown value of the protective device.

Where and how to install diverters is also important. The many varying conditions and systems which occur in practice cannot be covered in the short space of the present chapter and the subject is one which demands the services of specialist engineers, to advise on a particular network the points at which diverters should be placed to give protection against internal or external overvoltage. An appendix in BS 2914 gives a useful outline and guidance. To obtain advice however, it is essential that the fullest data be given concerning the system, particularly that concerning the neutral of the system and how it is earthed. Other information essential to a study is that relating to the insulation level of the apparatus to be protected, altitude of location, details of transmission lines or cables, system data, etc.

As to the actual installation, it is, in general, necessary that diverters be installed as near to the apparatus to be protected as possible in order to minimise the risk of a lightning stroke striking a point between the diverter and the apparatus. It is also necessary that the leads from the line conductors to the diverters, and from the diverters to earth, be short and as straight as possible. In order that the residual voltage on the line should be low, the earth resistance must be maintained low. Inadequate earthing will bring about a reduction in the protective level afforded since the IR value it represents must be added to the diverter protective level incorporated. The earthing system for the transmission line, substation and surge diverters should be made common, together with any counterpoise embodied.

IMPULSE VOLTAGE LEVELS

A study of current literature discloses that many designs of switchgear previously outside the range where an impulse 'withstand' level (i.e. a voltage at which no flashover occurs on the primary insulation) has been thought necessary, are now coming into this range. British practice for many years has been to require, in the case of circuit-breakers, such levels (with appropriate proving tests) in the case of outdoor designs only and for voltages of 22 kV and above. The limitation to outdoor types relates largely to the fact that such circuit-breakers are associated with overhead transmission lines which are described as being 'electrically exposed', i.e. exposed to external overvoltages such as those due to lightning.

174

Indoor switchgear, on the other hand, is normally associated with systems using underground cables and has been described as 'non-exposed'.

Under the condition where the distribution network is *wholly* of cable, external overvoltages can be regarded as unlikely, but there are many installations today where indoor switchgear is associated with overhead lines, an example being the packaged substation illustrated in a later chapter, where the overhead lines enter the substation via through=bushings. An alternative case is that where overhead lines terminate at a pole or tower outside the substation, the link between the lines and the indoor switchgear being made by a short length of cable, typically as shown in Fig. 6.20(b). For such an arrangement it has been claimed that the presence of this cable is in itself sufficient to prevent external voltages reaching the terminal apparatus in the substation. While

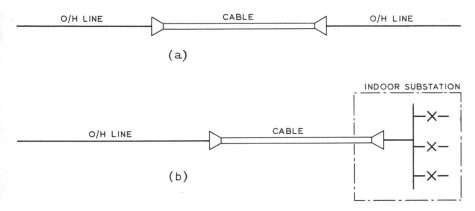

Figure 6.20. Examples of overhead line/cable combinations

the cable does exert a damping influence both in this case and in that represented in Fig. 6.20(a), recent investigations[1] show that under certain conditions the mere presence of cable may complicate the problem rather than ease it.

There is therefore justification for designing indoor switchgear to specific impulse levels in addition to outdoor types. In many countries this has been accepted practice over a number of years, appropriate 'withstand' levels being tabulated in national and international standards and, furthermore, for all systems voltages of 3·3 kV and above. In so far as indoor switchgear is concerned, the requirement has been confined to 'electrically exposed' switchgear and while future British practice will line up with this generally, it is likely that *all* indoor switchgear will be designed to an impulse level but with alternative values for 'exposed' and 'non-exposed' use in the voltage range of 3·3 to 11 kV. In the interests of standardisation and bulk production it appears likely that manufacturers will be content with one design at these voltages, i.e. that with the highest insulation level, so that prior knowledge of an installation is not essential to the manufacturer against a particular contract.

Table 6.2 is a tabulation of present day and estimated future impulse 'withstand' levels based on internationally accepted practice and related to rated system voltages. Because the cost of high-voltage switchgear is very considerable and because a large proportion of this cost is represented by the primary insulation, impulse levels are constantly under review with a view to cost reduction.

For this reason therefore, the data given in Table 6.2 should at all times be checked against current standards.

It is seen that for system voltages above 88 kV and up to 220 kV, two levels of insulation are given, i.e. 'full' and 'reduced'. A generally accepted definition of the latter is that it refers to that reduction in test impulse voltages which, under otherwise unchanged conditions, would be possible on changing a network from one with an isolated neutral or one earthed through an arc suppression coil (see Chapter 7) to one which is solidly earthed and assuming surge

Table 6.2
PRESENT DAY AND ESTIMATED FUTURE
IMPULSE 'WITHSTAND' LEVELS

Rated system voltage (kV r.m.s.)	Highest system voltage (kV r.m.s.)	Impulse withstand voltage (kV peak)	
3·3	3·6	45 (30)*	
6·6	7·2	60 (45)*	
11·0	12	75 (60)*	
13·8	15	95	
22	24	125	
33	36	170	
66	72·5	325	
		Full insulation	Reduced insulation
88	100	450	380
110	123	550	450
132	145	650	550
220	245	1 050	900
275	300	—	1 050
330	360	—	1 175
400	420	—	1 425
500	525	—	1 800
750	765	—	2 300
1 000†	1 100	—	2 800

*The values in parentheses are alternatives for non-exposed installations
†Estimated

diverters are employed. At higher voltages, these conditions are assumed and only the 'reduced' level specified.

For a given application, the impulse 'withstand' level (i.e. the basic insulation level) of an installation as a whole will be selected, and if protection against external overvoltages is provided, the surge diverters giving this protection must prevent voltages in excess of the 'withstand' level reaching terminal apparatus which otherwise might be damaged; by this means satisfactory insulation co-ordination is achieved.

Insulation is related to the highest system voltage (column 2 in Table 6.2) and this is defined as the highest line to line r.m.s. voltage which is sustained under normal operating conditions at any time and at any point on the system. Standard surge diverter ratings take these highest values into account, but if due to special circumstances, still higher system voltages are likely to be frequent, a surge diverter of a higher voltage rating may be necessary.

Apparatus designed to a specified impulse level will be type tested as will be noted later, and to pass such a test satisfactorily the electrical clearances to earth and between phases must clearly be adequate. In outdoor installations however, there are elements which cannot be type tested, e.g. the completed busbar and connection structures. While the insulators themselves will be individually impulse tested, clearances must be determined by design in relation to the impulse level of the installation, the nature of the electrodes bounding the clearances, the degree of pollution to be expected and the altitude above sea level at which the apparatus is to be installed.

Having designed switchgear to an appropriate impulse level, it remains to carry out type tests on a finished product to satisfy both the designer and user

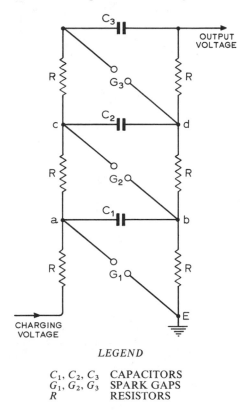

Figure 6.21. Basic circuit for impulse generator (courtesy A. Reyrolle & Co. Ltd.)

that the level has been met, i.e. that the insulation will withstand the applied voltage without flashover or puncture. Such tests require that the voltage wave form be one in which the voltage rises rapidly to its peak value, e.g. in 1 μs and thereafter decays to half peak value in say 50 μs. This is the 1/50 wave form as previously noted in Fig. 6.3 and is the normal (British) requirement for *external* overvoltage tests.

The tests applied comprise a series of impulses consisting of five consecutive positive impulses and five consecutive negative impulses, positive and negative being with regard to earth. If, during the series, a single flashover occurs, a

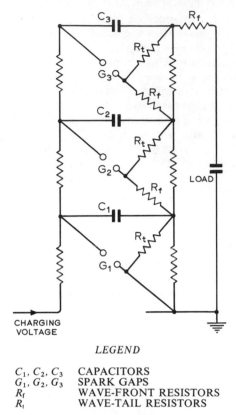

LEGEND

C_1, C_2, C_3 CAPACITORS
G_1, G_2, G_3 SPARK GAPS
R_f WAVE-FRONT RESISTORS
R_t WAVE-TAIL RESISTORS

Figure 6.22.   *Final circuit for impulse generator (courtesy A. Reyrolle & Co. Ltd.)*

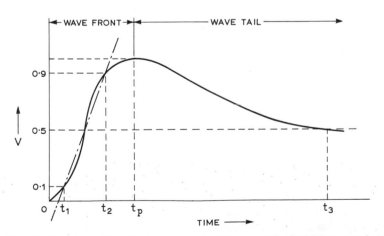

Figure 6.23.   *The method of measuring the time to wave peak of a 1/50 μs wave-form*

178

further set of five impulses may be applied and if there is no further break-down, the test is deemed to be satisfactory. The test voltages are applied firstly between each phase and earth in turn, the circuit-breaker (if such is being tested) being in the closed position, with the phases not being tested earthed. This is followed by tests between all terminals on one side of the breaker with all opposite terminals earthed.

To produce the high unidirectional voltage required, a surge or impulse generator is used. Such generators are based on a circuit devised by Marx in which a high-voltage output is produced from a number of capacitors which are first charged in parallel and then discharged in series by the sequential firing of interstage spark gaps. The basic connections of the circuit are shown in Fig. 6.21 in which three stages are assumed but which can be any number necessary to produce the required output voltage.

The applied d.c. charging voltage, which may be of the order 100–200 kV, is obtained from a transformer/rectifier combination with voltage regulation on the transformer primary. The application of this voltage allows the capacitors to charge to a predetermined voltage of $+V$ at which point spark gap G_1 breaks down. Point a is thus connected to E and point b takes up a voltage of $-V$. Since at this instant point c is at a voltage of $+V$, there is a voltage across spark gap G_2 of $2V$, and G_2 will break down. This cycle is repeated in rapid succession to give a final voltage of nV where n is the number of stages. When the final gap breaks down, the capacitors will discharge and the voltage will decay from its initial peak with a time constant depending on the values of resistors and capacitors.

In practical form, additional resistors are included in the circuit, typically as shown in Fig. 6.22. These are necessary in order to produce the wave forms of the required shape, the resistors R_f controlling the rate of voltage on the load, i.e. the insulation under test, while resistors R_t control the rate of discharge of the whole circuit. Resistors R_f are thus designated wave-front resistors and R_t the wave-tail resistors, noting that the latter are only connected in parallel with the capacitors after the spark gaps have fired. To ensure that gap G_1 breaks down first it may be set with a slightly lower gap, but for the highest voltages this can be unreliable and more sophisticated methods are usually adopted whereby the gap is triggered off[2].

The wave forms illustrated in Fig. 6.3 are seen to show a straight-line rise to voltage peak, and similarly the decay. A more practical representation would show the wave-form in the manner of Fig. 6.23, although this has been exag-gerated in an opposite direction. Here it is seen that there is a relatively slow rate of rise from zero time and that there is a comparatively flat portion on the wave-front just before the peak. This introduces some difficulty when measuring the time to peak value and this illustration is designed to show the accepted method of making such measurement.

Thus, two points are first distinguished, i.e. the time t_1 the voltage takes to reach 10% of the peak value and the time t_2 for it to reach 90%. The time to peak value t_p is then taken as $1\cdot25(t_2-t_1)$, thereby assuming that the wave front has a constant gradient between the 10 and 90% points. A line drawn between these two points makes the assumption that the wave starts where this line cuts the axis of zero voltage. The time to decay to 50% of peak voltage, t_3, is readily measured on the oscillographic record. A typical impulse generator is shown in Fig. 6.24, while Fig. 6.25 is a view of part of an impulse test laboratory.

In passing, and to indicate the magnitude of the voltages required for testing apparatus designed for use on systems today, it is of interest to note that a recent installation in an extension of this laboratory makes available an impulse generator which will give an output voltage of 4 000 kV to meet the requirements for apparatus rated at 750 kV and much higher.

Switching surges

Overvoltages due to lightning or other external causes have an amplitude which is *not* related to the system voltage and, as noted, their wave-form is usually that of a unidirectional impulse.

Figure 6.24. Impulse generator to give maximum output voltage of 1 700 kV arranged in parallel banks to give a complete impulse generator circuit of 1, 2, 3, 4, 6 or 12 stages

In Chapter 2 however, overvoltages of a very different nature have been noted, viz. those high-frequency transient voltages which follow the interruption of short-circuits and which have a magnitude which is related to the system voltage, or those which arise due to current chopping, and the switching of small inductive or capacitive currents. While the magnitude of such overvoltages (to earth) may be as high as five times the normal line to neutral peak voltage of the system, it is generally accepted that in practice they rarely exceed three times. Based on this lower multiple, the following examples show that the magnitude is of no mean order.

System voltage (kV r.m.s.)	Approximate overvoltage (kV peak)
11	27
33	81
66	162
132	325
275	670
400	980

Figure 6.25. View of an impulse-testing laboratory with a 380 kV air-blast circuit-breaker on test (courtesy A. Reyrolle & Co. Ltd.)

At the lower voltages, say up to 66 kV, it can be assumed that the standard power-frequency voltage tests which must be applied as routine, coupled with impulse tests, are sufficient to prove the ability of the insulation to withstand switching overvoltages of the likely magnitudes. As system voltages rise however, the possible magnitude of switching overvoltages is an important factor, particularly those arising when energising long overhead lines. For this reason, the problem of switching surges has been the subject of considerable study and in particular the means of providing protection against them or methods whereby the magnitude can be reduced. It is a problem which can be more readily studied today with the aid of digital computers.

As to protection, the use of surge diverters is widely advocated but this has required design changes in the components of the diverters to make them suitable to meet the different nature of the switching surge as compared with that due to lightning. Factors entering into this are the duration of switching surges and the greater frequency with which they can occur. Apart from this, the most suitable wave-form which the test voltage should have has to be determined, and as opposed to the standard $1/50$ μs wave acceptable for external overvoltages, one which has a wave-front of the order of 200 μs and a wave tail of 1 000 μs or more has to be used. Methods of reducing these overvoltages include resistance switching during fault interruption, as discussed in Chapter 2, and by switching (energising) a line through resistors which are short-circuited after a suitable time interval.

Switching problems are also considered in detail elsewhere[3-7].

REFERENCES

1. CHRISTOFFEL, M., 'The Effect of Power Cables on Overvoltages in High and Medium-Voltage Transmission Systems', *Brown Boveri Review*, **51** No. 6, June (1964)
2. TODD, M., 'Impulse Testing', *Reyrolle Review*, No. 158, March (1954)
3. CHRISTOFFEL, M., 'Insulation Co-ordination in High and Medium-Voltage Installations', *Brown Boveri Review*, **51** No. 6, June (1964)
4. ALTHAMMER, P. and PETITPIERRE, R., 'Switching Operations and Switching Surges in Systems Employing Extremely High Voltages', *Brown Boveri Review*, **51** No. 1/2, Jan./Feb. (1964)
5. BICKFORD, J.P., 'Switching Overvoltages on Transmission Lines', *Elect. Rev.*, 1 Sept. (1967)
6. BICKFORD, J.P. and DOEPEL, P.S., 'Calculation of Switching Transients with Particular Reference to Line Energisation', *Proc. I.E.E.*, **114** No. 4, April (1967)
7. VOGLER, L. and DANNENBERG, K., 'Lightning Arresters for Protection Against Switching Surges in Systems', *Elect. News & Eng.*, June (1968)

BIBLIOGRAPHY

CHRISTENER, H., 'Pressure Relief for Lightning Arresters', *Brown Boveri Review*, **51** No. 6, June (1964)
CHRISTENER, H. and MORF, A., 'New Lightning Arresters for Voltages from 4·5 to 750 kV, *Brown Boveri Review*, **51** No. 6, June (1964)
CLIFF, J.S., 'Insulation Co-ordination of High-voltage Equipment', *Elect. Rev.*, 18/25 Dec. (1970)
HICKS, B.C., 'Valve-type Surge Diverters', *Elect. Supervisor*, Oct. (1959)
Impulse-Voltage Testing, BS 923:1940
KOHLER, E. and BAUMONN, J., 'The Installation of Lightning Arresters', *Brown Boveri Review*, **51** No. 6, June (1964)
KÖPPL, G. and RUOSS, E., 'Switching Overvoltages in E.H.V. and U.H.V. Networks', *Brown Boveri Rev.*, **57**, Dec. (1970)
MONAHAN, T.F., 'The Design and Performance of Surge Diverters for the Protection of Alternating Current Systems', *J.I.E.E.*, No. 65, Part 2, June (1951)

NEWMAN, S.E. and PARISH, A.R., 'Insulation Co-ordination for High-voltage Situations', *English Electric Journal*, Sept. (1953)

OUYANG, M., 'Lightning Protection for Cable Connected High-voltage Distribution Substations by Surge Diverters', *Proc. I.E.E.*, **117** No. 8, Aug. (1970)

Recommendations for Insulation Co-ordination, I.E.C. Pub. No. 71

RYAN, H.M. and WHISKARD, J., 'The Clothier Ultra-high-voltage Laboratory', *Reyrolle Parsons Rev.*, **1** No. 1, Summer (1971)

STIGANT, S.A. and FRANKLIN, A.C., *The J & P Transformer Book*, Butterworths (1961)

Surge Diverters, BS 2914:1957

WEBB, M., 'Development of Testing Equipment for Higher Voltages', *Elec. Rev. Sup.*, 18 June (1971)

WILLIAMS, W.P., 'Switchgear for Extra-high-voltage Systems', *J. Sci. & Tech.*, **37** No. 2 (1970)

Chapter 7

Neutral point earthing

The majority of three-phase systems today operate with an earthed neutral, earthing being achieved either directly or through an impedance. Nevertheless, there are quite a number of systems operating with a free neutral, i.e. insulated systems, and the advocates of this method claim its superiority on the grounds that the supply can be maintained for a time on the two healthy lines while an earth-fault exists on the third. This argument is particularly true for an overhead transmission system when the failure of one line to earth is not so likely to develop into a fault between two or more lines. On a cable system, however, one line down to earth leads to heating and burning with the likelihood that, within a short time, an earth-fault will develop into a phase-fault and to avoid this possibility, quick acting earth fault protection is required.

The advantages of the earthed neutral are many and include the following:
1. When an earth-fault occurs, the fault current can return via the neutral point, and in so doing it can be utilised to bring about the discriminative operation of protective apparatus, thereby disconnecting the faulty circuit without disturbance to healthy parts of the system.
2. By reason of (1) the voltage on healthy parts of the system is held down to line to neutral voltage.
3. It avoids the transient overvoltages caused by earth-fault arcs (arcing grounds) on insulated neutral systems and which can be damaging to the system insulation as a whole.
4. Induced static charges are conducted to earth without disturbance.

Standard specifications recognise various conditions of system earthing in relation to insulation co-ordination (refer to Chapter 6). They are:
(a) The condition where at least one of the neutral points of a three-phase system is permanently earthed either solidly or through a resistor or reactor of low impedance. Such a system is considered to be effectively earthed if, during line to earth faults, the voltage to earth of the sound lines does not exceed 80% of the voltage between lines of the system. In general, this is only achieved when *all* transformer neutrals are solidly earthed.
(b) The condition where at least one of the neutral points of a three-phase system is earthed normally through an arc suppression coil. On such a system it is the intention that the majority of line to earth faults will be self-clearing without interruption to the supply. Where such faults are not self-clearing, three methods of system operation are recognised:

(i) Where the fault is automatically disconnected after a short delay (see Fig. 7.4 later).

(ii) Where non-automatic disconnection is used the faults are generally cleared quickly although they may be allowed to persist for several hours provided the total duration does not exceed 125 h/a with a maximum of 8 h in any 24.

(iii) Where the faults are allowed to remain for a longer duration than in (ii) but not approaching continuous operation with one line earthed.

(c) All neutral points of a three-phase system are insulated from earth.

(d) A single-phase system with one line earthed.

Standard circuit-breakers (particularly those for outdoor service) complying with BS 116, are those for use on systems earthed as in (a), (b)(i), (b)(ii) and (d). Where the earthing conditions are as noted in (b)(iii) and (c), special consideration has to be given to the circuit-breaker and other insulation levels (see Chapter 6).

Regulations issued by the Electricity Commissioners prohibit multiple earthing except in special circumstances and then only with the consent of the Minister of Posts and Telecommunications. This is due to the possibility of interference with communication circuits owing to the circulation of current between neutrals. Whether or not such interference is possible may be controversial and those in favour of multiple earthing point out that its advantage is that it practically eliminates the danger of losing the earthed neutral, a danger which is always present when only one machine or transformer out of a bank is earthed and, for one reason or another, may be disconnected from the system.

Single point earthing, on the other hand, also has its advantages. It permits earth-fault currents to be limited by the insertion of a single impedance in the earth connection. It maintains, thereby, a constant impedance value in the earth connection irrespective of the number of connected machines or transformers, or, when no external impedance is employed, limits the value of earth current to that which can be fed from one machine or transformer.

Solid earthing is normal practice in Great Britain for systems in excess of 33/66 kV and is, in general, the method adopted on medium-voltage systems. At the higher voltages, however, it can result in very heavy currents flowing to earth, values being comparable in magnitude with those for interphase faults. Because on overhead systems the majority of faults are earth-faults, heavy currents may be a severe shock to the system if faults are frequent, and therefore there is an argument for the introduction of some form of limiting resistance to reduce the fault current to a value necessary for the operation of the protective gear. Any higher resistance in the earth-return circuit will further restrict the current which can flow, so much so that its value may be insufficient to operate the protective apparatus.

When a system has its neutral earthed through a resistance this may be either of the metallic grid type or a liquid type. The former usually consists of a number of banks of high-resistance alloy steel grids of rigid construction with welded joints and specially designed to ensure rapid dissipation of the heat generated. Other forms are those using cast-iron grids or wound-strip resistors, the latter rarely being used and then only for normal-rated currents below, say, 250 A.

From an economic point of view, the liquid resistor is preferred. Figure 7.1 illustrates a typical unit[1] of this type designed for indoor or outdoor use and

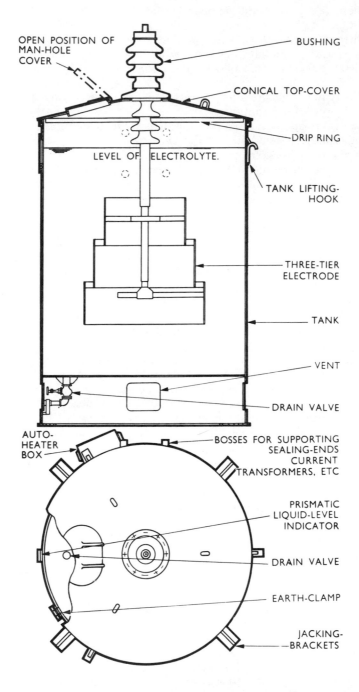

Figure 7.1. Sectional views of liquid neutral-earthing resistor (courtesy A. Reyrolle & Co. Ltd.)

it complies with the British Electricity Board's Specification B.E.B.S. S5. Based on the earthed tank principle, it consists essentially of a high-voltage bushing, a high-voltage electrode, the earthed tank and the electrolyte. The electrode is suspended in and completely immersed in the electrolyte, and earth-fault current flows through the latter between the electrode and the tank. The electrolyte consists normally of a weak solution of sodium carbonate (washing soda) in distilled water or a dilute solution of suitable salt in piped water. The use of the latter is not normally recommended as, unless it is reasonably pure and free from salts, chemical reactions are probable. If piped water has to be used, a sample should first be analysed and approved.

In the design illustrated the electrode is a three-tier construction designed to overcome problems caused by the negative temperature coefficient of the electrolyte. The three-step construction allows cool electrolyte from below to flow across the heated external surfaces of the upper tiers of the electrode without having been previously directly affected by the lower sections. The reduction in diameter in the direction shown increases the distance between the electrode and the tank at each step, thus helping to compensate for the fall in resistivity of the hot electrolyte rising from below.

On medium-voltage systems, e.g. 415 V, added resistance at the neutral earth is unnecessary. There will be some resistance in the earth-fault path, no matter how small, such as that at the earth plate, and this can limit the earth-fault current appreciably. A simple example shows that on a 415 V system, the voltage to earth is about 240 V and if the natural resistance of the earth return circuit is say 1 Ω, then the earth-fault current will be limited to 240 A. On the continent, reactance earthing is often used, the advantage claimed being that for corresponding ohmic values, the reactor is of smaller bulk than the resistor. No standard ohmic values for such devices exist, but in general, it is common practice to fix a value which will limit the earth current to the full-load rating of the largest generator or transformer, or alternatively, to about twice the normal current of the largest feeder.

On this basis, it is usual, with commercial current transformers and earth-fault relays, to protect up to 80/85% of the machine or transformer winding, the relay setting being 20/15%. Lower values are possible but stability may be thereby sacrificed due to the possibility of unwanted tripping by spill currents when heavy through faults occur. In any event, earth-faults in the windings at points less than 15 or 20% of the total winding length from the neutral are rare because the potentials above earth at such points are only these percentages of the full line to neutral voltage.

Assuming that it is agreed to limit the fault current to earth to a value equal to the full-load current of the largest machine or transformer, the value of impedance to be inserted in the neutral connection to earth is:

$$R = \frac{V}{I}$$

where R = neutral impedance (Ω)
$\quad\quad V$ = line/neutral voltage (V)
$\quad\quad I$ = full-load current of largest machine or transformer (A).

If a relay setting of 20% is chosen, this then affords protection to 80% of the windings on the largest machine, while a greater percentage of the windings of smaller machines running in parallel will be protected. If, at some later date, a still larger machine is added, it may be necessary to take steps to reduce the ohmic value of impedance in order to get maximum winding protection of the larger machine. To determine the percentage of winding unprotected on any machine, the following expression is used:

$$\% \text{ of winding unprotected} = \frac{100RI}{V}$$

where R = ohmic value of impedance
I = minimum relay operating current (A)
V = line/neutral voltage (V)

and noting that if a 20% relay setting is used then I is 20% of the full-load current of the machine being checked.

The problem of neutral point earthing of transformers may be resolved into two parts, i.e. high voltage and low voltage. That of high-voltage earthing is little different to that of generators, to provide the same degree of protection. That of low voltage has the added and important feature that it reduces somewhat the danger to life in that it prevents any voltage above normal appearing on the low-voltage winding, an important matter in domestic and industrial applications.

The importance of a low value of earth resistance in low-voltage systems has already been mentioned. In the 9th Edition of J. & P. Transformer Book* the following expression is given:

$$Z_N = \frac{V^2}{n \times \text{kVA} \times 1\,000}$$

where Z_N = impedance in neutral (Ω)
V = line voltage (V)
kVA = rating of transformer ,
n = neutral short-circuit current in terms of full-load line current.

Taking as an example a 2 000 kVA transformer with an earth-fault relay set at 40% then, with respect to the 400 V side:

$$Z_N = \frac{400^2}{0.4 \times 2\,000 \times 1\,000} = 0.2\,\Omega$$

This can be checked very simply as follows. By symmetrical component theory the zero-phase sequence impedance is:

$$3R + jX_o$$

where R = resistance
X_o = zero-phase sequence reactance.

Assuming for the moment that X_o is sufficiently small to be ignored, then the earth-fault current I_{EF} is given by:

$$I_{EF} = \frac{3E}{3R}$$

* This title deals with the problem of neutral point earthing of transformers in considerable detail and also covers the apparatus necessary when it is required to earth a part of a system where no neutral is available. See Reference 2 on page 194.

where E = line/neutral voltage (V)

$$\therefore \ I_{EF} = \frac{3 \times 231}{3 \times 0.2} = 1\ 155\ \text{A}.$$

The full-load current of the 2 000 kVA transformer at 400 V is 2 890 A and with a relay setting of 40%, the operating current is:

$$40/100 \times 2\ 890 = 1\ 155\ \text{A}.$$

It can be shown that when there are a number of machines operating in parallel, the value of earth-fault current varies with the number of machines operating at any one time. This can be demonstrated by symmetrical component theory. Here we have:

Z_1 = positive-phase sequence impedance
Z_2 = negative-phase sequence impedance
Z_0 = zero-phase sequence impedance.

For the purpose of demonstration assume that there are six alternators all equal in output and characteristics, and that arrangements exist whereby only one machine may be earthed at a time. The impedances of each machine may well be:

$$Z_1 = 20\%$$
$$Z_2 = 14.6\%$$
$$Z_0 = 6.4\%$$

Taking the case first where only one machine is operating, and assuming zero resistance in the neutral connection, then:

$$\text{Fault current} = \frac{3E}{Z_1 + Z_2 + Z_0}$$

$$= \frac{3E}{0.2 + 0.146 + 0.064} = 7.32E$$

Now let us assume that all six machines are operating in parallel but that only one is earthed, then:

$$\text{Fault current} = \frac{3E}{\left(\frac{0.2}{6}\right) + \left(\frac{0.146}{6}\right) + 0.064} = 24.4E$$

so that in the latter case the fault current is more than 3 times that of the first case, i.e. in the ratio 24.4 : 7.32.

It will be noted that in the foregoing, zero resistance has been assumed in the neutral connection. If there is resistance at this point, it may be that its value is so high in relation to the reactance that it is the resistance which determines the value of fault current. For example, assume we have two 2 000 kVA transformers which may operate singly or in parallel and that the resistance in the earth connection is 2 Ω. Keeping in mind that this value is in series with each line (i.e. $3R$ has to be included in the expression for zero-phase sequence impedance) we can assume that for each transformer:

$$Z_1 = 0+j0\cdot009$$
$$Z_2 = 0+j0\cdot009$$
$$Z_0 = 6+j0\cdot009$$

When one transformer is operating alone, the total impedance to the fault is:

$$Z_{total} = 6+j0\cdot027 \ \Omega$$

Where two transformers are operating in parallel, the total impedance will be:

$$Z_1 = 0+j0\cdot0045$$
$$Z_2 = 0+j0\cdot0045$$
$$Z_0 = 6+j0\cdot009$$
$$\therefore \ \overline{Z_{total} = 6+j0\cdot018 \ \Omega}$$

and, if calculated, it will be found that there is little difference between the two, the resistance value being so large as to swamp the reactance, so that for practical purposes the value of resistance only can be used.

On systems with an insulated neutral, a fault to earth does not constitute a short-circuit and it may be argued that disconnection is unnecessary. The only current flowing is the capacitance current of the healthy phases, the condition being indicated in Fig. 7.2. In the case of overhead lines, this current may be so small as to render automatic isolation by protective means difficult if not impossible. Such a fault has the effect of raising the voltage of the two healthy lines above the normal to earth and may result in insulation breakdown. Furthermore, it is an unstable condition which may lead to arcing grounds at supporting insulators, causing transient surge voltages to travel in both directions along the line, which may bring about further failure at line insulators or terminal apparatus. By the use of an arc-suppression coil as a means of earthing, the danger of arcing grounds is eliminated and under certain conditions the system can be left in service with one line to ground until it is convenient to disconnect and effect repair.

In the condition shown at Fig. 7.2, the capacitance current will lead the voltage of the faulty phase by nearly 90°. It follows that if an inductance of appropriate value is connected in parallel with the capacitances, the current in the fault will be either very considerably reduced or cancelled out. The diagram now becomes that shown in Fig. 7.3, for which the phasor conditions will be typically as shown in Fig. 7.4.

It has been stated that the inductance of the coil cancels out the capacitance current. This implies a condition whereby the inductance of the coil must be related to the capacitance of the system and therefore the coil must have an inductance L of:

$$L = \frac{I}{3\omega^2 C}\text{henries (H)}$$

where C = capacitance to earth of each phase (F)
$\omega = 2\pi f$
f = frequency (Hz)

190

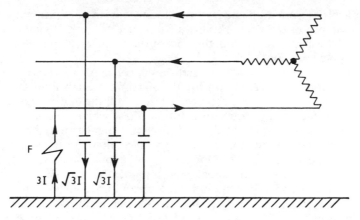

Figure 7.2

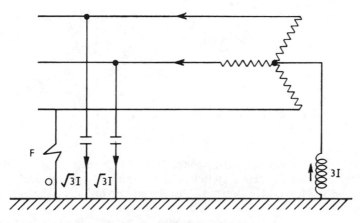

Figure 7.3

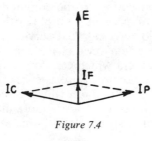

Figure 7.4

191

This leads to some difficulty when, due to varying operational conditions, the capacitance of the network varies from time to time. It can be overcome, however, by using a tapped coil, the appropriate tapping being selected for each change in network conditions.

The condition of allowing an earth-fault to persist, therefore, involves the use of a continuously-rated coil for the maximum earth-fault current which can pass, and this is readily achieved. There is still the danger, however, that a second earth-fault might occur on another phase which gives the condition of an interphase fault. To avoid this risk a circuit-breaker may be connected in parallel with the suppression coil, so arranged that the breaker is normally open. After an earth-fault has persisted for a predetermined time, a relay operates to close the circuit-breaker automatically, thus short-circuiting the suppression coil and allowing sufficient uncompensated current to flow for the operation of the protective gear. This scheme is illustrated in Fig. 7.5 and it may be noted that, if necessary, a resistance may be inserted in series with the

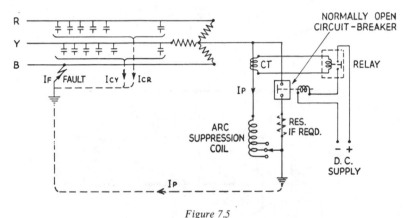

Figure 7.5

circuit-breaker, as shown by the broken lines. In Chapter 18, note will be taken of a range of 'fault-throwing' switches and, in suitable circumstances, this type can be used as a less costly alternative to the circuit-breaker as a short-circuiting device.

If arc-suppression coils are to be used on a system it is important that knowledge of this fact and how they are to operate be made known to the switchgear manufacturer in order that the latter may offer apparatus of adequate insulation level (see Chapter 6).

In order to ensure that only one neutral point is earthed where a number of machines or transformers operate in parallel, a circuit-breaker can be connected in each neutral before connection to the common earth bar, with interlocks between breakers which will prevent multiple earthing. Circuit-breakers in the neutral connection should have a rated service voltage equal to the phase voltage of the three-phase system to which it is connected, and should be capable of interrupting the fault current which can flow to earth.

·At this point it is of interest to note the existence of a very-high-speed ammeter developed by Edgcumbe Peebles Ltd., which connected in the neutral via a suitable current transformer, acts as a ground fault detector. The instrument, shown in Fig. 7.6, has a high-speed rectifier-operated moving-coil movement,

192

and when operating, the pointer is driven to the point of maximum current in 5 cycles (0·1 s), at which point it is held by a magnetic clutch until reset by hand. Damping is such that there is no overswing. On interconnected systems an instrument of this type installed at each system neutral provides a series of readings on the occurrence of a ground fault, thus showing the distribution of fault current. From this a close approximation can be determined as to the location of the fault.

The connections for this instrument are shown in Fig. 7.7. Normal full-scale deflection is at 5 or 10 A but the sensitivity can be increased to give full scale deflection at 0·5 or 1·0 A by operating the press key.

Incidentally, it may be noted that this instrument (connected one in each line) is of value in short-circuit testing (see Chapter 5) as it enables immediate readings of the short-circuit current to be made without waiting while oscillograph records are scaled.

The earth connection proper should receive full consideration, particularly on medium-voltage systems where a low value of resistance is essential if reasonable protective relay settings are to be obtained. Common practice is to bury several earth plates or pipes in parallel in order to obtain low resistance values. The cross-section of earth leads must be such as to carry the maximum fault current for the period of time determined by the protective gear.

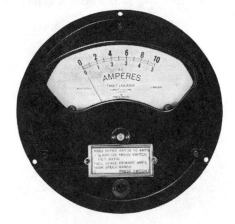

Figure 7.6.   High-speed ammeter (courtesy Edgcumbe Peebles Ltd.)

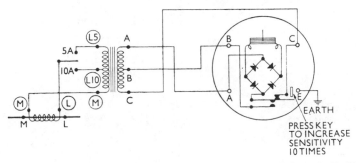

Figure 7.7.   Connections for high-speed ammeter in neutral (courtesy Edgcumbe Peebles Ltd.)

Earth plates, if used, may be copper or cast-iron, from 1–2 m (3–6 ft) square and they should be buried in an upright position with charcoal or crushed coke to a thickness of about 0·3 m (1 ft) or more. The strip connection to the plate or plates should be riveted, or preferably welded, and not soldered, and should be of the same metal to avoid electrolysis. When pipes are used, these should be 2–2·5 m (6–8 ft) long and buried as deep as possible; they can be driven quite easily by electric or pneumatic hammers specially designed for the purpose.

A low resistance is essential to keep down the potential gradient in the earth surrounding the plates or pipes under fault conditions. Most of the resistance exists in the immediate vicinity of the plates or pipes. Regular checking of the earth contact resistance is essential. It is by no means constant and alters with the amount of moisture in the soil and is therefore subject to seasonal variations.

REFERENCES

1. REYROLLE, A. & CO. LTD., U.K. Pat. 774 124 (8.5.57)
2. STIGANT, S.A., LACEY, H.M. and FRANKLIN, A.C., *The J & P Transformer Book*, 9th edn., Butterworths, London (1961)

BIBLIOGRAPHY

CLOTHIER, N.W., LEESON, B.H. and LEYBURN, H., 'Safeguards Against Interruption of Supply', *Journal I.E.E.*, **42** No. 497, May (1938)
TAYLOR, H.W. and STRITZL, P.F., 'Line Protection by Petersen Coils', *Journal I.E.E.*, **82** and **83** Nos. 496 and 503 (1938)

Chapter 8

Busbars and busbar connections

Two materials are commercially suitable for use as busbars and connections in switchgear practice, i.e. copper and aluminium, the relative properties of which are noted in Table 8.1.

Table 8.1
THE RELATIVE PROPERTIES OF COPPER AND
ALUMINIUM

Property	Copper	Aluminium
Weight per unit length for equal conductivity	1·0	0·50
Conductivity for equal areas:		
electrical	1·0	0·61
thermal	1·0	0·56
Tensile strength (hard drawn)	1·0	0·40
Hardness (hard drawn)	1·0	0·44
Modulus of elasticity	1·0	0·55
Coefficient of thermal expansion	1·0	0·39
Melting point	1·0	0·61

This table shows that for equal conductivity, aluminium is lighter than copper and while this is an advantage in some applications, it is not usually important in indoor types of switchgear up to 33 kV. Here, weight is not a decisive factor so much as bulk, particularly in metal-clad or other enclosed types, and as aluminium conductors must have about 60% greater sectional area than copper for the same current rating, the latter material is often preferred. In other circumstances where space is of less consequence, aluminium finds many applications, a particular example being for busbars and connections in outdoor open-type switchgear installations.

Aluminium has the advantage that it is not subject to progressive oxidation, the oxide film being continuous, very hard, adherent and stable, thus sealing the metal from further oxidation. This is important in installations operating in high temperatures or in polluted atmospheres.

When copper is used, hard-drawn types are preferable to cold rolled because of better surface finish and because the process results in increased strength. When using aluminium, a choice is available between that designated EIE

195

which is similar to pure aluminium and that designated E91E, an alloy which includes additions of magnesium and silicon. This alloy has the strength of copper as normally used and is generally chosen for rectangular bars which have to withstand the stresses which arise due to the passage of high fault currents, but, for equal sectional area, it has current ratings of 3% lower than EIE. Both metals are supplied to size within very close limits as laid down in the appropriate British Standards.

Current carrying capacity (a.c.)

At one time, the current carrying capacity of busbars and connections was based on a rough and ready rule of 1 000 A/in^2 for copper and 750 A/in^2 for aluminium. Tables of current ratings published by the Copper Development Association in the first edition (1936) of its handbook *Copper for Busbars*, and calculated from formulae derived in tests carried out at the National Physical Laboratory, clearly indicated that approximations of the kind noted were, for small conductors, very pessimistic, i.e. densities well over 1 000 A/in^2 could be sustained with acceptable rises in temperature, while for larger conductors optimistic ratings were likely. The use of approximations was also found to be wrong in the case where multiple conductors had to be used for a particularly heavy current. It was shown that it could not be assumed that the use of two or three conductors of a given size would provide a current rating two or three times that of a single conductor of that size.

It was recognised that the factor which controls the current rating is that of a safe temperature, and today BS 159:1957 specifies that the temperature rise when carrying rated-normal current at rated frequency shall not exceed 50°C and that this be based on an ambient temperature having a peak value not exceeding 40°C and an average value not exceeding 35°C measured over a 24 h period.

The foregoing discussion can be illustrated by noting the data in Table 8.2. The temperature to which a conductor will rise is affected by many factors. In

Table 8.2
RATINGS (A) FOR ALUMINIUM AND COPPER
CONDUCTORS ON DIFFERENT BASES

Bar size (*in*)	*Basis*			
	750 A/in²	*1 000 A/in²*	*50°C rise on a 35°C ambient*	
	Aluminium EIE	*Copper*	*Aluminium EIE*	*Copper*
$2 \times \frac{1}{4}$	375	500	692	868
$3 \times \frac{1}{4}$	562	750	998	1 230
$4 \times \frac{3}{8}$	1 125	1 500	1 600	1 937
$5 \times \frac{1}{2}$	1 875	2 500	2 300	2 755
$6 \times \frac{1}{2}$	2 250	3 000	2 700	3 219
$8 \times \frac{1}{2}$	3 000	4 000	3 480	4 126

Notes (1) For demonstration purposes, inch dimensions, as in an original table published by the British Aluminium Co. Ltd., have been retained.
(2) Current ratings based on temperature rises for bar sizes in metric dimensions are noted in later tables.

brief they include the number and arrangement of laminations, whether rectangular bars are mounted on edge or laid flat, whether exposed to still or free air
or surrounded by insulation, the proximity of the surrounding enclosure and
the material of which the latter is made, i.e. magnetic or non-magnetic. In an
outdoor open-type installation, the temperature rise will be inhibited by cross
winds. It is found that if, in suitable applications, the conductors are painted
with dull-black paint (matt finish non-metallic), the current carrying capacity
can be increased by about 20% without increase in temperature rise.

The amount of heat generated in a conductor is proportional to its resistance
and to the square of the current it carries, while the temperature rise depends
on the rate at which the heat is dissipated, the latter taking place in varying
degrees by convection, radiation and conduction. Conductors completely surrounded by insulation will have the heat removed by conduction in the first

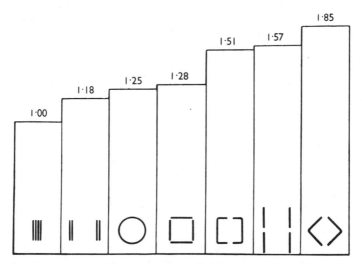

Figure 8.1.   Comparative a.c. ratings of various conductor arrangements of equal cross-section,
i.e. 4 in² (2580 mm²) (courtesy The Copper Development Association)

place, while those exposed to air will have the heat dissipated by convection
and radiation. This exposure to air is, in determining British current ratings,
based on *still* but unconfined air, but higher ratings are possible if it is assumed
that the conductors are exposed to unrestricted circulation of free air[1].

The maximum rate of heat dissipation with rectangular sections is given when
the bar is thin, as this provides a long perimeter for a given cross-sectional
area. When a number of rectangular bars are used in parallel, each bar is shielded
by an adjacent bar so that less heat is dissipated, and a point can be reached
where further increase in the number of laminations does not sensibly increase
the overall current rating. For this and other reasons, other formations are
often used, such as those indicated in Fig. 8.1, each formation shown being of
equal cross-sectional area. From this illustration it is seen, for example, that
two-channel sections as in the fifth column from the left have a current rating
50% greater than the conventional laminations in the first column. These
relationships should however be regarded as an indication only, as much
depends on other conditions such as those noted earlier.

Two other problems arise in the determination of a.c. ratings. Both are related to the fact that the apparent resistance of a conductor carrying a.c. is increased in comparison to its resistance to d.c. This is because there is an uneven distribution of current through the sectional area of the conductor due to effects produced by inductance.

The first problem arises out of what is known as *skin effect*. When an alternating flux exists, a back e.m.f. is induced by virtue of this flux cutting the conductor. The e.m.f. is produced in the conductor by its own magnetic flux, and while the internal parts of the conductor are cut by the alternating flux from all parts of the conductor, the outlying parts are not, the line linkages decreasing as the edges of the conductor are reached. Thus, the conductor elements possess more and more reactance the nearer they get to the interior of the conductor so that uneven current distribution occurs through the cross-section, the current tending to 'crowd' into the 'skin' and outer edges of a single-bar conductor and in the outer laminations of a multiple-bar conductor. The effects of this phenomena can be countered by using other conductor configurations, e.g. a hollow square, as noted in Fig. 8.1.

Alternatively, a tubular conductor may be ideal, the principle being to locate as much of the metal as possible equidistant from the magnetic centre of the conductor. When using tubular conductors, there is little advantage to be gained by using a tube whose wall thickness is much greater than the depth of penetration[2, 3], the greatest advantage being obtained by increasing the tube diameter and reducing the wall thickness.

The second problem is one which produces analogous results due to mutual induction between two conductors carrying current in opposite directions or of different phases, and this is known as the *proximity effect*. The condition here is that each conductor is cut by the flux from its neighbour and this leads to the current concentrating in those portions of each conductor nearest to the other. Here again, the effect can be minimised by choosing the best configuration for each conductor and, more particularly, by adopting a wide spacing between conductors. When conductor spacings are close as in medium-voltage switchgear where the electrical clearances demanded are small and when heavy current ratings are involved, the proximity effect may be pronounced. In their book[2] Thomas and Rata stated that:

> 'Proximity effect can be safely regarded as introducing a change of 5% or less in the rating if the current is less than 2 000/3 000 A and the voltage exceeds 1 000 V because the busbar will not then be too large nor will the spacing be too close'.

From what has been said, it will be clear that the a.c. rating for any given section of conductor is dependent on many variables. It may vary depending on the type and design of the switchgear in which the conductors are used, and most switchgear manufacturers will have produced their own rating tables for different forms of conductor when used in various types of enclosure and taking into account the many factors discussed. For our purpose it must suffice to give, as a guide, Tables 8.3 and 8.4 showing the current ratings for a range of copper and aluminium rectangular bars based on the proposed metric dimensions and assuming them to be mounted in still but unconfined air. As we have noted earlier, conductors comprising multiple laminations will not carry a current equal to that of the rating of the single laminations multiplied by the number of laminations. Thus, for copper, the single bar ratings in Table 8.3 need to be

Table 8.3
APPROXIMATE A.C. RATINGS FOR SINGLE
RECTANGULAR COPPER BARS IN STILL BUT
UNCONFINED AIR

Conductor size (mm)	Sectional area (mm²)	Approximate rating (A)
2·5 × 12·5	31·25	159
16·0	40·0	195
20·0	50·0	235
25·0	62·5	287
31·5	78·75	347
40·0	100·0	426
50·0	125·0	516
63·0	157·5	630
4 × 16·0	64	254
20·0	80	305
25·0	100	367
31·5	125	445
40·0	160	542
50·0	200	660
63·0	252	802
80·0	320	900
100·0	400	1 185
6·3 × 25·0	157·50	473
31·5	198·45	569
40·0	252·0	693
50·0	315·0	832
63·0	396·9	1 010
80·0	504·0	1 220
100·0	630·0	1 465
125·0	787·5	1 755
160·0	1 008·0	2 145
10 × 50·0	500	1 060
63·0	630	1 260
80·0	800	1 525
100·0	1 000	1 800
125·0	1 250	2 150
160·0	1 600	2 620
200·0	2 000	3 140
250·0	2 500	3 710
16 × 100·0	1 600	2 220
125·0	2 000	2 640
160·0	2 560	3 180
200·0	3 200	3 760
250·0	4 000	4 500
315·0	5 040	5 370

Note. Table courtesy The Copper Development Association and *The Electrical Review.*

Table 8.4

APPROXIMATE A.C. RATINGS FOR RECTANGULAR ALUMINIUM BARS (EIE-M) IN STILL BUT UNCONFINED AIR

Conductor size (mm)	Sectional area (mm²)	Approximate rating (A)					
		1 bar	2 bars	3 bars	4 bars	5 bars	6 bars
2·5 × 12	30	118	210	285	360	425	480
16	40	151	275	395	490	580	655
20	50	183	320	450	575	675	770
25	62·5	223	390	540	685	800	910
30	75	263	480	660	840	990	1 115
40	100	342	610	860	1 080	1 260	1 425
4 × 12	48	156	290	420	536	620	700
16	64	198	340	470	600	710	815
20	80	238	410	570	720	850	955
25	100	290	530	755	950	1 110	1 250
30	120	339	600	845	1 060	1 245	1 400
40	160	434	750	1 050	1 320	1 550	1 750
50	200	532	905	1 260	1 575	1 825	2 035
6 × 12	72	200	350	480	610	720	825
16	96	252	450	640	805	960	1 075
20	120	301	550	790	1 000	1 170	1 320
25	150	364	640	900	1 120	1 315	1 485
30	180	424	730	1 025	1 290	1 520	1 720
40	240	545	935	1 310	1 630	1 900	2 130
50	300	660	1 130	1 580	1 950	2 255	2 505
60	360	782	1 350	1 870	2 200	2 630	2 885
80	480	995	1 700	2 310	2 745	3 070	3 330
100	600	1 215	2 090	2 770	3 190	3 490	3 745
120	720	1 415	2 415	3 180	3 640	3 985	4 270
160	960	1 830	3 100	4 050	4 600	5 025	5 340
10 × 40	400	720	1 230	1 710	2 110	2 425	2 670
50	500	870	1 500	2 060	2 505	2 850	3 100
60	600	1 015	1 750	2 350	2 795	3 120	3 380
80	800	1 250	2 215	2 940	3 355	3 675	3 950
100	1 000	1 565	2 650	3 465	3 940	4 315	4 635
120	1 200	1 810	3 050	4 010	4 560	4 980	5 290
160	1 600	2 310	3 940	5 170	5 870	6 300	6 620
200	2 000	2 795	4 750	6 160	—	—	—
250	2 500	3 365	5 720	—	—	—	—
16 × 100	1 600	1 950	3 260	4 250	4 890	5 340	5 660
120	1 920	2 255	3 850	5 030	5 700	6 130	6 450
160	2 560	2 840	4 830	6 260	—	—	—
200	3 200	3 395	5 780	—	—	—	—
250	4 000	4 095	6 500	—	—	—	—

Notes (1) Based on bars mounted with the long side vertical and a gap between the bars equal to the bar thickness.
(2) Current ratings for E91E bars are about 3 % lower.
(3) Table courtesy The Aluminium Federation.

Table 8.5

MULTIPLYING FACTORS FOR A.C. COPPER BARS

Total area of cross-section (mm²)	Multiplying factors		
	2 bars	3 bars	4 bars
500	1·78	2·45	3·13
1 000	1·72	2·36	3·00
1 500	1·65	2·24	2·84
2 000	1·60	2·16	2·70
2 500	1·55	2·10	2·60
3 000	1·52	2·02	2·52
3 500	1·48	1·98	2·48
4 000	1·44	1·96	2·45

multiplied by one of the factors given in Table 8.5 to obtain the current rating of a multiple bar arrangement. In the case of aluminium bars, the ratings for multiple-bar arrangements are noted directly in Table 8.4.

Joints

Perhaps the most widely used method of making a joint between unit lengths of busbars or between a conductor and a busbar is that of bolting or clamping two rectangular sections, a method which is simple and flexible and in which the joint can easily be dismantled if required. Other methods include rivetting or welding, but with these the joint has to be regarded as permanent. When rod or tubular bars are used, special fitments will be required.

Whatever method is used, the efficiency of the joint depends on a few essential precautions which are:
1. The contact pressure must be ample and be maintained.
2. The surfaces of the conductors must be clean.
3. With flat conductors, the overlap should be equal to or greater than the width of the bars or ten times the bar thickness, whichever is the greater.
4. Joints between aluminium conductors must be treated to exclude moisture.

In the design of a joint, the gross contact area is not of primary importance because the surfaces will not be perfectly flat, so that current is transferred through numerous point contacts formed by irregularities on the surfaces and the effectiveness of these depends on the pressure applied and its distribution, due regard being paid to the stresses set up in bolts when these are used. Bolts will be of a different metal to that of the conductor and if the stress intensities in the materials of the joint are high when cold, they may well be excessive when the joint is warm so that a permanent set in one part may occur. It has to be remembered also that the bolts will not be at the temperature of the conductor since they are not directly heated by the currents.

For joints between copper conductors, bolts of bronze or other copper alloy can be used. These are resistant to corrosion, have higher electrical and thermal conductivities than steel and have a coefficient of thermal expansion closely approximating to that of copper. By this means a more uniform pressure is maintained with changes in temperature.

For joints between aluminium conductors, bolts of aluminium alloy HE30-WP to BS 1476 are recommended, again because their expansion due to temperature change is the same as that of the conductor. With these bolts, steel nuts may be used.

The overlap at bolted joints between flat conductors is determined by the number of bolts required to obtain the necessary pressure and its distribution. The efficiency of the joint can be preserved by smearing the surfaces with 'Vaseline' and scratch brushing just prior to making the joint. Joints may, with advantage, be tinned to give protection against corrosion or where high-current densities are unavoidable.

For joints between aluminium conductors, a proprietary joint compound as recommended by the aluminium supplier may be smeared on the surfaces to be joined. When a joint is made between dissimilar metals, e.g. copper to aluminium, electrolytic action will occur if moisture is present so that the joint must be made moisture-proof by the application of grease or a joint compound.

Expansion and contraction

Variations in temperature cause conductors to expand or contract and this may cause damage to the conductors or the supporting structure. In the case of short lengths, the problem is not important within the normal range of temperatures, the changes in length will be very small and can be taken up by a certain amount of flexibility in the supporting structure. With long runs however, some form of expansion joint should be introduced at intervals, typically as shown in Figs. 8.2 and 8.3.

Clearances

The recognised *minimum* clearances to earth and between phases for a variety of conditions are given in Tables 8.6 to 8.10. They assume an altitude not exceeding 1 000 m (3 300 ft) and should be increased by 3% for each 300 m (1 000 ft) higher than this. Atmospheric pollution by smoke, chemical fumes, salt-laden spray, etc. may require that larger clearances be provided.

As the notes below the tables indicate, the clearances to be provided depend on a number of conditions, as for example on whether a system is exposed or non-exposed to overvoltages of atmospheric origin or whether the system is effectively or non-effectively earthed. These subjects are noted in more detail in Chapters 6 and 7. On a system having a permanently insulated neutral the possibility exists of arcing faults occurring between one line and earth. With such faults, high overvoltages can be produced and special consideration must be given to the busbar insulation, particularly where transmission is by overhead lines. When, as in some designs of outdoor substation, the busbars comprise stranded conductors supported by insulator strings, allowance has to be made for conductor swing.

In Table 8.7 a note indicates that clearances less than those enumerated can be used if, in addition to immersion in oil or compound, the busbars are covered with solid insulation capable of withstanding the appropriate power-frequency test voltage. The latter are noted later in Table 8.11.

FLEXIBLE CONDUCTORS

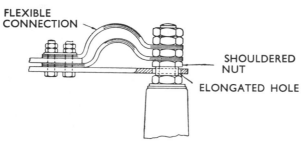

FLEXIBLE
CONNECTION

SHOULDERED
NUT

ELONGATED HOLE

Figure 8.2.   Forms of expansion joints

Figure 8.3.   Expansion joint for 1 200A busbars

Table 8.6

CLEARANCES FOR OPEN AND ENCLOSED INDOOR AIR-INSULATED BUSBARS AND CONNECTIONS

Rated voltage up to and including (kV)	Minimum clearance to earth in air				Minimum clearance between phases in air			
	Open		Enclosed		Open		Enclosed	
	in	mm	in	mm	in	mm	in	mm
0·415	$\frac{3}{4}$	19	$\frac{5}{8}$	16	1	26	$\frac{3}{4}$	19
0·6	1	26	$\frac{3}{4}$	19	$1\frac{1}{4}$	32	$\frac{3}{4}$	19
3·3	2	51	2	51	2	51	2	51
6·6	$2\frac{1}{2}$	64	$2\frac{1}{2}$	64	$3\frac{1}{2}$	89	$3\frac{1}{2}$	89
11·0	3	77	3	77	5	127	5	127
15·0	4	102	4	102	$6\frac{1}{2}$	165	$6\frac{1}{2}$	165
22·0	$5\frac{1}{2}$	140	$5\frac{1}{2}$	140	$9\frac{1}{2}$	242	$9\frac{1}{2}$	242
33·0	$8\frac{3}{4}$	223	$8\frac{3}{4}$	223	14	356	14	356

Notes (1) Based on Table 3 of BS 159:1957.
(2) Millimetre dimensions rounded up to whole figures.
(3) The clearances are for electrically non-exposed installations. For electrically exposed installations special consideration is required—see Appendix C in BS 159:1957. When, for special or more onerous conditions of service, Class B clearances are employed on associated circuit-breakers (see BS 116:1952) then the clearances of bare busbars and connections should be correspondingly increased.

Table 8.7

CLEARANCES FOR BUSBARS AND BUSBAR CONNECTIONS IMMERSED IN OIL OR COMPOUND

Rated voltage up to and including (kV)	Minimum clearance to earth		Minimum clearance between phases	
	in	mm	in	mm
0·6	$\frac{1}{2}$	13	$\frac{1}{2}$	13
3·3	$\frac{1}{2}$	13	$\frac{3}{4}$	19
6·6	$\frac{3}{4}$	19	1	26
11·0	1	26	$1\frac{1}{2}$	38
15·0	$1\frac{1}{4}$	32	$1\frac{3}{4}$	45
22·0	$1\frac{3}{4}$	45	$2\frac{1}{2}$	64
33·0	$2\frac{1}{2}$	64	$3\frac{1}{2}$	89

Notes (1) Based on Table 7 of BS 159:1957.
(2) Millimetre dimensions rounded up to give whole figures.
(3) Clearances shall not be less than above unless the conductors concerned are covered with solid insulation (additional to the oil or compound) which is capable of withstanding the appropriate power frequency test voltage specified in *Table 8.11*.

Table 8.8
CLEARANCES FOR OPEN-OUTDOOR BUSBARS AND BUSBAR CONNECTIONS NOT EXCEEDING 15 kV RATED VOLTAGE FOR ELECTRICALLY EXPOSED OR NON-EXPOSED INSTALLATIONS

Rated voltage not exceeding (kV)	Minimum clearance to earth in air		Minimum clearance between phases in air	
	in	mm	in	mm
6·6	5½	140	7	178
11·0	7	178	9	229
15·0	8½	216	10½	267

Notes (1) Based on Table 4 of BS 159:1957.
(2) Millimetre dimensions rounded up to give whole figures.
(3) These clearances are to be regarded as minimum values which may be used in any circumstances. When the method of mounting insulators is not such as to prevent lodgement of birds or vermin it may be necessary to employ larger clearances.

Table 8.9
CLEARANCES FOR ALL OPEN-OUTDOOR BUSBARS AND BUSBAR CONNECTIONS OF 22–88 kV RATED VOLTAGE AND FOR NON-EFFECTIVELY EARTHED SYSTEMS OF 110 kV AND ABOVE

Impulse voltage withstand level, peak value (kV)	Rated voltage (kV)	Minimum clearance to earth in air		Minimum clearance between phases in air	
		in	mm	in	mm
150	22	11	279	13	330
200	33	15	381	17	431
250	44	19	482	22	558
350	66	27	685	31	786
450	88	34	863	39	969
550	110	42	1 068	48	1 219
650	132	50	1 270	58	1 473
750	165	58	1 473	67	1 702
1 050	220	82	2 082	94	2 368

Notes (1) Based on Table 5 of BS 159:1957.
(2) For rated voltages of 22 and 33 kV, the above clearances are to be regarded as the minimum values in any circumstances. When the method of mounting insulators is not such as to prevent lodgement of birds or vermin it may be necessary to employ larger clearances.

Table 8.10

OPEN-OUTDOOR BUSBARS AND BUSBAR CONNECTIONS
FOR USE ON EFFECTIVELY EARTHED SYSTEMS OF
110 kV AND ABOVE

Impulse voltage withstand level, peak value (kV)	Rated voltage (kV)	Minimum clearance to earth in air		Minimum clearance between phases in air	
		in	mm	in	mm
450	110	34	863	39	989
550	132	42	1 068	48	1 219
650	165	50	1 270	58	1 473
900	220	70	1 770	81	2 029
1 050	275	82	2 082	94	2 388

Note. Based on Table 6 of BS 159:1957

Table 8.11

POWER FREQUENCY TEST
VOLTAGES AT WORKS

Rated voltage (kV)	Test kV r.m.s.
0·6	2
3·3	9·5
6·6	17
11	27
15	36
22	52
33	76
44	100
66	150

Notes. (1) Based on Table 8 of BS 159:1957.
(2) The test voltages are applied between phases and each phase to earth, in turn, with other phases earthed.

Creepage distances

The minimum creepage distance over insulation which should be provided in indoor types of switchgear cannot be laid down too specifically, because so much depends on the design and the conditions under which it may have to operate. One of the problems to be contended with is that of dust and damp, so that the essential creepage distance will depend on the degree of protection the switchgear provides against this hazard, which is clearly greater in open types and less in enclosed types. The configuration of the insulating parts can have a considerable bearing on the problem, noting also that dust is less likely to collect on vertical surfaces than on those which lie flat. If the dust or dirt is free from carbon or metal and in a dry state, creepage distances can be much less than when moisture is present.

Surface tracking is another problem, and here the degree of resistance to such tracking of the insulating material is important, some having considerably greater anti-tracking properties than others. Surface tracking is also influenced by contamination, and resistance to it in laminated materials is influenced by the direction of the voltage stress.

BS 159:1957 notes these problems in Appendix G and includes Table 8.12 purely as a guide to apply only when the insulation is of porcelain or synthetic

Table 8.12
CREEPAGE DISTANCES TO EARTH
IN AIR FOR OPEN AND ENCLOSED
BUSBARS FOR INDOOR-TYPE
SWITCHGEAR

Rated voltage up to and including (kV)	Minimum creepage distance in air, phase to earth	
	in	mm
0·415	$\frac{3}{4}$	19
0·6	1	26
3·3	2	51
6·6	$3\frac{1}{2}$	89
11	5	127
15	6	153
22	8	204
33	12	304

Notes. (1) Based on Table 11 of BS 159:1957.
(2) Millimetre dimensions rounded up to whole figures.
(3) Increase by at least 50% when applied to insulation between phases.

resin which is resistant to tracking and adequately protected from dust and damp. It has been noted in other chapters that where busbars and other parts can be encapsulated in epoxy resin, some part of the creepage problem is at once resolved. In outdoor types of switchgear, creepage is a problem largely related to the design of outdoor bushings, supporting insulators, etc. whose surfaces are affected by atmospheric conditions, the insulators requiring frequent cleaning in heavily-polluted atmospheres. BS 159:1957 refers its readers to BS 223:1956 (High-voltage Bushings) in respect to creepage distances for outdoor switchgear.

The effects of short-circuits

The magnitude of the current which flows on the occurrence of a short-circuit, can, as we have seen in Chapter 3, be exceedingly high, and the passage of this current even though it persists for a very short time, must be considered both in determining the sectional area of the busbar and conductor material and in the design of supporting structures.

The first of these problems is thermal, in that the conductor temperature may rise, if the sectional area is inadequate, to a dangerous level, while the second problem concerns the electromagnetic forces of attraction and repulsion set up between adjacent conductors of different polarity or phase and which tend to distort the conductors and severely stress the supporting structure.

Considering first the thermal problem, it has to be noted that this is directly related to the r.m.s. value of the fault current and the time it has to be carried. What the latter will be depends very largely on the total break time of the interrupting device which operates to isolate the fault. If it is a circuit-breaker, some delay in operation may be imposed by the protective system, e.g. time-graded relaying for discrimination purposes as discussed in Chapter 11, so that several seconds may elapse before final clearance. If, on the other hand, the interrupting device is an h.r.c. fuse, the total break time can be exceedingly short, e.g. 0·005 s or less, depending on the magnitude of the fault current and the degree of asymmetry (see discussion in Chapter 10). For times such as the foregoing, it may be assumed that all the heat is absorbed by the conductor, there being insufficient time for it to be dissipated by radiation or convection.

The thermal problem is therefore to determine the sectional area of the conductors to carry the calculated fault current for a defined time with a temperature rise which is safe, not only for the conductors themselves, but also for any insulation which may be in contact with or near to the conductors and for sweated joints such as at cable sockets. What a safe temperature limit is must be decided taking into account all factors in a particular design of switchgear and while some designers suggest that a temperature rise of 175/200°C is permissible, others suggest a safer limit is 100°C. This latter figure has merit when it is remembered that the conductor may, prior to the fault, be running at 80–90°C so that the final temperature would be 180–190°C. It may be noted in passing, that solder as used at cable sockets, will tend to soften at 180°C and will run out at higher temperatures.

A formula for calculating the temperature rise in °C/s is that given below, the only difficulty being that of ascertaining the initial temperature of the conductor, i.e. at the instant of fault, so that an intelligent estimate may have to be made:

$$T = k \left(\frac{I}{A}\right)^2 (1+\alpha\theta).10^{-2}$$

where T = Temperature rise per second (°C)
I = Current, r.m.s. symmetrical (A)
A = Sectional area of conductor (mm^2)
α = Temperature coefficient of resistivity at 20°C/°C
  = 0·00393 for copper
  = 0·00386 for aluminium
  = 0·0036 for aluminium alloy
θ = Temperature of the conductor at the instant at which the temperature rise is being obtained (°C)
k = 0·52 for copper; 1·166 for aluminium.

Alcan Industries Ltd. have produced a series of curves, reproduced here in Fig. 8.4, from which the value

$$I/A \sqrt{t}$$

can be deduced directly for a known initial temperature and a desired final temperature, for both copper and aluminium (Noral CISM). These curves are based on the formula

$$I\sqrt{t} = kA \sqrt{\log_e \left[\frac{1+\alpha(\theta_F-20)}{1+\alpha(\theta_I-20)}\right]}$$

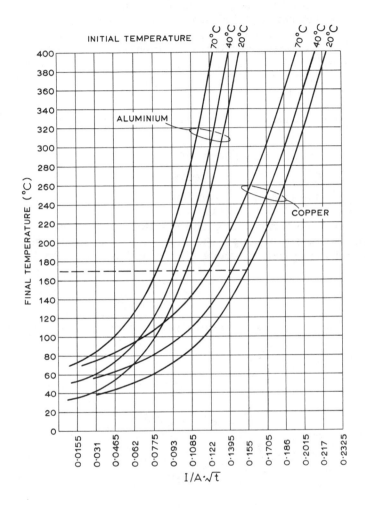

INITIAL TEMPERATURE

70°C 40°C 20°C   70°C 40°C 20°C

ALUMINIUM

COPPER

FINAL TEMPERATURE (°C)

$I/A\cdot\sqrt{t}$

LEGEND

I   CURRENT, R.M.S. SYMMETRICAL *(kA)*
A   SECTIONAL AREA OF CONDUCTOR *(mm²)*
t   TIME *(s)*

Figure 8.4.   Curves to determine a minimum conductor area for a known initial temperature and a desired final temperature when carrying high short-circuit current. Curves are for conductors in metric dimensions (courtesy Alcan Industries Ltd.)

209

where I = Current, r.m.s. symmetrical (kA)

k = 0·226 for copper

= 0·149 for aluminium (Noral CISM)

= 0·142 for aluminium alloy (Noral D 50 S-TF)

α = Temperature coefficient of resistivity at 20°C/°C (values as previously noted)

A = Sectional area of conductor (mm²)

θ_I = Initial temperature (°C)

θ_F = Final temperature (°C)

t = time (s).

As an example of the use of these curves, let us assume that the essential data is:

I = 46 kA r.m.s. symmetrical

t = 3 s

θ_I = 70°C

θ_F = 170°C (i.e. a rise of 100°C)

Projecting a line across from 170°C on the vertical scale to the point of intersection with the curves for copper and aluminium at an initial temperature of 70°C, and from these points projecting down to the base, we obtain the following readings:

Copper $I/A \times \sqrt{t}$ = 0·122

Aluminium $I/A \times \sqrt{t}$ = 0·0775

With these readings, the sectional area (A) for each metal is determined as follows:

Copper

$$\frac{46}{A} \times \sqrt{3} = 0.122$$

$$\therefore A = \frac{46 \times 1.73}{0.122} = 651 \text{ mm}^2$$

Aluminium

$$\frac{46}{A} \times \sqrt{3} = 0.0775$$

$$\therefore A = \frac{46 \times 1.73}{0.0775} = 1\,026 \text{ mm}^2$$

Considering next the electromagnetic forces, it is now the *peak* current in the first major loop at the instant of short-circuit which determines the maximum forces to which the conductors are subject. As we have noted elsewhere, this peak value may be 2 or 2·55 times the r.m.s. symmetrical value, and if we take as an example a fault level of 31 MVA at 415 V, the short-circuit currents will be of the order of:

Symmetrical r.m.s. current   =   43 300 A

Initial peak current at 0·3 p.f.   =   86 600 A

Initial peak current at 0·15 p.f. = 110 415 A

A.C. SINGLE-PHASE CIRCUIT, FULLY OFFSET
ASYMMETRICAL WAVE (CONDITION FOR MAXIMUM
FORCE). ALSO SINGLE-PHASE SHORT-CIRCUIT
(LINE/LINE) ON A THREE-PHASE BUSBAR

$$F_m = \frac{16 \times I^2 \times 10^{-4}}{S} \text{ N/m}$$

A.C. THREE-PHASE CIRCUIT, HORIZONTAL BUSBARS.
FULLY OFFSET ASYMMETRICAL WAVE IN PHASE A
(CURRENT WAVE CANNOT BE FULLY OFFSET
IN ALL PHASES)

$$F = \frac{12 \times I^2 \times 10^{-4}}{S} \text{ N/m}$$

A.C. THREE-PHASE CIRCUIT, HORIZONTAL BUSBARS.
CONDITIONS OF ASYMMETRY TO GIVE MAXIMUM
FORCE ON OUTSIDE PHASE A OR C

$$F_m = \frac{12 \cdot 9 \times I^2 \times 10^{-4}}{S} \text{ N/m}$$

A.C. THREE-PHASE CIRCUIT, HORIZONTAL BUSBARS.
CONDITIONS OF ASYMMETRY TO GIVE MAXIMUM
FORCE ON CENTRE PHASE B

$$F_m = \frac{13 \cdot 9 \times I^2 \times 10^{-4}}{S} \text{ N/m}$$

A.C. THREE-PHASE CIRCUIT WITH EQUILATERAL
TRIANGULAR SPACED BUSBARS.
CONDITIONS OF ASYMMETRY TO GIVE
MAXIMUM FORCE ON ANY PHASE

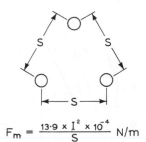

$$F_m = \frac{13 \cdot 9 \times I^2 \times 10^{-4}}{S} \text{ N/m}$$

LEGEND

F FORCE BETWEEN CONDUCTORS *(N/m)*
F_M FORCE OBTAINED WHEN CONDITIONS OF ASYMMETRY ARE SUCH THAT
       THE MAXIMUM POSSIBLE FORCE IS OBTAINED *(N/m)*
I R.M.S. CURRENT *(A)*. THE FACTOR REPRESENTING THE PEAK VALUE
       OF THE WAVE IN TERMS OF THE R.M.S. VALUE FOR MAXIMUM ASYM-
       METRY IS CONTAINED IN THE NUMERICAL TERMS OF THE FORCE
       EQUATION. HENCE THE R.M.S. VALUE SHOULD BE USED IN ALL
       CALCULATIONS
S SPACING BETWEEN CONDUCTORS (CENTRES *(mm)*)
NOTE: FORMULAE ARE CORRECT FOR CIRCULAR CONDUCTORS. FOR RECT-
       ANGULAR CONDUCTORS A SPACE FACTOR K MUST BE APPLIED—SEE
       TEXT AND FIG. 8.6

Figure 8.5. Formulae for calculating the instantaneous peak short-circuit forces on conductors,
based on the metric system (courtesy Alcan Industries Ltd.)

211

The formulae for calculating the instantaneous peak forces under various conditions are given in Fig. 8.5 from the book *Aluminium Busbars*[2], and a study of this shows that the forces are proportional to the square of the current so that it is obvious that their magnitude can be quite high.

In using these formulae, the current I to be included is the r.m.s. symmetrical value, the factor representing the peak value for maximum asymmetry being contained in the numerical term in the equation.

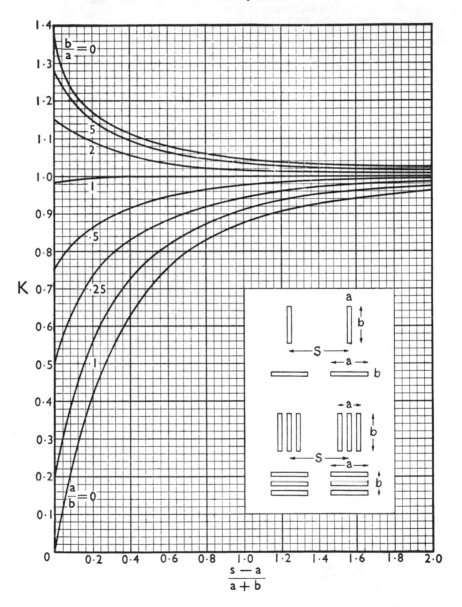

Figure 8.6. *Shape factor for rectangular conductors. All dimensions must be in the same units (courtesy The Copper Development Association)*

Noting also that the formulae hold good only for circular conductors, it is necessary to introduce what is known as a space factor (K) for rectangular bars. This factor can be determined from Fig. 8.6, firstly by determining the ratio

$$\frac{S-a}{a+b},$$

and then from this value on the base scale projecting upwards to the point of intersection with the curve appropriate to the ratio a/b. From this point a projection to the vertical scale gives the factor K, and taking the first formula in Fig. 8.5 as an example, it is introduced thus:

$$F_{\mathrm{m}} = \frac{16 \times I^2 \times 10^{-4} \times K}{S} \ \mathrm{N/m}$$

These formulae show that increasing the spacing between phases gives reduced electromagnetic forces which, while desirable, can only be obtained at the cost of larger busbar enclosures.

It is of interest to note that the worst condition is for a fault across two lines of a three-phase circuit or across both lines of a single-phase circuit.

REFERENCES

1. RICHARDS, T.L., 'The Current Rating of Rectangular Copper Busbars with Metric Dimensions', *Elec. Rev.*, 6 March (1970)
2. THOMAS, A.G. and RATA, P.J.H., *Aluminium Busbars*, Hutchinson, 25, (1960)
3. *Copper for Busbars*, Copper Development Association, Pub. No. 22, 47

BIBLIOGRAPHY

Aluminium Busbars, British Aluminium Co. Ltd., Pub. No. L4
Aluminium for Busbars, Earthing and Lightning Conductors, British Aluminium Co. Ltd., Pub. No. M4
Busbars and Busbar Connections, BS 159:1957
High-voltage Bushings, BS 223:1956

Chapter 9

Busbar systems and switching systems

The busbar system selected for any particular application will depend largely on:
1. The degree of flexibility of operation required.
2. The degree of immunity from total shut-down desired.
3. The relative importance of the location.
4. First cost, where economics are a primary consideration.

In a major plant, e.g. generating station or primary distribution centre, an elaboration of the busbar system is nearly always justified. Here, a shut-down results in the disconnection of consumers over a wide area, and a system which enables reconnection in the shortest possible time is essential. In the small substation the number of connected consumers may be small and the dislocation due to a shut-down is thereby reduced. First cost is also a primary consideration in small substations and therefore the elaborations of a major station are not warranted.

In the following pages will be found the main basic layouts. There are various ways in which two or more of these can be combined and such combinations find useful application in certain circumstances.

Single busbar

The simplest of all busbar connections is that where a single set of busbars extend the length of the switchboard without break, and to which all generator, feeder and transformer circuits are connected. This method is general for d.c. switchboards, and is one usually chosen for the smaller a.c. substation or generating station.

The single busbar scheme is shown in Fig. 9.1. It is to be noted that if at any time a busbar fault occurs, all feeders will be deprived of supply. Busbar cleaning and maintenance will involve a complete shut-down. In compound-filled types of switchgear, busbar faults and the need for cleaning should not arise, so that for this type, single busbars are often suitable. A further point not to be over-looked is that under fault conditions the combined plant of the station feeds into the fault and this may place some limitation on the size of station which can use continuous busbars, i.e. without sectionalising. In Fig. 9.1 means of isolating the circuit-breaker are indicated only on the busbar side. If, on feeders or transformers, there exists any possibility of a feedback, double isolation must be used. This point should be particularly watched in transformer circuits where they may be paralleled on the m.v. side for distribution—such paralleling may arise through an indirect route and not necessarily at a common point such as the m.v. switchboard.

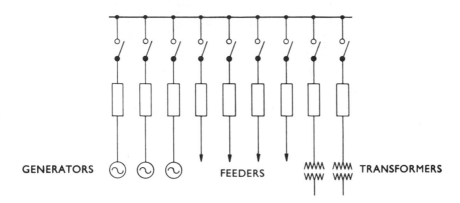

GENERATORS   FEEDERS   TRANSFORMERS

Figure 9.1. Single-busbar system

Sectionalised single busbar

The simple act of sectionalising the busbar results in many advantages. The chief one is the facility it provides in operating the system in that one (or more) sections can be completely shut down for maintenance or repair without interfering with supply from other sections. The number of sections will largely depend on the importance of the station or on the limitation of short-circuit value desired (see Chapter 3). It is an important advantage of sectionalising that circuit-breakers of lower breaking capacity may be used by running normally with sections electrically segregated. If feeders to any one point are duplicated, it is usual to connect these to different sections. If sectionalising has been adopted in order to obtain a reduction in fault value, care must be taken not to parallel feeders off different sections of the main switchboard at the remote point, i.e. sectionalising may also be necessary at the remote point. In general, the sectionalising switch should be a circuit-breaker so that the sections may be uncoupled even if a load transfer happens to be being made. An air-break isolator, so often used for sectionalising, is not suitable for this purpose, and if used, should be suitably interlocked so that it can only be opened or closed under no-load conditions. Air-break isolators should preferably be confined to m.v. systems.

Where a circuit-breaker is used, it should have double isolation, in order that the circuit-breaker may be completely isolated from adjacent sections. A simple sectionalised single busbar scheme is shown in Fig. 9.2 which also indicates how fire risks may be reduced by housing the sectionalising circuit-breaker within fireproof walls. It will be appreciated that the sections must be synchronised before the section switch is closed.

215

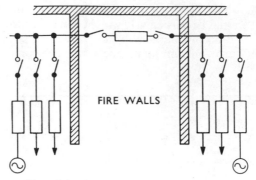

Figure 9.2.   Sectionalised single-busbar system

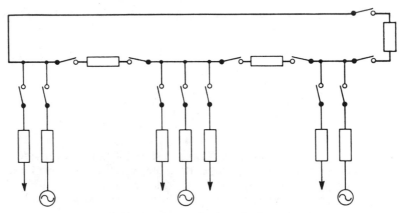

Figure 9.3.   Sectionalised ring-busbar system

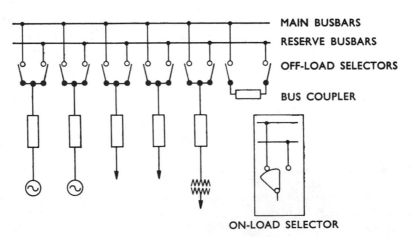

Figure 9.4.   Duplicate busbar system

216

Ring busbars

From the sectionalised scheme, the next step to give greater flexibility is to join the ends of a multi-sectionalised busbar, to form a ring, as shown in Fig. 9.3. By this means, generating plant on any section can be utilised to supply the feeders on any adjacent section.

Duplicate busbars

In the more important stations, the use of duplicate busbars is almost universal. The advantages of the scheme from an operating and maintenance point of view more than outweigh the additional cost. Usually, one set of bars is designated *main* and the other *reserve* or *hospital*. This infers that normally the 'main' bars are in use with the other set available in the event of trouble. Apart from cleaning and maintenance, the existence of a second set of bars is of considerable value when, for some reason, a particular circuit demands special treatment, such as testing out a new feeder, or the running of an existing feeder at a higher voltage than normal to compensate for an abnormal voltage drop. Similarly, it is possible to carry out commissioning tests on new plant on the reserve busbars without interfering with normal services on the main bars.

Duplicate busbars involve the use of selector switches at the switchgear. In cubicle gear, these take the form of ordinary isolating switches. In metal-clad gear, removable plugs are sometimes supplied, these being moved by hand to one position or another. Alternatively, oil-immersed selectors are used—one type being an 'off-load' arrangement where a single blade, hinged at one end, is moved by means of an external handle to one or other set of contacts connected to the main or reserve busbars. In another form, the blade is in the shape of a fan and makes contact with one set of contacts before breaking on the other, and is an 'on-load' type. The two sets of busbars must be paralleled before operating the selector switches, and this is done through a busbar coupler switch, as shown in Fig. 9.4. This switch may or may not have automatic features, but in any case should be interlocked with the selector switches. This is usually accomplished by means of keys, suitably trapped until the busbar coupler is closed. This interlock can be combined with a synchronising scheme.

In an alternative form of duplicate busbar scheme, duplicate circuit-breakers are used for each circuit. This scheme does not require a busbar coupler switch, but it is costly and is generally only used in major stations. It is a scheme which gives greatest facility for circuit-breaker maintenance. The layout is shown in Fig. 9.5. Methods of busbar selection are considered further on pages 232–236.

Sectionalised duplicate busbars

This scheme is shown in Fig. 9.6 and provides considerable flexibility. Any section of busbar can be isolated for maintenance while any section can be paralleled with any other through the reserve busbars. Normally, sectionalising of the reserve bars is unnecessary, although this can be done if required. Busbar coupler switches can be provided on each section.

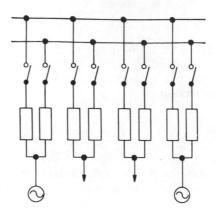

Figure 9.5

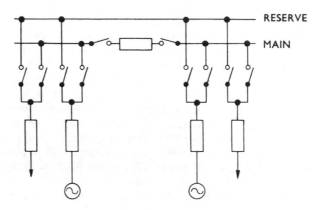

Figure 9.6

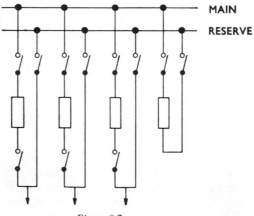

Figure 9.7

218

Duplicate busbars with by-pass isolators

Instead of using duplicate circuit-breakers, a scheme may be used in which a by-pass isolator is incorporated as shown in Fig. 9.7. It is only suitable for cubicle-type switchgear and the by-pass isolating switch is generally connected to the reserve busbars. If it is required to take a circuit-breaker out of service, the circuit may be kept in service by closing the by-pass isolator after the circuit has first been cleared both at the breaker and its isolating switches, and then closing the busbar coupler. As the circuit still demands protection, this is usually provided at the busbar coupler, by means of back-up overcurrent protection.

Group switching

It often happens that when the station capacity increases, existing switchgear will have insufficient breaking capacity. If there are a considerable number of feeder circuits, it becomes a costly item to replace the circuit-breakers by new ones, and a group switching scheme is often resorted to. This scheme is shown in Fig. 9.8, where groups of feeders are connected to the generators through circuit-breakers of ample breaking capacity. It will be clear that if a fault occurs

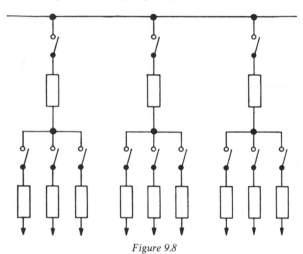

Figure 9.8

on any of the feeders, the group circuit-breaker must open to clear it. This is a disadvantage in that all feeders connected to that group circuit-breaker are out of service until the faulty circuit is cleared. In order to ensure the opening of the group circuit-breaker, a scheme of interlocking is necessary, usually accomplished through relays. This scheme will permit a feeder circuit-breaker to clear an overload within the capacity of that circuit-breaker.

Before adopting the group switching scheme, it is essential to check that the feeder circuit-breakers can carry the maximum fault current until cleared on the group circuit-breaker. It must also be remembered that a feeder circuit-breaker may be closed on to a fault, a duty for which it may not be suitable.

A modification of the scheme, and one to be recommended, includes reactors between the group feeder and the secondary busbars, as shown in Fig. 9.9.

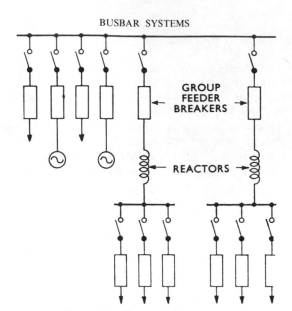

Figure 9.9.   Group switching system

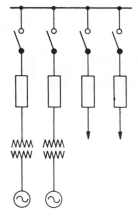

Figure 9.10.   Generator and
transformer switched as a unit

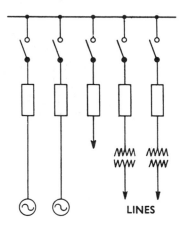

Figure 9.11.   Transformer and line
switched as a unit

Transformer switching

In networks where transformers are employed to step up to a suitable transmission voltage, a variety of switching schemes are available. Two of these are shown in Figs. 9.10 and 9.11. The scheme which allows for switching the transformer and line as a unit is adopted to economise in switchgear, as none is required on the h.v. side. It has the obvious disadvantage that a transformer breakdown also involves the loss of the line. The practice of treating a generator and transformer as a unit has the same disadvantage, as trouble with one involves the other. It has the advantage that heavy-current switchgear at

220

relatively low voltage is not required. The two can be adequately protected as a unit, and magnetising current rush on switching-in is eliminated. All the schemes for transformer switching, though shown for single busbars, can be elaborated by the use of duplicate busbars and sectionalising.

Mesh scheme

A scheme which has been adopted in major stations is known as the *mesh* scheme, shown in Fig. 9.12. It economises in the use of circuit-breakers (by comparison with a duplicate busbar scheme) but the total number of circuit-breakers is the same as the number of circuits (see also Fig. 9.20). The saving is in the elimination of the busbar coupler. To make any circuit dead, two circuit-breakers must be opened, i.e. the two adjacent to the circuit in question. Protection must include for the tripping of two circuit-breakers.

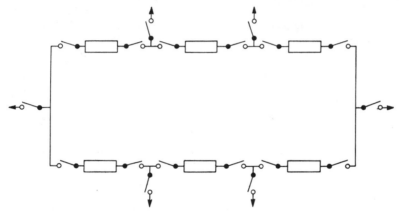

Figure 9.12

Reactor schemes

Many of the schemes so far considered can have generator, feeder or busbar reactors included in order to reduce the fault level to a safe figure. Details of the use of reactors are given in Chapter 3, while typical diagrams are given in Figs. 9.13 to 9.16.

The busbar systems so far described relate mainly to those employed on high-voltage networks. While it is rarely necessary to adopt duplicate busbars or the more complicated mesh or ring schemes for low-voltage (400–600 V) switchboards, it is nevertheless true that sectionalised busbars are of considerable importance, particularly in relation to the need to reduce fault values. In addition, sectionalising effectively reduces the transformer ratings to bring down the normal load currents to be carried by both cables and switchgear, which in itself is a desirable feature.

The use of two or more small transformer units instead of one large unit has the further advantage that if one smaller transformer is lost due to breakdown or other cause there is no *total* loss of supply as would be the case if the one and

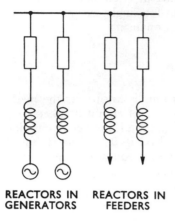

REACTORS IN GENERATORS   **REACTORS IN FEEDERS**

Figure 9.13.   Reactors in generator and feeder circuits

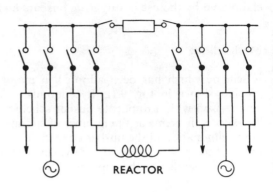

REACTOR

Figure 9.14.   Reactor in busbars with short-circuiting switch

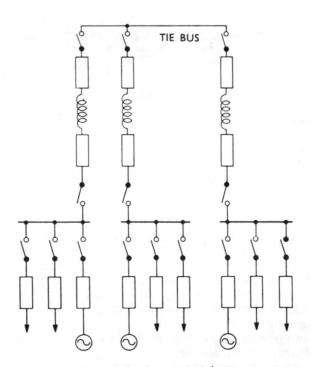

TIE BUS

Figure 9.15.   Reactors in tie bars

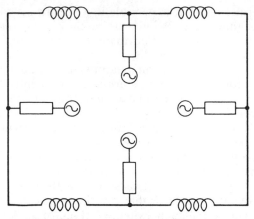

**MEANS OF ISOLATING OR SHORT-CIRCUITING
REACTORS OMITTED FOR SIMPLICITY**

Figure 9.16.   Reactors in ring bars

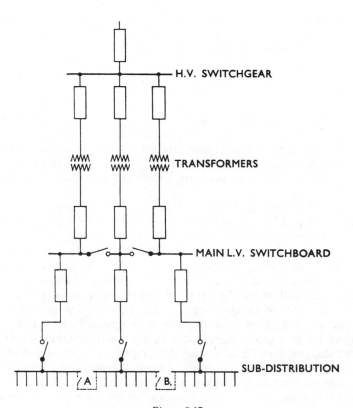

Figure 9.17

223

only large transformer failed. It is possible in a scheme such as that shown in Fig. 9.17 to assume three 650 kVA units taking the place of one 1 500 kVA unit and the load factor being such that normally only two transformers would be in service leaving the third as a standby.

Sectionalising to obtain a reduction in fault values can only be effective if the transformer and sectionalising circuits are adequately interlocked. Under no circumstances must it be possible to have all of them closed at the same time; in fact in the scheme in Fig. 9.17 out of the five circuits it must be possible to have only three or less closed at any one time, while in a scheme with two transformers and one sectionaliser, only two out of three must be closed. Such interlocking is usually achieved by the use of figure locks and keys.

In some circumstances it may be an advantage to have facilities to join the busbars at the sub-distribution point, as shown by the dotted lines at A and B in Fig. 9.17. The advantage of this is that it makes it possible to have one of the feeder circuit-breakers at the main switchboard out of service for maintenance purposes. This, however, means that further interlocking will be necessary to ensure that only three of the five circuits (three incoming and two section) can be closed at the sub-distribution boards at any one time.

Schemes with load-breaking switches

In the foregoing, the assumption has been made that circuit-breakers of appropriate breaking capacity will be freely used in each and every circuit. This is a practice which will prevail in many industrial applications and for certain distribution systems, but there are many circuits in high-voltage networks which can usefully employ a load-breaking fault-making switch, with or without h.r.c. fuses, to replace the more costly circuit-breaker.

For system voltages of up to 33 kV, this possibility is not new as many designs of oil switch capable of load breaking and fault making have been used for many years in ring main units in combination with fused switches or full oil circuit-breaker units. Some typical circuits of this type are given in Fig. 9.18, each example showing what is known as *non-extensible* units. In other assemblies, busbars are included so that they are then 'extensible', i.e. further switching units can be added.

In another direction, air-break switches having the same technical ability have been developed for voltages up to about 24 kV. This type has been familiar in continental countries for a long time and more recently has been taken up in Britain. Basically they comprise an air-break isolator designed for high-speed opening and closing, load currents being interrupted by a gas generated by the arc acting on the material of which the arcing contact nozzle is made aided by a self-generated puff of air. This type of switch finds many applications as a substitute for a circuit-breaker, e.g. on the high-voltage side of a dry-type transformer as used in the now popular packaged substations or as a main incoming switch to a distribution board or high-voltage motor-control board.

In most designs, h.r.c. fuses of the striker-pin type can be associated with the switch, and trip coils of the shunt or no-volt type can be fitted. This latter facility enables an intertrip between a circuit-breaker on the low-voltage side of a transformer and the air-break load-switch on the high-voltage side to be provided.

The load-breaking fault-making switch, whatever its form, must meet the following requirements:

1. It must be capable of breaking currents equal to its normal current rating at load power factor and system voltage.

2. It must be capable of interrupting small inductive and capacitive currents, i.e. disconnecting unloaded transformers, cables or overhead lines.

3. It must be able to make, i.e. close, on to a terminal short-circuit. This is its fault-making ability.

4. Its short-time rating must be such that it can carry the maximum fault current for the time the fault is being cleared by an interrupting device elsewhere on the system. This time is usually taken as 3 s.

These basic requirements have been met with relative ease on load switches of the types described, and for the voltage range noted. To meet them at higher voltages is not so easy, but the urgent need to economise in the use of extremely costly power circuit-breakers has provided an incentive to evolve designs of load switches which today are available for voltages of up to 750 kV. This has been made possible very largely by advances in other directions, e.g. the permanently pressurised air-blast and the sulphur hexafluoride (SF_6) circuit-breakers. From the former, the interrupter heads used for isolation purposes have been used for the load-breaking fault-making duty, with compressed air providing the insulating, arc quenching and actuating medium, and the switches being available for the voltage range 72·5 to 765 kV[1]. In the design using SF_6 gas, this serves as the insulating and arc-quenching medium while compressed air is used as the actuating medium. In this design interruption and isolation are separate functions, isolation being achieved on sequentially-operated isolator blades[2,3].

Load switches such as these only differ functionally in comparison with a circuit-breaker in that they cannot interrupt short-circuit currents and the

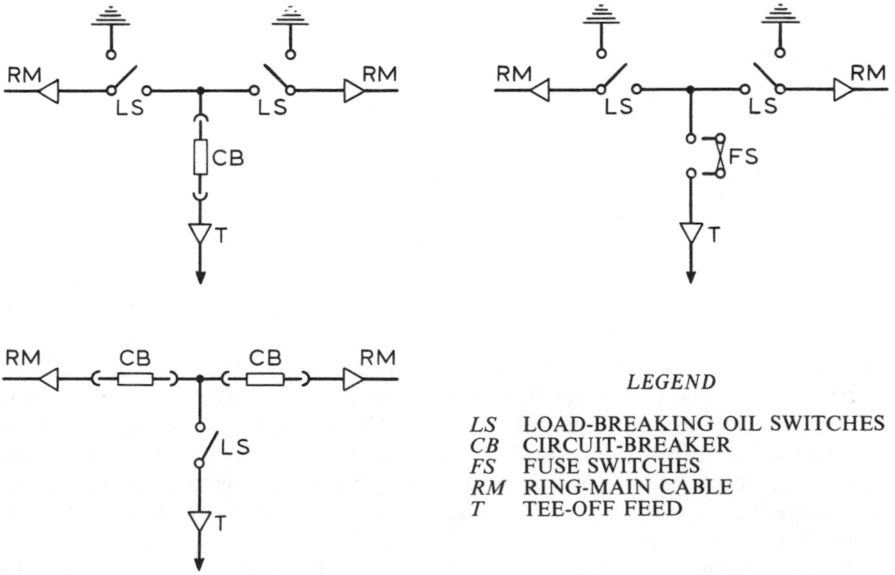

LEGEND

LS LOAD-BREAKING OIL SWITCHES
CB CIRCUIT-BREAKER
FS FUSE SWITCHES
RM RING-MAIN CABLE
T TEE-OFF FEED

Figure 9.18. Typical ring-main circuits using load-breaking fault-making oil switches

225

protective systems must ensure that such currents are interrupted by an appropriate breaker before a load switch opens to isolate the fault. To permit their use to the greatest extent, it is required that they should be capable of operation as three-pole units or that any selected single pole of a three-pole unit can be operated alone, they must, for some applications, have cyclic ability, e.g. open/close/open/time interval/close/open and the switching and arcing times must be compatible with those of modern circuit-breakers.

Given these attributes, many applications have been found for the load switch, either as a convenient means of increasing the operational flexibility of switching in applications where the minimum number of circuit-breakers is already achieved, or as a substitute for circuit-breakers to bring down the overall cost of an installation. Other applications have been found in shunt switching, short-circuiting of series capacitors and tuned interconnectors. The economics of such applications are obvious when it is noted that the load switch costs approximately one third that of a power circuit-breaker. It must be noted however that while the basic applications appear relatively simple, other problems arise, particularly those of protection[4].

Figure 9.19 illustrates a fairly simple application for load switches. Here, two transformers (for reasons of economy) are connected to one circuit-breaker and

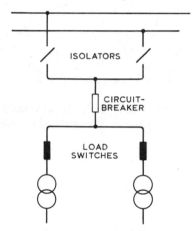

Figure 9.19. Load switches in transformer circuits backed by one circuit-breaker (the symbols used in the diagram also apply to Figures 9.20–9.23)

to enable either transformer to be taken out of service leaving the other operating without interruption, a load switch is included in each transformer circuit. A fault on either transformer would have to be cleared by the circuit-breaker but the protective system can include current relays which detect the faulty circuit and, after the breaker has cleared the fault, will cause the appropriate load switch to open. The circuit-breaker can now be automatically re-closed putting the healthy transformer back into service. This example could apply to two lines instead of transformers but here there is the possibility that the lines can be fed from both ends, requiring more complicated protection to ensure the circuit-breakers are opened at *both* ends before the load switches at *both* ends of the faulty line are opened.

On the British grid system, the mesh-connected substation shown typically at (*a*) in Fig. 9.20 has been extensively used because of its economical use of circuit-breakers. It is seen that four circuit-breakers only are used to control eight circuits whereas a conventional double-busbar system would require up to 11 for the same purpose. Unfortunately this scheme carries with it the disadvantage that when a fault occurs on one circuit two circuit-breakers must open to isolate the fault. This is also the case when one circuit requires to be disconnected normally, and in both cases there is a loss of one feeder and one transformer, i.e. the mesh is broken.

This is an application where operational facility is improved by replacing certain normal isolators by load switches, the revised arrangement now appearing as in Fig. 9.20(b). By this means and with suitable protective arrangements

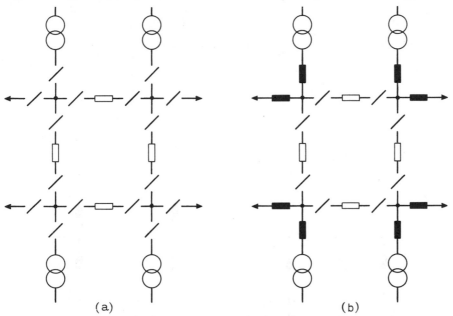

(a)   (b)

Figure 9.20. Mesh substations. (a) *without load switches,* (b) *with load switches*

and interlocks any one circuit can be isolated by opening one circuit-breaker and one load switch.

Figure 9.21 shows how load switches can be employed on the high-voltage side of transformers fed from a lower voltage source, leaving routine switching operations unaffected. Line faults are cleared in the normal way by the circuit-breaker in the faulty line, while busbar faults will be cleared by *all five* circuit-breakers opening. In the event of a transformer fault, say T_1, *all five* breakers will open simultaneously, but a lock-in memory element in the protective system 'remembers' which transformer protection has caused the total disconnection and will send a trip signal to the load switch in the faulty transformer circuit (i.e. load switch 4) and at the same time lock-out the low-voltage circuit-breaker 5 so that it cannot be reclosed. This achieved, the now open load-switch 4 sends a 'close' signal to all other circuit-breakers (1, 2, 3 and 7) thereby restoring the service via transformer T_2.

From this it is obvious that the usefulness of load switches depends largely on protective techniques coupled with auto-reclosing facilities. The latter may be three phase or single phase depending on varying conditions, and in some

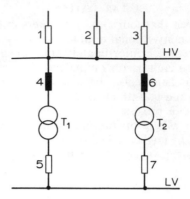

Figure 9.21. Load switches used in a transformer substation (courtesy Brown Boveri & Co. Ltd.)

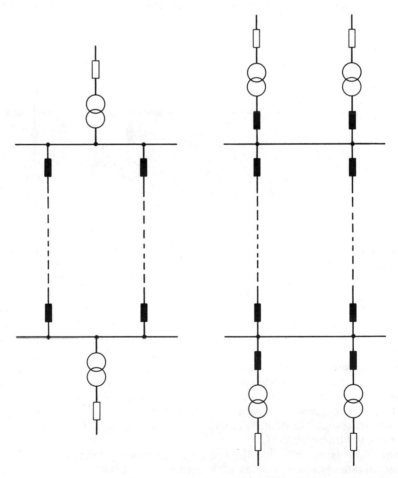

Figure 9.22. System tie lines using load switches (courtesy Brown Boveri & Co. Ltd.)

228

schemes the protective system may be elaborate, involving high-frequency carrier channels between two ends of transmission lines to ensure disconnection at both ends, each having a source of supply. Even so, the saving in circuit-breaker costs justifies the elaboration and two examples where this is so are shown in Fig. 9.22. The protection required for these has been discussed in detail elsewhere[4]. Other applications for load switches occur in connection with the modern practice of 'shunt switching' and for short-circuiting series capacitors.

Shunt switching, shown in Fig. 9.23(a) is a method of clearing faults by removing voltage from the source that feeds into the fault. This is achieved by temporarily connecting that source to earth by a shunt circuit-breaker connected to the busbars. It is a method particularly suited to radial feeders but it can be applied on interconnected systems as has been shown elsewhere[4,5]. It is primarily an economic method of clearing transient faults on transmission lines, i.e. faults arising from the breakdown of air insulation due to surges or to arcing across polluted insulators. Such faults are normally self-clearing, and any circuit-breaker which has been opened because of the fault can be reclosed almost immediately to restore the service.

This scheme can also be used in circumstances where existing circuit-breakers are found to have inadequate breaking-capacity. By shunt switching, the severity of duty on these is so reduced that replacement can be avoided.

The shunt breaker in the example shown comprises three separate poles each capable of individual operation although applications arise where combined operation is necessary. Under normal conditions the breaker is open and because it is not called upon to interrupt fault current it can be cheaper and lighter than a fully rated circuit-breaker. By its use, load switches can be used in the feeder circuits instead of circuit-breakers.

In Fig. 9.23(a) it is assumed that a line to earth fault occurs on phase B, feeder L_4. This can be detected by an earth-fault relay connected to a current transformer in the power transformer neutral and an associated phase-selector relay will cause pole B of the shunt breaker to close. The fault is thereby transferred to the busbars, shunting the fault and resulting in a rapid fall in voltage at the busbars and hence across the arc, so that current is not maintained. Thus the arc will die of its own accord.

The shunt-breaker pole is retained closed for a short time (milliseconds) to ensure complete de-ionisation at the arcing area and it is then opened automatically so that the system returns to normal, the load switch 4 in the faulty feeder not having opened. If, when the shunt-breaker pole opens, the fault has not been cleared, i.e. a restrike occurs, the sequence will be repeated but now the load switch is opened automatically and locks out. As the load switch opens in the interval of busbar short-circuit (applied by the shunt breaker), its operation is virtually at no-load and at zero recovery voltage.

If, instead of load switches in the feeders, circuit-breakers are used, operation will follow the same pattern but now the fault will cause the protective relay in the faulty circuit to commence its movement. However, before completing this and thereby signalling a tripping command to the circuit-breaker, the current which initiated movement will have been so reduced (possibly to zero), that the relay ceases to operate and resets without tripping the circuit-breaker. If necessary, resetting of the relay can be delayed so that if the arc is not extinguished, the relay will continue to operate and ultimately trip the breaker.

229

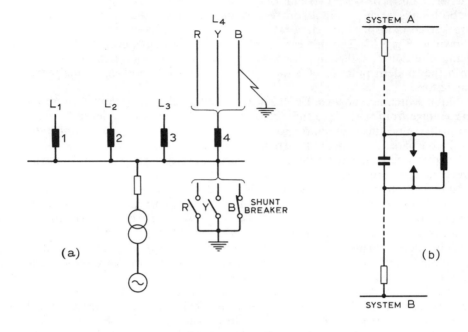

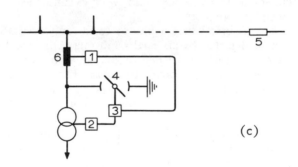

LEGEND FOR 'C'

1. MOTOR MECHANISM
2. TRANSFORMER FAULT RELAY
3. FAULT-THROWER TRIP

4. FAULT-THROWING SWITCH
5. REMOTE CIRCUIT-BREAKER
6. LOAD-BREAKING SWITCH

Figure 9.23. Further applications for load switches. (a) shunt switching using load switches in radial feeders, (b) load switch for short-circuiting series capacitor and the protective spark gap and (c) load switch with fault-throwing switch in tee-off circuit (courtesy Brown Boveri & Co. Ltd. and Switchgear & Equipment Ltd.)

Series capacitors are used in transmission lines to give a degree of compensation matched to system conditions, and provision has to be made whereby they are either in or out of circuit. This is controlled by the open or closed condition of a switch connected across the capacitor as shown in Fig. 9.23(b) and for such purpose a load switch is admirably suited as the currents to be made or interrupted are those in the region of normal rated values.

In this application however, the switch has a second function, namely to by-pass the protective spark gap where this breaks down. This occurs when, with the capacitor in circuit, a short-circuit occurs on the line, a condition which causes the voltage across the capacitor to rise suddenly and the spark gap therefore flashes over.

In these circumstances, the load switch must close at high speed and, as it is closing on to a short circuit, it must have adequate capacity in this respect. The flashover at the spark gap will be detected by current relays operated from current transformers in the spark-gap circuit, the relays giving a 'close' signal to the load switch. As the latter will be carrying the short-circuit current until such time as the fault is cleared by the opening of the line circuit-breakers (both ends) its short-time rating must match the maximum fault current. As soon as the line is cleared, the current relays in the spark-gap circuit will reset and the load switch will open.

The problem of short-circuit limitation on interconnected systems has been considered by Bonell and Friedlander[6] in a recent article and they have discussed the possibilities of tuned interconnectors in which a series-capacitor arrangement similar to Fig. 9.23(b) is employed but with a reactor in each half of the line. This gives a series resonance circuit such that a certain amount of power can flow with minimum voltage drop due to normal load current but the link will not allow more than a specified short-circuit current to flow.

On short-circuit, the capacitor by-pass switch closes as described earlier and on doing so, the resonant link is detuned and an increase in current through the link is prevented. This would appear to be an ideal application, where the load switch can again be used.

The protection of a transformer teed-off a line will often demand a circuit-breaker in the tee on the high-voltage side, but for relatively small loads this can be a costly item. If, on account of cost it is omitted and replaced by an off-load isolator, a fault in the transformer must be cleared by the opening of a distant circuit-breaker in the main feeder. This involves a pilot cable back to that circuit-breaker, again a costly item and furthermore it is not necessarily certain that a local fault in the transformer will be sufficient to cause operation in this way.

Such certainty can, however, be achieved by installing what is known as a *fault-throwing* switch in the tee-off as shown in Fig. 9.23(c). This switch is normally open but a suitable protective relay in the transformer circuit can, on operation, cause it to close thereby putting a line to earth or line to line fault on the system to ensure the opening of the remote circuit-breaker, whereupon the ordinary isolator in the tee-off can be opened, following which the remote circuit-breaker can be reclosed.

This system can be greatly improved however by again making use of the load-breaking switch in place of the ordinary isolator. Such a switch is represented in Fig. 9.23(c) and in this scheme the closing of the fault-throwing switch can be made to initiate the automatic opening (after a suitable time-delay to

231

ensure that the remote breaker has opened) of the load-breaking switch. The remote circuit-breaker can be of the auto-reclosing type, so that after a further short delay it can close to restore supply to healthy parts of the system with the faulty tee-off isolated.

A further advantage provided by the load-breaking switch is that it gives local control of the transformer circuit because, unlike the ordinary isolator, it can switch load and magnetising currents without difficulty.

Methods of busbar selection

Where duplicate busbars are employed, some means must be provided whereby the circuit is connected to one set of bars or the other. In open or cubicle types of gear, this simply means the supply of two sets of isolating switches as indicated in the diagrams in Fig. 9.4, etc., but in the various forms of draw-out or drop-down types, whether air-insulated or compound-filled, other methods are necessary and one of the earliest designs was that of plug changing. In this, a set of three plugs is provided which can, with the circuit-breaker isolated, be screwed into the upper or lower set of fixed spouts. This method is shown diagrammatically in Fig. 9.24 where the plugs are indicated as being in the upper orifices thus connecting the circuit-breaker to the upper set of busbars.

It is essentially an 'off-load' method of selection, involving perhaps the scaling of the unit to get at the plugs, and then handling them from one orifice to another.

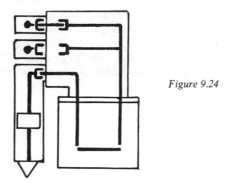

Figure 9.24

For the smaller current ratings this may not be a serious handicap, but at the larger current ratings the plugs tend to be rather heavy. It is a form of selection which is applied particularly in types with horizontal isolation and much ingenuity has been shown in devising interlocks to ensure that before a circuit-breaker is put back into service, *all three* plugs have been put into *one* row.

In an effort to provide an easier changeover, the oil-immersed selector switch has been developed. In a chamber carried above the oil circuit-breaker, a three-pole changeover switch is accommodated, the three poles being coupled and connected to an external operating mechanism. Two types of this design are used, one an 'off-load' type as shown diagrammatically in Fig. 9.25, where the changeover blades are of the 'break-before-make' type, and an 'on-load' type as shown in Fig. 9.26, where the blades are of the 'make-before-break' type. With 'on-load' selection by this method, it is usual to provide an interlock with

232

a busbar coupling switch so that the latter must be closed before changeover takes place at individual circuits. Where it is likely that certain generating plant may be connected some to one set of bars and some to the other, synchronising across the busbar coupler is necessary.

The disadvantages of the oil-immersed isolator are that it adds to the quantity of oil per unit, and involves a common connection to both sets of busbars within the selector chamber.

An alternative form of 'off-load' selection is that described as a transfer circuit-breaker. In this scheme the circuit-breaker is first isolated completely from one set of bars, bodily moved, and then reconnected to the second set of bars. In vertical isolation types, this involves lowering the breaker carriage, moving it either forward or backward, and then raising it to the desired set of busbars. Diagrammatically this is shown in Fig. 9.27.

In the horizontal-isolation type it is usual to fix two rows of fixed structures back to back, the circuit-breakers being in use on one row or the other, typically as shown in Fig. 9.28. To move the circuit-breaker involves the use of a transporter truck or a crane and the need for two rows of fixed structures involves considerable floor space.

A variation of the transfer breaker method is sometimes used where two separate circuit-breakers are used per circuit, with suitable interlocks between

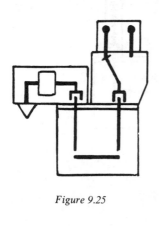

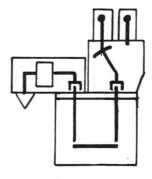

Figure 9.25   Figure 9.26

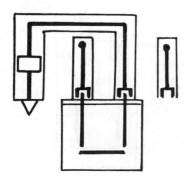

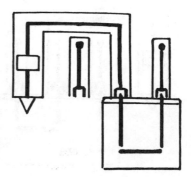

Figure 9.27

233

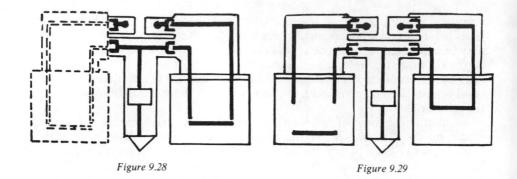

Figure 9.28   Figure 9.29

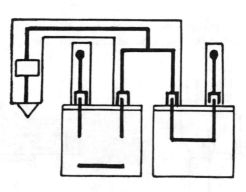

Figure 9.30

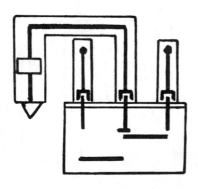
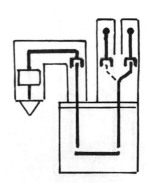

Figure 9.31   Figure 9.32

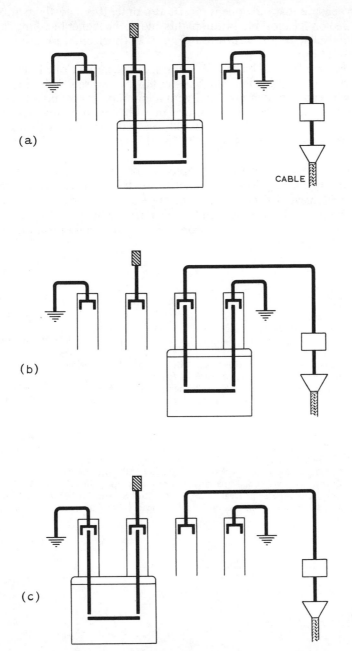

Figure 9.33.   Use of a transfer breaker for cable and busbar earthing. (a) normal service, (b) cable
earthed and (c) busbar earthed

the pair to ensure that only one is closed at a time. It is a costly method and is only justified on the most important plants and at the higher breaking capacities. This method of selection is shown in Figs. 9.29 (horizontal isolation) and 9.30 (vertical isolation).

Two other methods of busbar selection have been developed, the first comprising a specially designed circuit-breaker having two sets of fixed and moving contacts within a common tank and with a common centre point, generally as shown in Fig. 9.31. The other is a design which permits one set of circuit-breaker stems to be rotated through 180° to make contact with one or other set of busbars, as shown in Fig. 9.32. This is, naturally, an 'off-load' form of selection.

In later chapters, the methods adopted to provide integral means whereby the cable or the busbars can be earthed through the circuit-breaker in certain types of switchgear will be considered. Here we may note how a vertically-isolated circuit-breaker can be used for this purpose by transferring the breaker from its normal service position to one or other earthing positions as shown schematically in Fig. 9.33.

REFERENCES

1. KÖPPL, G., 'Load Switches in H.V. and E.H.V. Networks: Interesting Applications for a New Type of Unit', *Brown Boveri Review*, **54** No. 12, Dec. (1967)
2. JOYCE, W.J., '400 kV Load-break Fault-make Switch Isolator', *Elect. Rev.*, 7 June (1968)
3. ANON., 'Switching Isolators in HV Substations', *Elect. Rev.*, 26 July (1968)
4. BARCHETTI, H., FREY, W. and KÖPPL, G., 'High-voltage Load Switches for 72·5 to 750 kV', *Brown Boveri Review*, **55** No. 4/5, April/May (1968)
5. STALEWSKI, A., 'The Technique of Shunt Switching', *Elect. Rev.*, 17 March (1967)
6. BONELL, M.W. and FRIEDLANDER, E., 'Tuned Interconnectors', *Elect. Rev.*, 8 April (1966)

BIBLIOGRAPHY

BURCKHARDT, P. and KNECHT, H., 'Type DR36 Generator Breakers Rated 12 to 36 kA', *Brown Boveri Rev.*, **57**, Dec. (1970)
COLBERT, H.J., '3·3 kV On-load Isolators', *Elect. Rev.*, 29 March (1968)
HEINEMANN, T., 'Single-pole Rapid Reclosing', *Elect. Rev.*, 30 April (1965)
I.E.C., 'High-voltage Switches (Load-breaking Fault-making up to 765 kV)', *I.E.C.*, Pub. No. 265
MACKERTICH, P.J., 'Choosing Switchgear for Motor Control Systems', *Elect. Rev.*, 22 Jan. (1971)
'New Designs of High-voltage Substations and Overhead Lines Cut Costs', *Elect. Rev.*, 28 Aug. (1970)

Chapter 10

H.R.C. fuses

As a circuit interrupting device under conditions of short-circuit, the modern h.r.c. fuse is in many ways superior to the oil or air-break circuit-breaker. In the low and medium-voltage range it can successfully interrupt prospective fault currents (r.m.s. symmetrical) of up to at least 80 000 A, equivalent to 57·5 MVA at 415 V, which is the limit presently recognised in BS 88 : 1967 Part 1.

This specification lists four categories of duty, as noted in Table 10.1 for a.c. ratings of 250 and 415 V.

For use at higher voltages, typical ratings are 150 MVA at 3·3 kV and 250 MVA at 11 kV to BS 2692, but higher ratings are available, e.g. 250 MVA at 3·3 kV and 750 MVA at 11 kV. These higher ratings are equivalent to prospective fault currents (r.m.s. symmetrical) of 43 800 and 39 400 A respectively.

As noted in earlier chapters, the *peak* fault current in the first half-cycle of short-circuit can, for the condition of full asymmetry, reach a value of 2·55 times the r.m.s. symmetrical value and, assuming the highest ratings noted above, the peak currents can be those noted in Table 10.2.

Its superiority over other interrupting devices lies mainly in (a) its ability to limit the fault current to a value less than the prospective peak in the first half-cycle of short-circuit, (b) in consequence of (a) the fault is interrupted in less than

Table 10.1

Category of duty	Prospective current (A, r.m.s. symmetrical)	Power factor (lagging)
AC16	16 500	0·3
AC33	33 000	0·3
AC46	46 000	0·15
AC80	80 000	0·15

Table 10.2

Voltage (V)	MVA	r.m.s. symmetrical (A)	Initial peak amperes
415	57·5	80 000	204 000
3 300	250·0	43 800	111 690
11 000	750·0	39 400	100 470

one half-cycle (see Fig. 10.8) and (c) it does all this in a bulk of a few cubic inches and at relatively low cost. Whilst these attributes give it superiority as a short-circuit interrupting device, it should be considered as complementary to the circuit-breaker in situations where other forms of protection are of equal importance. The use of one or the other must also depend on considerations related to the system as a whole.

The fuse, by comparison with the circuit-breaker, suffers the disadvantage that replacement is necessary after operation. This is offset in situations where the fault level is high by the fact that the physical size of the fuse, and therefore its cost, is directly proportional to its current rating, whereas the dimensions of the circuit-breaker are determined by its breaking capacity irrespective of current rating. The fuse, being a thermal device, generates more heat than the current-carrying parts of a circuit-breaker of equivalent normal current rating and the effect of temperature rise of the fuse must be taken into account in relation to associated apparatus. Fuse-links are listed in BS 88 up to 1 200 A and are in common use up to this rating.

Current ratings of fuse-links for higher voltages have maximum ratings of the order of 350 A at 3·3 kV and 100 A at 11 kV, but where a circuit requires fuse-links in excess of these ratings, successful operation can be obtained by fuse-links in parallel.

The excellence of present designs is due to the extensive research and development which has been sustained since about 1926 when, good as fuses were at that time, it was realised that the rapid increase in fault power would demand higher breaking capacity in protective devices than then existed. About that time too, improved facilities for high-power testing under controlled short-circuit conditions were becoming available (see Chapter 5) to take the place of large secondary batteries which had been a recognised source of power for tests at high-current values. A paper by Grant[1] analysed the state of the art at that time and outlined many of the problems demanding investigation and it can be said with fairness that the fuse of today embodies the results of such investigation.

It is not within the scope of this book to discuss in any detail the process of circuit-breaking in an h.r.c. fuse except only so far as it is necessary to appreciate this process as it affects the application of fuses. It is of interest however to note that basically all h.r.c. fuses comprise a ceramic body to contain specially designed fuse elements, these being connected to metal and caps which serve also to seal the body after it has been filled with pure granulated quartz. Typical of this construction for medium-voltage designs is the fuse-link shown in cut-away form in Fig. 10.1, while Fig. 10.2 shows the external view of another make.

The elements, as noted later, are designed such that melting will occur at a point or points depending on the configuration or on purposely introduced low melting-point regions, the time required for melting depending on the magnitude of the current. Vaporisation of the metallic element occurs on melting and there is fusion between the metallic vapour and the filling powder leading to rapid arc extinction. This chemical reaction produces a substance of high resistance which becomes an insulator as the current is interrupted. Fuse-links for the higher voltages have elements of very different form as can be seen from Fig. 10.3. The pure silver element is of a spiral nature supported on a star core or former located in the end caps.

Because of the much wider use of fuses for medium-voltage applications,

238

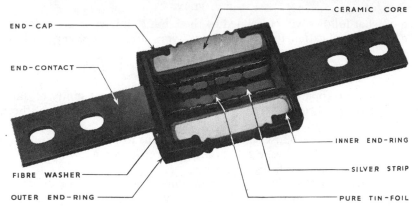

Figure 10.1. Sectional view of a typical medium-voltage cartridge fuse-link (courtesy A. Reyrolle & Co. Ltd.)

Figure 10.2. Medium-voltage cartridge fuse-link (courtesy English Electric Fusegear Ltd.)

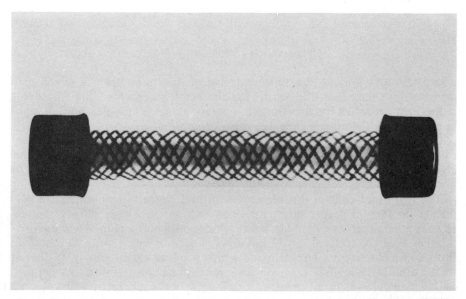

Figure 10.3. Typical radiograph of an 11 kV fuse-link (courtesy English Electric Fusegear Ltd.)

much of what follows will be related to these but at a later stage, note will be taken of the application for high-voltage types and some comparable data given.

In the application of h.r.c. fuses, there are three broad requirements to be studied:

1. *Protection* for apparatus and conductors against the possibility of damage due to the passage of current greater than normal. Such damage may be thermal or mechanical or both.

2. *Co-ordination* between fuses and other apparatus which can be tripped open by other overcurrent devices, e.g. a circuit-breaker or contactor.

3. *Discrimination* between fuses in series.

For a study of protection, it is at once important to note the existence of fuse-links having entirely different time/current characteristics. Typical curves to illustrate the difference between two particular designs are given in Fig. 10.4

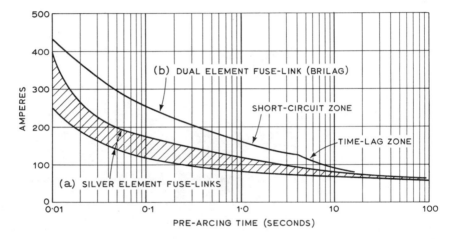

Figure 10.4.   *Typical time/current characteristics of single and dual-element fuse-links, each of 30A rating (courtesy Fluvent Electric Ltd.)*

where the curves at (*a*) are representative of fuse-links using a silver strip element while the curve at (*b*) shows the characteristic of a fuse-link employing a dual element which has two zones of operation, one for the clearance of high-current values, the other a time-lag zone for moderate over-currents.

Curve (*b*) is important in that there is discontinuity at the point of change-over from time-lag operation to the quick-acting (short-circuit) zone and this change is achieved in the design of the element which, as shown in Fig. 10.5, is in the form of dual elements.

The two outer ends of this element comprise copper strips which are perforated to form a construction for operation at the higher current values. Between them there is a time-lag insert which consists of a plug of low melting-point alloy which melts at 180°C and it is this section which melts on sustained but small overcurrents. The elements which produce curves similar to that at (*a*) are usually made of silver strip with a series of narrowings or necks, coupled with a plug of low melting-point which alloys with the silver strip when melting occurs, as shown typically in Fig. 10.6.

240

In another design, fuses with either quick-acting or slow-acting characteristics are available where the characteristic time-current curve is continuous (as in (a) of Fig. 10.4) in both types but the slow-acting characteristic curve is modified in its slope (for times greater than 1 s) to give longer pre-arcing times at the lower values of current. This change is obtained by the introduction of an alloying medium having a fusing temperature below that of silver. The difference between the element construction in these designs is shown in Fig. 10.7.

The arguments for and against the two sets of characteristics have been ventilated in some detail in a paper by Dean[2] and the discussion on that paper. One argument by those who prefer the dual-element fuse-link is that the time-lag action permits the use of fuse-links having normal ratings nearer to the normal full-load current of a motor than is possible with other types, and that this is so even with direct-on-line started induction motors taking six to eight times full-load current from the line at starting. Against this it is argued that

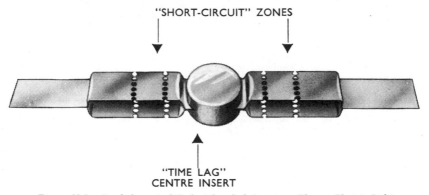

Figure 10.5. Dual element of 'Brilag' fuse-link (courtesy Fluvent Electric Ltd.)

Figure 10.6. Typical single element

by specification a contactor must itself be capable of breaking up to six or eight times the normal current rating of the contactor, i.e. the stalled current of the motor, and therefore should, in association with its overload device, be allowed to deal with overcurrents of these magnitudes.

The problem of fuse protection on motor circuits is of course complicated by the need to ensure that the fuse will not operate due to current surges when starting from rest or during the changeover from star to delta. These surges last some seconds and their magnitude depends on the method of starting and on the motor design, some direct-on-line motors taking six to eight times full-load current from the line while accelerating while others may take only two to three times. This question will be considered in more detail later.

To protect a cable also requires special consideration, particularly today when there is increasing use of p.v.c. insulated cables in medium-voltage instal-lations. Compared with paper insulated cables, p.v.c. types have a lower thermal

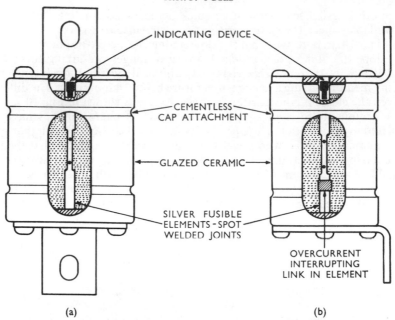

Figure 10.7. H.R.C. fuse-links. (a) *identically-graded elements for classes Q2 or R and* (b) *graded and interrupting elements for class P or Q1 (courtesy EMP Electric Ltd.)*

capacity and the I.E.E. regulations require that any fuse-links used should provide what is known as *close excess current* protection. A guide to the degree of protection afforded is given by the 'fusing factor'[3], a factor which is defined as the ratio, greater than unity, of the minimum fusing current to the current rating, i.e.:

$$\text{Fusing factor} = \frac{\text{minimum fusing current}}{\text{current rating}}$$

BS 88:1967 recognises four classes of fuse each having a different fusing factor as noted in Table 10.3.

From this it is evident that the lower the fusing factor, the closer is the degree of protection against small sustained overcurrents. Thus a 30 A fuse-link class P will have, at the worst, a minimum fusing current of 37·5 A, whereas for a class R fuse-link of this rating it will have, at the worst, a minimum fusing current of 75 A or at the best, 52·5 A.

Table 10.3

Class of fuse-links	Fusing factor	
	exceeding	not exceeding
P	1·00	1·25
Q1	1·25	1·5
Q2	1·5	1·75
R	1·75	2·5

The I.E.E. regulations therefore recommend that fuse-links protecting p.v.c. cables should have a fusing factor not exceeding 1·5, i.e. classes P and Q1. The other two classes are usually used in special cases such as motor circuits, or, in the case of class R, where back-up protection is sought for other protective apparatus. Both give what is known as *coarse excess current* protection, but give equal protection on short-circuits.

Whether h.r.c. fuse-links are of one type or the other, however, all exhibit (at values of prospective current above a known minimum) that most valuable characteristic known as 'cut-off'. This means that the short-circuit current is interrupted before it can reach the prospective value in the first half-cycle of short-circuit and is demonstrated in Fig. 10.8 from which it is seen that at (*a*) the rising current wave is stopped (element melts) and it dies away during the

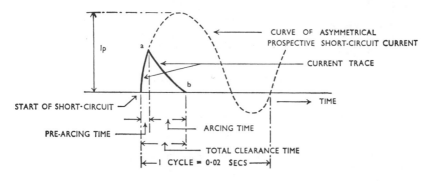

Figure 10.8. Cut-off feature in h.r.c. fuses

arcing period to zero at (*b*). The value at which 'cut-off' occurs may vary between designs and Fig. 10.9 shows the values for English Electric Type T fuse-links while Fig. 10.10 gives similar data for the 'Brilag' dual-element fuse-links. 'Cut-off' values vary firstly in relation to the normal rating of the fuse-link, secondly in relation to the prospective value of the short-circuit current and thirdly to the degree of asymmetry. The curves shown assume maximum asymmetry.

It is important to note that the values of prospective current are symmetrical r.m.s. and in Chapter 3 we have seen how to calculate these for any defined system. Thus, if we assume a fault value of 31 MVA at 415 V equivalent to 43 300 A (symmetrical r.m.s.), then a 30 A type T fuse-link in that circuit would 'cut-off' at approximately 3 500 A. Had no fuse been present then the peak current (I_p in Fig. 10.8) in at least one phase could reach 110 000 A. On the other hand if the fuse-link had been rated 300 A then 'cut-off' would not occur until 29 000 A or, going to the extreme, a 1 200 A fuse-link would 'cut-off' at about 80 000 A.

The real significance of 'cut-off' will be better appreciated by noting the data given in Chapter 8 concerning the electromagnetic and thermal effects on busbars and connections when these are carrying short-circuit current. It was shown, for example, that the electromagnetic forces set up tending to distort the busbar or connection structure, are related to the *square* of the current value and this being so, the design problem is radically eased if the current concerned is, as noted earlier, the 'cut-off' current of say 3 500 or 29 000 A instead of a

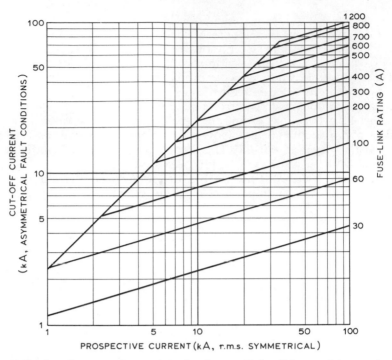

Figure 10.9. Cut-off current characteristics for the type T fuse-links tested in accordance with BS 88:1967 at 415 V (courtesy English Electric Fusegear Ltd.)

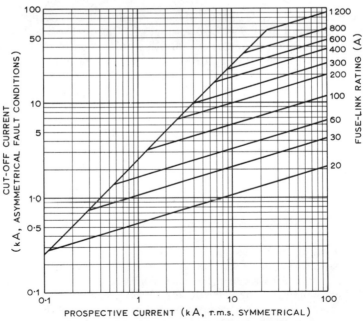

Figure 10.10. Cut-off characteristics for Aeroflex-Brilag fuse-links tested in accordance with BS 88:1967 (courtesy Fluvent Electric Ltd.)

possible peak value of 110 000 A. Even the worst condition of 80 000 A is an improvement.

In a paper by Jacks[4] it is pointed out that when the *pre-arcing time* of a fuse is less than 0·02 s, the *total operating time* is extremely difficult to determine. It is therefore suggested that the criterion for such short times should be the values representing the energy admitted* during operation and expressed in 'amperes² seconds' or more briefly I^2t. A range of such values is given in Fig. 10.11 for both total operating times and pre-arcing times. Here we shall be concerned only with the curve for total times, that for pre-arcing times being considered later when discussing discrimination.

The following formula, from the book *Copper for Busbars*, shows how the time t in seconds can be determined for the temperature of a copper conductor to rise $\theta°C$ above an ambient temperature of 30°C when carrying a short-circuit current of I amperes:

$$t = 2\cdot13\left(\frac{A}{I}\right)^2\left[\sqrt{(1+0\cdot00756\theta)}-1\right] \times 10^{10}$$

where A is the cross-sectional area in square inches.

Converting to the metric system where A will be the cross-sectional area in square millimetres, the formula becomes:

$$t = 5\cdot12\left(\frac{A}{I}\right)^2\left[\sqrt{(1+0\cdot00756\theta)}-1\right] \times 10^4$$

Using I^2t values for h.r.c. fuses from Fig. 10.11 and rearranging, a formula is arrived at which enables this minimum cross-sectional area of a conductor appropriate to the I^2t values to be determined thus:

$$A = \sqrt{\frac{I^2t}{5\cdot12\left[(\sqrt{1+0\cdot00756\theta})-1\right] \times 10^4}}$$

If we assume a circuit in which a 400 A h.r.c. fuse-link is present, the total I^2t of which is $1\cdot9 \times 10^6$, and assuming a permissible temperature rise of 100°C, then the minimum conductor section will be:

$$A = \sqrt{\frac{1\cdot9 \times 10^6}{5\cdot12\left[(\sqrt{1+0\cdot00756 \times 100})-1\right] \times 10^4}}$$

$$= \sqrt{\frac{1\cdot9 \times 10^6}{1\cdot664 \times 10^4}} = 10\cdot7 \text{ mm}^2$$

In a practical case, the continuous current-carrying capacity coupled with physical considerations would demand a conductor of much greater cross-sectional area, and for the case quoted a conductor not less than say 25 mm × 6·3 mm (1 in by $\frac{1}{4}$ in) with a cross-sectional area of 157·5 mm² (0·25 in²) would probably be chosen. This example illustrates that where h.r.c. fuses are present

* Refer to BS 88:1967 for a definition of 'specific energy'.

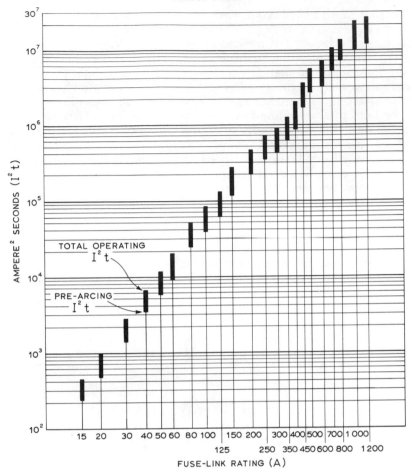

Figure 10.11. I^2t *characteristics for type* T *h.r.c. fuse-links tested in accordance with BS 88 : 1967 category 415 AC 80 (courtesy English Electric Fusegear Ltd.)*

in a circuit, the thermal problems associated with conductors carrying high values of short-circuit current for a short time, are virtually eliminated. Figure 10.12 gives the I^2t characteristics of the 'Brilag' (dual element) fuse-links.

Finally on protection, it should be noted that the problem of short-time ratings for cables is very considerably eased when these are protected by h.r.c. fuses as again the current to be carried is the 'cut-off' current and that only for the short time required by the fuse to interrupt the fault. The question of short-time ratings for cables has been noted in Chapter 3.

Co-ordination of fuses with other apparatus which has its own automatic devices for tripping open on overcurrent involves a study of two time/current characteristic curves, i.e. that of the fuse and that of the overcurrent device, usually thermal or magnetic, and sometimes a relay which is current transformer operated.

The fuse and the overcurrent device in such circumstances must share the duty of protecting a motor or cable in such a way that the breaking capacity of the automatic device (circuit-breaker or contactor), will be fully utilised. This is essential in that it is naturally much more convenient to reclose a circuit-breaker or contactor than to replace a fuse and the latter should only operate under conditions outside the ability of the other device. This leads therefore to a study of two characteristics superimposed and it will be found that a point of cross-over occurs and an example of this is shown in Fig. 10.13. This feature is of particular importance when fuses are associated with contactors used for motor starting. Here, the fuse rating will be chosen to ensure that it will *not* operate during the starting period of the motor when a current up to six or eight times full-load current is taken from the line for a short period of time. The overcurrent device on the starter will have a special characteristic to take care of the same condition so that the superimposed curves will now appear as shown typically in Fig. 10.14.

A study of this illustration shows that the time/current curves are given for two classes of fuse-link, namely Q1 and R. The former is a normal industrial class and given a rating of 125 A. The class R fuse-link on the other hand is for

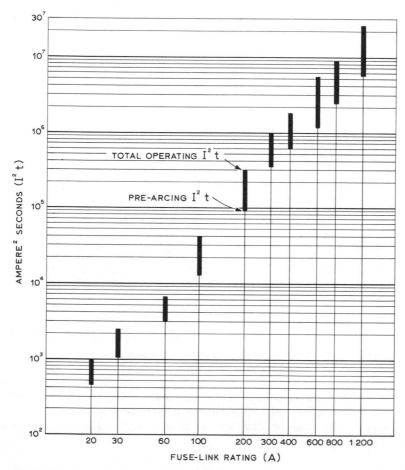

Figure 10.12. I^2t *characteristics for Aeroflex-Brilag h.r.c. fuse-links tested in accordance with BS 88:1967 category 415 AC 80 (courtesy Fluvent Electric Ltd.)*

247

motor-circuit protection only and has a double rating identified as 100M150 A. The first of these figures is its *continuous* current rating while the second figure prefixed by the letter M, is its rating for motor starting. Both types of fuse-link are based on the recommendations of English Electric Fusegear Ltd. for a 40 hp motor started direct-on-line and having a normal full-load current of 55 A at 415 V. These recommendations show that whereas the 125 A class Q1 fuse-link covers a range of full-load motor currents of 54·4 to 71·5 A, the 100M150 class R fuse-link covers a wider range, viz. 54·4 to 94·4 A.

In applications such as these the important feature is that the fuse is providing back-up protection for another circuit-interrupting device which has only limited ability but allowing that ability to be used to the full so that unnecessary

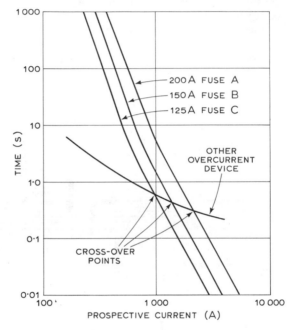

Figure 10.13. ·*Typical time/current characteristics of three h.r.c. fuse-links and some other overcurrent protective device*

fuse operation is avoided. It is of course possible that a fault may exist on a system at the moment this other device is closed so that it must have the ability to 'make' on to currents equal to the maximum value of 'cut-off' current of the fuse. To ensure this may mean the selection of a fuse rating lower than would be chosen by other considerations.

To some extent the question of co-ordination just considered can be regarded equally as a problem of discrimination and, indeed, no distinction is made in BS 88, but here it will be assumed that the major problem of discrimination is that which involves two or more sets of fuses in series. This subject has been dealt with rather fully in the paper by Jacks[4] in which he discusses not only the aspect of discrimination as may be determined from time/current characteristic curves, but also from the point of view of system layout, unequal loading causing one fuse to be running warm and the other cool, and the effect of installation abuses.

248

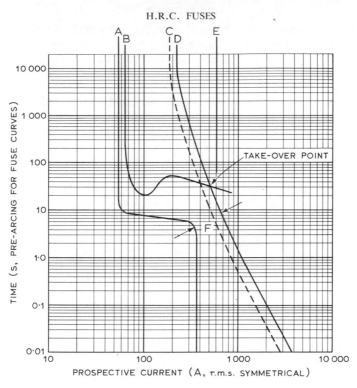

LEGEND

A   APPROXIMATE STARTING CURRENT OF *40 hp (30 kW) 415V* MOTOR SWITCHED DIRECT-ON-LINE. *FLC = 55A*, MAX. STARTING CURRENT = *385A*

B   TIME CURRENT CHARACTERISTIC FOR *60A* ELECTROMAGNETIC OVERLOAD WITH TWO-RATE TIME-LAG SET AT *115%*

C   TIME/CURRENT CHARACTERISTIC OF ENGLISH ELECTRIC TYPE T CLASS *Q1 125A* FUSE-LINK

D   TIME/CURRENT CHARACTERISTIC OF ENGLISH ELECTRIC TYPE T CLASS *R100M150* FUSE-LINK

E   SAFE INTERRUPTING CAPACITY OF A *75A* CONTACTOR

F   SAFE GAP WHICH ENSURES FUSE DOES NOT OPERATE DUE TO MOTOR STARTING-CURRENT

Figure 10.14.   Discrimination between h.r.c. fuse-links, magnetic overload, motor starting current and contactor ability

The simplest case for discrimination concerns two fuses in series, typically as shown in Fig. 10.15. Here fuse *A* is what is known as the *major* fuse, while *B* is designated *minor*. As discrimination is essential at any current within the breaking-capacity range of both fuses, the first essential is that the time/current characteristic* of fuse-link *B* must lie throughout its length below that of fuse-link *A* (see for example Fig. 10.13).

When high fault-currents have to be interrupted however, pre-arcing times are extremely short and we have already noted that at times less than about 0·02 s, determination of the total operating time is difficult to assess. As discrimination at high fault-currents can only be achieved when the pre-arcing time of

---

* Because of the multiplicity of fuse-links of different makes, no attempt is made here to include the curves showing time/current characteristics. These are normally given in makers publications, which should be studied.

the 'major' fuse is greater than the total operating time of the 'minor', reference to time/current characteristics is unreliable and therefore curves of I^2t values such as Figs. 10.11 and 10.12 are used to determine whether or not discrimination is possible. The following example shows how this is done.

A system is known to have a prospective fault level of 15 000 A (r.m.s. symmetrical), a value at which cut-off will be exhibited for the fuse-link chosen. Fuse-link B in Fig. 10.15 has been chosen rated at 200 A by load considerations and it is required to rate fuse-link A such that discrimination at the fault level will be assured. Reference to Fig. 10.11 shows that a fuse-link of 200 A rating has a *total* I^2t of approximately $4\cdot3 \times 10^5$ so that by our rule fuse-link A must have a pre-arcing I^2t greater than this. If we consider first the next higher fuse-link rating, i.e. 300 A, we see that its pre-arcing I^2t is only 4×10^5 so that

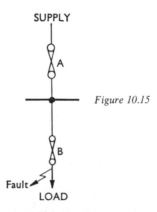

Figure 10.15

it will *not* discriminate. Choosing the next higher rating, 350 A, however, we see that this has a pre-arcing I^2t of 6×10^5, i.e. greater by a good margin than the total I^2t of the 200 A fuse-link B, and therefore fuse-link A must be rated not less than 350 A.

An extension of the example in Fig. 10.15 could be one where three fuses are in series as in Fig. 10.16. Here the principles already noted must be applied and for a fault at F_1, F_2, F_3 or F_4, fuses B, C, D or E must discriminate with fuse A, and for a fault at F_5, fuse F must discriminate with fuse D.

In his paper, Jacks points out that in certain circumstances it may be necessary to regard discrimination as of secondary importance and quotes a case as shown in Fig. 10.17. Here the 'minor' fuse rated at 600 A is selected to give back-up protection within the through-fault capacity of the associated contactor, whereas the 'major' fuse rated 800 A, chosen to clear faults in the busbar zone, would not protect the contactor.

Two such fuses would, however, give discrimination at the lower values of prospective current and because both are relatively large, discrimination will occur up to about 15 000–20 000 A, the values round about which these fuses start to exhibit cut-off.

In all that has been said on the subject of co-ordination and discrimination, the assumption has been made that the characteristic time/current curves of fuses and other tripping devices are strictly accurate making no allowance for manufacturing and other variations. To cover these, British Standards indicate permissible tolerances, e.g. $\pm 10\%$, so that when the curves of two devices are being compared by superimposition, such comparisons should be made between bands representing the overall tolerances, e.g. 20%. By this means it is possible to see whether the desired co-ordination or discrimination will be achieved should one device be at the upper limit of tolerance and the other at the lower limit. When making studies of this nature it may be advisable to ascertain the degree of accuracy achieved by a particular design as manufacturers may provide devices with performances well within the permissible limits of the appropriate British Standard.

It must also be remembered that published characteristic curves for h.r.c. fuses are based on tests which require the fuses and the conductors connected to them to be at approximately ambient temperature, generally less than 25°C, and must not have been carrying current prior to the tests. When in service, however, and at the time of operation, load will be being carried and therefore

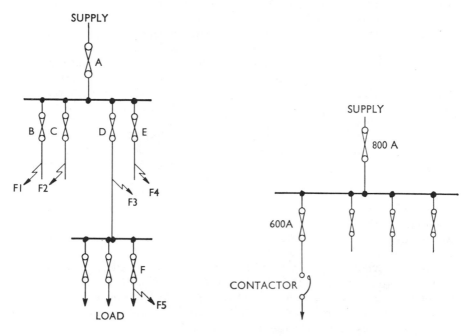

Figure 10.16

Figure 10.17

the fuse and conductor temperature will be above ambient and this will have the effect of reducing the pre-arcing and total operating times at certain current values. Guile[5] has studied this in relation to fuses with single wire elements and concludes that at prospective currents above about 15 times the minimum fusing current, the change due to pre-loading in total operating time for the fuse tested is very small and could be neglected. At low overcurrents, however, he found the reduction to be such as to be significant when considering close discrimination. An example is quoted of a fuse pre-loaded with its rated current and then subjected to a fault current of twice the minimum fusing current, and it was found that the total operating time was 30% shorter than that when unloaded. This clearly needs consideration under specified circumstances by reference to the fuse manufacturer in the absence of published data.

Another point to consider in the application of fuses is that the temperature rises allowed in BS 88 are based on an ambient temperature peak of 40°C with an average of 35°C over a twenty-four hour period. If fuses are known to be for use where higher ambient temperatures may exist, e.g. in tropical or sub-tropical climates or in others where the room temperature may be high on account of the processes in that room, a reduction in current rating may be necessary, the actual reduction being related to the ambient temperature. Because links in motor circuits are normally highly rated to avoid operation on starting, de-rating is rarely necessary.

As a guide to fuse selection for a particular type of load, the following may be regarded as representing average practice but due note must be made of the earlier discussion.

Fluctuating loads are those in which peaks of comparatively short duration occur. Examples of this type of load are found in transformer, fluorescent lighting, capacitor and motor circuits. For these, the fuse selected has to be of such rating that it will withstand the transient current surge on switching-in. Selection will depend to some extent on the fusing factor of the fuse proposed, but it is suggested that the chosen fuse should generally have a normal rating 50% above the normal full load current of the apparatus to be protected. A capacitor circuit is particularly difficult because, on switching in, there is a heavy current surge of a highly transient nature and of high natural frequency (see discussion in Chapter 2).

The selection of fuses for motor circuits will depend, of course, on the value of current taken at starting which, in turn, is dependent on the motor design and the method of starting (e.g. direct-on, star/delta, stator/rotor, etc.). In addition, correct selection depends on a knowledge of the length of time the motor takes to accelerate and for the current to fall to its normal full load value. These are factors which should be obtained from the motor manufacturers whenever possible. Given this information, it is possible to choose a fuse whose characteristic time/current curve lies at all points *above* the curve of the motor starting current.

This has been illustrated in Fig. 10.14 and it may be noted that it is essential to have an ample gap between the two curves at the point *F* where the curve of motor starting current starts to fall. If this gap is small and the motor is subject to frequent starting—with the possibility of stalling—then the fuse may suffer deterioration leading to subsequent unexplained operation.

When the starting current is not known, useful approximations are (*a*), that the starting current of a direct-on-line started motor is about 7 or 8 times the full load current for 10 s and (*b*) that the starting current of a motor with a 75% auto-transformer starter tapping is about 4 times the full load current and $2\frac{1}{2}$ times with a 60% auto-transformer starter tapping for 20 s. This latter figure also applies to star/delta starting while for slip ring motors (stator-rotor starters) a fuse selected to meet normal running conditions is adequate.

On the other hand a steady load is one which will fluctuate only a little from the normal value (as for example in heating circuits) and in such cases selection will depend on whether the fuse has to give overload *and* short-circuit protection or just short-circuit protection. If the former is required the fuse chosen should have a current rating as near to the normal circuit current as possible and be class P or Q1 (see Table 10.3). If for short-circuit protection only, then a fuse of higher normal rating may be chosen because at short-circuit values of current, the operating time will be very little more than for a fuse of lower rating and the advantage of a lower running temperature will be gained.

Although not basically different in so far as it is a fuse-link, reference should be made to a design which incorporates a striker pin. In this the striker pin is arranged to function after the fuse element proper has cleared the circuit, and in functioning the pin moves to upset the latching-in mechanism of a circuit-breaker causing the latter to open, or to operate an auxiliary contact in the control circuit of a contactor, or to operate an auxiliary contact to cause an audible or visual alarm to be given.

The striker pin is held after operation so that it cannot be ejected completely nor can it be pushed back into the fuse body. The force can be varied to suit the application ranging from several pounds for mechanical tripping to one or two pounds if to operate auxiliary contacts. After operation the striker pin acts additionally as an indicator to show which fuse has operated.

The striker pin assembly is generally as shown in Fig. 10.18 from which it will be seen that an ignition wire passes through a sealed compartment containing a charge of powder. Within the powder the ignition wire is slightly weakened and, after the main fuse elements (of relatively less resistance) have melted to clear the circuit, current is transferred to the ignition wire acting as a high resistance shunt, and this heating up causes the powder charge to be fired and forces the striker pin upwards to the limit of its travel. High-voltage fuses can also be provided with a striker pin, one design (E.M.P. Electric) using a thermal type which, in addition to functioning as a tripping device in association with other apparatus, will also detect any overheating of the fusible element due, for example, to an error in initial selection of fuse rating. Under these circumstances, the striker will operate. High-voltage fuses can be obtained suitable for use in air or, as in a number of fuse-switch applications, for immersion in oil.

The application of fuses with a striker pin ensures, when used in association with an automatic circuit-breaker or contactor, that if one fuse only operates, the three-phase circuit is disconnected, avoiding, in motor circuits, the hazards of 'single phasing'. Under these conditions it is known that a running motor will continue to run on the two remaining healthy lines but with an excess of current in those lines and in the motor windings.

It is appropriate here to note briefly that medium voltage h.r.c. fuses have been developed not only for power or lighting circuits but for many other purposes, as for example fuses in the secondary circuits of voltage transformers, for house service cut-outs, for the protection of coil circuits (contactor closing coils and the like) and for some special purpose applications such as those for use in aircraft and for the protection of semi-conductor rectifiers.

In Chapter 5, details have been given of the short-circuit tests which have to be made to prove the rating assigned to circuit-breakers. It is equally necessary to prove that h.r.c. fuses will behave as predicted under overcurrent and short-circuit conditions.

These tests are, in the case of a.c. fuses, single phase in a circuit having a prospective current not less than the breaking-capacity rating of the fuse (see Table 10.1). The test supply voltage is required to be not less than 110% of the fuse-link rated voltage, i.e. a fuse-link rated 415 V must be tested with the supply voltage at 457 V. In the test at the appropriate prospective current the circuit must be made at a rising voltage of 50% of the peak value, with a suitable tolerance. From Table 10.1 it will be seen that the power factor of the test

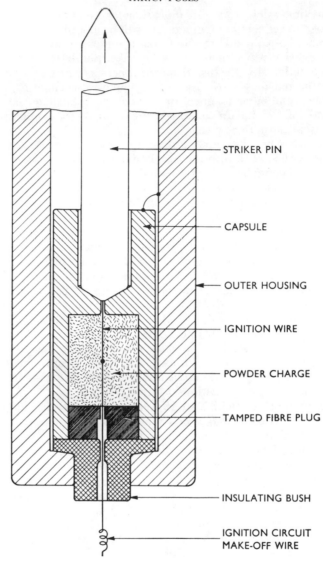

STRIKER PIN

CAPSULE

OUTER HOUSING

IGNITION WIRE

POWDER CHARGE

TAMPED FIBRE PLUG

INSULATING BUSH

IGNITION CIRCUIT
MAKE-OFF WIRE

Figure 10.18. Elements of striker assembly greatly enlarged (courtesy EMP Electric Ltd.)

circuit is defined, the severity at these lower values having been discussed in other chapters and being equally applicable to fuses.

If the fuse tested as above has a 'cut-off' current less than the numerical value of the a.c. prospective current, i.e. less than approximately 70% of the numerical value of the symmetrical peak associated with the prospective current, then further tests have to be made at some smaller prospective current such that the 'cut-off' current of this smaller prospective value is not less than the numerical value of the smaller prospective current.

In some types of fuse there is, within the range of duty, a prospective current, usually a moderate overcurrent, at which operation is inherently difficult.

254

Manufacturers usually check for this by carrying out tests at a prospective current not less than the minimum fusing current but not more than 1·4 times this value.

The tests as described will therefore prove the ability of a fuse:

(*a*) At the upper limit of prospective current for which the fuse is rated.

(*b*) At values of prospective current where 'cut-off' may not occur or may occur to such a limited extent that the 'cut-off' current exceeds the numerical value of the reduced prospective current but is less than the associated peak.

(*c*) At a very-low value of current not much greater than the minimum fusing current.

The test circuit for medium-voltage fuses is that indicated in Fig. 10.19. Oscillographic records of tests made on medium-voltage h.r.c. fuse-links are

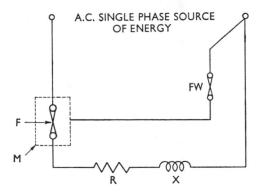

A.C. SINGLE PHASE SOURCE
OF ENERGY

FW

F

M

R   X

LEGEND

F	FUSE ON TEST	*X*	REACTOR (IF REQUIRED)
M	METAL CASE	*FW*	FINE-WIRE FUSE
R	RESISTOR (IF REQUIRED)		(40 S.W.G. OR SMALLER)

Figure 10.19. Test circuit as in BS 88 : 1967 for medium voltage h.r.c. fuse tests. During tests the metal case is connected to earth through FW

given in Figs. 10.20 and 10.21, the former showing the oscillographic record of a test as indicated at (*a*) above where the prospective current is 46 000 A, and 'cut-off' occurs at 20 000 A, the latter showing the record for a test as at (*b*) where the prospective current is only 11 000 A and the peak 'cut-off' current exceeds this, i.e. is 14 250 A.

It is of interest to note the two X-ray photographs reproduced in Figs. 10.22 and 10.23 to show the fused element condition after clearing the rated prospective current (33 000 A) and the much lower value of 2 500 A.

We have noted earlier and have discussed in some detail the cut-off and I^2t characteristics of medium-voltage h.r.c. fuse-links. It has been noted how the former limits the electromagnetic stresses and the thermal conditions in associated apparatus and the value of the latter in assessing discrimination between fuses in series.

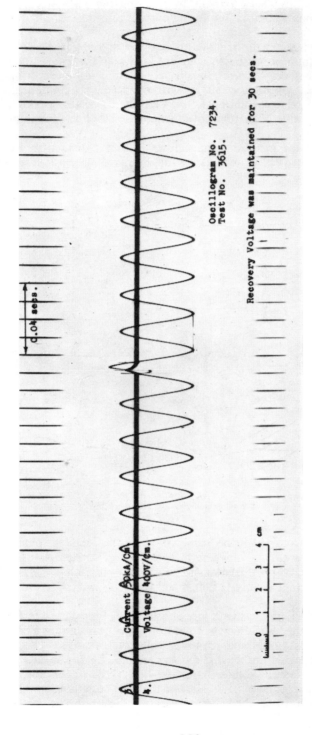

Figure 10.20. *Short-circuit test oscillogram for 'Brilag' fuse-link, 300A. Prospective current 46·0 kA, cut-off (peak) 20·0 kA and total operating time 0·0063s (courtesy Fluvent Electric Ltd.)*

256

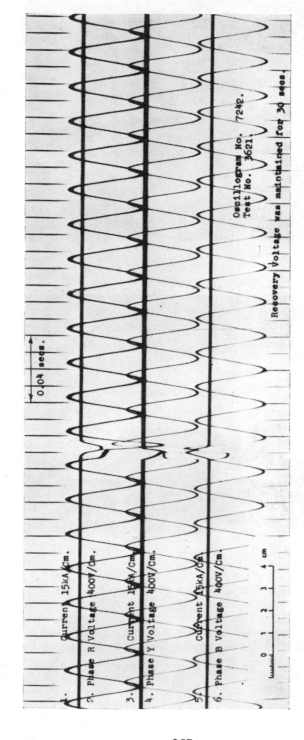

Figure 10.21. Short-circuit test oscillogram for 'Brilag' fuse-link, 300A, category A.C.5. Prospective current 11·0 kA, cut-off (peak) 14·25 kA and total operating time 0·0106s (courtesy Fluven: Electric Ltd.)

257

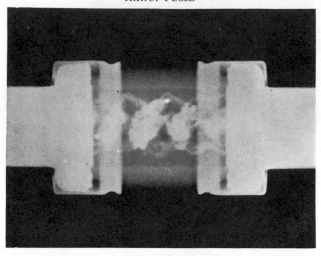

Figure 10.22. X-ray photograph of fuse after clearing 33 000A (r.m.s.) (courtesy A. Reyrolle & Co. Ltd.)

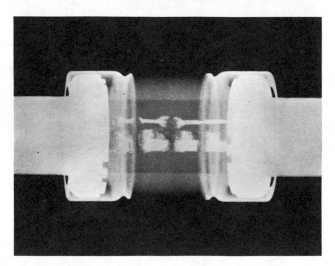

Figure 10.23. X-ray photograph of fuse after clearing 2 500A (r.m.s.) (courtesy A. Reyrolle & Co. Ltd.)

These characteristics, their attendant advantages and uses apply equally to high-voltage h.r.c. fuses, and Figs. 10.24 to 10.27 inclusive are included here to show the cut-off and I^2t characteristics for typical fuse-links. Apart from their use in high-voltage fuse-switches, rural fuse units (pole mounting), load-breaking switches, etc. they also find an application in series with air-break circuit-breakers in draw-out or drop-down switchgear equipments. The latter have been extensively used for the control of large high-voltage motors at 3·3, 6·6 and 11 kV such as are in common use today, notably power station services. Such is the size of the modern power station that even at auxiliary switchboards, the fault levels can be as high as 250 MVA at 3·3 kV, 350/500 MVA at 6·6 kV and 750 MVA at 11 kV.

Switchgear incorporating air-break circuit-breakers of these ratings will be noted in later chapters but they are rather expensive when regarded simply as a motor control unit, and in recent years the higher-voltage h.r.c. fuse has been combined with circuit-breakers in an endeavour to reduce the cost. In this way, the circuit-breaker and associated apparatus can be for a much lower fault level, e.g. 50 MVA at 3·3 kV, or 250 MVA at 11 kv, the back-up fuses being rated to suit the full system fault level. Such combinations are limited by (a) the range of current ratings of the h.r.c. fuses and (b) difficulties of accommodation within the switchgear unit design. Where this latter consideration is surmountable,

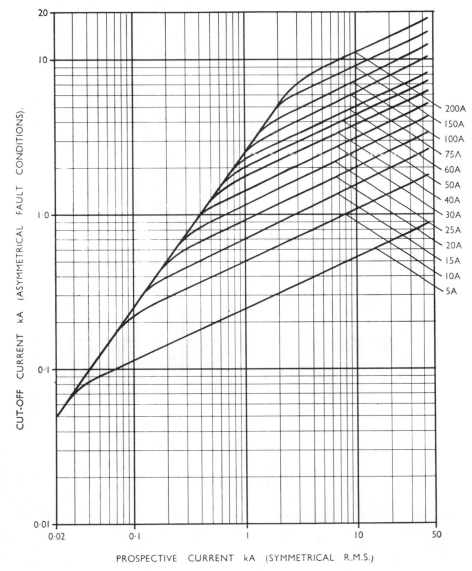

Figure 10.24.   Cut-off current characteristics of one range of 3·3 kV h.r.c. fuse-links for use in air at prospective currents up to 43·8 kA (courtesy English Electric Fusegear Ltd.)

259

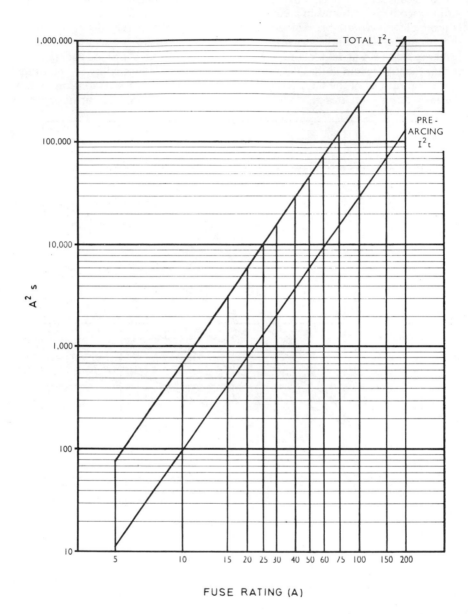

Figure 10.25. Maximum I^2t characteristics for one range of 3·3 kV h.r.c. fuse-links for use in air
(courtesy English Electric Fusegear Ltd.)

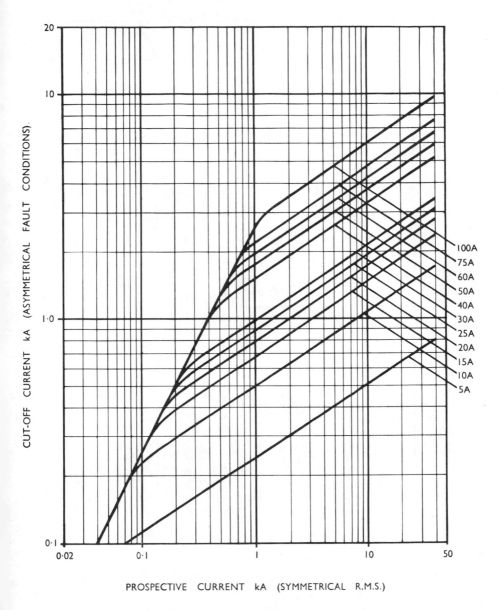

Figure 10.26. Cut-off current characteristics of one range of 11 kV h.r.c. fuse-links for use in air at prospective currents up to 39·4 kA (courtesy English Electric Fusegear Ltd.)

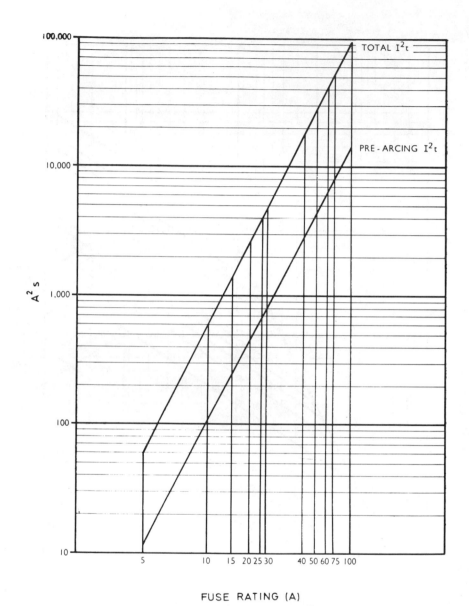

Figure 10.27. *Maximum I²t characteristics for one range of 11 kV h.r.c. fuse-links for use in air (courtesy English Electric Fusegear Ltd.)*

Figure 10.28. Rear view of an English Electric class E3 high-voltage air-break circuit-breaker carriage with h.r.c. fuses (courtesy G.E.C. Switchgear Ltd.)

fuse-links in parallel can be successfully used. In this way, Schwarz[6] has quoted data on tests with a 3 000 h.p. motor using three 350 A, 250 MVA fuse-links in parallel per phase at 3·3 kV and four 90 A, 750 MVA fuse-links in parallel per phase at 11 kV. In an article by Wright[7] it has been stated that the physical limitations of an existing design of switchgear unit are such as to preclude the use of fuses in series with an air-break circuit-breaker for motors above about 2 500 h.p. at 6·6 kV and 11 kV, particularly if the fuse-links are ideally placed, i.e. on the busbar side and forming an integral part of the draw-out circuit-breaker as shown in Fig. 10.28.

In other applications, high-voltage motor-starting equipments will be of the contactor type, and as a contactor has only a limited breaking capacity, e.g. up to six times its normal current rating, back-up h.r.c. fuses form an essential element of such units.

Finally, it is of interest to note that whereas our discussion on high-voltage h.r.c. fuse-links has been related to voltages up to 11 kV (this being the range normally associated with various forms of switchgear) BS 2692 covers a much wider range, i.e. up to 132 kV. Such a range is, for example, listed by E.M.P. Electric, starting at 2·4 kV with current rating at this lower end of the voltage range extending to 400 A and progressively reducing to 30 A at 88–132 kV. The interrupting capacities range from 230 MVA at 2·4 kV to 2 000 MVA at 132 kV.

REFERENCES

1. GRANT, L.C., 'High-power Fusible Cut-outs', *J.I.E.E.*, **64** (1926)
2. DEAN, R.H., 'Recent Developments in Medium-voltage h.r.c. Fuse-links', *Proc. I.E.E.*, **105** Part A, No. 21, June (1958)
3. DEAN, R.H., 'Fusing Factors of h.r.c. Fuses', *Elect. Rev.*, 9 Dec. (1966)
4. JACKS, E., 'Discrimination Between h.r.c. Fuses', *Proc. I.E.E.*, **106** No. 38, Part A, Aug. (1959)
5. GUILE, A.E., 'The Effects of Pre-loading on Fuse Performance', *Proc. I.E.E.*, **102** Part A, No. 1, Feb. (1955)
6. SCHWARZ, K.K., 'Further Development in the Design and Performance of High-voltage Terminal Boxes', *Proc. I.E.E.*, May (1968)
7. WRIGHT, A., 'Fuses in Series with Circuit-breakers', *Reyrolle Rev.*, No. 189 (1966)

BIBLIOGRAPHY

BAXTER, H.W., *Electric Fuses*, Edward Arnold
Cartridge Fuses for Voltage Ratings up to 660 V, BS 88:1967
FEENAN, J., 'Trends in the Design of High-voltage High-rupturing Capacity Fuses', *Proc. I.E.E.*, **118** No. 1, Jan. (1971)
GIBSON, J.W., 'The High-rupturing Capacity Cartridge Fuse with Special Reference to Short-circuit Performance', *J.I.E.E.*, No. 88 Part 2 (1941)
JACKS, E., 'The Role of the h.r.c. Fuse in the Protection of Low and Medium-voltage Systems', *The English Electric Journal*, **17** No. 3, Sept. (1961)
JACKS, E., 'H.R.C. Fuse Protection for High-voltage Power Circuits', *Electronics and Power*, April (1964)
LAPPLE, H., *Electric Fuses*, Butterworths, London (1952)
LYTHALL, R.T., 'Excess-current Protection by h.r.c. Fuses on Medium-voltage Circuits', *J.I.E.E.*, **93** No. 29, Part 2 (1945)
LYTHALL, R.T., 'High-voltage Motor Control Gear', *Elect. Rev.*, 29 Sept. (1967)
Cartridge Fuses for Voltage Ratings up to 600 V, BS 88:1967
Fuses for Alternating Current Circuits Above 660 V, BS 2692:1956

Chapter 11

Protective gear

When anything abnormal occurs on an electrical system, some action is necessary to isolate the abnormal condition either instantaneously or, in some circumstances, after a predetermined time delay. Such action must be automatic and selective, i.e. it must segregate the faulty section or piece of equipment leaving the healthy remainder in normal service. This is the function of protective gear which, in one form or another, is designed to sense the presence of dangerous conditions and based on this sensing, to isolate the circuit.

In very broad terms, the abnormal conditions against which protection is required may be summarised as follows:
(a) The condition of overloading which, if persistent leads to overheating of transformer or machine windings, busbars, connections and insulated cables.
(b) The failure of insulation to an extent where a dangerous leakage of current can occur to earth.
(c) The failure of insulation to the extent where a short-circuit occurs between two or three phases.
(d) The loss of, or a serious drop in, system voltage causing, for example, motors to stop.
In the case of conditions (b) and (c) external events may produce similar results, e.g. if vermin obtain access to bare conductors.

Many electrical circuits can be given adequate protection against these conditions by the application of relatively simple trip coils or relays, but these have limitations which lead to the need for more complex and special protective schemes, examples of which are those applied to highly interconnected power systems such as the 'Grid' system in Great Britain. For our purpose here it is convenient to consider first the simpler schemes and follow with some details of those of greater complexity. In passing we may note that perhaps the simplest of all protective devices is the fuse, types of which can be used either to cover *both* conditions (a) and (c) or to cover *mainly* condition (c). These alternatives have been considered in a fairly full discussion on the fuse as a protective device in Chapter 10, so that further discussion here is unnecessary.

It is doubtful whether the fuse will act as a protective device for condition (b) as so much depends on the resistance of the earth circuit and, even in good initial circumstances, deterioration can occur. Given a very low value of earth path resistance, fuses of relatively low normal current rating (probably not exceeding

265

80 A) can give a degree of *earth-fault* protection but will not give any against *earth-leakage* where it is required to detect small values of current.

Next in order of simplicity is the direct-acting overload trip coil which, with some limitations which will be noted, can protect simple radial feeder or motor circuits against the abnormal conditions (*a*) and (*c*). In certain types of switchgear, mainly in the medium-voltage range, these coils can be of the series or whole-current pattern, in which the coil is connected in series with the main circuit. Operating on the electromagnetic principle the coil acts as a solenoid with a central plunger, the latter being free to lift under electromagnetic influence to impinge on the circuit-breaker trip mechanism. There are, however, certain limitations as to the use of this type of coil, the first being that for high currents the production of a single-turn coil having sufficient conductor section is not easy—in one design for 800 A such a coil has been produced by suitably machining a solid block of copper—and the second being that at low currents a large number of turns of small cross-sectional area are necessary, such a coil is subjected to considerable stresses (electromagnetic and thermal) on the passage of short-circuit current, so much so that the breaking and making capacity and the short-time rating of the associated breaker may have to be related to the withstand ability of the series coils.

When these limitations apply and always in higher voltage switchgear, the direct-acting trip coil may be arranged for operation from the 5 A or 1 A secondary of a current transformer, the primary winding of which will be suited to the normal current rating of the circuit. This arrangement virtually isolates the trip coil from the primary circuit, the coil being completely relieved of stresses under short-circuit conditions as, at heavy currents, the transformer will saturate to place a limit on the secondary current. A further advantage is that should the normal rating of the primary circuit be changed, it may only be necessary to change the current transformers, the trip coil remaining undisturbed.

In both types of direct-acting trip coil, the operating current value is usually adjustable either by varying the magnetic gap or, in some designs, modifying the tension of a restraining spring. Calibration markings will be provided to indicate the various setting points, varying from the lowest coinciding with the rated normal current to the highest at three times this value.

If no other steps are taken, trip coils of either type will operate practically instantaneously (note that interruption by the circuit-breaker is not instantaneous because the latter will have an inherent minimum break-time of a few milliseconds) as soon as the current reaches the setting value. In the majority of circuits this is unwarranted and, indeed, in some cases where switching-in current surges occur, instantaneous operation would make it impossible to switch in a transformer or start a motor. All electrical apparatus can withstand some degree of overloading for a short time without damage, the heavier the overload the shorter the time it can be withstood. It is desirable, therefore, that some form of time delay device be added to the trip coil assembly which will give long delay times (relatively) at low values of overload, and shorter (maybe instantaneous) delay times as the current increases to short-circuit values. In other words, the retarding device should have an inverse time/current characteristic.

This may be achieved in two ways. Firstly, when a series connected overload trip coil is used, an oil dashpot can be attached in which there is a piston connected to the lower end of the solenoid plunger. This piston, immersed in

266

oil, provides retardation in such a way that the time of operation is related to the pull on the plunger, this pull being directly related to the current in the coil.

When the trip coil is current-transformer operated, time delay is obtained by connecting a time fuse across the trip-coil terminals, i.e. in parallel. This fuse should have an inverse time/current characteristic and will normally carry the current-transformer secondary current to by-pass the trip coil. As and when sufficient current occurs to 'blow' this fuse, the whole current is then transferred to the trip coil which operates to trip the breaker.

A standard specification has been issued by the British Electricity Boards (B.E.B.S.—S 14 (1966)) covering time fuses* used on higher-voltage circuit-breakers controlling step-down distribution transformers, the fuses having time/current characteristics in accordance with a given set of curves and indicating how the fuses shall be selected to ensure that discrimination is achieved with h.r.c. fuses used on the medium-voltage distribution. The foregoing discussion is illustrated by the single line diagrams shown in Fig. 11.1.

Reverting for a moment to the oil dashpot form of time delay it may be noted that for use in temperate climates and where there is no wide range of operating temperatures, a mineral oil of suitable characteristics may be used satisfactorily

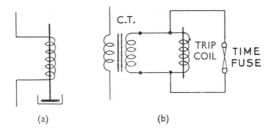

Figure 11.1. Trip coils. (a) *Series (whole) current trip coil with oil-dashpot time lag and* (b) *current-transformer operated direct-acting trip coil with time fuse*

in the dashpot. Such oils, however, have a rather steep viscosity/temperature curve, i.e. as the temperature rises so the oil becomes less viscous and there can be a significant reduction in the time delay characteristic. This is particularly important if the apparatus is to be used in tropical or sub-tropical climates when high ambient temperatures can exist and possibly vary over wide limits, where normal oils may have so diminished in viscosity as to give little or even no time delay. One solution to this problem lies in the use of a silicone fluid which has a relatively flat viscosity/temperature characteristic when compared with that of mineral oil, a point demonstrated in Fig. 11.2.

The simple nature of the direct-acting trip coil is such, however, as to make it unsuitable in certain circumstances as, for example, where a high degree of accuracy in both current and time settings is essential or where two or more circuit-breakers in series are required to trip discriminatively. Accuracy may not be too important in many circuits and relatively wide tolerances can be accepted. The need for discriminatory tripping on the other hand may arise in even the simplest of systems such as that shown in Fig. 11.3 where one incoming feeder with 400 A overload coils gives supply to two outgoing feeders each with 200 A coils.

* Previously designated *time-limit* fuses.

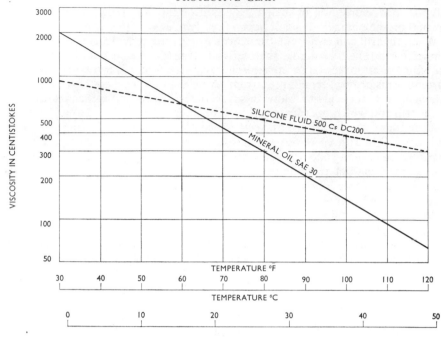

Figure 11.2. *Relative variation in viscosity with temperature change between silicone fluid 500cSt DC200 and mineral oil SAE 30*

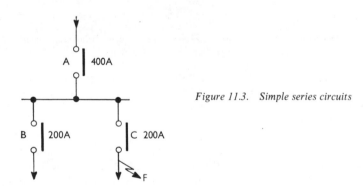

Figure 11.3. *Simple series circuits*

If we assume that a fault occurs on feeder *C*, as marked *F*, it is clear that the resultant current will flow through the two circuit-breakers *A* and *C* in series and unless the time delay on *A* exceeds that on *C* by a safe margin, both breakers will open. This, of course, is not necessary as to clear the fault, only breaker *C* need be opened, leaving *A* closed to maintain the supply to feeder *B*. To ensure discrimination, the time delay at *A* should be at least 0·2 s longer than at *C* for the same value of current, but when the latter is of short-circuit magnitude it is unlikely that any difference can be achieved, and both will operate instantaneously.

This problem can be solved by the use of special time-delay devices but much more satisfactory results are obtained by the use of relays which have an

inverse definite-minimum time-delay characteristic and which provide, incidentally, a very high degree of accuracy in relation to both current and time
settings. It must be noted, however, that the employment of a separate relay
requires additional tripping facilities at the circuit-breaker, arranged to be
energised from a separate source of supply, e.g. a 30 V tripping battery as shown
in Fig. 11.4(a).

Here it will be seen that when the relay operates to close its contacts, the
circuit to the trip coil is completed and a plunger is lifted to act on the trip
mechanism of the breaker. When a circuit-breaker in a particular part of a
system is fitted with a no-volt trip coil, this may be used instead of the shunt
type coil and battery, the contacts on the relay in such a case being arranged to
open on operation and open-circuit the no-volt coil as in Fig. 11.4(b). A further

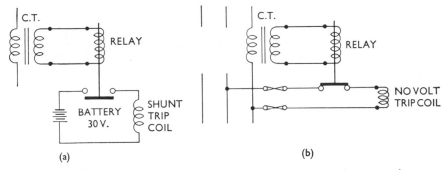

(a) (b)

Figure 11.4. Circuit-breaker tripping schemes when protective relays are used

*Figure 11.5. Relay and trip coil wired
for series tripping*

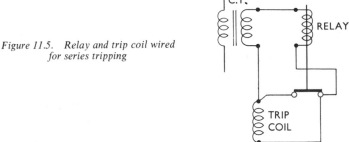

alternative is to arrange a current-transformer operated direct-acting trip coil
which is normally short-circuited by a pair of contacts on the relay as shown
in Fig. 11.5. Operation of the relay opens these contacts to remove the short-
circuit and the full current transformer output is now passed to the trip coil to
operate the circuit-breaker.

The inverse definite minimum time relay (known as I.D.M.T. for brevity)
has a characteristic time/current curve based on standard values given in
BS 142[1] and reproduced here as Fig. 11.6.

This basic curve shows that when the current reaches short-circuit magnitude,
no further reduction in operating time occurs below about 2·2 s, i.e. it has a
definite minimum time of operation. The relay is fitted with an adjustment

269

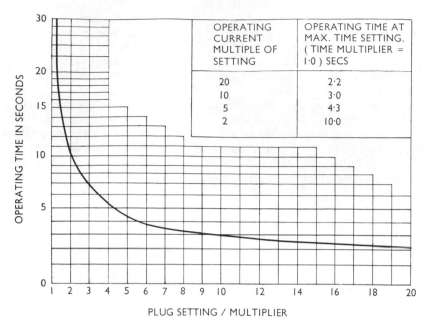

OPERATING CURRENT MULTIPLE OF SETTING	OPERATING TIME AT MAX. TIME SETTING. (TIME MULTIPLIER = 1·0) SECS
20	2·2
10	3·0
5	4·3
2	10·0

Figure 11.6.   Basic time/current characteristics of I.D.M.T. relay

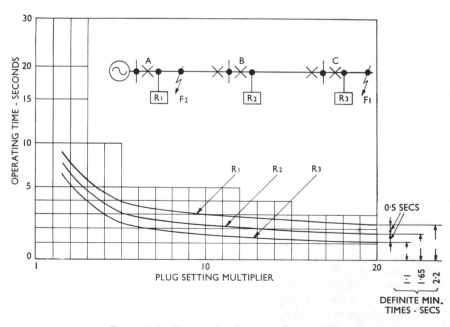

Figure 11.7.   Time grading between relays in series

270

known as the *time multiplier*, a device which controls the position to which the rotor in the relay resets after operation and thereby determining the travel the rotor has to make before it closes its associated contacts. This adjuster has a scale marked from 0·05 to 1·0 and it is at this latter value (unity time multiplier) that the curve in Fig. 11.6 is representative. Thus, if at unity time we obtain a definite minimum of 2·2 s, at 0·5 on the time multiplier we shall get a definite minimum of 1·1 s and at 0·05 obtain 0·11 s definite minimum. This gives, therefore, a range of definite minimum times of 0·11 to 2·2 s and with a number of relays in series, using a different time multiplier for each, discrimination can be obtained between them regardless of the current magnitude.

In practice, it is essential that the difference in definite minimum times between adjacent series relays shall be such as to cover the operating and arcing time of the circuit-breaker clearing the fault, an allowance for relay over-run and a further allowance for manufacturing tolerances. These factors may quite easily account for a total time of about 0·4 s, and for safety a difference between series relays of 0·5 s is often employed. This means that with a range of definite minimum times of 0·11 to 2·2 s, not more than five relays will be possible in series but relays can be obtained having higher upper limits, e.g. 4 s, thus permitting the use of more relays in series.

In some circumstances, the differential of 0·5 s can safely be reduced, as for example when it is known that the circuit-breaker has a high-speed clearance time (0·2 s has been assumed for this in our value of 0·5 s) or when the relays have an over-run time less than the permissible 0·1 s given in BS 142[1].

For the purpose of demonstration, however, it will be assumed that a difference of 0·5 s is allowed as between the I.D.M.T. relays associated with circuit-breakers A, B and C in Fig. 11.7. Using time multipliers of 1·0, 0·75 and 0·5 respectively for relays R_1, R_2 and R_3, we obtain three time-current curves as shown and indicating that for a fault at F_1, relay R_3 and circuit-breaker C will operate to clear the fault leaving breakers B and A in service.

Reverting to Fig. 11.3, it would be permissible to apply an I.D.M.T. relay at circuit-breaker A and ordinary direct-acting magnetic overloads with oil dash-pot time-lags at circuit-breakers B and C provided that the correct time discrimination is maintained at maximum fault level. Typical time/current characteristics would be similar to those in Fig 11.8.

The operating coil in an overcurrent I.D.M.T. relay is tapped to correspond to different current settings, usually covering the range 50–200% in seven equal steps although other ranges are available. The tappings are brought out to a plug bridge (shown in Fig. 11.9) for easy selection, and for any current above that chosen, the rotor will rotate and complete a pair of contacts in the breaker trip-coil circuit at the end of its travel. At currents less than the setting, movement is prevented by a restraining spring. Thus, this current-setting device enables discrimination to be maintained at low overloads where two circuit-breakers in series have current transformers of the same ratio.

If we refer back to Fig. 11.7 and recall what has been demonstrated in Chapters 3 and 4, it will be clear that the value of fault current at F_1 will be determined by the impedance of the generator plus that of the intervening cables or overhead lines between breakers A and C. If we now assume the fault to occur at F_2 however, the only impedance is that of the generator and therefore the fault current can be considerably greater. Because relay R_1 at breaker A has the longest time characteristic, this heavier fault current will be maintained for a relatively

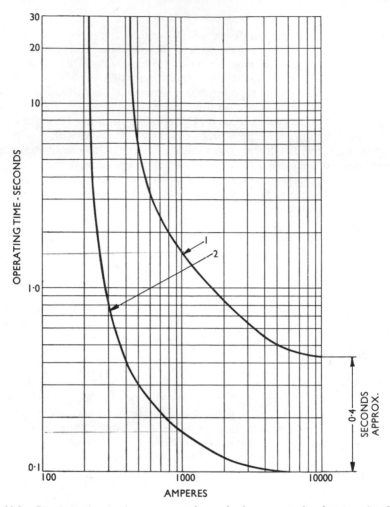

Figure 11.8. Discriminating time/current curves for overload protection—breakers in series. Curve 1 is a time/current curve for I.D.M.T. relay at breaker A in Figure 11.3. Curve 2 is a time/current curve for solenoid overload coil with oil dashpot on breakers B and C in Figure 11.3

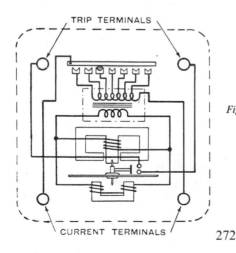

Figure 11.9. Connections for non-directional I.D.M.T. relay

272

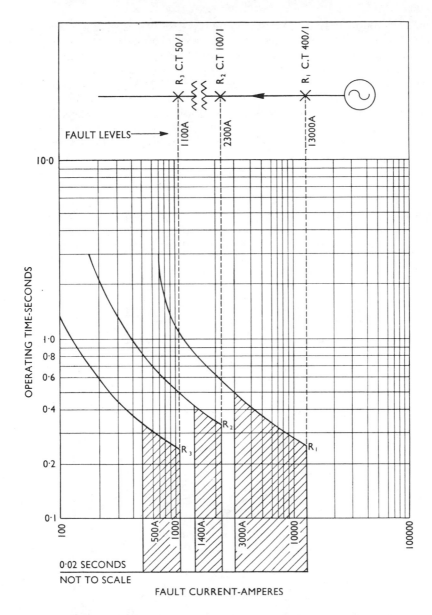

FAULT LEVELS⟶

OPERATING TIME-SECONDS

0·02 SECONDS
NOT TO SCALE

FAULT CURRENT-AMPERES

I.D.M.T. RELAYS ALL SET AT 125%
R1 SET AT 500 A ON 0·125 T.S.M.
R2 SET AT 125A ON 0·15 T.S.M.
R3 SET AT 62·5A ON 0·1 T.S.M.

INSTANTANEOUS HIGH SET RELAYS
R1 SET AT 3000 A
R2 SET AT 1400A
R3 SET AT 500A

T.S.M.=TIME SETTING MULTIPLIER

NOTE: THE EFFECT OF THE INSTANTANEOUS ELEMENT IS TO REDUCE THE OPERATING TIME IN
THE SHADED AREAS TO 0.02 SECOND THUS GIVING HIGH-SPEED OPERATION OVER A LARGE
PORTION OF THE CIRCUIT.

*Figure 11.10. Characteristics of combined I.D.M.T. relays and high-set instantaneous relays (after
Figure 3 of article by R. W. Newcombe in 'The English Electric Journal', March, 1956)*

long period unnecessarily. To overcome this disadvantage, relay manufacturers have developed an instantaneous overcurrent element which can be added to the normal I.D.M.T. relay and which can be set to give instantaneous tripping at high values of overcurrent, for example at 20 times normal full-load and operating in 0·02 s, instead of waiting for the I.D.M.T. relay to operate. It will be obvious that this high-set instantaneous relay element to override the inverse relay at specified current values can be applied equally to relays R_2 and R_3, the instantaneous current-setting getting progressively lower as we leave the source supply. Figure 11.10 serves to illustrate how I.D.M.T. relays with instantaneous high-set trips can be applied on a transformer feeder.

While many applications for the I.D.M.T. relay can be met by one having the standard characteristic noted in Fig. 11.6, there are other applications where a modified characteristic would be more suitable. This has led to the development of relays having either (i) a very inverse characteristic, or (ii) an extremely inverse characteristic. A comparison of these with the standard is given in Fig. 11.11, noting that each curve is shown at the unity time-multiplier setting.

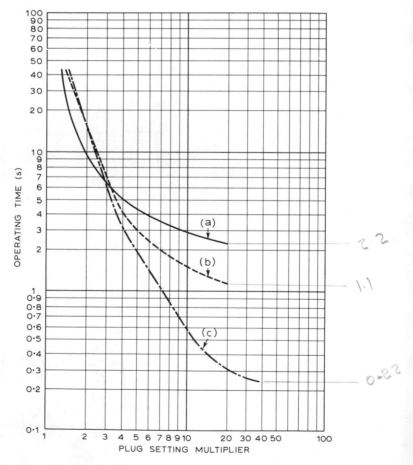

Figure 11.11.   Comparison between characteristics of (a) inverse, (b) very inverse and (c) extremely inverse D.M.T. relays at T.M.S. = 1·0

274

A relay with a very inverse characteristic is particularly suitable in cases where there is a substantial reduction of fault current as the distance from the power source increases. Its curve shows that the operating time is almost doubled for a reduction in current from seven to four times the plug multiplier setting, thus permitting the use of the same time-setting multiplier for several relays in series while maintaining adequate difference in tripping times between adjacent circuit-breakers.

The extremely inverse relay is most suitable on feeders subject to peak-current surges when switching in. The characteristic is such as to allow time grading with h.r.c. fuses, an example being that where, on a rural distribution network, automatic reclosers are used to restore service following a transient

Figure 11.12. Precision-type direct-acting overcurrent release assembly (courtesy Brown Boveri & Co. Ltd.)

fault. On these networks, fuses may be used in tee-off feeds to consumers and it is a requirement that the auto-recloser should open before the fuse operates in the faulty tee-off. This switching scheme is discussed in more detail in Chapter 21.

Other applications include its use in conjunction with a negative-phase sequence network applied for the protection of large generators and its use on generator circuits as a protection against internal and external faults. In the latter application its characteristic gives adequate protection at the lower values of current while providing ample time for discrimination with other relays on the system.

On medium-voltage systems, the use of I.D.M.T. relays is a costly alternative to the simple direct-acting overload devices discussed earlier. There are, however, many applications where something better than the latter is necessary and this need has led to the development of more sophisticated designs of direct-acting devices which, while not having the accuracy and close calibration tolerance of the I.D.M.T. relay, can provide similar characteristics and allow a very considerable measure of co-ordination and discrimination. This development has been recognised in national and international standards.

Their use has been largely linked with the modern medium-voltage air-break circuit-breaker and one such device is a chassis-assembled 3-pole arrangement as shown in Fig. 11.12. This is contained within the base of the circuit-breaker as seen in Fig. 11.13, and can be removed complete and replaced by another having different characteristics, should a change of electrical conditions warrant it.

The design is based on the use of four basic overcurrent elements, three of which have definite-minimum-time characteristics and the fourth being a high-set instantaneous release. The D.M.T. releases, designated long, medium and short, have characteristics as shown typically in Fig. 11.14, each release being designed to cover a range of D.M.T. at a specified multiple of the pick-up current, the range being adjustable but set at the required D.M.T. by the

Figure 11.13. Front view of air-break circuit-breaker with overcurrent assembly as in Figure 11.12, in base (courtesy Brown Boveri & Co. Ltd.)

276

factory. The pick-up setting is also adjustable and can be chosen by the user. The data appropriate to these releases is given in Table 11.1.

In suitable circumstances, any one D.M.T. release per pole may by itself satisfy the protective requirements, as for example on simple radial feeders where the medium range release with its D.M.T. range of 0·15 to 0·75 s at 10 times the pick-up current is adequate and wide enough to provide discrimination between circuit-breakers in series. It is a feature of the design however, that any two D.M.T. releases per pole, e.g. long and short or medium and short, can be assembled in tandem thus providing different characteristics as between overload and short-circuit conditions.

When discussing the I.D.M.T. relay, note was taken of the advantages to be gained by fitting a high-set instantaneous element in that relay. These advantages can be obtained with this direct-acting design by a tandem arrangement using one D.M.T. release and the high-set instantaneous release per pole, e.g. a long D.M.T. plus the instantaneous element.

On medium-voltage systems, a combination of this type is additionally valuable in that, for example, a main feeder may give supply to a number of sub-circuits controlled by apparatus of limited fault capacity, e.g. moulded case circuit-breakers, and here instantaneous interruption at an appropriate value of fault current will protect the lower rated apparatus. Cables associated with these sub-circuits may be of relatively small cross-section and will therefore have a very limited short-time rating (refer to Chapter 3 for discussion) and here again, instantaneous tripping of the main circuit-breaker at an appropriate value will avoid possible damage to those cables and avoid the use of much greater sectional area.

If the sub-circuits are fused, i.e. controlled by fuse-switches or they comprise motor-starting apparatus incorporating h.r.c. fuses, the cables beyond the fuses are adequately protected against short-circuit currents, but even here the presence of an instantaneous release can be of value in that it gives protection against a busbar fault on the sub-distribution board. If applied for this purpose, the setting of the instantaneous release must be high enough to ensure it does not take over the protective function of the h.r.c. fuses, i.e. it should not operate when faults occur *beyond* the fuses.

The use of the medium range D.M.T. release has been noted earlier. The long range release, apart from giving overload protection, is particularly suitable for circuits where current surges of short duration occur on switching in, e.g. motor control circuits where the motor is switched direct-on-line. Its time range extending to 70 s at six times the pick-up current is adequate for quite difficult starts over a relatively long accelerating period.

The short range release, on the other hand, is specifically for selective short-circuit protection and normally would always be used in tandem with one of the other two D.M.T. releases.

Constructionally, the instantaneous release is a solenoid whose pivoted armature is held open by a spring. When the current reaches a magnitude equal to or greater than the pick-up setting, magnetic force overcomes the spring, attracting the armature and in turn tripping the breaker. The pick-up setting is determined by adjusting the tension of the restraint spring.

The D.M.T. releases are similar in principle but are fitted with a delay mechanism of the dashpot type in which silicone fluid is used to provide consistent operation over a wide temperature range. The time delay is obtained by the slow transfer of the fluid through a calibrated orifice, but as the accuracy is dependent on the viscosity of the fluid and as this is affected in some degree by temperature (see Fig. 11.2) it is necessary to provide a form of temperature compensation. To meet this, compensation is achieved by a needle which controls the orifice opening in such a manner that the delay mechanism is independent of temperature over a wide range. The mechanism is basically the same for each D.M.T. release, the design time-range being determined by using a silicone fluid of appropriate viscosity, coupled with variations in the cross-section of the orifice.

Differing in detail, but offering equal protective facilities, is a design by English Electric (G.E.C. Switchgear Ltd.). Here again the basic element is an instantaneous release as previously described, this being adapted to provide

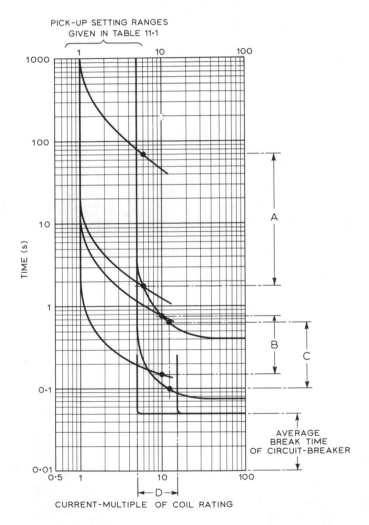

Figure 11.14. Time/current characteristics of D.M.T. direct-acting series overcurrent releases. See Table 11.1 for explanatory notes (courtesy Brown Boveri & Co. Ltd.)

PROTECTIVE GEAR

three types of release by the addition of special delay mechanisms. The releases so formed are designated D.M.T., Dual Characteristic and Pre-set Selective and are accommodated at the base of medium-voltage air-break circuit-breakers.

To provide a release with a D.M.T. characteristic, the instantaneous release is combined with a delay attachment described as a non-agitating positive-displacement oil-compression dashpot[2]. Using silicone fluid, the time-delay range is dependent on the viscosity of the fluid used. The dashpot is connected to the direct-acting trip through a cam-roller mechanism and the D.M.T. setting (specified as that obtained at 10 times the coil rating) is varied by adjusting the cam.

The D.M.T. setting can be adjusted down to instantaneous if required, the range upwards being dependent on the coil rating, e.g. with coils rated 1 000 A and above, a setting of up to 2 s D.M.T. can be obtained and for coils in the range 300–800 A, the range is up to approximately 0·6 s. For coils below 300 A and

Table 11.1
DATA RELATIVE TO FIG. 11.14

	A	B	C	D
	Long	Medium	Short	Instantaneous
Time range (s)	1·7–70 at 6 times pick-up current	0·15–0·75 at 10 times pick-up current	0·1–0·6 at 2·5 times pick-up current	—
Pick-up ranges (times coil rating) I.E.C.	0·6–1·0		3·0–6·0	8–16
N.E.M.A.	0·8–1·25		4·0–10·0	5–15
OTHER	0·8–1·6 1·0–2·0	0·8–1·6 1·0–2·0		
The curves shown in Fig. 11.14 given at pick-up setting	1·0	1·0	5	5–15

dependent on the magnitude of fault current, a release of the dual characteristic type may be recommended. The pick-up setting is independently adjustable between 100% and 300% of the coil rating.

The time/current characteristic of this D.M.T. release is of the very inverse form, as shown at A in Fig. 11.15, enabling discrimination with h.r.c. fuses and circuit-breakers in series to be obtained. The D.M.T. remains substantially constant irrespective of the pick-up setting chosen.

The dual-characteristic release is an arrangement similar to the D.M.T. but is so designed that the time delay is only effective up to a predetermined value of current, beyond which tripping is instantaneous, as shown by curve B in Fig. 11.15. The value of current at which instantaneous tripping occurs can be pre-set over a range of 5 to 15 times the coil rating. This range enables a choice to be made which is clear of the starting current taken by direct-on-line induction motors, a setting of 12 times being usual. A D.M.T. range of 0·30 s or 0·15 s can be provided, specified at six times the coil rating, and affording a choice to cover the accelerating time of most induction motors.

This device is particularly suitable where a good overload characteristic is required coupled with an instantaneous fault trip to protect sub-circuit cables

279

of low cross-section and sub-circuit apparatus of limited short-circuit rating. It is valuable also where the overcurrent coils are of a low rating, e.g. below 300 A and have a correspondingly low short-time rating. The pick-up current can be set in the range 85% to 300% of the coil rating.

The pre-set selective unit is similar to the dual characteristic device, except that instead of tripping instantaneously at a pre-set current it trips with a delayed characteristic in the short-circuit zone so that the time/current tripping curve consists of two separate characteristics, as shown in curve C in Fig. 11.15, both time delays are independently adjustable. This is particularly valuable in that it allows overcurrents of foreseeable duration to be catered for, e.g. induction-motor starting currents, while the facility of a short time-delay in the short-circuit zone avoids tripping the circuit-breaker on through-faults, i.e. a fault which should be cleared by some other device nearer to the point of fault. The characteristic is also such that discrimination with h.r.c. fuses of much higher rating than is possible with the D.M.T. device can be achieved.

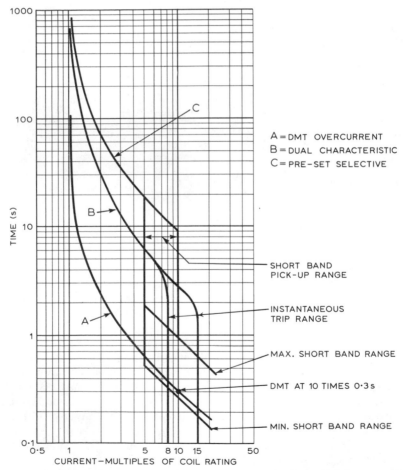

Figure 11.15. Time/current characteristics of 'English Electric' time-controlled direct-acting series-overcurrent tripping units set at 100% pick-up (courtesy G.E.C. Switchgear Ltd.)

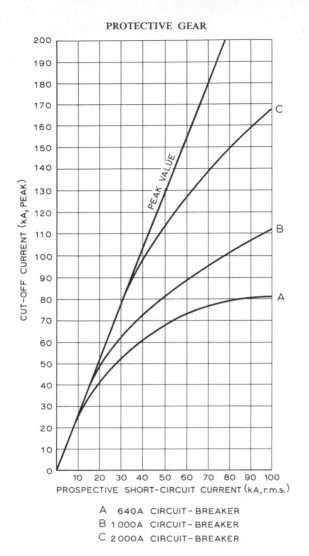

Figure 11.16. Cut-off characteristics of 'Brush-Delle' high-speed current-limiting circuit-breakers (courtesy Brush Switchgear Ltd.)

The time delay and pick-up settings for the overload zone are those noted for the dual-characteristic unit while the time delay for the short-circuit zone is calibrated at 10 times the coil rating with a pick-up setting range of 5–10 times. To achieve this performance, two armatures are provided, one of normal dimensions for the overload range and a smaller high-current armature for the short-circuit zone range coupled with an ability in the dashpot release mechanism to act as a mechanical relay and control the time delay under operating conditions with the application of a small force[2].

In Chapter 14 we shall note a design of medium-voltage air-break circuit-breaker ('Brush-Delle') of the 'current limiting' type in which, by virtue of its design, the prospective fault current is 'cut-off' at some value below the prospective peak in the first half-cycle (major loop) of short-circuit, i.e. having the

281

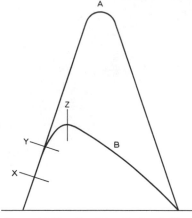

LEGEND

CURVE *A*: PROSPECTIVE SHORT-
CIRCUIT CURRENT
B: ACTUAL SHORT-CIRCUIT
CURRENT THROUGH CIRCUIT-
BREAKER AND SYSTEM
POINT *X*: INITIATION OF ULTRA-RAPID
TRIP
Y: REPULSION FORCES EXCEED
THE SPRING PRESSURE OF
THE CONTACTS, WHICH
OPEN TO CAUSE RESISTIVE
ARCING
Z: COLLAPSE OF FAULT-
CURRENT DUE TO ACTION
OF ULTRA-RAPID TRIP

Figure 11.17. Conditions in first half-cycle of short-circuit with 'Brush-Delle' high-speed current-limiting circuit-breaker (courtesy Brush Switchgear Ltd.)

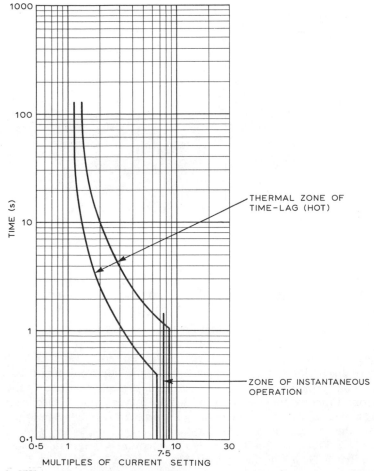

Figure 11.18. Time/current characteristics of thermal magnetic tripping device of high-speed current-limiting 'Brush-Delle' circuit-breaker (courtesy Brush Switchgear Ltd.)

282

characteristics of the h.r.c. fuse (see Fig. 10.8) and the resulting advantages. The cut-off characteristics for three breaker ratings are noted in Fig. 11.16.

This is achieved by designing the breaker in such a manner that its contacts form part of the conductor loop so that the electromagnetic forces cause partial opening by self-repulsion. This occurs at an instant in time approximately 0·25 of a cycle after the short-circuit occurs, thus inserting the resistance of the arc into the fault-current circuit with consequent reduction of the current. If left at this however, contact separation would be incomplete and the reduced current would continue to flow via the arc until current zero, at which point the forces of repulsion would cease and the contacts would reclose.

To prevent this, an ultra-rapid magnetic trip-device set to operate at a level below that of self-repulsion is fitted so that the holding-in mechanism is unlatched to allow the contacts to accelerate rapidly to the fully-open position. Variations of the magnetic release permit settings to be obtained most suitable for the application, e.g. 2·5 times normal full-load current for the protection of recti-fiers, moulded-case circuit-breakers, etc., 7 times for general purpose feeders and 14 times for heavy-current breakers on incoming feeders. The sequence of events described is illustrated in Fig. 11.17.

The foregoing however, offers no protection against small overloads so that a thermal/magnetic release is fitted for this purpose and operated by built-in current transformers. The thermal part of this device has an inverse characteris-tic as shown in Fig. 11.18 while the magnetic element operates almost instantane-ously at a fault level about 7·5 times the nominal primary rating of the current transformers. Variations of the thermal element allow for characteristics of the inverse or very inverse form. Pick-up settings are in the range of 1·0 to 1·6 times the nominal rating.

The abnormal conditions considered to this stage are those of simple overload or faults (short-circuits) involving two or three phases on a three-phase system. At least initially, however, most fault conditions arise due to an insulation failure on one phase allowing current to flow to earth, a condition which may lead rapidly to a fault between phases and, in passing, of danger to personnel. It is therefore desirable to consider some form of protection which will detect a fault to earth and disconnect it from the system in the shortest possible time.

For a limited number of circuit-breakers in the medium-voltage range, this form of protection can be achieved by a single direct-acting trip coil but, as in the case of an overload coil, it is unsuitable where discrimination is necessary and generally it is not too sensitive. Greater sensitivity can be obtained by using a moving-coil relay operated from a full wave a.c./d.c. rectifier but for dis-crimination and sensitivity a relay of the I.D.M.T. type offers the best solution.

The single trip coil or relay employed for earth leakage or earth-fault pro-tection will be connected in the secondary circuit(s) of one or more current transformers as shown in Fig. 11.19. In this illustration, (a) and (b) represent two forms of core-balance current transformer, that at (a) with the three primary conductors passing through a simple ring core without break while at (b) the core has three primary windings to which the primary conductors are connected. At (c) is shown how a single current transformer may be inserted in the neutral earth connection of a generator or transformer, a scheme which, when applied to a transformer, can be arranged to trip-out the circuit-breakers on both the primary and secondary sides. At (d) and (e) schemes are shown using three or four individual current transformers on three-wire or four-wire circuits respectively. In each of these except that at (c) the principle of operation is based on the fact that in a balanced circuit, currents in the three lines sum up to zero as shown in complexor form in Fig. 11.20. When a fault between one line and earth occurs, this balance is upset and the out-of-balance, or residual current, is fed to the relay and if this current is equal to the relay setting, operation occurs to cause disconnection of an associated circuit-breaker.

A balanced circuit as in Fig. 11.20 does not necessarily require that each current phasor R.Y.B. must be equal in magnitude or phase. With loads which are unbalanced, the current in each line may indeed be unequal but, so long as the system is healthy, i.e. no earth-fault or leakage exists, the three phasors representing these currents will still form a closed triangle and the protective gear will not function. Only when current from one line flows via earth and the earthed neutral point of the system is the balance upset and the three phasors will then not form a closed triangle.

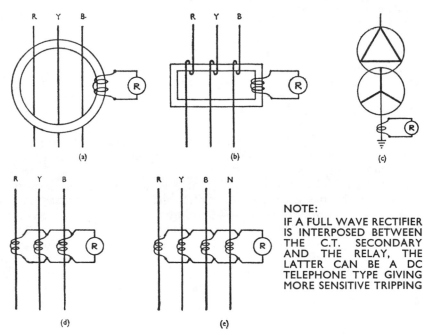

NOTE:
IF A FULL WAVE RECTIFIER IS INTERPOSED BETWEEN THE C.T. SECONDARY AND THE RELAY, THE LATTER CAN BE A DC TELEPHONE TYPE GIVING MORE SENSITIVE TRIPPING

Figure 11.19.   Basic forms of earth-fault protection

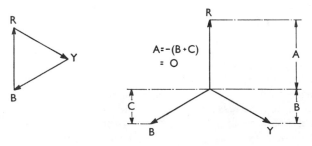

$$A = -(B + C)$$
$$= O$$

Figure 11.20.   How currents in a healthy balanced three-phase circuit sum up to zero

This theory, outlined in simple language, is related to symmetrical components as discussed in Chapter 4 involving zero-phase sequence current. It is important to note that these forms of protective gear do *not* give protection against so-called *single phasing*, i.e. an open circuit on one line. Note also that technically there is a difference between (a)(b) and (d)(e) in Fig. 11.19 in that with (a) and (b) it is the fluxes in the core which are normally balanced whereas in (d) and (e) the balance is between the three or four secondary currents.

Applied to an open-ended radial feeder this type of protection functions to isolate that circuit and no other when a fault occurs on the feeder. If applied

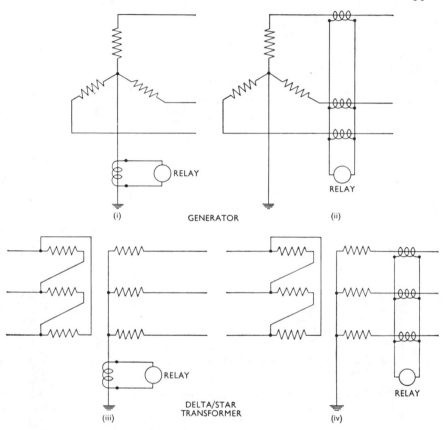

Figure 11.21. Unrestricted earth-fault protection

to an incoming feeder it will function to disconnect that feeder and the supply to the switchboard will be lost, even though the fault is on outgoing feeders. This is true also if applied to generator or transformer circuits, as in Fig. 11.21, in any of the forms shown. In all these cases the earth-fault may occur at points well beyond the immediate circuit to which the protection is applied but because the protective gear cannot discriminate, the circuit-breaker controlling the source of supply may be opened unnecessarily.

It follows from what has been said that earth-fault protection should be applied to individual outgoing feeder circuits and not to an incoming feeder which gives supply to a group of circuits and, if it is applied to a generator or

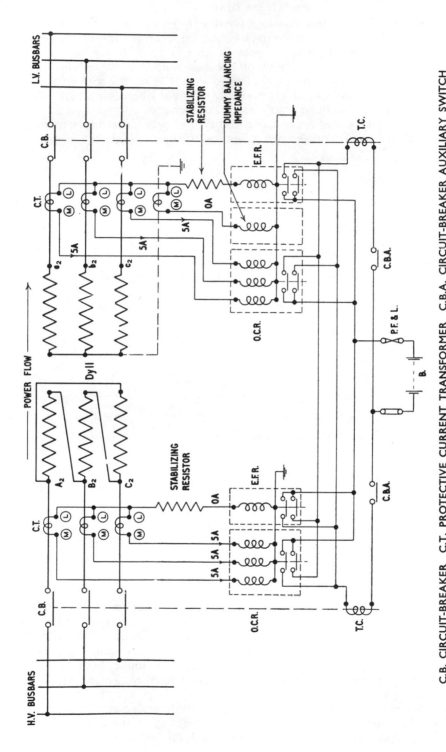

C.B. CIRCUIT-BREAKER C.T. PROTECTIVE CURRENT TRANSFORMER C.B.A. CIRCUIT-BREAKER AUXILIARY SWITCH
T.C. TRIP COIL O.C.R. OVERCURRENT RELAY E.F.R. EARTH FAULT RELAY
P.F. & L. PROTECTIVE FUSE AND LINK B. BATTERY

Figure 11.22. Overcurrent and earth-fault protection of a three-phase delta/star connected transformer

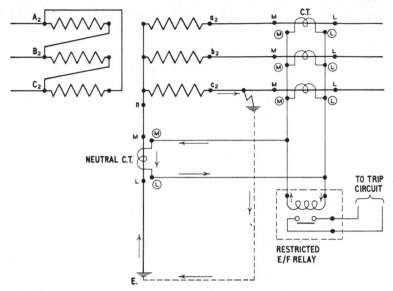

SHOWING OPERATION ON FAULT INSIDE ZONE

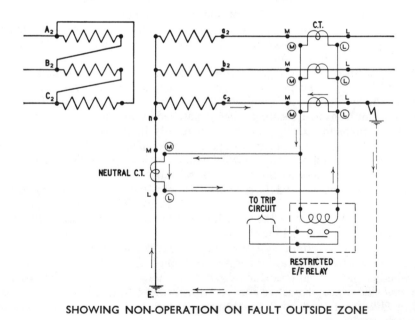

SHOWING NON-OPERATION ON FAULT OUTSIDE ZONE

Figure 11.23.   Principle of restricted earth-fault protection of transformers

transformer circuit, it should be of the type known as *restricted* earth-fault protection. Figure 11.22 shows how overcurrent and earth-fault protection may be applied to the primary and secondary sides of a three-phase delta/star power transformer.

On the primary (delta) side, the use of three current transformers, connected as shown to the earth-fault relay, gives restricted protection, i.e. to the delta winding only as this is unearthed. On the secondary side, however, we must add a fourth current transformer in the neutral connection to earth if we wish to restrict the earth-fault protection here to the secondary windings and connections thereto. This fourth current transformer is connected in parallel with the three line current transformers and the protective system will now discriminate between faults *external* to the protected zone and those *within* the zone, operating only for the latter as indicated in Fig. 11.23.

For the sake of simplicity, the secondary current in the upper diagram is shown to be wholly circulating through the relay. In fact, a part of this current divides to pass through the secondary windings of the three line current transformers which are in parallel with the one in the neutral connection[3]. The exact division will depend on the relative impedances of the relay coil and the secondary windings but it must be remembered that this division of current will have an effect on the relay settings.

It will be noted in Fig. 11.22 that (a) a dummy balancing impedance has been connected in series with the neutral current transformer on the secondary side of the power transformer and (b) a stabilising resistor has been connected in series with the earth-fault relay. The purpose of (a) is to balance the line and neutral current transformers when an *external* fault occurs and the dummy impedance must be equal to that of one of the overcurrent relay elements. The stabilising resistor (b) is applied where the earth-fault relay is of low impedance such that 'spill' currents may be sufficient to operate the relay in circumstances not calling for such operation.

In any form of balanced protection, stability must be maintained during a 'through fault', i.e. the passage of fault current to another (possibly remote) part of the system and demanding clearance at that other point. Unless the three current transformers are perfectly matched in ratio and other characteristics, these through currents, often of extremely high magnitude, can readily cause a 'spill' current to appear at the relay and if of sufficient magnitude, cause it to operate. This is a particular hazard when a sensitive earth-fault relay is set to operate at 1 A or less as no matter how well the current transformers are designed and manufactured the primary current will not be reproduced perfectly in each secondary and a 'spill' current will result. The stabilising resistor is therefore added to increase the impedance of the relay circuit and to reduce the value of spill current reaching the relays.

Many medium-voltage systems operate as four-wire and here restricted earth-fault protection for a star winding is applied in one of two ways depending on whether the neutral is earthed directly at the winding or at some point on the *load* side of the protective current transformers. Both conditions are noted in Fig. 11.24 from which it will be seen that either five or four current transformers must be employed.

When both overcurrent and earth-fault protection is applied to a circuit by I.D.M.T. relays, two overcurrent and one earth-fault elements are generally combined in a single relay, connected as in Fig. 11.25. The earth-fault element

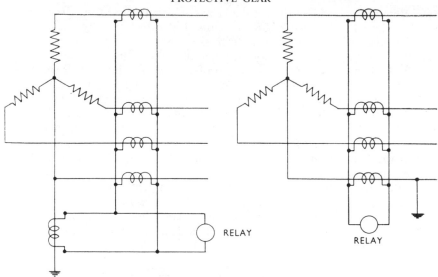

Figure 11.24. Restricted earth-fault protection applied to a four-wire system using five or four current transformers

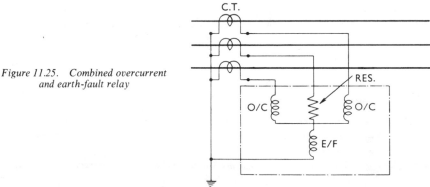

Figure 11.25. Combined overcurrent and earth-fault relay

will be very similar to those we have discussed for overcurrent conditions but the operating coil will be tapped to cover a range of 10% to 40% in seven equal steps. Its application on a time graded basis arranged to give discrimination with relays in series will also be as discussed for overcurrent.

The use of I.D.M.T. relays for the protection of simple 'open end' feeders and for feeders in *series* has so far been considered. It will, however, be clear that if applied to two or more feeders in *parallel* some other feature will be necessary to ensure that *only* the faulty feeder is disconnected. A typical system of this type is shown in Fig. 11.26 where three feeders are connected in parallel between a generating station and a remote supply point.

I.D.M.T. relays for overcurrent or overcurrent and earth-fault protection can be applied to a system such as this but to ensure discrimination, those at the receiving end must be of a directional type. In the diagram shown in Fig. 11.26 relays R_1, R_2 and R_3 at the sending end are recognised as non-directional by reason of the double-ended arrows indicating that they will operate for fault

289

power flow in either direction, i.e. the relays so far discussed. At the receiving end, the relays R_4, R_5 and R_6 are recognised as directional by reason of the single-ended arrows pointing away from the busbars towards the source and indicating that they are only operative when the power flow is in that direction.

Let it be assumed that a fault occurs on feeder B at point F. This can be fed via three paths, (a) direct from the power source along feeder B, (b) indirect through feeder A to the receiving end and then back along feeder B and (c) indirect through feeder C to the receiving end and back along feeder B. To isolate the fault, the circuit-breakers at each end of feeder B must open while all other breakers remain closed.

When the fault occurs, all non-directional relays (R_1, R_2, R_3) will start to operate. At the receiving end, relays R_4 and R_6 will not operate as the flow is against the arrow, and only relay R_5 will start to operate. But we do not want the circuit-breakers at the source end of feeders A and C to open, and this is ensured by reason of the fact that the fault current flowing through them will be lower than that in B due to the greater impedance between the source and

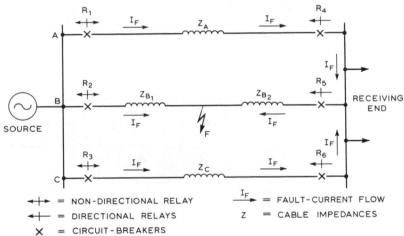

Figure 11.26. Application of directional and non-directional relays for parallel feeder protection

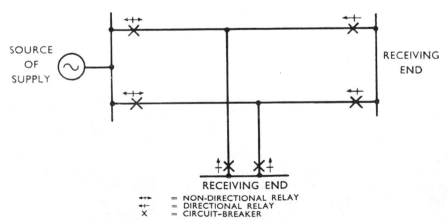

Figure 11.27. Parallel feeders with tee-off feeders

290

the fault via the receiving end. Thus the impedance via feeder A will be $Z_A + Z_{B_2}$ against the lower impedance Z_{B_1} in the direct feed. This means that relays R_1 and R_3 will take longer to reach the point of giving a trip impulse to their associated breakers, than relay R_2. Thus the sending-end breaker B opens and as relay R_5 will have caused its breaker to open, the fault is isolated, while relays R_1 and R_2 stop operating and will reset. To ensure that the directional relays at the receiving end operate (as indicated for R_5) they are usually given lower time and current settings than the non-directional types at the source. When a tee-off feed as shown in Fig. 11.27 is involved, directional and non-directional relays can be used as indicated.

To make the I.D.M.T. relay sensitive to direction of flow, a voltage element is added and is arranged so that it controls the current element, the internal connections being shown in Fig. 11.28 and operating on the wattmeter principle.

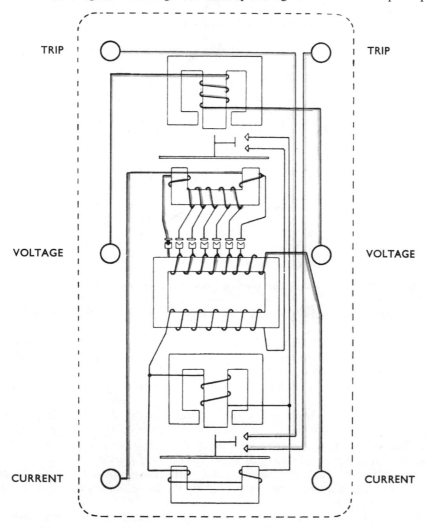

Figure 11.28. Internal connections for directional I.D.M.T. relay

291

By this means, with current flowing in one direction, the voltage element is inoperative and inhibits operation of the current element, but when current flows in the opposite direction, the voltage element operates to close a pair of contacts to initiate operation of the current element.

For the operation of a non-directional relay, only three current transformers are necessary. For directional relays, however, a voltage supply is essential, involving a three-phase voltage transformer as shown in Fig. 11.29. With directional earth-fault relays, however, when only one relay element is used to protect against earth faults on any of the three phases there is the problem of ensuring that the voltage applied to the directional-element voltage coil corresponds in phase to that of the current in the current coil. This voltage will be

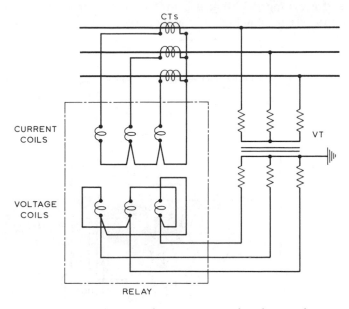

Figure 11.29. *Current and voltage transformer connections for a directional overcurrent relay*

the residual voltage of the system and will be the phasor sum of the three line to earth voltages.

Two methods of achieving this are shown in Fig. 11.30. In diagram (*a*) it will be noted that the neutral point of the high-voltage star winding is earthed and on a system where the neutral is also earthed, an earth-fault on one line short-circuits the winding connected to that line. In a normal (three-limb) transformer, the resultant flux due to two healthy lines returns through the transformer limb of a faulty line, inducing a heavy short-circuit current in the winding on that limb. This induces a voltage which is reflected in the corresponding secondary winding, and the voltage across the open point of the delta will not be the true residual. In order to obviate this it is necessary to provide a low reluctance return path of sufficient cross section to carry the maximum value of unbalanced flux without saturation. This is achieved by the use of a five-limb transformer as shown in Fig. 11.31.

The use of an open delta-connected tertiary winding to give a true residual voltage is demonstrated in Fig. 11.32. It is necessary to consider three cases,

292

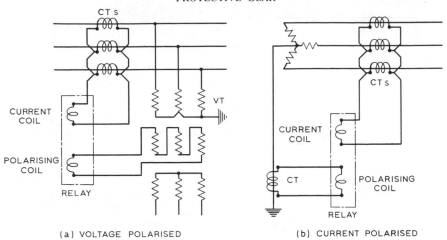

Figure 11.30. Current and voltage-polarising connections for a directional earth-fault relay

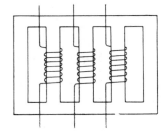

Figure 11.31. Elementary diagram of five-limb transformer

(a) where the system is healthy, (b) where there is an earth-fault on one phase of the system and the supply neutral is not earthed, and (c) where there is a fault on one phase of the system and the supply neutral is solidly earthed.

(a) Under healthy conditions all three phases will be balanced and the residual voltage of the system will be zero. The three e.m.f.s in the delta winding will form a closed triangle and the residual voltage V_R across the relay will be zero (see Fig. 11.32(a)).

(b) If there is an earth-fault on phase C of the system when the supply neutral is unearthed, then phase C will be at earth potential and the neutral point of the supply will be at a potential equal to the normal phase voltage, as shown in Fig. 11.32(b). The phase to earth voltage will now equal the normal line to line voltage, i.e. it will be $\sqrt{3}$ times as great as normal and the phase displacement between A_2A_1 and B_2B_1 will now be 60° instead of the normal 120°. As the phase to earth voltage has increased by $\sqrt{3}$, so the flux in the core will increase by $\sqrt{3}$, as also will the induced e.m.f. in each phase of the tertiary winding. These e.m.f.s will be displaced 180° from the primary and will sum up to give a resultant voltage:

$$V_R = \sqrt{3} \cdot \sqrt{3}V_T = 3V_T$$

i.e. three times as great as the normal tertiary-phase voltage.

If the secondary of the voltage transformer is rated at 110 V then the normal phase voltage will be $110/\sqrt{3}$, i.e. 63·5 V and the residual voltage across the

293

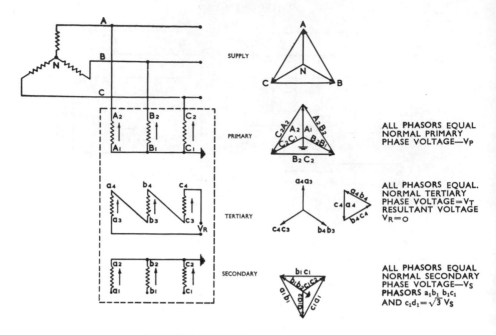

SUPPLY
PRIMARY
TERTIARY
SECONDARY
ALL PHASORS EQUAL NORMAL PRIMARY PHASE VOLTAGE—VP
ALL PHASORS EQUAL. NORMAL TERTIARY PHASE VOLTAGE=VT RESULTANT VOLTAGE VR=O
ALL PHASORS EQUAL NORMAL SECONDARY PHASE VOLTAGE—VS PHASORS a1b1 b1c1 AND c1d1=√3 VS
(a) HEALTHY SYSTEM
PHASORS A2A1 & B2B1 =√3 VP
PHASORS a4a3 & b4b3 =√3 VT
PHASOR VR =√3 . √3VT=3 VT
PHASORS a2a1 & b2b1 =√3 VS
PHASOR a1b1 =√3 VS
(b) EARTH FAULT ON PHASE C
SUPPLY NEUTRAL UNEARTHED

Figure 11.32 (above and opposite). Principle of the residual voltage transformer

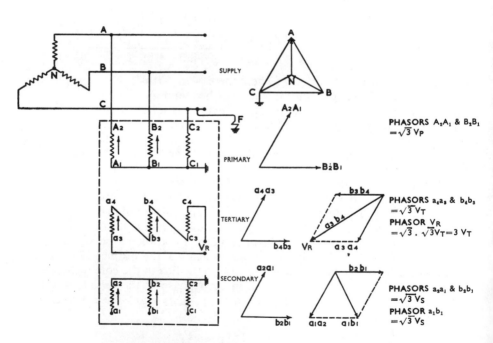

SUPPLY

PRIMARY

PHASORS A_2A_1
& $B_2B_1 = V_P$

TERTIARY

PHASORS a_2a_4
& $b_2b_1 = V_T$
RESULTANT PHASOR
$= V_R$

SECONDARY

PHASORS a_2a_1 b_2b_1
$= V_S$
PHASOR a_1b_1
$= \sqrt{3} V_S$

(c) EARTH FAULT ON PHASE C
SUPPLY NEUTRAL SOLIDLY EARTHED

relay will be three times this value, i.e. 190 V. It is noted from the phasor diagram that the resultant line to line voltage of the secondary winding will not exceed 110 V.

(c) If there is an earth-fault on phase C of the system and the supply neutral is solidly earthed, then (neglecting the impedance of the fault and of the supply) the voltage across phase C will disappear completely and the phasor diagram appear as in Fig. 11.32(c), the other phase voltages remaining at their normal values. The e.m.f.s in the tertiary winding will be displaced by 120° and will sum up to give a residual voltage V_R equal in magnitude to the normal phase voltage V_T, i.e. $V_R = 63.5$ V. It will also be seen that the resultant voltage across the secondary winding will not exceed 110 V.

Cases (b) and (c) represent two extreme conditions, i.e. where the system is either unearthed or is earthed solidly. If the neutral is now earthed through a resistance or impedance, the residual voltage across the tertiary winding will be a value somewhere between 63.5 and 110 V, depending on the value of resistance or impedance in the neutral.

Directional overcurrent and earth-fault protection as described for parallel feeders is also an ideal form of protection for ring main circuits, a simple form of which is shown in Fig. 11.33. Here a single source of supply feeds a ring cable which is interrupted in its course at four transformer substations. At the power source, two circuit-breakers control the ring main, each being fitted with non-directional relays.

At each substation the ring is broken by the insertion of two circuit-breakers and these are fitted with directional relays such that operation occurs only when fault current of appropriate magnitude flows *away* from the substation,

295

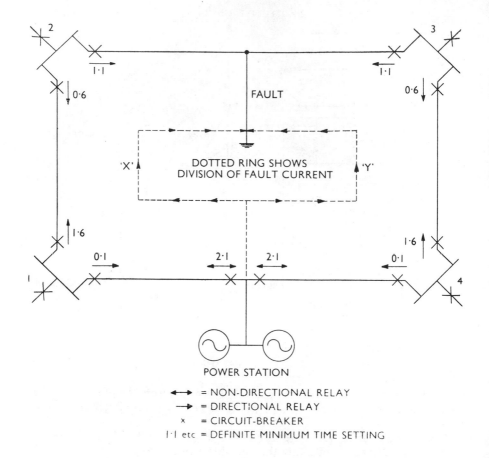

FAULT

DOTTED RING SHOWS
DIVISION OF FAULT CURRENT

'X'   'Y'

POWER STATION

↔ = NON-DIRECTIONAL RELAY

→ = DIRECTIONAL RELAY

×   = CIRCUIT-BREAKER

1·1 etc = DEFINITE MINIMUM TIME SETTING

Figure 11.33.   Directional protection applied to a simple ring main

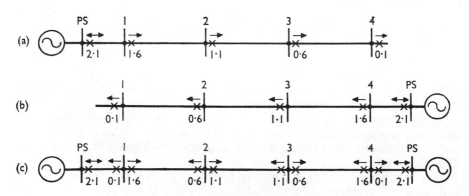

Figure 11.34.   Development of ring-main scheme

as indicated by the arrows. Thus, if a fault occurs on the cable between sub-stations 2 and 3, only the circuit-breakers at each end of this cable will open, leaving *all* substations in service but isolating the faulty cable. At each relay a figure, e.g. 1·1, is given. This is the selected definite minimum time setting of the relay and it will be noted that, starting at the source of supply in either direction, the outgoing relay settings are progressively reduced. This principle is shown in Fig. 11.34 where the ring is developed into two radial feeders (*a*) and (*b*) and superimposed at (*c*), which is the ring main developed into a straight line.

Assuming a fault at *F* between substations 2 and 3, fault power is fed via two paths *X* and *Y*, dividing in inverse ratio to their impedances. The fault power feeds through every substation but at each of these one set of relays will be inoperative because the power flow is against the arrow, while the other set will be operative because the power flow is with the arrow.

Considering the fault power flow in the direction *X* first, the relays at the power source and on the outgoing side of substations 1 and 2 have definite minimum time settings of 2·1, 1·6 and 1·1 s respectively. The 1·1 s relay on the outgoing side of substation 2 will obviously be the first to complete its operation, trip-out the associated circuit-breaker and thus clear the fault feed in this direction, the relays at the power source and substation 1 immediately resetting.

Considering now the feed in the direction *Y*, the relays at the power source and on the outgoing sides of substations 4 and 3 have definite minimum time settings of 2·1, 1·6 and 1·1 s respectively, thus ensuring that the circuit-breaker on the outgoing side of substation 3 with its 1·1 s setting will clear the fault leaving the remaining relays to reset.

In some circumstances, a ring main of the type shown in Fig. 11.33 may have the additional feature of an interconnector between two selected substations as shown in Fig. 11.35. The arrangement of relays around the ring is as previously noted but on the interconnector, relays of the non-directional type are used, and with a low definite-minimum time setting.

Because the relays in the tie are non-directional and will have a minimum time setting (0·1 s) a fault anywhere on the system will cause the tie to be isolated at both ends.

In Fig. 11.33, a fault has been assumed to occur at the mid-point of the ring so that the impedances of the two halves will be equal. In Fig. 11.36 however, the fault has been moved to a point close to the power source between this and substation 1. For this condition, the fault current through breaker *A* will be at its maximum as the impedance between the source and the fault will be very small. For reasons discussed earlier, the relay at breaker *A* may well have a high-set instantaneous element so that breaker *A* opens first to isolate the fault from one end. This leaves the fault fed right round the ring main until breaker *B* opens. While the relay here has a low time setting, it is essential to check the magnitude of the current reaching the relay and to select a current setting accordingly, allowing a good margin. This is because the impedance of the complete ring main will (or may) very considerably reduce the fault current reaching breaker *B*. In our diagram, the supply source envisages two generators, but considerations such as the foregoing should be based on the condition with minimum plant in operation, i.e. one generator.

It has been shown in Figs. 11.22 and 11.23 how earth-fault protection can be applied to a star winding (of a generator or transformer) in such a way as to limit the protection afforded to a defined zone. Zonal protection is an important

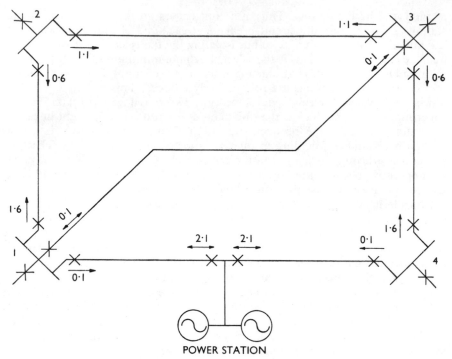

Figure 11.35. Directional protection applied to a ring main with interconnector (legend as for Figure 11.33)

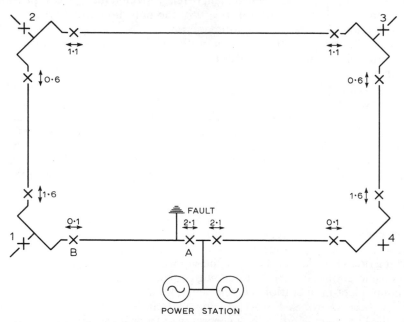

Figure 11.36. The condition for a fault near the power source on a ring main with directional protection (legend as for Figure 11.33)

feature of the well-known Merz-Price circulating current system, a differential scheme which can be applied to protect generators, transformers and feeders against phase to phase or earth-faults.

The system is discriminating in that it disconnects only the apparatus or feeder which is faulty and is stable for any faults beyond the protection zone, i.e. through-faults.

When applied to a generator, the scheme is very simple. The fundamental principle is that, under healthy conditions, the current entering at one end of a machine winding is identical, both in phase and magnitude, with that leaving the winding at the other end. On the occurrence of an internal fault this equality

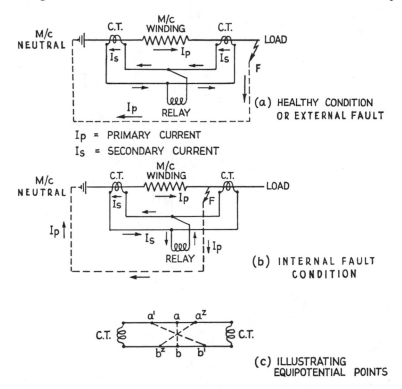

I_p = PRIMARY CURRENT
I_s = SECONDARY CURRENT

Figure 11.37.   Explanatory diagram illustrating the principle of circulating current protection

is disturbed and, when the unbalance reaches the necessary value of relay operating current, the plant is disconnected from the system by opening the main circuit-breaker.

Figure 11.37 is an explanatory diagram showing the principle of the circulating current system. It will be noted that current transformers (which have similar characteristics and ratio) are connected on both sides of the machine winding and a relay is connected across the pilot wires between the two current transformers. Under healthy or through-fault conditions the current distribution is as shown at (a), no current flowing in the relay winding. Should a fault occur as shown at (b), the conditions of balance are upset and current flows in the relay winding to cause operation. It will be noted that at (b) the fault is shown at a point between the two current transformers, the location of which determine

299

the extent of the protected zone. In order that the symmetry of the burden on the current transformers shall not be upset and thus cause an out-of-balance current to pass through the relay, causing operation when not intended, it is essential that the relay be connected to the pilot wires at points of equipotential. This is illustrated at (c) in Fig. 11.37, such equipotential points being those as *a* and *b*, *a'* and *b'*, etc. In practice it is rarely possible to connect the relay to the actual physical mid-point in the run of the pilots and it is usual to make the

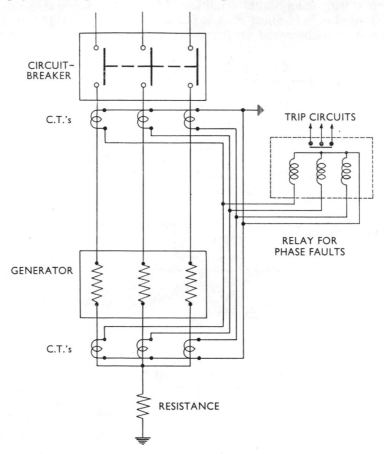

Figure 11.38. Merz-Price system of circulating current protection applied to a generator

connection to convenient points at the switchgear and to insert balancing resistances in the shorter length of pilot wire. The resistances should be adjustable so that accurate balance can be obtained when testing before commissioning the plant.

Figure 11.38 shows the protective gear connections for a three-phase machine. It will be noted here that there are two sets of three-current transformers, one set being mounted in the neutral connections (usually in the alternator pit), and the other being mounted in the switchgear equipment. Thus, not only are the machine windings within the protected zone but also the external connections to the switchgear.

The relay used in this scheme is usually an instantaneous attracted armature type with a setting range of 10 to 40 %. To ensure that the relay does not operate when a fault occurs externally to the protected zone, a stabilising resistor may be fitted in series with the operating coil. While normally such incorrect operation is improbable, there may be a condition where one set of current transformers saturate during an external fault, and the stabilising resistors will be of such value as to ensure that unwanted operation does not occur.

The current transformers, connected in star as shown, will be chosen to have similar characteristics and preferably they should not be used for any other function than that of protection. If used for other purposes as well, e.g. instrumentation, unequal secondary loading may occur.

When circumstances are such that the current transformers on the line side have dissimilar characteristics from those at the neutral end of the windings, relatively large spill-currents may flow through the relay winding, and if large enough may cause operation on faults external to the protected zone. In this case the relay should be of the biased differential type, the connections being

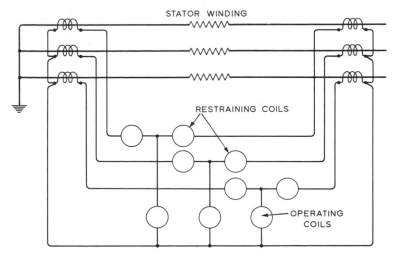

Figure 11.39. The principle of a percentage-biased differential relay in a circulating-current protective scheme

as shown in Fig. 11.39. This relay comprises two restraint coils and one operating coil per phase; the torque produced by the operating coil which tends to close the relay contacts is opposed by the restraint-coil torque.

Under through-fault conditions, i.e. external faults outside the protected zone, the relay setting is increased so that spill current will not cause relay operation. For internal faults however, the torque produced by the restraint coil is ineffective and the relay closes its contacts when the setting current flows in the operating coil.

In order to provide for the detection of earth faults, the modified system shown in Fig. 11.40 has been developed, use being made of an earth-fault relay element operating on the residual principle.

When generators are directly connected to the distribution system, the scheme can provide high-speed discriminative earth-fault protection with low settings. Since the earth-fault current is limited by the earthing resistance, there is a substantial difference in fault magnitude between earth faults and phase faults, and to ensure stability on through faults, relatively high phase-fault settings must be used.

Earth-fault protection for generator stator faults can be provided in other ways and is influenced by the method of neutral-point earthing. The preferred practice in the U.K. is resistor earthing as in earlier diagrams and with this a current transformer is mounted in the generator neutral as shown at (a) in

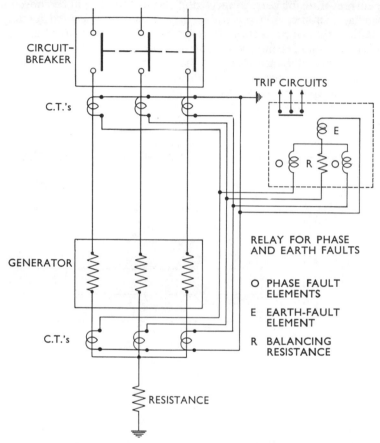

Figure 11.40. Modified scheme as Figure 11.38 to include earth-fault protection

Fig. 11.41 and connected to an earth-fault relay. When a generator is directly connected to the distribution system an I.D.M.T. relay can be used but must be graded with other earth-fault relays on the system. When, as with many large generators supplying high-voltage transmission systems, the generator is tied to a delta/star transformer, an instantaneously attracted armature relay can be used and, as the earth-fault loop is restricted to the generator stator and the transformer primary winding, no discrimination with other earth-fault relays is necessary. The percentage of the stator winding protected depends on the value of the neutral resistor, i.e. the percentage of generator full-load current it is designed to pass and the relay setting. If, as is often the case, the resistor is designed for 100% full-load current and the relay is set at 20% of generator full-load, then 80% of the stator winding is protected. If the setting is reduced to say 5%, the stator winding is protected up to about 95%.

In other countries, neutral earthing through the primary of a distribution transformer is preferred as shown at (b) in Fig. 11.41, with the fault current restricted to a very small value. This scheme[3], practicable only where the generator is directly connected to the delta winding of the main transformer, ensures minimum damage to the stator core. The relay is an inverse time-voltage neutral-displacement relay such as the English Electric type *VDG14* which is a frequency-compensated induction-disc unit with adjustable inverse time/voltage characteristics.

When a generator and a step-up transformer are directly connected, i.e. without any switchgear at generator voltage, it is usual to include both the generator and the transformer in a common differential protective scheme, the protected zone extending from the generator neutral to the circuit-breaker on

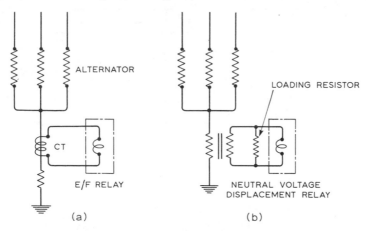

Figure 11.41. Stator earth-fault protection. (a) Resistance-earthed system and (b) distribution-transformer-earthed system

the high-voltage side of the transformer. The connections for such a scheme are shown in Fig. 11.42 and here, as will be noted again later, problems arise as the delta/star transformer introduces a phase shift, and account must be taken of the current transformation in the transformer.

Phase shift is compensated by connecting the current transformer secondaries in star in the generator neutral, i.e. on the delta side of the transformer, and those on the star side of the transformer in delta. The primary ratings of the current transformers will differ by the transformation ratio of the power transformer while the secondary ratings must also differ, e.g. if the secondary rating of the star-connected current transformers is 5 A, the secondary rating of those connected in delta must be $5/\sqrt{3}$ or 2·89 A, or alternatively 1 A star to 0·578 A delta.

The majority of units connected in this manner are extremely large so that the current on the generator side is similarly high, of the order of thousands or even tens of thousands of amperes. To transform primary currents of this order directly to 5 or 1 A requires a current transformer of a considerable number of turns which in turn leads to difficulties in construction and accommodation. To reduce the number of turns therefore the main current transformers on the

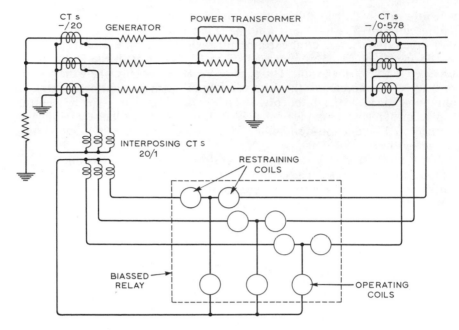

Figure 11.42. *Overall-biased differential protection for a generator/transformer*

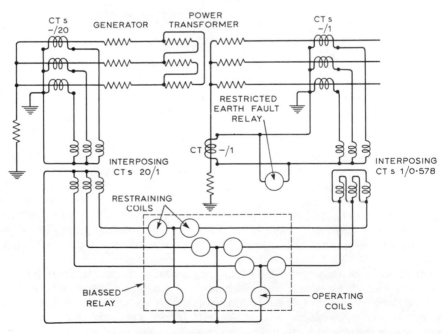

Figure 11.43. *Combined biased differential and restricted earth-fault protection for a generator/transformer*

generator side will have a secondary rating of say 20 A and as shown in the diagram, the output is fed to an interposing current transformer with a ratio of say 20:1.

The power transformer will be equipped with tap changing facilities so that it becomes impossible to match the current ratios as between the high- and low-voltage sides at all tappings. Owing to this, unbalance currents will be present and the use of a percentage-biased differential relay is essential.

When the high-voltage star winding of the power transformer is resistance earthed, the differential protective scheme in Fig. 11.42 is not very effective and the addition of restricted earth-fault protection is normal practice. A scheme of this type is shown in Fig. 11.43 and earlier comment on the amount of the winding protected applies equally here. It is seen that the main current transformers are star-connected on both sides, the 30° phase shift being taken care of by the star-delta connected interposing transformers.

If we now consider the problems of protection across a power transformer alone, note may first be taken of what is described as a rough balance scheme.

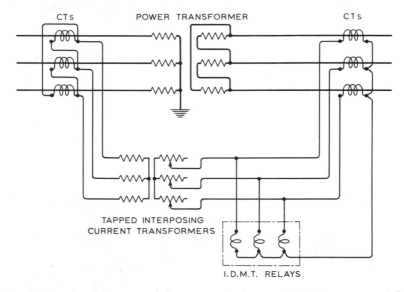

Figure 11.44.   Transformer rough-balance protection (courtesy G.E.C. Measurements Ltd.)

It is one which can be applied to transformers already protected by I.D.M.T. relays for overcurrent and restricted earth-fault protection, and where this has become inadequate. To avoid the cost of providing a separate differential scheme, the existing relays and current transformers can be reconnected in a basically conventional circulating-current balance scheme as shown in Fig. 11.44. By this means lower fault settings and faster operating times can be obtained for internal faults and it will also provide discriminative clearances under external fault conditions.

We have noted earlier the problems which have to be solved when circulating current protection is applied to a generator/transformer combination, i.e. phase shift due to the delta/star transformer connection and how the current transformer connections and secondary ratings are chosen. These same problems

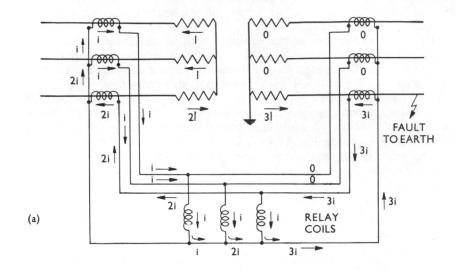

(a)

SHOWING OPERATION WHEN PROTECTIVE C.T's ARE CONNECTED IN STAR AND
AN EARTH-FAULT OCCURS EXTERNAL TO THE POWER TRANSFORMER, THE RATIO
OF WHICH IS ASSUMED TO BE UNITY.

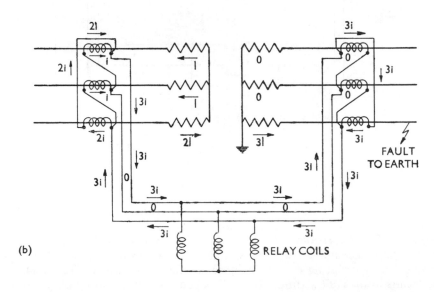

(b)

SHOWING STABILITY WHEN PROTECTIVE C.T's ARE CONNECTED IN DELTA AND
AN EARTH-FAULT OCCURS EXTERNAL TO THE POWER TRANSFORMER.

*Figure 11.45.   Stable and unstable conditions on through earth-faults with circulating current protec-
tion applied to a star/star transformer, due to methods of connecting current transformers*

306

arise when applying this form of protection to a transformer as a unit and are solved in the same way.

If the power transformer is connected delta/delta, there is no phase shift between primary and secondary line currents and protection is applied as for a generator but with correction for the differences in magnitude. Similarly, there is no phase shift in the case of star/star connected power transformers but here, phase correction is applied at *both* sets of current transformers, the reason being that only by this means can the protective system be stable under external earth-fault conditions. Thus, both sets of current transformers will be delta connected so that the secondary currents in the pilots from each set will be displaced in phase by 30° from the line currents but both will coincide, a necessary requirement of circulating current protection. It is obvious that similarity in phase could be achieved if both sets of current transformers are connected in star but it can be shown that in this case, the protective system would be stable on through faults between phases but *not* for earth faults. This is demonstrated numerically in Fig. 11.45, noting that at (a) the secondary currents entering and leaving the pilots are not the same at both ends and therefore do not sum up to zero at the relays, whereas at (b) the reverse is true and no current appears in the relay coils.

The 2:1:1 current distribution shown in Fig. 11.45 on the unearthed side of the star/star transformer, is only true for such a transformer which has a closed-delta tertiary winding. This winding, not shown in the diagrams, is included to provide a short-circuit path for the flow of harmonic components in the magnetising current. The distribution applies also when the core is a three-phase type as opposed to the shell type.

As is well known, the switching-in of a power transformer causes a transient surge of magnetising current to flow in the primary winding, a current which has no balancing counterpart in the secondary circuit. Because of this a 'spill' current will appear in the relay windings for the duration of the surge and if of sufficient magnitude it will lead to isolation of the circuit.

Such unwanted operation can be avoided by adding time delay to the protection, but as the inrush current persists for some cycles, such delay may render the protection ineffective under true fault conditions. A better solution lies in the use of a relay designed with harmonic restraint, a relay of this type being the English Electric type *DMH* for which a connection diagram is given in Fig. 11.46.

Of the harmonics appearing in the inrush current, the second harmonic predominates and this is detected by the relay and used to restrain its action, thus discriminating between a fault and the normal magnetising inrush. The relay employs rectifier bridge comparators in each phase which feed their outputs through transistor amplifiers to sensitive polarised relays. The input to the polarised units is the resultant of:
1. An operating current which is a function of the differential current.
2. A restraining current, the value of which depends on the second harmonic content of the differential current.
3. A bias current, which is a function of the through current and stabilises the relay against heavy through faults.

The relay is also provided with an instantaneous overcurrent unit in each phase to protect against faults heavy enough to saturate the line current transformers, under which conditions the harmonics generated would tend to restrain the main unit. The overcurrent units have a fixed setting of eight times the current transformer secondary rating and are themselves fed from saturable current transformers to prevent operation on peak inrush current which may momentarily exceed this value.

Operation of the main unit is briefly as follows. Under through-current conditions current is passed by the two restraint-rectifier bridges through the polarised relay in the non-operating direction. Under conditions of internal

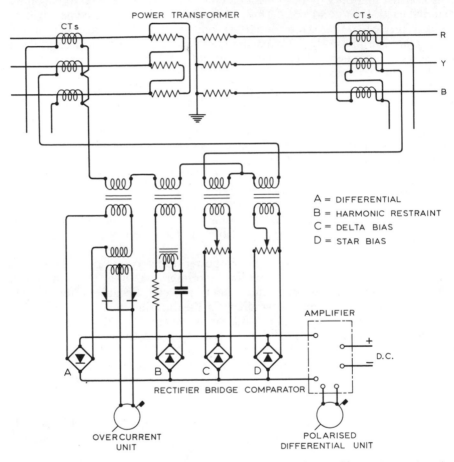

A = DIFFERENTIAL
B = HARMONIC RESTRAINT
C = DELTA BIAS
D = STAR BIAS

Figure 11.46. Differential protection for a power transformer with second harmonic restraint using English Electric type DMH high-speed biased relay. Connections are shown for the one phase only and are repeated for the other two phases (courtesy G.E.C. Measurements Ltd.)

fault, there will be a difference between the primary and secondary currents and the difference current flows in the operating circuit so that the operating rectifier passes a current to the polarised relay in the operative direction. Operation depends on the relative magnitude of the total restraint and differential currents, and the ratio of these currents to cause operation is controlled by a shunt resistor across the restraint rectifiers. Under magnetising inrush conditions, the second harmonic component is extracted by the tuned circuit and the current is passed to the relay in the non-operating direction.

In addition to the second harmonic component, the inrush current contains a third harmonic component, its proportion being large, but less than the second. No restraint against this however is provided as there would be a danger that the relay might be delayed in operating under heavy internal fault conditions due to current transformer saturation producing third harmonics in the secondary waveform.

When circulating current protection is applied to a power transformer, the relay is arranged to cause the circuit-breaker on *both* sides of the transformer to open, thus clearing the transformer completely under fault conditions.

Only brief mention has been made of the problem which arises when a power transformer is provided with facilities for tap changing. It has been noted that for stability under healthy or through-fault conditions, identical outputs from each group of current transformers are an essential feature of circulating current protection. It is clearly impossible for the current transformers to be matched at all tap positions unless these (the c.t.s) are also correspondingly tapped. This solution is impracticable if only because of the nature of the task of changing current transformer tappings each time a tap change is made on the power transformer. The latter function is often automatic so that it would then be necessary to make the tap changes on the current transformers automatic and simultaneous. Because of this and the normal inequalities which occur between current transformers, many schemes for the protection of transformers have been devised in which steps have been taken to eliminate the difficulties, and some of these schemes will be noted later.

For the circulating-current schemes under discussion, the problem is largely solved by the use of biased differential relays as discussed earlier, a diagram including such a relay for a delta/star power transformer being given in Fig. 11.47.

Circulating-current protection can be applied on feeder circuits provided pilot wires are, or can be, made available between the two ends of the feeder. This is an obvious objection and often costly. If the feeder is long then the burden on the current transformers becomes excessive but in theory the scheme functions exactly as in our earlier description where one group of transformers at one end of the feeder compares the current at that point with that at the other end of the feeder where another group of current transformers is located. A difference exists, however, in that a relay is required at *both ends* of the feeder whereas for generator and transformer protection only one relay is employed.

Because of the expense of pilot cables the development of pilot wire systems has been concentrated largely on schemes requiring a minimum number of cores, most new schemes requiring only two.

A scheme of this kind is shown in Fig. 11.48 using privately owned pilot cables* and a relay at each end of the feeder. It is, as the diagram shows, basically a single-phase circulating current scheme adapted for three-phase operation through summation transformers. It is seen that each line-current transformer energises a different number of turns on the primary winding of the summation transformer with a resulting single-phase output from the secondary. The secondary turns are usually made much greater than the primary so as to reduce the current circulating in the pilot.

A polarised relay, shown diagrammatically in Fig. 11.48 has two windings for restraint (bias) and operation respectively. The current which circulates

* Some schemes are designed for use with telephone cores rented from the G.P.O.

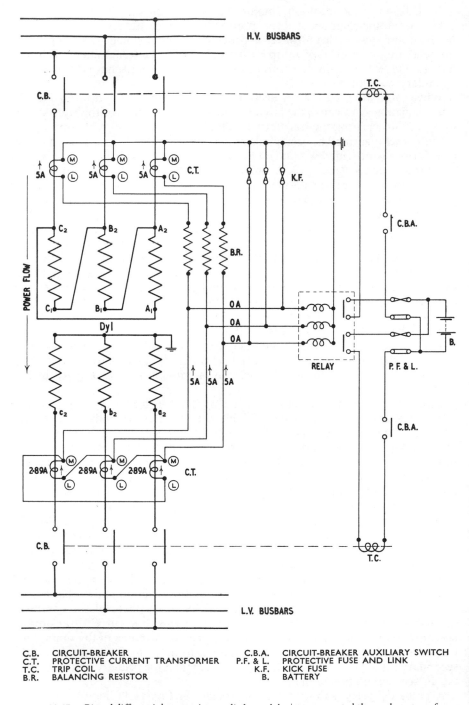

H.V. BUSBARS

L.V. BUSBARS

C.B.	CIRCUIT-BREAKER	C.B.A.	CIRCUIT-BREAKER AUXILIARY SWITCH
C.T.	PROTECTIVE CURRENT TRANSFORMER	P.F. & L.	PROTECTIVE FUSE AND LINK
T.C.	TRIP COIL	K.F.	KICK FUSE
B.R.	BALANCING RESISTOR	B.	BATTERY

Figure 11.47.   Biased differential protection applied to a delta/star connected three-phase transformer

310

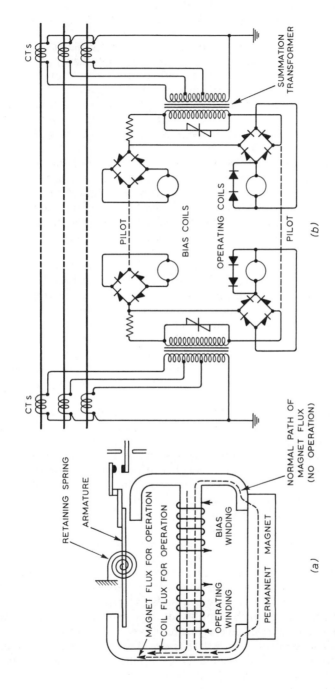

CTs

SUMMATION
TRANSFORMER

PILOT

BIAS COILS

OPERATING COILS

PILOT

CTs

(b)

RETAINING SPRING

ARMATURE

MAGNET FLUX FOR OPERATION

COIL FLUX FOR OPERATION

BIAS
WINDING

OPERATING
WINDING

PERMANENT
MAGNET

NORMAL PATH OF
MAGNET FLUX
(NO OPERATION)

(a)

Figure 11.48. Circulating current feeder protection using a two-core private pilot cable with 'English Electric' type DMW polarised relay. (a) Magnet circuit and (b) circuit connections (courtesy G.E.C. Measurements Ltd.)

311

through the pilots flows in the bias windings of the two relays (one at each end of the feeder). Out of balance currents such as those that occur in the event of an internal fault are provided with a path through the operating windings connected across the pilots.

In the relay, a permanent magnet provides flux which circulates in two parallel paths, one of low reluctance formed by the core through the windings and one of high reluctance which contains the armature which is held open by a spiral restraining spring. The rectifier which supplies the bias winding is in series with the pilot circuit while another is in the differential circuit for the operating winding. The connections of the two windings are such that the ampere turns in each are in opposition and the relay operates when the operating ampere turns exceed the bias ampere turns by the setting ampere turns.

As various types of pilot may be used, a link arrangement in the relay permits an alteration to the connection of a resistor and capacitor in the relay so that stability and good operating characteristics can be obtained for each type of pilot. When a fault occurs within the protected zone the fault current may be fed from one or both ends, but in either case the ampere turns on the operating winding greatly exceed the bias ampere turns, and operation occurs. The protection provided covers both phase and earth faults.

Before leaving this discussion on differential protection it may be useful to consider briefly the need for some form of back-up protection. In all cases it can be assumed that such additional protection is applied to cover the possibility, however remote, of a failure on the part of the differential protection to operate with a fault within its zone, or the failure of circuit-breakers elsewhere on the system to clear local faults. Although busbar protection (see later discussion) is now employed in many large schemes, it is by no means universally applied and back-up protection on generators and transformers normally covered by differential protection affords a means of protection against busbar faults, disconnecting the machine or transformer in such event. Back-up protection is usually afforded by I.D.M.T. relays, care being needed to ensure that time discrimination is obtained in relation to the protective relays on the feeder network, the time setting on the back-up relay being higher than the highest setting of any feeder relay. Because of this, some difficulty may be experienced with an I.D.M.T. relay affording back-up protection on a generator or generator/transformer circuit, as long before the time setting has been reached, the short-circuit current may have fallen to the steady state value due to decrement. It must therefore be ensured that the back-up relay will operate with this much-reduced value of current.

Under-voltage protection is not normally applied to circuits other than those which control motors. Here, it is essential to trip the circuit-breaker (or contactor) in the event of a supply failure and thereby prevent danger to personnel should the supply be restored without warning. In such cases, a deliberate action on the part of the operator is essential before the motor can be restarted. Under-voltage protection can be employed to provide an interlock to ensure, for example, that all rotor resistance is in circuit before starting a slip-ring motor by means of a drum controller or, where reduced-voltage starting is employed, e.g. auto-transformer, that full voltage is not applied to a stationary machine. Another aspect of under-voltage protection is that where some external condition causes a serious but transient dip in voltage to occur. Depending on the drop-out value of the under-voltage trip coil or relay, this may cause unnecessary

312

stoppages and, in such cases, it is feasible to time-delay the trip coil or relay for a short period. This may of course result in loss of speed and it may be that, due to the nature of the load, the motor will not pick-up again.

Having noted various methods of providing simple overcurrent and/or earth-fault protection and the slightly more complicated differential schemes for generators, transformers and feeders, it is appropriate to look at what other protection can be provided and at some specialised systems. Some of the schemes we shall note are developments based on the circulating current principle, while others are those which have been designed especially to meet conditions arising out of modern high-voltage power transmission and interconnected power networks such as the Grid, where high-speed operation, transient stability and other characteristics are essential. It will be convenient to consider these further details and schemes under headings corresponding to those noted above.

GENERATOR PROTECTION

Some of the faults which may occur on an a.c. generator in service are:
1. Failure of insulation on the stator windings or associated connections.
2. Failure of insulation on the rotor.
3. Overspeed.
4. Generated overvoltage.
5. Unbalanced loading.
6. Field failure.
7. Failure of prime mover.

Stator winding faults

These comprise short-circuits between phases or to earth, and short-circuits between turns, the latter rapidly developing into earth-faults. It is essential that the main circuit-breaker between the machine and the busbars is opened immediately when a stator fault occurs so that other generating plant on the system can be prevented from feeding into the faulty machine. At the same time it is necessary to suppress the rotor field to prevent the machine itself from feeding into the fault. If the neutral of the machine is earthed through an automatic circuit-breaker, it is an advantage to provide for the opening of this circuit-breaker and thereby assist with rapid clearance of earth-fault current.

The minimum primary operating current at which the earth fault protective gear operates governs the amount of stator winding protected and, in the case of machines operating on a system in which the neutral point is earthed through a resistance, the value of the earthing resistance and the minimum operating value of the protective gear must be correlated to give the maximum degree of stator winding protection.

For phase faults, overcurrent or some form of differential protection or a combination of both, can be applied. When both are applied, the overcurrent relays will act as back-up protection as previously discussed. Earth-fault protection should be of the restricted type sensitive to earth-faults in the stator winding or in the associated connections and not to earth-faults outside the zone of protection.

313

As already mentioned above, provision has to be made to suppress the field in the shortest possible time after an internal fault has been detected. The method of achieving this is to cause automatic opening of a suitable switch or circuit-breaker in the field circuit, as shown in Fig. 11.49.

It will be seen here that the trip-coil circuit on the field switch is completed by auxiliary contacts on the protective relay. The opening of this switch results

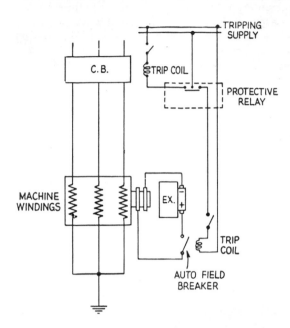

Figure 11.49. Simplified connections for automatic field suppression

in high rotor voltage and, in the case of built-up or laminated rotors, this may cause insulation failure and a field discharge resistance must therefore be used. When a solid rotor is used the effect is not usually dangerous and resistance is not normally employed, noting that the use of resistance slows up the process of field suppression.

Failure of insulation on the rotor

This is usually in the form of a single fault to earth and only in the remote possibility of a double fault is damage likely. On very large generators it is often considered advisable to provide some form of earth-fault detector, as a second fault to earth occurring in another part of the field winding constitutes a short-circuit requiring an immediate shut down of the machine. A suitable detector is an earthed negatively-biased relay connected between the field circuit and earth as shown in Fig. 11.50.

A relay of this type is the English Electric type *VME* which can detect leakage currents of a few milliamperes. A self-contained d.c. injection supply establishes a small bias on the alternator field circuit so that all points are negative with respect to earth. When a fault occurs, current flows in the bias circuit and is detected by the sensitive balanced armature movement of the polarised relay.

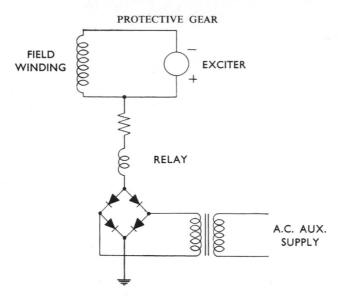

Figure 11.50.   Rotor earth-fault detection by the negative biasing method

Because of its unusual ratio of withstand voltage to pick-up voltage, detection of the very small leakage current noted above is possible without risk of over-heating during a fault at field-forcing voltage. The relay also functions as a self-powered rotor earth-fault relay in the absence of the d.c. injection supply, covering a large proportion of the field winding, possibly up to 95%.

Overspeed

This leads to overvoltage and may arise due to a sudden loss of load. In certain circumstances (e.g. total loss of load coupled with high steam pressure at the stop-valve) the rise in speed may be so considerable that the action of the governors or the closing of the emergency valve will not prevent the rise. Some form of overspeed device must therefore be provided to safeguard the machine under these circumstances and arranged to trip the main circuit-breaker.

Generated overvoltage

Generated overvoltage of significant duration or magnitude does not generally occur on turbo-generator equipment and it is not usual to provide protection against such conditions. In the case of hydro-electric generators, however, the inherent slow action of the control governors leads to a considerable lapse of time before normal speed is restored after a sudden loss of load to the system. The increase in speed due to loss of load gives a corresponding increase in voltage, which may lead to damage of connected apparatus and will over-stress the insulation of the generator winding. Some form of protection is therefore recommended for such generators. It should be arranged to disconnect the machine from the system and to open the field system if the generator voltage rises 20% above normal.

315

Unbalanced loading

This arises from causes such as faults between two lines or one line to earth on the system external to the generator. The unbalanced currents, even though of a value much less than the rated normal current of the machine, induce double-frequency eddy currents in the rotor, resulting in dangerous overheating. Protection can be given against such conditions by the use of negative-phase sequence protection in which a filter network detects the flow of negative-phase sequence currents in the generator windings, but is not responsive to balanced conditions, i.e. to positive-phase sequence currents.

In Chapter 4 we have shown that any unbalanced system can be considered to be comprised of three balanced systems as follows:

1. A three-phase system of forward phase sequence known as the *positive-phase sequence.*
2. A three-phase system of reverse phase sequence, known as the *negative-phase sequence.*
3. A system without time interval between phasors, known as the *zero-phase sequence.*

It has also been shown that:

(*a*) The positive component only is present with balanced three-phase conditions and corresponds to normal load conditions.
(*b*) The positive and negative components are both present with unbalanced phase to phase conditions corresponding to faults between lines.
(*c*) The positive, negative and zero components are all present with unbalanced phase to neutral conditions corresponding to a line to earth fault on a system with an earthed neutral.

From the foregoing, it will be noted that the negative phase sequence component is present in *both* conditions likely to produce unbalance in a three-phase system and, therefore, a relay that is sensitive to this component and not to the positive component will protect the machine against conditions of single phase loading. An equipment designed for this purpose is shown in Fig. 11.51 comprising a filter network with matching transformers and a relay unit consisting of a heated body, a sensitive relay responding to the temperature of the heated body and an instantaneous alarm relay element.

In this scheme the output from the filter network is fed into a small coil of resistance wire and so raises its temperature. By suitably proportioning the heated body, its time/current characteristic for a given temperature rise is made to match the ability of the protected generator to withstand the flow of negative phase sequence currents. When the temperature of the heated body reaches a given level a sensitive relay element, connected to a thermocouple, operates.

The alarm relay, connected directly to the matching transformer, closes its contacts to give early indication of an unbalanced condition and in the case of low values of negative-phase sequence current, the control engineer has an opportunity to take action before circuit-breaker tripping occurs. The latter can only take place when the contacts on *both* the alarm and the temperature-responsive relay are closed.

316

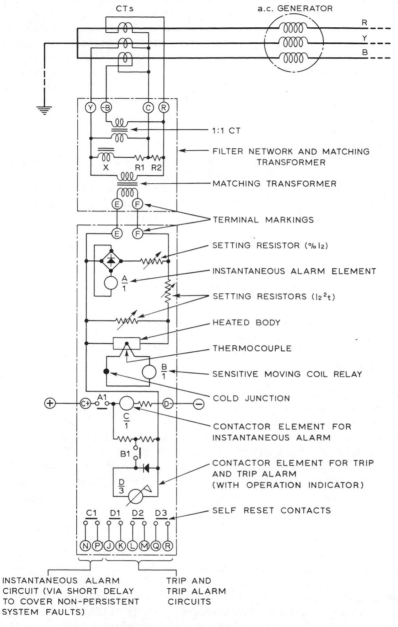

Figure 11.51. Schematic diagram of negative-phase sequence-protective gear with G.E.C. relay type HNP (courtesy G.E.C. Measurements Ltd.)

Failure of the prime mover

In the case of a turbo-generator, no serious effect will be sustained by allowing the turbine rotors to be motored by the generator running as a synchronous motor for a short time provided the lubricating system etc., continues to function. In the case of back-pressure turbo generators, however, protection against inverted running should be included. On such machines, after closing the combined emergency and stop valves upon failure of the prime mover the generators should be disconnected from the busbars, otherwise the turbine rotors would be rotating in trapped steam of back pressure density which would cause a dangerous increase in temperature of the rotor and casing.

Diesel-engine driven alternators should also be protected against inverted running to guard against motoring in the event of a mechanical seizure.

The effect of prime mover failure is to cause the machine to 'motor' by taking power from the system. There is therefore a reversal of power and the condition can be detected by a power relay with a directional characteristic. Such a relay would also operate for power-swing conditions and when a machine is being synchronised, and to prevent such operation a time delay must be introduced, either by a separate relay or by the use of an inverse-time reverse-power relay.

TRANSFORMER PROTECTION

When a fault occurs within a transformer (or other oil-filled equipment such as reactors or capacitors), heat is produced which in turn liberates gases from the oil either gradually or violently according to the nature of the fault. If the apparatus is fitted with an oil conservator a gas-activated relay fitted in the pipe connection between the main oil tank and the conservator can be arranged to indicate the presence of the gases firstly by completing an alarm circuit and secondly to cause the controlling circuit-breaker(s) to trip out. This form of protection is known as 'Buchholz', and a typical relay is shown in Fig. 11.52.

In this relay each of the two chambers houses an oil bucket with a mercury switch attachment. Each bucket is kept level under normal conditions by a balance weight and the mercury switches will be open. When a slight or incipient fault occurs in the transformer, small bubbles of gas will be generated and these, attempting to pass from the tank to the oil conservator, will be trapped in the relay housing.

As this gas accumulates, the oil level in the relay will fall, leaving the top bucket full of oil. As this bucket will not now be fully immersed, the extra weight due to the contained oil will overcome the balance weight and cause the whole assembly to tilt, thereby causing the mercury switch to close and complete the alarm circuit. When a serious fault occurs, the gas generation is rapid, causing the displaced oil to surge through the relay. This oil flow will impinge on the baffle plates and cause the bottom bucket assembly to tilt, closing the mercury switch in the trip circuit to the breakers. If a transformer suffers a loss of oil, causing the oil level to drop below the level of the relay, the buckets of the two elements will be left full of oil, and first the alarm and then the surge element will operate to close the alarm and trip circuits.

The use of a 'Buchholz' relay on transformers is generally recommended for

318

units above about 1 000 kVA where these are fitted with conservators, as by this means incipient faults can be detected before great damage is caused.

In our earlier discussion concerning circulating-current (differential) protection we noted various problems such as:

(a) The currents on opposite sides of the transformer differ in phase angle and magnitude depending on the inter-connection of windings and the transformer ratio.

(b) The transformation ratio is often variable as governed by tap-changing equipment.

(c) The magnetising current inrush on switching-in appears only on the primary side and has no counterpart on the secondary side. The differential protection, therefore, detects this as an internal fault and causes unwanted tripping of the circuit-breaker. This inrush current can attain a magnitude many times the steady state magnetising current which may be as low as 2 to 4% of the normal full-load current[4].

We have seen how (a) and (b) can be overcome by using a differential protective system with biased relays and problem (c) can be taken care of by having

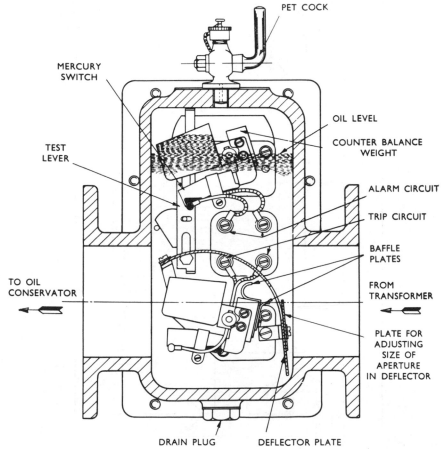

Figure 11.52. Diagrammatic illustration of an English Electric 'Buckholz' relay with alarm circuit closed (courtesy G.E.C. Measurements Ltd.)

time delayed relays to ensure stability. Unfortunately, this time delay is also operative when an internal fault occurs on a transformer and when it should be isolated from the system as quickly as possible.

It is in an effort to overcome all these problems and yet retain the ideal of the differential protection scheme with its discriminating features, but with high-speed operation, that a number of transformer protective schemes have been perfected of which the following is an example. This is the Reyrolle scheme known as *High-speed Duo-bias Differential Transformer Protection*. It is

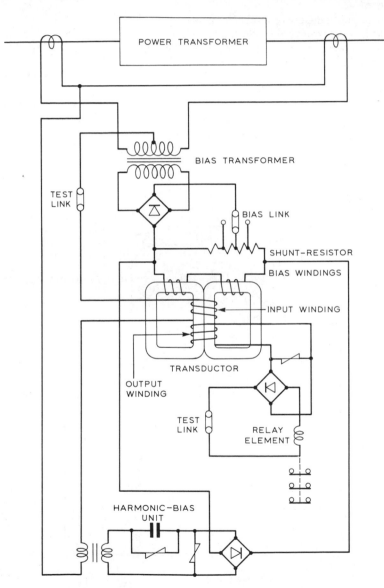

Figure 11.53. Single-phase diagram of 'Duo-bias' transformer protection (courtesy A. Reyrolle & Co. Ltd.)

basically a conventional current-balance scheme on the lines previously discussed but it uses a special relay compensated so that it overrides the complications associated with transformer protection. Figure 11.53 is a single-phase diagram of the Duo-bias relay used in this scheme, its functioning under various conditions being as follows.

Under load or through-fault conditions, the current-transformer secondary currents circulate through the primary winding of the bias transformer, and the rectified output of the latter is applied to a bias winding of a transductor via a shunt-resistor. Out-of-balance current flows from the centre tap on the primary winding, energising the transductor input winding and the harmonic bias unit.

On the transductor, the input and output windings are inductively linked but there is no such linking between these and the bias windings. So long as the transformer being protected is sound, the bias winding is energised by full-wave rectified current which is proportional to the load or through-fault current and this bias current saturates the transductor. Out-of-balance currents in the transductor input-winding, produced by power transformer tap-changing

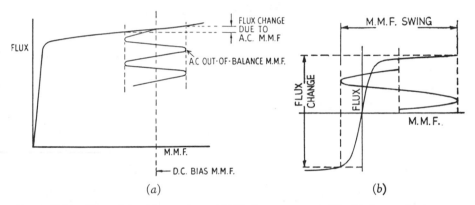

Figure 11.54. Fluxes due to (a) operating and (b) biasing ampere-turns 'Duo-bias' protection (courtesy A. Reyrolle & Co. Ltd.)

or by current transformer mis-match, superimpose an alternating magnetomotive force upon the d.c. bias m.m.f. as shown in Fig. 11.54, but the resulting change in working flux density is small and the output to the relay is negligible.

The tappings on the shunt resistor are used for adjusting the relationship between the bias transformer primary current and the input to the transductor bias winding. This resistor also serves to suppress ripples in the bias m.m.f. due to the ripple in the bias current, providing a low impedance non-inductive shunt-path across the highly inductive bias winding for the a.c. content of the bias current.

If a fault develops in the power transformer, the operating m.m.f. produced by the secondary fault-current in the transductor input-winding exceeds the bias m.m.f., resulting in a large change in working flux density. This produces a correspondingly large voltage across the relay winding and the resultant current operates the relay.

Relay operation cannot occur unless the operating m.m.f. exceeds the bias m.m.f. and as the latter is proportional to the load or through-fault current, the required operating m.m.f. (and hence the operating current) is also proportional to the load or through-fault current. Figure 11.55 illustrates the operating characteristics of the relay with the 20%, 30% and 40% percentage-bias slopes corresponding to the 20%, 30% and 40% shunt-resistor tappings, noting that the bias current I_1 is the component of current which circulates around the balancing loop between the current transformers and that the operating current I_2 is the out-of-balance component which flows in the operating winding.

The harmonic-bias unit (seen in Fig. 11.53) is a tuned circuit which responds to the second harmonic component of the magnetising current. When magnetising, inrush current flows through the relay operating circuit, the rectified output of the unit is injected into the transductor bias-winding and restrains the relay.

Transformer differential relays generally have a basic setting which is the fault current required to operate them with no through current in the differential

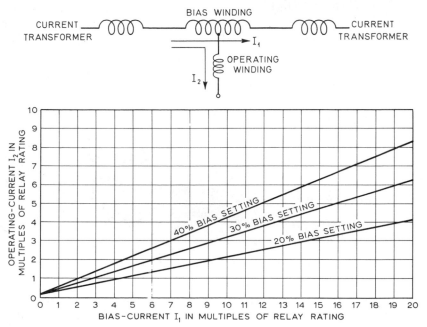

NOTE. THE BIAS CURRENT I_1 IS THE COMPONENT OF CURRENT WHICH CIRCULATES AROUND THE BALANCING LOOP BETWEEN THE CURRENT TRANSFORMERS. THE OPERATING CURRENT I_2 IS THE OUT-OF-BALANCE COMPONENT WHICH FLOWS IN THE OPERATING WINDING.

Figure 11.55. Basic characteristics of the 'Duo-bias' relay (courtesy A. Reyrolle & Co. Ltd.)

system and internal fault-current fed from only one set of current transformers. In the case of the Duo-bias relay this setting is 20% of the relay rating. The actual value of fault current at which a differential relay will operate is thus the basic setting under no-load conditions, but when load current is flowing the setting will be higher, depending upon the amount of the load and on the bias setting in use. With an internal earth-fault in which the current is limited by a neutral-earthing resistor, the load current might well be little affected by the fault and under such conditions the effect of load current on the setting has to be taken into account.

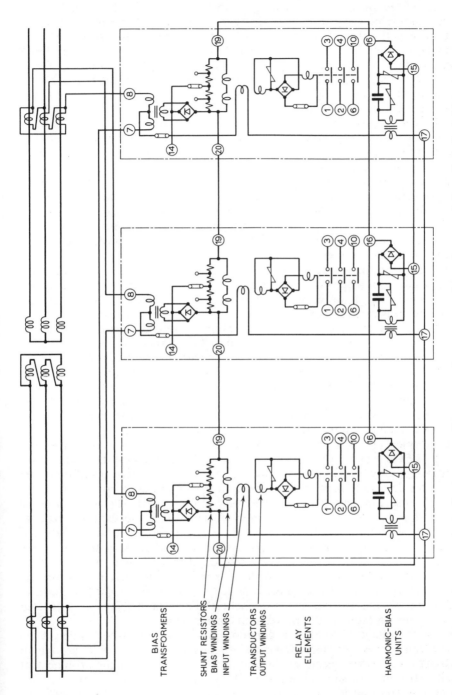

BIAS
TRANSFORMERS

SHUNT RESISTORS
BIAS WINDINGS
INPUT WINDINGS

TRANSDUCTORS
OUTPUT WINDINGS

RELAY
ELEMENTS

HARMONIC-BIAS
UNITS

Figure 11.56. 'Duo-bias' protection for a two-winding power transformer (courtesy A. Reyrolle & Co. Ltd.)

323

Figure 11.56 illustrates the three-phase assembly of Duo-bias relays applied for the protection of a two-winding power transformer. When applied to a three-winding power transformer, the relays are identical except for a change of tapping on the primary winding of the bias transformer. A separately mounted assembly comprising two additional bias-transformers and associated rectifiers is required so that there is a separate bias-transformer for each phase of each group of current transformers, there now being three sets of the latter, one set on the delta side as in Fig. 11.56 and one set in each of the star outputs. The summated rectified outputs of all three bias transformers is fed through the transductor bias-windings so that the relay is biased by the *total* current flowing in the transformer regardless of its distribution between the windings. When a high-speed back-up feature is required a high-set overcurrent element can be added to some types of Duo-bias relay.

When a power transformer is resistance earthed, the current available on an internal earth-fault for operation of a differential protection may be relatively low and the percentage of the winding protected against such faults may be inadequate. It is obviously desirable that the percentage protected should be as high as possible and the degree obtained has been previously discussed in relation to generator windings.

When differential protection is applied to a power transformer, the percentage of the winding under protection against earth faults will be much less for a given fault setting than if supplementary restricted earth-fault protection is added. This is demonstrated in Fig. 11.57 which shows that in order to cover a reasonable percentage of the winding with a differential relay an extremely sensitive setting would be necessary, e.g. to cover up to 80% of the winding a fault setting of approximately 2·5% is necessary, whereas with a separate restricted earth-fault relay a setting of 20% would give the same cover. Sensitive settings with differential relays are, however, not practical because of the limitations imposed by tap changing, current transformer inequalities, magnetising current inrush, etc., and it is generally recommended that where the earth-fault current is restricted, supplementary earth-fault relays should be included.

Two typical arrangements for supplementary earth-fault protection are given in Fig. 11.58 and 11.59. The first of these is for a straightforward delta/star power transformer for which, as we have noted elsewhere, the current transformers on the delta side would be normally connected in star and delta connected on the star side, if separate earth-fault protection is not included. The addition of the latter means that the current transformers must now be connected in star on both sides and an auxiliary star/delta transformer interposed in the differential circuit to compensate for the 30% phase shift between primary and secondary sides. The earth-fault relay is connected, on the delta side, in the residual circuit from the Duo-bias relays to the star point of the current transformers while on the star side it is connected directly to the line current transformers and to the current transformer in the neutral. Earth-fault relays so connected operate only on faults in the power transformer zone.

On high-voltage systems, it is common practice to earth both sides of the power transformer, the star side neutral directly and the delta side through an earthing transformer[4] as shown in Fig. 11.59. It is seen that the arrangement on the star side is the same as in Fig. 11.58 but on the delta side a zero-sequence shunt is introduced in the differential circuit, as zero-sequence currents (see Chapter 4) may flow in the current transformers to an external earth-fault

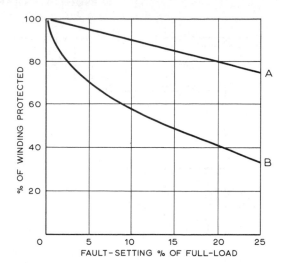

LEGEND

A RESTRICTED E/F RELAY
B DIFFERENTIAL RELAY

Figure 11.57. Percentage of transformer winding protected against earth faults

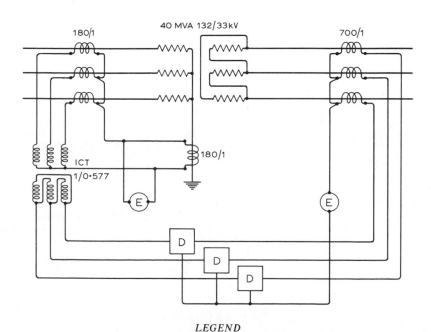

LEGEND

D 'DUO-BIAS' DIFFERENTIAL RELAYS
E EARTH-FAULT RELAYS
ICT INTERPOSING-CURRENT TRANSFORMERS

Figure 11.58. Typical arrangement of 'Duo-bias' differential protection with supplementary earth-fault protection across a star/delta transformer (courtesy A. Reyrolle & Co. Ltd.)

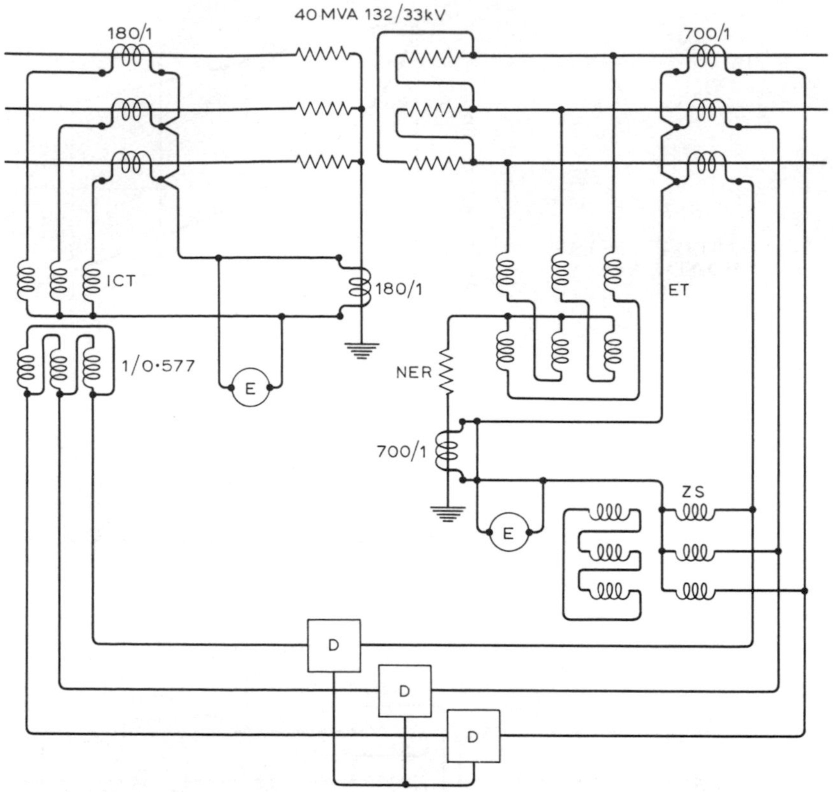

PROTECTIVE GEAR

40 MVA 132/33kV

LEGEND

D   'DUO-BIAS' DIFFERENTIAL RELAYS
E   EARTH-FAULT RELAYS   ET   EARTHING TRANSFORMER
ICT INTERPOSING-CURRENT   NER NEUTRAL EARTHING RESISTOR
     TRANSFORMERS   ZS   ZERO-SEQUENCE SHUNT

Figure 11.59.   As Figure 11.58 but with both windings of the transformer earthed, the star side directly, the delta side through an earthing transformer (courtesy A. Reyrolle & Co. Ltd.)

without there being corresponding currents on the star-connected side. To preserve stability of the protection under this condition, the zero-sequence current must not appear in the differential circuit and the zero-sequence shunt effectively removes this current from that circuit. The delta side earth-fault relay is now connected to the line and neutral current transformers and the zero sequence shunt, in the manner shown in the diagram.

FEEDER PROTECTION

We have shown how discriminating overcurrent and earth-fault protection can be applied to series, parallel or ring-main feeder circuits by various means depending on circumstances, using time-graded and/or directional or non-directional relays. We have also noted the application of the circulating current system of protection as applied to generator and transformer circuits and, in passing, that this can be applied to feeder circuits subject to the availability of pilot cables running the full length of the cable, often perhaps, for many miles. This means that considerable resistance can exist in the pilots and lead to difficulties with a circulating current scheme. Moreover, with long pilots, many difficulties arise due to capacity currents which tend to flow in the relay circuit unless the pilots are sheathed or special devices are employed to neutralise them.

Because of these problems the system known as *balanced voltage* came into favour in which the relays, located at each end of a feeder, are connected in series through the pilots and so arranged that no current flows in the pilots under normal conditions and, in present-day schemes, with a bias feature to overcome the inherent out-of-balance currents due to pilot capacitance and current transformer inequalities.

Some of the available forms of protection will be noted but many others exist, as a study of specialised books on protective gear and of manufacturers literature will show. Schemes involving the use of pilot cables running the full length of the feeder and others which avoid their use will be discussed. It may be noted that the latter are generally of a complicated nature and are used generally on extra-high-voltage transmission systems where distances are considerable and the use of pilot cables is therefore impracticable.

Pilot-wire schemes

A pilot-wire scheme operating on the balanced-voltage principle is the G.E.C. Measurements Ltd./A.E.I. 'Translay' system, requiring a two-core pilot cable.

The name 'Translay' is evolved from the fact that the relay embodies a transformer feature. It provides complete protection against both earth and phase faults and can be applied to single or three-phase feeders, transformer feeders, feeders with a tee-off and parallel feeders. It is based on the established principle of the current entering at one end of a feeder being equal at any instant to that leaving at the other.

In its simplest form, operation of this system can be followed by reference to the simplified diagram, Fig. 11.60, for a single-phase feeder. It should be noted that for the sake of clarity, tripping circuits have been omitted. Under healthy conditions, current transformers 10 and 10a carry equal currents, and the coils, 11 and 11a, induce equal e.m.f.s in the windings, 12 and 12a. These latter windings are in opposition via the pilot wires with the operating windings, 13 and 13a, in series with them. Thus no forward torque is exerted on the disc. On the occurrence of a fault, the current through one transformer is greater than that through the other. A small current circulates through the operating windings and pilots, and when it reaches the set value causes the relay to close the tripping circuit and to disconnect the feeder.

This system, which is usually employed on a three-phase circuit, has a single-element relay at each end of a feeder which gives protection against both faults between phases and faults to earth. The connections are those shown in Fig. 11.61, in which again, for the sake of clarity, the tripping circuits are omitted. Operation under fault conditions is as follows:

Assuming a fault F between phases R and Y, fed in the direction of the arrows, the currents that flow in sections 1 of the relay primary windings, i.e. 11 and 11a, induce e.m.f.s in windings 12 and 12a which, being now additive, cause a current

327

to circulate in the operating coils, 13 and 13a, and the two pilot wires. Both the upper and lower electromagnets thus become energised and, if the fault current exceeds the value corresponding to the scale setting in use, the relays operate to trip their associated circuit-breakers. A fault between Y and B phases causes sections 2 of windings 11 and 11a to be energised and the relays to operate, while a fault between R and B phases causes operation by energising sections 1 and 2 of windings 11 and 11a, the fault setting in this case being one-half of that for the R-Y and Y-B cases.

In the event of an earth fault on phase R, the resultant secondary current from the current transformer in phase R flows through the sections 1, 2 and 3 of windings 11 and 11a—assuming power flow to be in the directions indicated by the arrows. As the e.m.f.s induced in windings 12 and 12a are now additive, a current will circulate in the operating windings 13 and 13a by way of the two

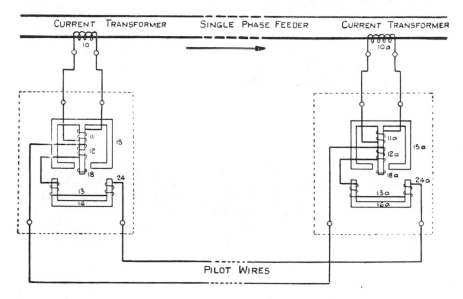

Figure 11.60. Simplified diagram of 'Translay' feeder protection (courtesy G.E.C. Measurements Ltd./A.E.I.)

pilots, thereby causing operation of the relays. The fault setting will be approximately half of that represented by the scale setting which is based on a fault on phase B, for which only section 3 is energised. In the case of an earth fault on phase Y, current will flow only in sections 2 and 3 on windings 11 and 11a, and the fault setting will now be approximately two-thirds of that represented by the scale setting.

This form of protection can be applied to teed feeders (where the current entering is balanced against that leaving by two sources), to transformer feeders (where transformer and feeder are switched as a unit without an intervening circuit-breaker), and to parallel feeders (where a 'Translay' element is combined with a directional element). The relays used for these schemes differ slightly.

Another balanced-voltage scheme is the 'Solkor-A' system (A. Reyrolle & Co. Ltd.) which also employs a two-core pilot cable. In this, as in the Duo-bias scheme of transformer protection, a transductor is used enabling the comparison of operating and restraining currents to be made statically, eliminating relays with complex magnetic systems and movements. The connections for the protective system are given in Fig. 11.62.

The name *Solkor* is indicative of the fact that current transformers with solid cores are employed. This is not unusual today, but in some older forms of feeder protection the current transformers had to have cores with a distributed air gap, as for example in the now obsolete 'Split-Pilot' form of protection.

At the end of the feeder the secondary currents from the current transformers are summed in the primary winding of a summation transformer. The tappings on this transformer primary are so arranged that an output voltage will occur for all fault conditions and the magnitude of this voltage will be proportional to the input ampere-turns.

The secondary windings of the summation transformers at each end of the feeder are connected in series with the pilots in such a way that the secondary voltages oppose each other during normal load or through-fault conditions

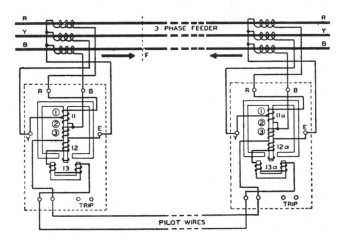

Figure 11.61. 'Translay' protection applied to a three-phase feeder (courtesy G.E.C. Measurements Ltd./A.E.I.)

(see Fig. 11.62) and no current circulates between ends. Under internal fault conditions, however, this balance of voltage is disturbed and a current circulates around the pilot loop. If this current is large enough it causes the relays at both ends to operate.

The input circuit of the relay is energised via a relay transformer which insulates the relay from the pilot circuit. Thus, any high voltages which may be induced in the pilots due to their proximity to a primary circuit are prevented from appearing at the relay terminals. A tuning capacitor is connected across the primary winding of the relay transformer causing the relay to respond mainly to the 50 Hz component of the pilot current.

At low primary through-currents the summation transformer output is sinusoidal and the system is a pure differential one in which both the magnitude and phase angle of the primary currents at the two ends of the feeder are compared. At high through-currents the summation transformer saturates; the effect of this is to limit the 50 Hz component of the output to a nearly constant

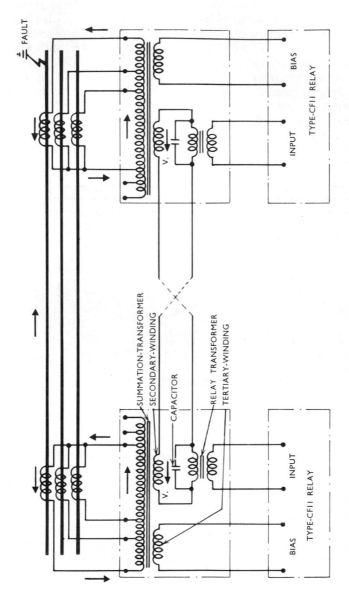

Figure 11.62. Connection diagram for 'Solkor-A' feeder protective system (courtesy A. Reyrolle & Co. Ltd.)

330

value. Since the tuning of the relay input-circuit confines the scheme to comparison at 50 Hz only, any increases in the magnitude of summation-transformer input at one end relative to the other will not be detected, i.e. the scheme changes to phase angle comparison of the primary currents at the two ends.

While under through-fault conditions the voltages at the two ends are equal, and theoretically no current will circulate between ends, the voltage appearing across the pilot-cores will cause currents to flow through the capacitance between cores which will give rise to currents in the operating-circuits of the relays. However, due to the limiting effect of the saturable summation transformer, the 50 Hz component of this capacity current will be relatively small, while currents at higher harmonics will be by-passed by the tuning capacitor.

To increase the inherent stability of the protection further, the relay incorporates a bias circuit, the current in which causes the relay to restrain. The bias circuit is energised from a tertiary winding on the summation transformer so that its output is proportional to the voltage across the secondary winding of the summation transformer, and hence to the through-fault current.

The summation transformer, the relay transformer and the tuning condenser are mounted in what is called a *solkor-box*.

The main feature of the relay (shown diagrammatically in Fig. 11.63) is that the input and bias currents are compared statically in a transductor and the

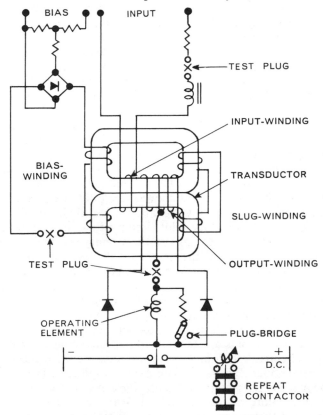

Figure 11.63. Transductor relay (type CF 11) as used in 'Solkor-A' protective system shown in Figure 11.62 (courtesy A. Reyrolle & Co. Ltd.)

331

resultant is fed to a simple d.c. contactor. The input and output windings of the transductor are inductively linked but there is no inductive linking between these windings and the bias windings, i.e. while currents and voltages in the input winding can be transformed into the output winding, no such transformation can occur between these windings and the bias windings. During through-fault conditions the current in the bias windings will produce a d.c. bias m.m.f. which will saturate the cores of the transductor as shown in Fig. 11.54. Spill current in the input winding will superimpose an alternating m.m.f. upon the d.c. bias m.m.f., but the resulting change in working flux density will be small and consequently the output to the relay is negligible.

In the event of an internal fault, the input current is now relatively large, so that the operating m.m.f. in the transductor exceeds the bias m.m.f. resulting in a large change in the working flux density. This produces a correspondingly large voltage across the d.c. contactor winding and the resultant current causes operation.

The slug-winding serves to suppress any ripple that may be present in the bias m.m.f. because it provides a comparatively low-impedance shunt-path for the a.c. component of the bias current.

It follows from the above that operation of the relay can only occur when the magnitude of the operating m.m.f. in the transductor exceeds that of the bias m.m.f. As the bias m.m.f. is proportional to the load or through-fault current, the required operating m.m.f. and hence the required operating current, is also proportional to the load or through-fault current.

The relay incorporates a repeat contactor having three contacts for direct tripping and alarm purposes. A hand-reset flag indicator is also provided.

The plug bridge enables the basic setting of the relay to be increased from the normal 55 mA to 80 mA. The latter setting is required when the protected feeder has 'bleed-off'*.

Three test points are provided at the bottom of the relay to facilitate the checking of the currents in the various parts of the relay circuit.

The summation transformer, relay transformer and capacitor are fitted in a compound-filled metal case suitable for mounting directly on the switchgear or at some other convenient point. The normal level of insulation between the pilot circuit and other circuits, and between the pilot circuit and earth, is 4 kV. Where a high level of pilot circuit insulation is required, isolating transformers can be inserted at each end of the pilot circuit with an insulation level of 15 kV.

There is a choice of three tappings on the primary winding of the summation transformer for connection of the neutral of the current transformers. These enable a choice of earth-fault settings to be made, which in any case should be no more sensitive than required, i.e. half the minimum earth-fault current. The settings for phase faults are constant on any tapping.

Subject to certain conditions of loading and the inability to feed fault current into the protected line, this form of protection can be applied to a main feeder from which tee-off circuits are taken, without balancing current transformers in the tee-off circuits. A fault in a tee-off will operate the protection if the fault current is large enough. If fuses are used in the tee-off circuits, it may be possible by the normal methods of time grading to achieve discrimination with the 'Solkor-A' protection, or alternatively, it may be necessary to increase the operating time of the protection by fitting additional time-delay relays.

* A load taken from the main feeder circuit by way of one or more tee-off circuits.

The increasing use of lightly insulated cables for communication circuits, remote control and telemetering has suggested the use of the same or similar cables for protection. These cables are, as a rule, privately owned and therefore the terminal equipment is not subject to the stringent requirements imposed when national communication pilots are used (see later comment).

The Reyrolle 'Solkor-R' protection has been specifically designed to meet these pilot cable conditions, i.e. relatively low insulation, relatively high core resistance and privately owned, but its use is not in any way restricted to these conditions and it can be applied equally well to any feeder using any ordinary kind of privately owned pilot cable.

The basic protective circuit is that shown in Fig. 11.64. As we have noted in our general discussion on the circulating current principle, the protective relay operating coils are connected in shunt with the pilots across points which have the same potential when current circulates round the loop. In this scheme, equipotential relaying points during *external* faults exist at one end during one half-cycle of fault current and at the other end during the next half-cycle. During

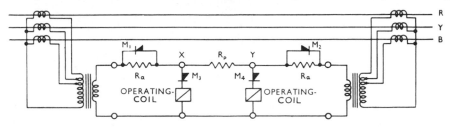

Figure 11.64. Basic circuit of 'Solkor-R' high-speed feeder protection (courtesy A. Reyrolle & Co. Ltd.)

the half-cycles when the relay at either end is not at the electrical mid-point of the pilot system, the voltage appearing across the relay is in the reverse direction to that required for operation.

At each feeder end, the secondaries of the line current transformers are connected to the primary of a summation transformer. For various types of current distribution in the three current-transformers, a single phase quantity appears in the summation transformer secondary and is applied to the pilot circuit. Thus the comparison of currents entering and leaving the feeder is on a single phase basis. In the basic diagram, the resistance of the pilot cable is represented by R_p the rest of the loop comprising the resistors R_a and the rectifiers M_1 and M_2. The operating elements which are made unidirectional by rectifiers M_3 and M_4, are connected in shunt with the pilots at points X and Y.

When a fault occurs external to the protected zone, an alternating current circulates around the pilot loop. On alternate half-cycles one or other of the resistors R_a at the two ends of the pilot is short-circuited by its associated rectifier M_1 or M_2, and the total resistance in the pilot loop at any instant is therefore substantially constant and equal to $R_a + R_p$. The effective position of R_a however, alternates between the two ends being dependent on the direction of current. This change in position of R_a makes the voltage distribution between the pilot cores different for successive half-cycles of the pilot current, the effective circuits on successive half-cycles being shown in Fig. 11.65 at (*a*) and (*b*).

These diagrams also indicate the resulting potential gradient between pilot

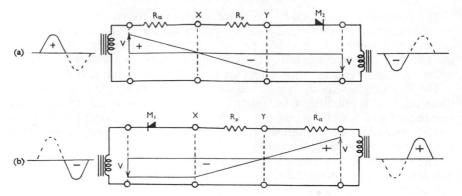

Figure 11.65. *Behaviour of basic circuit under external fault conditions.* (a) *and* (b) *show effective circuits during alternate half-cycles (courtesy A. Reyrolle & Co. Ltd.)*

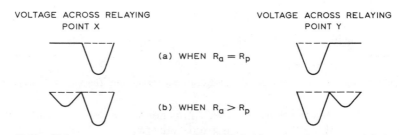

Figure 11.66. *Voltage across relaying points* X *and* Y *during one cycle of external fault current (courtesy A. Reyrolle & Co. Ltd.)*

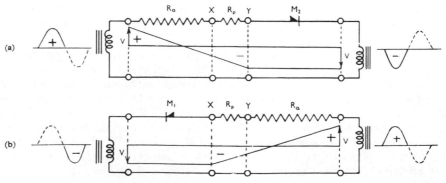

Figure 11.67. *Behaviour of basic circuit under external fault conditions when* R_a *is greater than* R_p. (a) *and* (b) *show effective circuits during alternate half-cycles (courtesy A. Reyrolle & Co. Ltd.)*

cores when R_a is equal to R_p, and it will be seen that the voltage across the relays at points X and Y is either zero (because the relay is at an electrical mid-point) or in the reverse direction for conduction of current through rectifier M_3. Therefore, when $R_a = R_p$, a reverse voltage appears across the relay circuit during one half-cycle and zero voltage during the next. The voltage across each relaying point X and Y during a complete cycle is shown in Fig. 11.66(a).

In practice, resistors R_a are made greater than the pilot loop resistance R_p and this causes the point of zero potential to occur within resistors R_a as shown in Fig. 11.67, and the voltage across X and Y throughout a complete cycle is now that shown in Fig. 11.66(b). Thus, instead of having zero voltage across each relay on alternate half-cycles, there is on both half-cycles a voltage in the reverse direction to that required for operation and as this voltage must be overcome before operation can take place the effect is to enhance the stability on through faults.

When a fault occurs *within* the protected zone and with current fed equally from both ends, the effective circuits during successive half-cycles are those shown at (a) and (b) in Fig. 11.68. From this it is seen that pulses of current pass

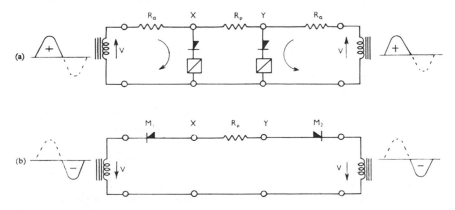

Figure 11.68. Behaviour of basic circuit under internal fault conditions fed from both ends. (a) and (b) show the effective circuits during alternate half-cycles (courtesy A. Reyrolle & Co. Ltd.)

through each relay on alternate half-cycles and the relays at both ends will operate. If the current is fed from one end only, the relay at the remote end (in series with the pilot loop resistance R_p) is energised in shunt with the relay at the feeding end. The relay at the feeding end operates at the setting current and the relay at the remote end at approximately 2·5 times the setting current. Providing therefore, that the fault current is not less than 2·5 times the fault setting, the relays at both ends operate to completely isolate the circuit. Figure 11.69 is a schematic diagram of the complete protective system.

While differential pilot wire protective systems have been developed to a high degree of perfection and their use in all suitable circumstances is universal because of the relative simplicity of relay design and components, there are nevertheless some limitations dictated by the pilot cables themselves. Apart from the obvious high cost involved over long distances, technical considerations have to be taken into account such as the loop resistance of the pilots (dependent on conductor size) and the total intercore capacity in microfarads. The acceptable limits will vary as between protective systems, and are largely dependent on relay design, etc. so that no values can be quoted as standard and reference to the manufacturer must be made. As an example however, for the scheme shown in Fig. 11.48 using the English Electric type *DMW* relay, the maximum loop resistance is given as 1 000Ω while the intercore capacity must not exceed 2·5 μF.

For reasons such as the above, pilot wire protection is generally limited to feeders not exceeding about 20 miles (32 km) in length and may be as low as 10 miles (16 km) with some types and sizes of rented pilots. With regard to the latter, the Post Office authorities lay down certain limits of voltage and current which may be applied to a pilot, e.g. the arc voltage must not exceed 130 V

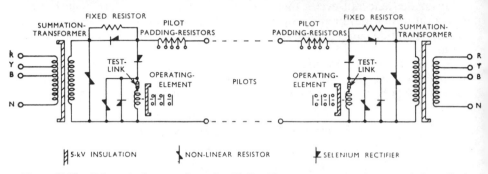

Figure 11.69.   Schematic diagram of complete 'Solkor-R' protective system (courtesy A. Reyrolle & Co. Ltd.)

(peak) and the alternating current is limited to 60 mA (r.m.s.), limitations not always easy to meet when designing a protective scheme.

It has to be remembered that pilot wire protection is very dependent on reliable pilots. When these are privately owned, access to them by the user for regular check purposes is easy, and given such checks, can be regarded as giving maximum reliability. On the other hand, rented pilots are not so accessible, as they are in the care of another owner and probably routed through one or more junctions. It may be noted that schemes are available which keep pilots under constant supervision, giving appropriate alarms, should for example, the pilots be open circuited or short circuited or should the cores get crossed.

DISTANCE PROTECTION

For long feeders associated with high or extra-high-voltage distribution and transmission systems, other means of protection must be sought which do not require pilot wires. One such scheme is that known as *distance protection* which, as the name suggests, is a form which measures the distance between a relaying point and a fault and dependent on that measurement, the relays will be operative or inoperative.

Since impedance is an electrical measure of distance along a feeder between two points, i.e. the ratio of V/I, the relay can be designed to compare these values. Space alone makes it impossible to give more than an outline of the basic principles and how these are applied, noting that studies of the theoretical aspects are given in detail in other works[3,5-9]

Principle of measurement

Figure 11.70 may be used to illustrate a typical condition. Here a chain of feeders fed from a single source is in a series arrangement. If a fault occurs at F, the fault current I will flow from the source through *all* the circuit-breakers (represented by crosses), i.e. its magnitude will be constant at each switching point. On the other hand, the voltages progressively reduce as indicated to voltages V_3, V_2 and V_1 at successive switching points as we get further away from the source, and will approach zero at the point of fault. If current and voltage transformers are now connected at each switching point R_3, R_2 and R_1 the two quantities can be measured and compared in a suitable device, and when V/I is below a given value, an output from that device can be used to initiate the trip circuit of the associated circuit-breaker or, if the ratio is above the given value, operation will be restrained.

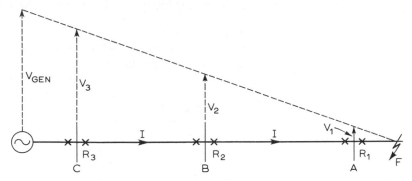

Figure 11.70. Simplified basic principle of distance protection

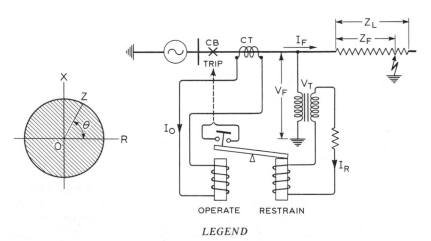

LEGEND

Z_L TOTAL IMPEDANCE OF LINE	I_F PRIMARY FAULT CURRENT
Z_F IMPEDANCE TO POINT OF FAULT	$V_F = I_F \times Z_F$

WHEN $I_0 > I_R$ OPERATION OCCURS

Figure 11.71. How a balanced-beam relay can be used to measure the impedance of a line up to a point of fault. The circle characteristics of a plain impedance relay are shown on the left; operation occurs for any value of impedance within the shaded circle. OZ is the 'reach' of the relay

The simplest way to examine such measurement is to assume that a balanced beam relay is used as shown in Fig. 11.71. Here there are two coils, one an operating coil receiving a secondary current proportional to the primary fault current, and the other a restraint coil energised by a secondary voltage equal to the product IZ_f where Z_f is the line impedance up to the point of fault.

Such a relay would be designed so that the operating torque is proportional to current and the restraint torque proportional to voltage, both torques being dependent on the number of ampere-turns applied to each coil. Under normal conditions the restraint torque due to voltage is greater than the operating torque due to current, so that the relay cannot operate. Under fault conditions the operating torque is increased due to fault current and the restraining torque is decreased due to reduced voltage. For a given current there will be a voltage at which the torques will be equal and a further reduction in voltage will tilt the beam to close the contact in the tripping circuit. The ratio of V/I at which the relay just operates is the relay setting sometimes referred to as the relay *reach*.

If we now revert to Fig. 11.70 it is seen that if the relay is set to operate at V_1/I where V_1 is the voltage obtained for a fault at the end of the feeder remote from R_1, the relay will operate for faults along that feeder because the voltage at R_1 will always be less than V_1. The relays at R_2 and R_3, being also set to operate when the values of V_2 and V_3 respectively are equal to V_1, will remain inoperative because whilst they are influenced by the same current the voltage at these points will always be higher than V_1 thus restraining operation.

On most systems where distance protection is applied, faults can be fed from both ends of the feeder. It is necessary therefore to have relays at each end of the feeder. With relays at each end of the feeder, of the type just described, there is nothing to prevent the relay to the left of busbar A operating for a fault at F since the voltage and current for this relay are the same as for the relay at R. The tripping of the circuit-breaker at the left of busbar A would result in the loss of supply to busbar A unnecessarily, and to prevent this happening all relays are made directional.

Measuring elements

The basic measuring element in distance protection is known as a *comparator*. There are two types in use, viz. *amplitude* and *phase-angle* comparators. The first of these is a device which is sensitive to the amplitude of two input signals with no regard to the phase angle between them. A device of this type is the balanced-beam relay discussed earlier, but other forms are more frequently used, e.g. transductors, a rectifier-bridge, and more recently, a transistor comparator. In the phase-angle comparator, response is related only to the phase angle between two inputs and is unrelated to the respective amplitudes.

The balanced-beam relay as shown in Fig. 11.71 is an early form of amplitude comparator having an impedance characteristic shown on the resistance-reactance diagram. The relay operates for any value of impedance within the shaded circle so that if the line OZ represents the transmission-line impedance having an angle θ, the relay will operate for any fault on the transmission line. Since the origin O represents the position of the relay it can be seen that the relay is non-directional and its operation to trip the circuit-breaker must therefore

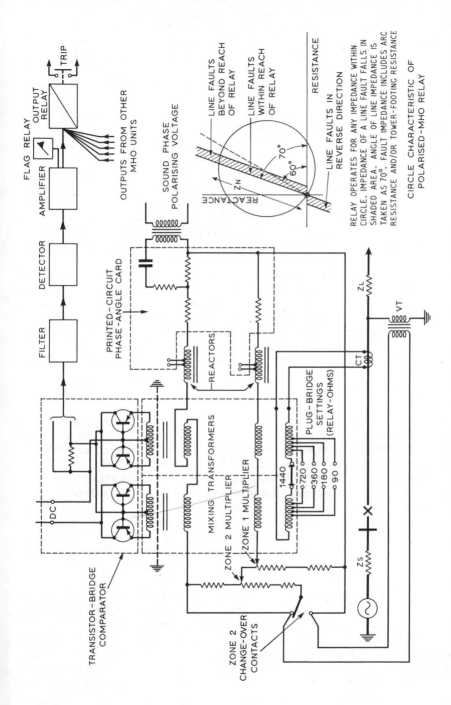

Figure 11.72. Schematic diagram for a polarised mho unit. Zones 1 and 2 are in type TH transistorised distance protection (courtesy A. Reyrolle & Co. Ltd.)

339

be controlled by another directional relay. In schemes using the balanced-beam relay two relays have to operate before tripping can take place.

In modern schemes of distance protection measuring elements having mho* characteristics are used. In these elements both features, the impedance measuring and the directional, are combined. Two inputs to the comparator are obtained from two mixing transformers, each with one or more primary windings supplied by current or voltage so that mixing of both is accomplished to obtain a required characteristic.

In a typical three-zone scheme, two types of mho relay are used, one designated *polarised mho* shown in Fig. 11.72 which operates for faults in zones 1 and 2 and the other designated *offset mho* shown in Fig. 11.73 which operates for faults in zones 1, 2 and 3.

The polarised-mho relay is so called because the voltage which determines the directional feature is taken from the phase which is not directly affected by the fault, e.g. in an earth-fault element measuring a red phase to earth fault the 'polarising' voltage will be that of a blue phase. This design of the relay ensures that the directional characteristic is maintained even when the restraining voltage falls to zero as would be the case for a fault close to the relaying point, i.e. a terminal fault.

Figure 11.72 is a diagram of connections of the polarised-mho relay showing the primary windings of mixing transformers and the secondary outputs fed to the comparator. The windings connected to the C.T. are tapped to provide a choice of impedance setting, to match it to the impedance of the protected feeder. There are two sets of windings connected to the V.T., the lower set providing the restraining output, and the upper set the polarising (or directional) feature. Both sets of windings are fed through reactor and resistor networks which determine the characteristic angle of the relay. The upper set of windings is also fed by a polarising voltage through a resistor and capacitor network which corrects its phase shift with respect to the restraining voltage.

The characteristic for this relay is again a circle but now its circumference passes through the origin of a resistance-reactance diagram as shown in the inset. As the origin corresponds to the relaying point it can be seen that the relay is directional, for it will only detect faults within the circle. The line Z_N may be taken as representing the line impedance at a typical angle. Ideally the characteristic angle of the relay should match the impedance angle of the protected feeder. In practice, quite often relays are employed with angles of 45°, 60° or 75° depending on which of the angles is closer to matching the impedance angle of the protected feeder. It should be noted from the inset that small mismatching of angles leads only to a small acceptance error in the reach of the relay. In the relay just described the characteristic angle can be altered by changing a printed card.

Figure 11.73 is a diagram of connections of the offset-mho relay. It can be seen that the circuitry is somewhat simpler than that of the polarised-mho relay. The primary windings of the mixing transformers connected to the C.T. are tapped to enable the choice of impedance settings to be made. The primary winding of one of the mixing transformers connected to the V.T. provides restraining voltage fed through a reactor and resistor network which determines the characteristic angle of the relay. The potentiometer 'zone 3 multiplier'

*The term *mho* was originally derived from the fact that the mho characteristic, when plotted on an admittance instead of impedance diagram, gives a straight line.

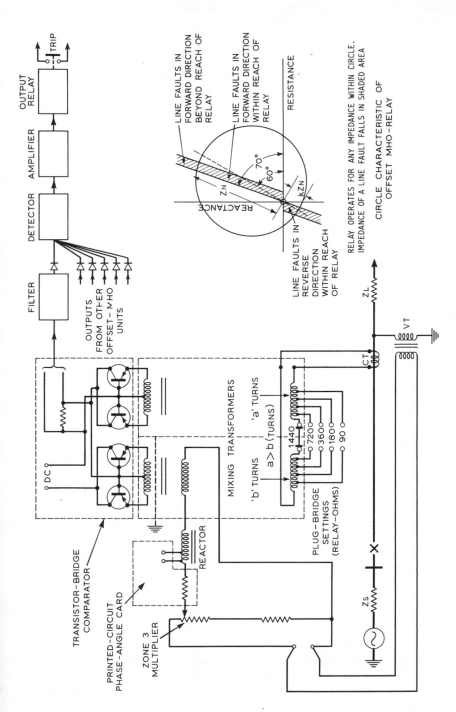

Figure 11.73. Schematic diagram for an offset mho unit. Zone 3 is in type TH transistorised distance protection (courtesy A. Reyrolle & Co. Ltd.)

341

provides continuous adjustment of impedance settings between the steps provided on windings connected to the C.T.

The characteristic of this relay is similar to that of the polarised-mho relay but the circle is shifted (offset) so that it encloses the origin in a resistance-reactance diagram. The relay will therefore detect faults on either side having a longer reach Z_N in the direction of the protected line and a shorter reach kZ_N in the reverse direction. The factor 'k' will normally be of the order of 0·1 to 0·15.

Zoning

A variety of time-distance characteristics are used in distance schemes for the purpose of discrimination, but the one most generally used for important high-voltage lines is the stepped characteristic illustrated in Fig. 11.74. In this figure, feeders AB and BC are for simplicity assumed to be of equal length. The relays A and B measure the distance to the fault when fault current flows in the direction left to right and have time-distance characteristics for this direction as shown *above* the base line OO. Thus the relay at A trips its associated

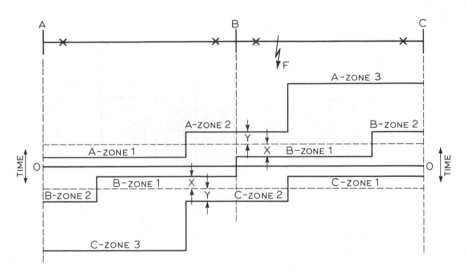

LEGEND

A, B, C   RELAYING POINTS
X   CIRCUIT-BREAKER OPERATING TIME
Y   MARGIN OF DISCRIMINATION

Figure 11.74. Typical distance/time graph for 3-zone protection. Note that zones 2 and 3 are independently adjustable

circuit-breaker immediately, for all faults which occur within the first 80% of feeder AB. For faults which occur in the remaining 20% of the feeder and in the first 20% of feeder BC, relay A initiates tripping after a short time-delay. A further time-delay is introduced for still more remote faults. Additional relays at B and C have similar characteristics but measure only when fault-current flows in the opposite direction as shown by the characteristics *below* the base line.

The discriminative properties of this scheme can be understood by considering a fault such as at *F* in feeder *BC* when fault current flows from *A* to the fault. The relay at *A* starts to operate, but before the tripping circuit can be completed the relay at *B* trips its circuit-breaker and the fault is cleared. The time margin of discrimination provided is indicated by *Y*.

It will be noted that the zone 1 of each relay is arranged to extend over 80% of a feeder. The main reason for this is because practical distance relays and their associated current and voltage transformer equipment have unavoidable errors especially under transient conditions, and a margin of safety has to be allowed to avoid incorrect tripping for faults just inside the next feeder. The zone 2 is extended well into the next feeder to ensure definite protection for that part of the feeder not covered by zone 1. The zone 2 may in some cases have the additional function of providing protection for the remote busbars. The object of zone 3 is to provide general back-up protection for the rest of the adjacent feeder. In schemes where offset-mho relays are used the offset in the reverse direction enables the relay to operate when the voltage falls to zero, say for a terminal three-phase fault. In that case the relay becomes a simple current operated device, the restraining ampere turns being smaller than those for operating.

Typical scheme

The arrangement shown in Fig. 11.74 requires three basic features, viz. response to direction, response to impedance and timing. These features need not necessarily be provided by three separate relay elements but they are fundamental to all distance protective systems. It can be shown that for the relays to measure the same distance for all types of faults the applied voltages and currents must be different, e.g. for faults involving more than one phase the appropriate phase-to-phase voltage must be applied, but for earth faults the phase-to-neutral voltage is necessary for correct measurement. It is common practice therefore, to provide two separate sets of relays, one set for phase faults and the other for earth faults. In practice, each set of relays is usually further divided into three, since phase faults may concern any pair of phases, and similarly any phase can be faulted to earth.

A typical arrangement of relays based on this is shown in Fig. 11.75. In this, three phase-fault and three earth-fault polarised-mho relays are used for zones 1 and 2 and three phase-fault and three earth-fault offset-mho relays for zone 3. The operation of offset-mho relays starts the two timing relays *T*. If the fault lies within the reach of zone 1, both the offset mho and the polarised-mho relays operate simultaneously. The polarised-mho relay trips the circuit-breaker immediately and both relays reset. For zone 2 faults, the offset-mho relay operates instantaneously and energises timing relays. As soon as the first timing relay operates it extends the reach of the polarised-mho relay which operates and trips. If the fault is cleared the timing relays reset when the offset-mho relay resets. For zone 3 faults, only the offset-mho relay operates and tripping takes place when the second timing relay operates. The time-distance and impedance characteristics of a three-zone scheme is shown in Fig. 11.76.

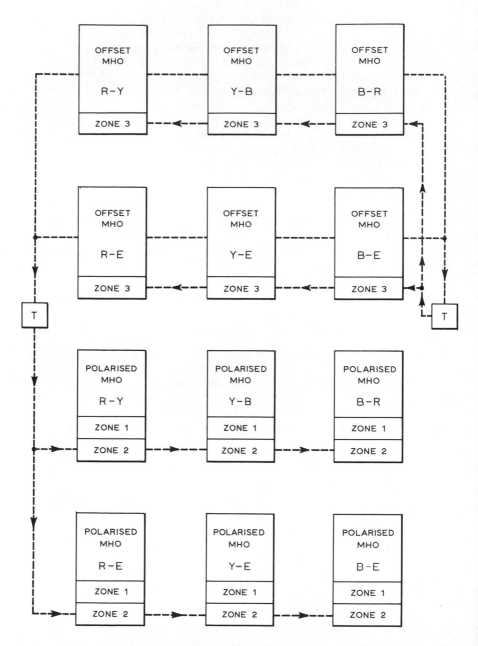

Figure 11.75.   Block diagram of a typical scheme of distance protection (courtesy A. Reyrolle & Co. Ltd.)

The relay shown in Figs. 11.72 and 11.73 may be used in the arrangement just described. In a transistorised scheme their output circuits beyond the comparators will be as shown. The output from the comparators is first fed to a filter circuit to attenuate the a.c. ripple. The smoothed output is then passed to a transistorised detector circuit which is basically a trigger circuit controlled by

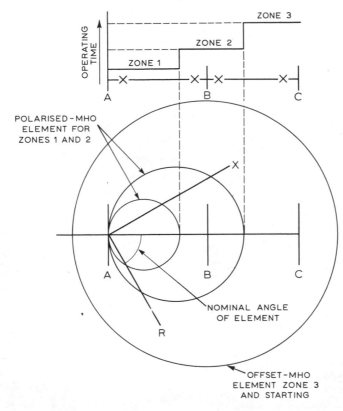

*Figure 11.76.   Time/distance and impedance characteristics for a 3-zone scheme using mho relays
(courtesy A. Reyrolle & Co. Ltd.)*

the output voltage from the comparator, i.e. when I_o exceeds I_R the increase in output voltage triggers the detector. The output signal from the latter is then amplified to operate the output and flag relays.

There are six flags operated by the polarised-mho relays and they show the faulty phase or phases for zone 1 and zone 2 faults. For zone 2 faults a 'zone 2' flag, operated by the zone 2 timing relay, is shown in addition to the flag operated by a polarised-mho relay.

The offset-mho elements do not operate flags so that only one detector and amplifier are necessary, common to all six offset-mho relays. The tripping operation of zone 3 is shown by a flag on the zone 3 timing relay.

All relays, etc. are contained within a single housing as shown in Fig. 11.77(*a*), the relay elements being of the plug-in type and shown in more detail in Fig. 11.77(*b*) and (*c*). Each plug-in assembly carries its mixing transformers, reactors, setting potentiometers, plug bridge and test sockets. At the side of each assembly are two printed-circuit cards, one the comparator filter, the other the phase-angle card. Below the relay assembly, further printed-circuit cards cover the amplifier and detector sections of the output circuits and a marshalling card holds the six blocking diodes seen in Fig. 11.73. A transistor timing unit comprises two plug-in printed-circuit cards. All the transistor circuits are fed from an external power supply at, nominally, 12 V d.c. typically from a modern sealed battery with continuous trickle charge.

A separately mounted compensating current-transformer (not shown in the diagrams) is connected between the secondaries of the line current-transformers and the current circuits of the measuring elements. Its purpose is to isolate

(a)

Figure 11.77.   Relay elements used in type **TH** *transistorised distance projection.* (a) *Complete relay cover removed,* (b) *mho element and* (c) *offset-mho element (courtesy A. Reyrolle & Co. Ltd.)*

346

(b)

(c)

347

current-transformers from the transistor circuits and to step-down the secondary current to a lower level. It has also a 'zero sequence' winding for earth-fault measurement compensation which ensures that the distance reach of the protection is the same for earth faults as for phase faults.

Use of protection with signalling links

In some circumstances, e.g. where there is a risk of system instability, or where high-speed auto-reclosing is employed, the zone 2 delayed tripping may not be acceptable. By the addition of some form of signalling equipment at each end of the feeder, the protection can be accelerated to give instantaneous tripping for faults over the whole of the protected feeder.

There is a very wide choice of signalling equipment but the most commonly used is the voice-frequency link using private or hired pilots and the high-frequency carrier link using the power line.

Several schemes are available but they can roughly be divided into two groups, viz. tripping schemes and blocking schemes. The principle of the tripping scheme, the one which is used in the majority of cases, is illustrated in Fig. 11.78.

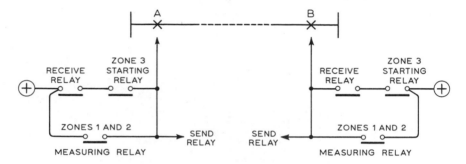

Figure 11.78. Accelerated distance-protection tripping scheme (courtesy A. Reyrolle & Co. Ltd.)

With the three zones of distance measurements set as previously described, a fault near the end of the protected feeder will cause the zone 1 relay at that end to trip the breaker instantaneously. Additionally it will operate a 'send' relay which initiates the sending of a signal to the other end of the feeder. At the other end the 'receive' relay operates to trip the circuit-breaker. To ensure that tripping is not obtained for incorrect operation of the signalling equipment the 'receive' relay is interlocked with the zone 3 measuring relays (which are instantaneous in operation).

Effect of loss of voltage from transformer supply

High-speed distance relays capable of operating for fault currents less than full load are liable to mal-operation if the voltage-transformer supply on one or more phases is lost due to the blowing or removal of the fuses, so care must be taken in the design and layout of the wiring. If desired a supervisory scheme can be added which detects the loss of a fuse and blocks tripping.

Operation under power swing conditions

Where the protected circuit interconnects two power sources and a power swing occurs, the increases and decreases of the three-phase current and the terminal voltages are seen by the impedance-measuring relay as a three-phase fault with a continually changing position.

Among the various characteristics that are normally used, the mho characteristic is the least susceptible to mal-operation under power swing conditions. Generally, mal-operation will not occur during a stable swing. However, tripping will be initiated on the occurrence of an unstable power swing when the phase displacement between the power systems approaches 180°. When required, separate relay equipment can be supplied to block tripping during power swinging and to give controlled tripping following a pole slip when the voltages of the machines are approximately in phase again.

PHASE-COMPARISON CARRIER-CURRENT PROTECTION

As an alternative to distance protection, a system of phase-comparison carrier-current protection is often used on high-voltage transmission lines. It is a system comparable with pilot-wire schemes in that the conditions at both ends of a line are compared, and depending on the result of that comparison, the circuit-breakers remain closed or are tripped open. In a pilot-wire scheme, as we have noted, the currents entering and leaving the protected zone are compared, and when they differ by a predetermined value, relay operation occurs and circuit-breakers are tripped. In a carrier-current system however, the amplitudes of the currents are not used as a criterion; instead a carrier is used to determine the phase angle between the currents at the two ends of the line. Thus, the secondary current (from line current transformers) at each end of the protected feeder is arranged to modulate a high-frequency carrier signal in

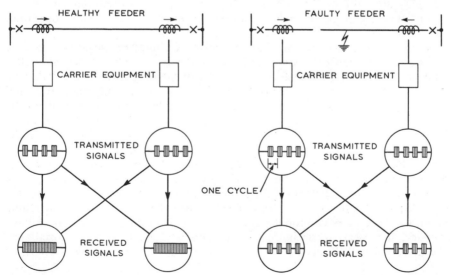

Figure 11.79. The principle of phase-comparison protection (courtesy A. Reyrolle & Co. Ltd.)

such a way that the carrier is transmitted over the power lines in blocks corresponding to the alternate half cycles of power frequency. The frequency of the carrier signal is of the order of 70–400 kHz and the connection to the overhead line is made by suitable coupling equipment.

The current transformer connections are such that for an external fault, i.e. a through fault, the transmitted blocks of modulated carrier from each end occur at alternate half cycles giving rise to an interlace to form a continuous carrier signal, and the protection does not operate. This is illustrated in principle in Fig. 11.79 (left).

In the case of an internal fault, fed from both ends, as in Fig. 11.79 (right), there will be a phase shift at one end approaching 180° so that the blocks of carrier at both ends will be transmitted more or less during the same half cycle. The received signal will thus contain gaps as shown and this is taken as the criterion for tripping. If the fault is fed from one end only, the carrier will be sent from that end only and the signal on the line will contain gaps as for a fault fed from both ends, and tripping will occur.

As may be anticipated, such a scheme demands considerable equipment and Fig. 11.80 is a block diagram of that required at each end of the line. Static circuitry has been introduced in this scheme to improve performance and reliability and at the same time, reduce the physical size. The full technical description of the operation of the many elements making up the complete equipment is too lengthy to be narrated here but two items are worthy of note.

Because the authorities in many countries prohibit the sending of a continuous carrier signal, it is necessary to provide starting equipment to detect a fault, and when detected, control the carrier signal. To ensure correct discrimination under marginal through-fault conditions, the protection is brought into operation in two stages. The carrier is initiated by a static low-set starting circuit (LS in Fig. 11.80) and the trip circuit is prepared by a similar high-set starting circuit (HS in Fig. 11.80), the latter set to operate at 150% of the low-set circuit setting. Thus, in the event of a marginal through-fault, where the current at the two ends may differ due to say line-charging current, it is ensured that the low-set circuits at both ends of the feeder operate to establish a carrier link before either end is free to trip.

Figure 11.81 shows that the starting network comprises negative-sequence and positive-sequence* networks, both connected as shown to the delta-connected line-current transformers. In the event of a three-phase balanced fault, the negative-phase sequence network will have virtually no output and the settings of the starting circuits will be controlled by the output from the positive-phase sequence network. For other faults, i.e. phase to earth or interphase (unbalanced faults) the negative-phase sequence network will have the larger output and will control the unbalanced fault settings.

This diagram also shows the modulator network. This is a negative-minus-positive sequence network whose function is to provide a single 50 Hz voltage from the three input currents of the main current transformers to modulate the high-frequency signal obtained from the oscillator. The modulator is a switching circuit which receives two input signals, one a 50 Hz signal from the modulator network, the other a continuous high-frequency signal from the oscillator. The effect of the 50 Hz signal is to suppress the high-frequency signal at alternate

---

* Chapter 4 considers negative and positive-phase sequences.

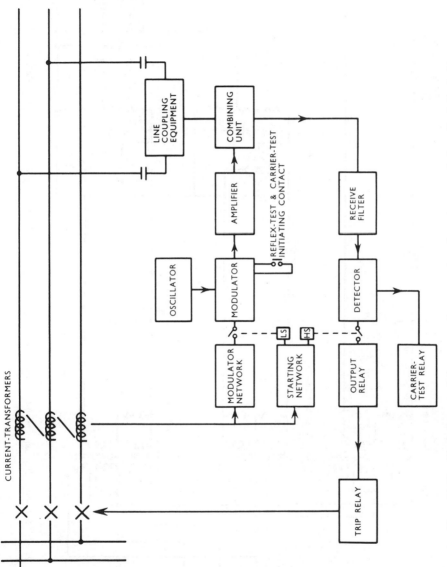

Figure 11.80. Block diagram of phase-comparison protective scheme (courtesy A. Reyrolle & Co. Ltd.)

351

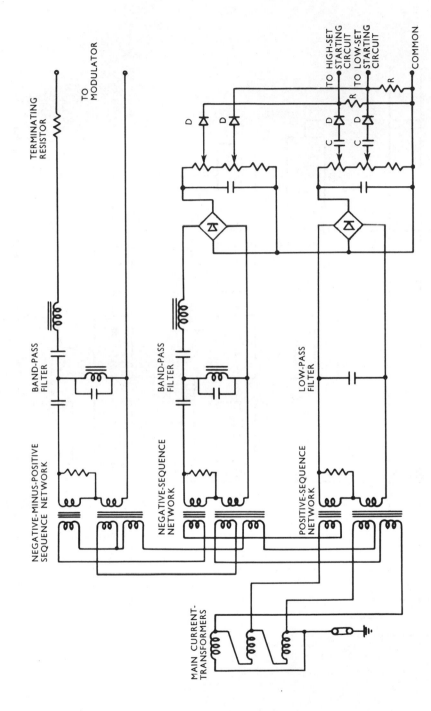

Figure 11.81. Schematic diagram of modulator and starting networks for phase-comparison protection (courtesy A. Reyrolle & Co. Ltd.)

half cycles of the 50 Hz frequency so that the output from the modulator comprises blocks of high-frequency signals, the blocks and quiescent periods being of normal half cycle duration as explained in relation to Fig. 11.79.

The detector unit is designed to detect the gaps in the carrier signal and to energise the tripping relay if the minimum gap is exceeded. Operation occurs when the phase displacement between the local and remote ends is nominally greater than 30°.

Figure 11.82 shows the line-coupling equipment required for two-phase injection (this is normal practice), the high-frequency coaxial cable being connected to the combining unit shown in Fig. 11.80. The line traps shown are

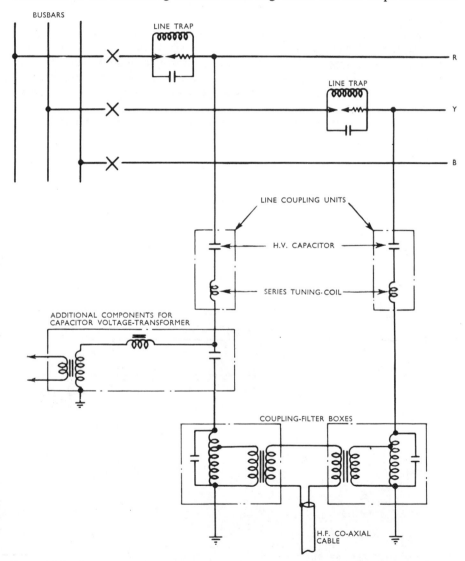

Figure 11.82. Line coupling equipment (phase-to-phase injection) for phase-comparison protection (courtesy A. Reyrolle & Co. Ltd.)

353

tuned to permit the passage of power-frequency current and to block the passage of high-frequency currents so that the carrier signals are confined to the protected line. The spark gap and non-linear resistor connected in series across the choke and capacitor protect the latter against breakdown due to high voltages induced across the coil by surges on the line. In Chapter 23 we shall note the use of capacitor voltage transformers for use on extra-high-voltage systems and Fig. 11.82 shows how the line-coupling unit can form a part of such a transformer.

BUSBAR PROTECTION

The types of protection so far discussed have been concerned with the protection of the section of the electrical network with which they are associated, i.e. generators, transformers and feeders. This is shown in diagrammatic form in Fig. 11.83 from which it will be noted that at any switchboard there may be a most vital section without protection against possible faults—a section known as the *busbar zone*.

While the possibility of faults in the busbar installations is, particularly in metal enclosed types of switchgear and with insulated busbars, less than at

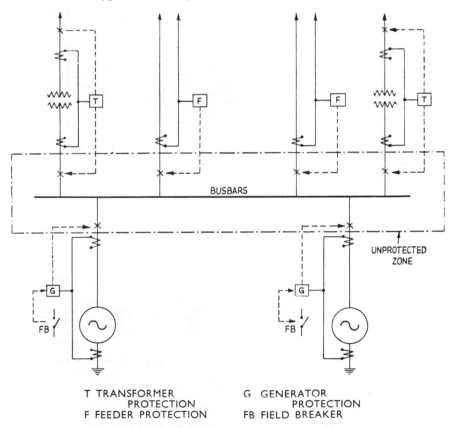

T TRANSFORMER
    PROTECTION
F FEEDER PROTECTION

G GENERATOR
    PROTECTION
FB FIELD BREAKER

Figure 11.83. Unprotected zone in power station

other points on a system, it has to be borne in mind that should they occur, the effects may be widespread causing considerable damage due to a high concentration of fault MVA. It is for reasons such as these, along with others, that sectionalising is resorted to so that trouble, if it does occur, is confined to a section of the busbar only.

In enclosed types of switchgear, most busbar faults involve one phase to earth due to insulation failure, overvoltages, etc. In open type switchgear, faults between phases can arise due to foreign objects spanning the busbars, e.g. in outdoor switching stations, a branch of a tree which has been blown down.

Many schemes have therefore been developed to provide protection in the busbar zone, some relatively simple such as frame leakage protection for metal enclosed switchgear, and others more elaborate for larger installations, such as the electronic type[10]. Whether simple or elaborate, the protection should ensure high-speed clearance to minimise damage and maintain system stability, be stable when faults external to the switchgear occur, discriminate in sectionalised schemes between busbar zones, isolate *all* circuits from a faulted busbar zone and be free of any possibility of incorrect operation.

Whether busbar protection is provided or not will depend largely on the importance of the installation and its relation to other parts of the network. Thus it will rarely be found on simple industrial installations or if it is used,

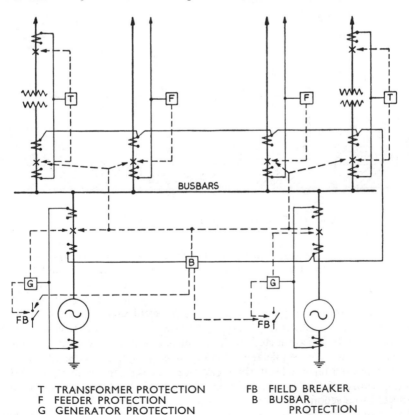

T   TRANSFORMER PROTECTION
F   FEEDER PROTECTION
G   GENERATOR PROTECTION
FB FIELD BREAKER
B   BUSBAR
        PROTECTION

Figure 11.84. Overlap protection to cover busbar zone

will not be an elaborate form, while in major power stations, primary substations and distribution centres its use is common, the added cost of an elaborate scheme being justified by the importance of the installation.

The ideal system of applying protective gear to a power system is for each component to be protected by a high-speed discriminative scheme which provides for each adjacent protective scheme to overlap (as shown in Fig. 11.84) thus leaving no item unprotected, but isolating only the section which is faulty. Economic considerations, however, often dictate that deviation from the ideal must be accepted.

To some extent, back-up protection added as a safeguard for the differential protection normally applied on generator and transformer circuits will cover

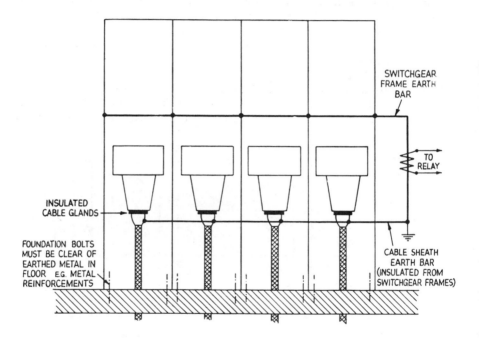

Figure 11.85. 'Leakage to frame' bus-zone protection

busbar faults, but because the back-up relays (e.g. overcurrent) may need to be time-graded with other relays further out in the system, clearance times will be extended so that damage will result. Thus, if in Fig. 11.84 it is assumed that an overcurrent relay is added as a second line of defence for the differential protection on both the generator and feeder circuits, relays on the generator circuits must have a longer time-setting than that on any feeder to ensure that the latter only will be disconnected in the event of a fault on the feeder, leaving the generators in service. While the back-up overcurrent relay on the generator will operate on a busbar fault, the clearance time will be relatively long. Other complications arise when the busbars are sectionalised and when feeders are connected to a second source of supply at a remote point.

As we have seen in the discussion on distance protection, busbars coming within the reach of zone 2 protection are covered, but here again time-delay is involved and while this may be of shorter duration than in the case of an over-current relay it may still be long enough to allow damage to be done.

When busbar protection is deemed essential therefore, it should preferably be applied separately. For many installations sufficient cover can be obtained by using frame leakage protection. It requires that the switchgear framework be lightly insulated from earth and that insulated cable glands be used, typically as shown in Fig. 11.85 which assumes metal-clad switchgear to which the protection can be most readily applied. The insulated framework is now earthed through the primary of a current transformer, the secondary output of which is fed to an instantaneous relay. When the latter operates, *all* circuit-breakers

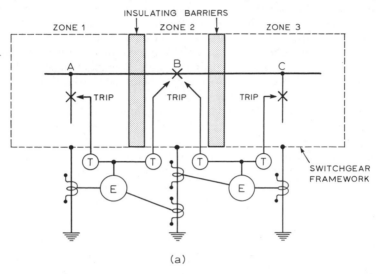

(a)

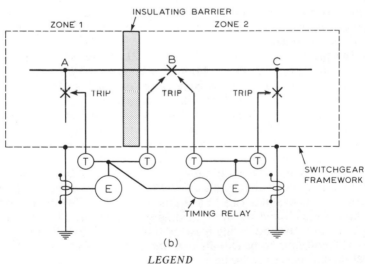

(b)

LEGEND

E FRAME-LEAKAGE RELAYS   *T* TRIPPING RELAYS

Figure 11.86.   Basic frame-leakage protection for metal-clad switchgear with sectionalised single busbars. (a) Three-zone scheme and (b) two-zone scheme

connected to the busbars will be tripped open. This form of protection covers earth faults only, i.e. a fault between a busbar and the switchgear frame causing current to flow to earth through the current transformer primary.

Normally no special insulation between the framework and earth is necessary as the concrete foundation provides all that is required, e.g. about 5–10 Ω, but it is essential that the holding-down bolts are kept clear of any metal reinforcements which may have been used. On the other hand a much higher degree of insulation is necessary on the main cable glands and here it should be capable of withstanding a flash test of at least 8 kV and possibly as high as 10–12 kV. This is particularly important when single-core cables are used as high voltages can be induced in the cable sheaths under through-fault conditions which can cause unnecessary operation of the frame-leakage protection if a flashover occurs between the glands and the earthed framework.

When this form of protection is applied to sectionalised busbars, some elaboration is necessary. In a single busbar layout, the busbar must be divided into zones, preferably three as shown in Fig. 11.86(a) or, if overall cost is a primary consideration, into two as in Fig. 11.86(b).

In a three-zone scheme it is seen that the framework of the bus section switch unit is insulated from that of the remaining switchgear on both sides, while in a two-zone scheme, insulation is introduced on one side only.

Considering the three-zone scheme first, it will be seen that a fault in zone 2 on either side of the breaker will trip all circuit-breakers, i.e. A, B and C. If the fault occurs in either zone 1 or zone 3, only the circuit-breakers connected to the busbars of the faulty zone *plus* the section breaker will trip, i.e. A and B for a zone 1 fault or B and C for a zone 3 fault.

In the two-zone scheme, a fault on zone 1 or zone 2 busbars will, as before, trip the breaker in the faulty zone plus the section breaker, but here there is a blind spot between the section breaker and the insulating barrier, making full discrimination impossible. It can be partly overcome, however, by introducing sequential tripping via a timing relay, set low at say 0·4 s. With this arrangement, the breaker A can be caused to trip if fault current continues to flow after breakers B and C have opened.

For switchgear with duplicate busbars with a bus-section breaker in the main bars only, and with the addition of a bus-coupling breaker, a scheme as shown in Fig. 11.87 can be employed. Here, auxiliary switches on the busbar selector switches in individual circuits are used to prepare the trip circuits for the appropriate circuit-breakers. In this scheme, operation of a zone relay initiates tripping of all circuit-breakers connected to the faulty busbar section *plus* the section switch and any circuit-breakers which may be connected to the reserve busbar at that time.

For frame-leakage schemes to function it is essential that at least one earthed source of supply be available, and, if there is only one such source, that it be connected in scheme (b) of Fig. 11.86 to the zone containing the section breaker. Preferably there should be an earthed source of supply on both sides as this ensures that any fault occurring between the section breaker and the insulating barrier will continue to be fed after isolation of the zone 2 and allow the fault to be cleared as described earlier.

The earthing arrangements of a frame-leakage scheme should have one common electrode of low resistance and adequate rating, for both the switchgear frame and the system neutral points. This ensures sufficient current for the scheme to operate and limits the rise in frame potential. If the system neutral is earthed through a resistance, the earthing connection from the switchgear frame should be made between the bottom of the earthing resistor and the earthing electrode.

One problem with the frame leakage scheme is that relay operation can occur without a bus fault occurring, e.g. any rise in frame potential above true earth may be sufficient to cause the relay operating current to flow. A check feature is therefore often incorporated which inhibits such tripping and ensures this for busbar faults only. In Fig. 11.88 it is seen that a current transformer is included in each neutral earth point, and is connected to a neutral check relay

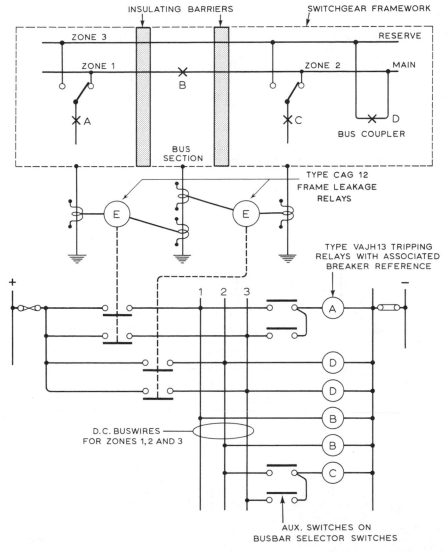

Figure 11.87. 'English Electric' frame-leakage scheme for duplicate busbars with metal-clad switch-gear (courtesy G.E.C. Measurements Ltd.)

359

whose normally open contacts are in series with those of the frame leakage relay so that if the latter should operate for spurious reasons, tripping of circuit-breakers will not occur as the neutral check relay contacts will still be open. Only when the two sets are closed will operation occur, a condition indicating that earth current is flowing from the frame back to the neutral. The neutral check relay will of course close its contacts when there is an earth fault elsewhere on the system, and for this reason it must be of the self resetting type.

Where the type of switchgear does not lend itself to frame-leakage protection, a simple earth-fault scheme for a non-sectionalised busbar can be used operating

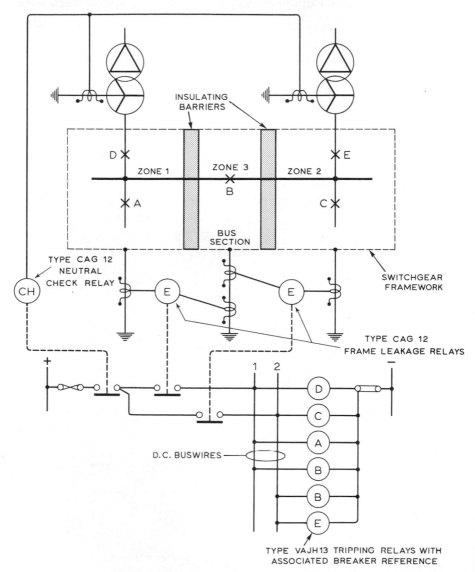

Figure 11.88. '*English Electric' frame-leakage scheme with neutral check (courtesy G.E.C. Measurements Ltd.)*

on the circulating current principle. Figure 11.89 shows such an arrangement where three current transformers (one per phase) are included in each circuit with all secondary windings connected in parallel and then to an instantaneous relay. Under healthy conditions, the currents in the secondaries of each set of current transformers equates to zero so that no current flows in the relay. If an external earth fault occurs as at F_1, the current output from each transformer in the faulty phase circulates through the pilots but not through the relay. If the fault is internal, i.e. on the busbars as at F_2, then the secondary currents in the incoming circuits are unbalanced, the imbalance flowing through the relay.

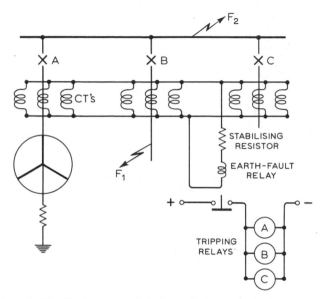

Figure 11.89. Single-zone earth-fault circulating-current busbar protection

The relay recommended for this scheme, and extensions of it which will be noted later, is a high-stability voltage-operated high-impedance type, some of the details of which are noted later.

When an earth-fault scheme of this type is applied to a sectionalised single-bus installation, two sets of current transformers are necessary in the bus-section unit in addition to those in the incoming and outgoing circuits, typically as shown in Fig. 11.90. The secondary connections of the groups of current transformers are paralleled in two sections as shown, each section with its own relay. The protection is therefore given to two zones which overlap, discrimination between the two zones being obtained by means of the bus-section transformers which unbalance the faulty side and cause operation of the relay associated therewith.

The scheme can be extended to double-bus switchgear, and if this includes a bus-coupler breaker, this also must have a set of three current transformers on *each* side of it, as for the section switch in Fig. 11.90. In this arrangement, three overlapping zones of protection are provided, i.e. two zones adjacent to the section switch in the main busbars and the third covering the reserve busbars (non-sectionalised) and with the discriminating zones selected via auxiliary switches on the busbar selector isolators.

361

When it is required to provide busbar protection for both phase and earth-faults, the simple scheme noted in Fig. 11.89 can be modified so that the current transformer secondaries of each phase are paralleled as in Fig. 11.91, a three-phase relay being connected across the paralleled groups to provide a spill circuit and arranged to trip all circuit-breakers on a faulty zone. For important installations, where the fault level is high and where high-speed clearance and system stability is a paramount consideration, some elaboration is considered essential and while the differential system is maintained using high-impedance voltage-operated relays, other features are added. Perhaps the most important

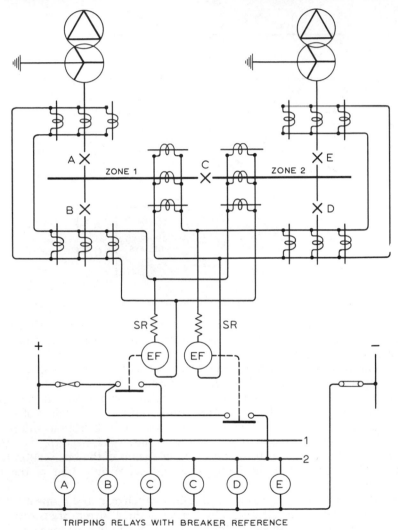

TRIPPING RELAYS WITH BREAKER REFERENCE

LEGEND

EF EARTH-FAULT RELAYS
SR STABILISING RESISTORS

Figure 11.90. Two-zone earth-fault circulating-current busbar protection for sectionalised single bus

362

of these is a separate check system backing-up the main protection and so connected that both the check and main features must operate before any tripping can occur. This necessitates fitting six current transformers in each outgoing and incoming circuit instead of the three noted in Fig. 11.91, the bus-section switch also having six as in the frame-leakage scheme. As seen in Fig. 11.92, three sets of secondary buswires are used, one set each for zones *A* and *B*, and the third set for the common check feature, plus a neutral buswire for the main and check features.

These buswires are energised from the groups of current transformers in each circuit and the bus-section and from them connections are taken to zone *A*, zone *B* and the check relays, the connections providing phase and earth-fault protection. Operation is on the principles noted earlier, viz. for external faults, the currents entering and leaving a zone are equal and the current transformers affected will circulate current through the buswires. The system is designed such

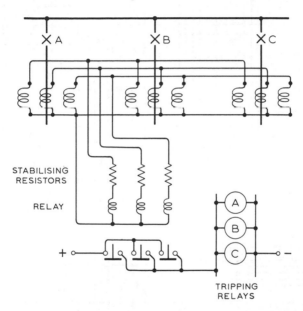

Figure 11.91. Single-zone phase and earth-fault circulating-current busbar protection

that the voltage necessary to operate the relay is greater than the voltage across the buswires under maximum through-fault conditions so that relay operation is prevented. If a fault occurs inside the protected zone, the balance of secondary current is upset and the relay will operate. The check feature operates similarly, but as the diagram shows, the feature is common to both zones so that as far as checking is concerned, the complete busbar installation is concerned as one overall zone.

As all circuit-breakers connected to a faulty zone and the bus-section breaker must be tripped by the zone plus check relays when they operate, *each* incoming and outgoing circuit-breaker must be provided with a tripping relay and the bus-section breaker with two such relays, i.e. one connected to each zone protection. For clarity, the tripping relays are omitted in Fig. 11.92; they will be connected typically as those shown in Figs. 11.88–11.91.

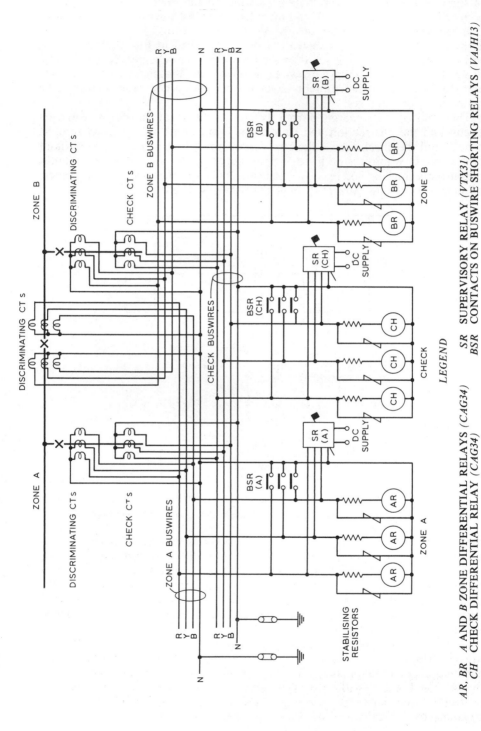

LEGEND

AR, BR A AND B ZONE DIFFERENTIAL RELAYS (CAG34)   SR SUPERVISORY RELAY (VTX31)
CH CHECK DIFFERENTIAL RELAY (CAG34)   BSR CONTACTS ON BUSWIRE SHORTING RELAYS (VAJH13)

Figure 11.92. 'English Electric' high-impedance voltage-differential busbar-protective scheme (courtesy G.E.C. Measurements Ltd.)

An additional feature considered essential is that some form of continuous supervision of the current transformers and a.c. wiring should be provided to ensure that all is in order when the protection is called upon to operate. In the scheme shown in Fig. 11.92 this is achieved by a static-transistorised relay connected across the protection-zone buswires. This relay will close its contacts when the voltage appearing across the buswires exceeds the main relay voltage setting. Operation of the relay takes the affected zone out of service by short-circuiting the appropriate buswires and at the same time causes an alarm to be given. The type of faults covered by this supervision are open-circuited current transformers, broken or crossed-current transformer pilots. A three-phase bridge rectifier is included to operate a timing circuit which provides a 3 s time-delay so that unwanted alarms are not given on the occurrence of busbar faults. Also, due to its low setting, the supervisory relay may be unstable under heavy external-fault conditions and the time-delay prevents an unwanted alarm prior to the fault being cleared by the protective relays appropriate to the external fault, e.g. on a feeder circuit.

In addition to the alarm just described, provision is made to give both visual and audible alarms of busbar faults (with indication as to which zone is affected), failure of trip or alarm supplies and whether the protection has been taken out of service in either zone; a manually operated switch is provided for the latter purpose.

For a duplicate busbar scheme in which the main busbar is sectionalised and between each section of main busbar and the reserve busbar there is a bus-coupling circuit-breaker, the arrangements for protection are very similar except that now there are three zones of protection, i.e. each section of the main bar and a third comprising the reserve bar. Thus there are a set of buswires for each zone plus a set for check purposes.

Each bus-coupler circuit-breaker must have two sets of three current transformers, one set on each side of the circuit-breaker as in the case of a section switch. In addition, auxiliary switches, operated by the busbar selector isolators, have to be connected in the current transformer secondary circuits so that the latter are connected to the appropriate zone buswires, e.g. zone A main or zone C reserve, and zone B main or zone C reserve.

It is obviously important that a busbar protective scheme remains stable under the most adverse through-fault conditions as unnecessary operation resulting in a shut down at the switchgear causes serious disruption of supply. To ensure maximum stability, two items are of major importance, (a) the current transformers and (b) the protective relay. The former must all have similar magnetising characteristics to ensure that the primary current is similarly transformed in all circuits and they must all have similar knee-point voltage levels, to ensure that unequal saturation is avoided. All current transformers in a bus zone must have the same ratio so that the currents in the secondary circuits are correctly summated regardless of any diversity in fault current levels entering or leaving the bus zone.

As we have noted in an earlier chapter, at the onset of a fault, the current rises rapidly to a peak value and the rate of change is very high, particularly in those phases exhibiting a high degree of asymmetry. Thus the current transformers in different phases may approach or even reach saturation level and because of variations in the magnetising characteristics of the transformers, a high un-balance current may result. Unequal saturation can produce non-sinusoidal

365

circulating currents with peaks sufficiently high to cause operation of an instantaneous relay.

To overcome these hazards, voltage-operated high-impedance relays are used in circulating-current protective schemes and such a relay is commonly used in busbar protection and elsewhere. It will be set to operate at a voltage slightly higher than that developed by the current transformers under the maximum external fault conditions. To avoid the hazards produced by current transformer saturation, a tuned relay can be used which rejects harmonic currents, and such a relay is shown in Fig. 11.93. Here it is seen that the input from the current transformers is fed to a tapped auto-transformer to provide seven current ratings. This auto-transformer energises the operating coil of the relay via a series resonant circuit comprising a choke and a capacitor, the

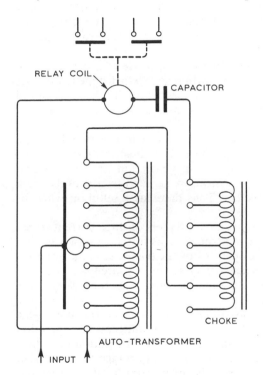

Figure 11.93. 'English Electric' type CAG14 *high-stability circulating-current relay—one pole only (courtesy G.E.C. Measurements Ltd.)*

circuit being tuned to supply frequency. By allowing the auto-transformer to saturate above the relay setting, a slight time delay occurs before the relay operates so that the relay armature operates on the slower part of its time/current curve.

Wherever possible, the current transformers used for circuit protection and those used for busbar protection should be arranged (physically) so that they provide overlapping zones of protection. Ideally the current transformers should overlap around the circuit-breaker as shown at (*a*) in Fig. 11.94 and this can easily be arranged in large bulk-oil circuit-breakers where the transformers are accommodated on the bushings. With some metal-enclosed types space may also permit this, but with air-blast and small-oil-volume breakers, separate and costly current transformers would need to be used, so that frequently the secondary windings for both circuit and bus-zone protection are assembled with a common primary.

This means that both will only be on one side of the circuit-breaker, i.e. the circuit side as at (b) or the busbar side as at (c). With the transformers on the circuit side, a fault between the transformers and the circuit-breaker will only be detected by the busbar protection, since to the circuit protection this is an external fault. Similarly, when the current transformers are on the busbar side (c) a fault between them and the circuit-breaker is detected only by the circuit protection.

If we consider (a) it is clear that a fault on the circuit side between the current transformers and the circuit-breaker will be 'seen' by both the busbar and

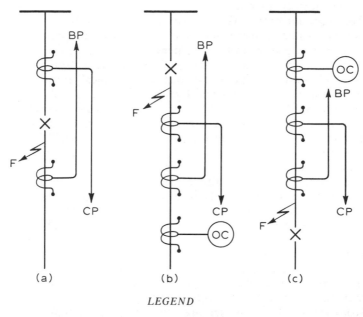

(a)   (b)   (c)

LEGEND

BP   BUSBAR PROTECTION   OC   INTERLOCKED OVERCURRENT
CP   CIRCUIT PROTECTION   F   FAULT

Figure 11.94.   Location of current transformers in relation to the circuit-breaker for busbar and circuit protection overlap

circuit protection, and, subject to the breaker at the remote end of the feeder being tripped simultaneously (by intertripping), the fault will be completely isolated. Such intertripping would be essential on scheme (b) because here the circuit protection does not operate and although the circuit-breaker in our diagram opens, due to the busbar protection the fault can still be fed from the remote end. If, instead of a feeder circuit we are concerned with a generator or transformer circuit, an interlock overcurrent relay controlled by the busbar protection can be arranged to shut down the generator or trip the breaker on the other side of the transformer if the fault can be fed by a parallel path on that side.

For the condition at (c) a fault between the transformers and the circuit-breaker will cause the feeder circuit-breaker to trip, but the fault can still be fed from the busbars and can only be completely isolated by the busbar protection being made to trip all the circuit-breakers associated with the appropriate zone. To achieve this, an interlocked overcurrent relay is energised from the separate set of current transformers to trip the circuit-breakers associated with the busbar protection. This relay should be operative only when the circuit protection is held in the operated condition.

CURRENT AND VOLTAGE TRANSFORMERS FOR PROTECTIVE PURPOSES

To fully assess the very different technical requirements between current and voltage transformers used for metering and instrumentation, i.e. measurement, and those used for protective purposes, it is essential that a detailed study be made of the current British Standards[11,12]. In this brief commentary our concern will be with protective transformers, noting that in Chapter 23 those for metering and instrumentation are considered, along with some general factors common to both and including illustrations of typical transformers for use in or with various types of switchgear over a wide range of voltages.

So different are the requirements in some respects that, except for the simplest forms of protection, separate current transformers in particular and voltage transformers in some cases are recommended. They should be regarded as a constituent part of a protective scheme in that the correct functioning of the latter is bound up with the performance of the transformers under anticipated fault conditions. In some specialised forms of protection, e.g. distance, the technical requirements of the manufacturer of that protection must be ascertained and met. Even in simpler schemes where the magnitude and balance of currents are the criterion, e.g. earth-fault protection and differential schemes, it is, as noted earlier, important that the characteristics of the current transformers be closely matched if unwanted operation of the protection is to be avoided. We have noted also that for the correct operation of directional protection, the voltage transformer used needs to be of a type with appropriate windings to ensure the application of a correct reference voltage.

In so far as current transformers are concerned, the major difference in requirement between those for instrumentation and those for protection is that with the former, specified accuracies (see Chapter 23) are essential over a range of primary current from about 5% full load up to 125%, whereas for protective purposes we are concerned with accurate secondary reproductions of the primary currents from about full load up to those of short-circuit magnitude, the latter being many times full load as we have seen in the chapter dealing with short-circuit calculations. As we have also seen, short-circuit currents can be asymmetrical, sometimes completely so, and this condition leads to severe flux swing[3].

It is therefore a primary requirement that protective current transformers should have a high saturation level, whereas those for instrumentation should, preferably, saturate at a low level, thus protecting the connected instruments or meters against overcurrents. The point at which a current transformer begins to saturate is known as the *knee-point* on a curve of its magnetising characteristic, and is, by definition, the point where the exciting current increases by 50% for a 10% increase in secondary voltage, typically as shown in Fig. 11.95. It is clear that when the core saturates, a disproportionate amount of the primary

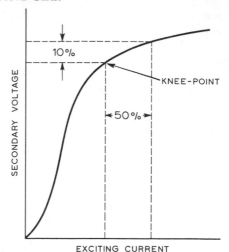

*Figure 11.95. Knee-point of the excitation
characteristic of a current transformer*

current is required to magnetise the core; indeed the whole of the primary current may be required for this purpose so that there is no secondary output.

In passing, it may be noted that manufacturers of distance forms of protection specify that the current transformers used must develop a minimum secondary voltage at the knee-point and give a formula from which this value is to be calculated. As an example, for the Reyrolle transistorised scheme described earlier, the minimum knee-point voltage V_{NP} is given by the formula:

$$V_{NP} > \frac{X}{R} \times I_{F2} \times B_T$$

where

$\frac{X}{R}$ = Ratio of reactance to resistance of the system for a fault at the end of zone 1,

I_{F2} = Secondary fault current and

B_T = Total burden, i.e. the sum of lead resistance, current transformer internal resistance and the relay burden.

From this it follows that a protective current transformer should maintain its accuracy (within prescribed limits of error) up to some primary current which is expressed as a multiple (5, 10, 15 or 20)* of its rated primary current. BS 3938: 1965 defines this as *the rated accuracy limit factor* and to determine what this should be for a given application requires an assessment of the *maximum* value of primary current up to which accuracy must be maintained.

Three classes of accuracy have been standardised in BS 3938, viz. *S*, *T* and *X*, the limits of error for *S* and *T* being those given in Table 11.2. It is noted that whereas with instrument current transformers, limits of phase error are specified (see Chapter 23), no such limits are given here. A note in the BS indicates that 'dependent on several factors in combination, the phase errors under actual working conditions may have any value between zero and a maximum value which is determined by the value of composite error specified in column 3. These maximum values of phase error for classes *S* and *T* are about 3 min and

* Classes *S* and *T* only.

6 min respectively, but experience indicates that these are rarely approached in practice'.

Class X transformers are for special applications and may be of the low or high-reactance type and their performance is specified in different terms[13]. For general purposes, rated outputs higher than 15 VA and rated accuracy limit factors higher than 10 are not recommended.

For transformers in classes S and T, a correlation between output and the accuracy limit factor is possible as in general the product of these numerical terms should not exceed 150, e.g. 15×10. Any decrease in the burden on a transformer allows a higher accuracy limit factor and vice versa. In some cases,

Table 11.2
LIMITS OF ERROR OF PROTECTIVE CURRENT
TRANSFORMERS AT RATED OUTPUT, A p.f. OF 0·7
LAGGING AND AT RATED PRIMARY CURRENT
(BS 3938, TABLE 10)

Accuracy class	Current error at rated primary current (%)	Limits of composite error at accuracy limit primary current (see Appendix K, BS 3938) (%)
S	±3	5
T	±5	10
X	For special applications, and may be of the low or high-reactance types and the performance is specified in different terms (see Section 12 and Appendix L of BS 3938)	

the burden of the protective relay is affected by the tap setting, e.g. with very inverse time overcurrent relays such as the English Electric type *CDG13* relay, where the burden at current setting on the highest tap is 3 VA but only 1 VA on the lowest tap. Where the product as above exceeds 150, a current transformer may be very costly and/or unduly large.

With wound primary types of current transformers, the 'short-time factor' has a bearing on this problem, as when this factor is high it may not be possible to attain a product of 150. This factor is the ratio of the rated short-time current to the rated primary current and is determined by the ability of a given design to withstand the electromagnetic forces tending to damage the transformer mechanically and the thermal effects tending to overheat the windings and damage or destroy the insulation, both effects resulting from the passage of high values of fault current. The first of these conditions, independent of time, is determined by the highest peak value of current in the first half-cycle of short-circuit, the number of turns in the primary winding and the configuration of the coil, the lowest forces being experienced when the primary winding has the least number of turns. Table 11.3 shows that the highest short-time factors are associated with the lower rated outputs and accuracy limit factors. The thermal problem is related to the r.m.s. value of short-time current, its duration and the insulation media.

Bar primary current transformers rarely present any problem in so far as short-time factors are concerned because the primary winding is effectively one turn and heavy short-circuit currents can be withstood for periods of 3 s.

This type of current transformer (and this includes the ring type fitted over the bushings as in high-voltage bulk-oil circuit-breakers) is normally used for primary currents of 600 A and above. For lower values of primary current there must be an upper limit of the expected rated output as this, for a given accuracy, is dependent on the ampere-turns, and as the number of turns is one then it is dependent on the primary current. Table 11.4 shows some maximum practicable outputs for bar primary transformers of low primary rating. It assumes that the diameter of the bushing insulation over which the core and secondary windings are fitted does not exceed 3·5 in (89 mm), typically as for circuits up to 33 kV.

It should be noted that the performance of a current transformer is normally related to the rated primary current of the transformer. In most cases the

Table 11.3
MAXIMUM SHORT-TIME FACTORS OBTAINABLE ECONOMICALLY WITH WOUND PRIMARY CURRENT TRANSFORMERS (SEE TABLE 12, BS 3938)

Accuracy class and accuracy limit factor	Rated output	Short-time factors obtainable corresponding to the rated duration		
		0·5s	1·0s	3·0s
S_{15} or T_{20}	5	350	250	150
	7·5	300	200	125
	10	275	190	115
	15	250	175	100
S_{10} or T_{15}	5	400	275	175
	7·5	350	250	150
	10	325	225	140
	15	300	200	125
S_5 or T_{10}	5	600	425	250
	7·5	525	400	225
	10	475	350	200
	15	400	275	175
T_5	5	1 000	700	400
	7·5	925	650	375
	10	850	600	350
	15	750	525	300

Table 11.4
POSSIBLE MAXIMUM OUTPUT (VA) OF BAR PRIMARY AND BUSHING-TYPE CURRENT TRANSFORMERS (SEE TEXT AND TABLE 13 OF BS 3938)

Metering CTs accuracy class	Protective CTs accuracy class and accuracy limit factor	Rated primary current (A)						
		60	75	100	150	200	300	400
AM	S_{15} or T_{20}	—	—	—	—	5	10	15
BM	S_{10} or T_{15}	—	—	—	5	7·5	15	15
CM	—	1·5	1·5	5	10	15	15	15
C	S_5 or T_{10}	—	5	10	15	15	15	15
D	T_5	5	10	15	15	15	15	15

Table 11.5

LIMITS OF VOLTAGE AND PHASE ERRORS FOR ALL VOLTAGE
TRANSFORMERS (SEE TABLE 6, BS 3941)

Accuracy class	0·9 to 1·1 times rated primary voltage, 0·25 to 1·0 times rated output at unity power factor		0·8 to 1·2 times rated primary voltage and at any output not exceeding rated output and at unity power factor	
	Voltage error (% ±)	Phase error (min ±)	Voltage error (% ±)	Phase error (min ±)
AL*	—	—	0·25	10
A	0·5	20	—	—
B	1·0	30	—	—
C	2·0	60	—	—
D	5·0	—	—	—

*Not capacitor types

Table 11.6

ADDITIONAL LIMITS OF VOLTAGE AND PHASE ERRORS FOR
DUAL PURPOSE VOLTAGE TRANSFORMERS (SEE TABLE 7, BS 3941)

Accuracy class	0·05 to 0·9 times rated primary voltage		1·1 to V_T* times rated primary voltage	
	0·25 to 1·0 times rated output at unity p.f.			
	Voltage error (% ±)	Phase error (min ±)	Voltage error (% ±)	Phase error (min ±)
E†	3	120	3	120
F†	5	250	10	300

*V_T is a voltage factor determined by the minimum operating voltage, which in turn is dependent on the system and the voltage-transformer-winding earthing conditions. These factors vary between 1·1 and 1·9, the conditions being enumerated in Table 3 of BS 3941.
†Transformers of classes E and F are also required to comply with one of the classes A, B or C in Table 11.5. Class E is for applications where only small limits of error are permissible over an extended voltage range. Class F is for application where larger limits of error are permissible over an extended voltage range.

Table 11.7

LIMITS OF VOLTAGE AND PHASE ERRORS FOR THREE-PHASE
RESIDUAL-VOLTAGE TRANSFORMERS (SEE TABLE 12, BS 3941)

Applied primary voltage (% of rated voltage)	Residual burden at unity p.f. (% of rated value)	Voltage error (%)	Phase error (deg)
100	100–25	±10	±10

372

latter will be reasonably close to the normal full load current of the primary circuit, but if there is a significant difference the effects of this on the performance need to be studied, particularly on the fault setting and on stability. On systems where the fault current is high and full load current is low, it may be necessary to choose current transformers with primary current ratings related to the fault current rather than ratings related to full load currents.

Voltage transformers will, in general, comply with limits of voltage and phase error whether for metering and instrumentation or for protection, these limits being noted in Table 11.5. However, when they are used for the dual purpose, additional limits must be met as noted in Table 11.6. It is seen that two additional classes are included (*E* and *F*) and such transformers therefore will be given a dual classification, one from Table 11.5 and the other from Table 11.6, e.g. *AE*, *AF*, *BE*, *BF*, etc.

In certain types of protection, e.g. directional earth fault, what is known as a residual voltage transformer (refer to Figs. 11.30 and 11.32) must be used. By definition this is a three-phase transformer (or three single-phase transformers) having a secondary winding connected in open (broken) delta so as to produce between the appropriate secondary terminals a voltage representation of the residual voltage existing in the three-phase voltage applied to the primary terminals.

In most applications, the open-delta secondary windings will be in addition to the normal secondary, i.e. it will be a tertiary winding as indicated in Fig. 11.32. The limits of voltage and phase error for the residual voltage transformer are as given in Table 11.7.

REFERENCES

1. *Electrical Protective Relays*, BS 142 (1966)
2. BEDDOE, S., 'Direct Acting Overcurrent Tripping', *Elect. Rev.*, 10/17 Aug. (1962)
3. VARIOUS, *Protective Relays Application Guide*, G.E.C. Measurements Ltd.
4. STIGANT, S.A., LACEY, H.M. and FRANKLIN, A.C., *The J. & P. Transformer Book*, 9th edn., Butterworths, London, 543 (1961)
5. WILSON, A., 'Recent Developments in Transistorised Equipment for Electrical Protection, *Reyrolle Rev.*, No. 185 (1964). Available as reprint No. RR 113
6. HAMILTON, F.L., LEGG, M. and PATRICKSON, J.B., 'Application of Transistor Techniques to Relays and Protection for Power Systems', *Reyrolle Rev.*, No. 190 (1967). Available as reprint No. RR 121
7. PATRICKSON, J.B., 'Modern Concepts in Power System Protection', *Reyrolle Rev.*, No. 186 (1965). Available as reprint No. RR 116
8. PATRICKSON, J.B., 'The Protection of Transmission Lines—Present Needs and Future Trends', *Reyrolle Rev.*, No. 185 (1964). Available as Pamphlet No. 1384
9. ELLIS, N.S., 'Distance Protection of Feeders', *Reyrolle Rev.*, No. 168 (1957). Available as Pamphlet No. 1301
10. *Brown Boveri Review*, **55** No. 11/12, Nov./Dec. (1966)
11. *Current Transformers*, BS 3938 (1965)
12. *Voltage Transformers*, BS 3941 (1965)
13. *Current Transformers*, Section 12 and Appendix *L*, BS 3938 (1965)

BIBLIOGRAPHY

ACKER, J. and RITTER, F., 'Breaker Back-up Protection', *Brown Boveri Rev.*, **58**, June (1971)
BALKWILL, B.J., 'Overcurrent Protection', *Elect. Rev.*, 5 April (1968)
CRANE, P.H.G., *Switchgear Principles*, Macmillan (1957)
Electrical Protective Systems for a.c. Plant, BS 3950 (1965)

GRAY, W. and WRIGHT, A., 'Voltage Transformers and Current Transformers Associated with Switchgear', *Proc. I.E.E.*, **100** No. 75, June (1953)

HAHN, C., 'The Protection of Generators', *Brown Boveri Rev.*, **51** No. 5, May (1964)

HEGAZY, M., 'New Principle for Using Full-wave Rectifiers in Differential Protection of Transformers', *Proc. I.E.E.*, **116** No. 3, March (1969)

LEGG, M., 'Construction and Application of Solid State Protection Equipment', *Elect. Rev.*, 21 Aug. (1970)

NAYLOR, J.H., 'Developments in Transmission Protection Methods and Equipment', *Elect. Rev.*, 21 Aug. (1970)

PATRICKSON, J.B., 'Replacing Electro-magnetic Systems by Electronics in Protection', *Elect. Times*, 22 Jan. (1970)

SEELY, S., 'Effect of Stray Flux on Current Transformers', *J. Sci. & Tech.*, **37** No. 3 (1970)

VARIOUS, 'Protective Relays for Electrical Installations', *Brown Boveri Rev.*, **53** No. 11/12, Nov./Dec. (1966)

WARRINGTON, A.R. van C., *Protective Relays: Their Theory and Practice*, Chapman and Hall (1962)

WELLMAN, F.E., *The Protective Gear Handbook*, Pitman

Chapter 12

Bulk-oil circuit-breakers

In spite of the extensive development of air break and air-blast circuit-breakers in their respective voltage ranges, the bulk-oil circuit-breaker is still the most widely used type of interrupting device for power networks up to 66 kV and is still favoured in many quarters for voltages much higher.

Quite a significant number of such circuit-breakers are in fact in service in many parts of the world on systems operating at voltages in the range 110–330 kV, and there is little doubt that were it not for the problem of short-circuit testing at the high interrupting capacities required, the design could be extended to cover voltages beyond this.

To carry out such tests in the past has meant recourse to unit testing as described in Chapter 5. This in turn means that the breaker must have a number of identical breaks per pole with resistance shunted across each break. An example of a circuit-breaker having alternatively four or six breaks per pole will be noted later and from this it will readily be appreciated that to increase the number beyond six can lead to a very complex design. It is possible however, that once its validity has been proved in relation to bulk-oil circuit-breakers, synthetic testing (also described in Chapter 5) may provide a solution, if indeed an extension of rating and voltage is found desirable and necessary. It has to be remembered however that larger designs will be of considerable size and weight, that maintenance problems will increase and that difficulties may be encountered in providing suitable foundations to withstand the reaction during fault clearance.

The nature of the duty to be performed by a circuit-breaker when interrupting, or making on to, currents of short-circuit magnitude or when switching small inductive or capacitive currents has been discussed in Chapter 2. Here it is our purpose to consider the design features of some modern examples of the bulk-oil circuit-breaker, all of which have been proved capable of performing the duties expected of them up to the limit of their rating. Before doing so however it is of interest to glance back and recall the very early circuit-breakers noted in Chapter 1 and in particular that shown in Fig. 1.3.

This should then be compared with a modern design in the same general voltage range such as that shown in Fig. 12.1. It is not known what interrupting capacity, if any, would have been assigned to the design in Fig. 1.3 but it is known that that in Fig. 12.1 has proved ratings of 100 MVA at 3·3 kV, 250 MVA at 6·6 kV and 350 MVA at 11 kV. An attempt to close the breaker in Fig. 1.3

on to a peak fault current would probably end in disaster whereas that in Fig. 12.1, with its modern closing mechanism, has proved its ability to perform this difficult task.

Instead of the plain and flimsy double-break contact system in the early design, the modern version shown has a single-break system (examples of modern double-break designs will be noted later) with interruption taking place in side-vented arc-control devices. The difference in tank and top plate design is readily observed, the present day top plate enclosing all but the

LEGEND

A MAINTENANCE HANDLE FOR SLOW CLOSING AND OPENING
B CIRCUIT-BREAKER RAISING AND LOWERING HANDLE
C NORMAL OPERATING MECHANISM
D RATCHET SPANNER FOR RAISING AND LOWERING THE TANK

Figure 12.1.   Modern 11kV bulk-oil circuit-breaker of the single-break type. Tank lowered and one arc-control device removed (courtesy A. Reyrolle & Co. Ltd.)

final link in the operating mechanism. Gone are the corrugated porcelains and instead the through bushings are of the condenser-wound bakelised paper type.

The design of most early oil circuit-breakers was based largely on certain empirical formulae, operating experience and a number of basic factors regarded as being of importance and on a comparison of which competitive offers were judged by the user. These factors included:

(a) Volume of oil

(b) Speed of break

(c) Length of break

(d) Head of oil above contact break

(e) Volume of air cushion above oil

(f) Electrical clearances.

With the coming of high-power short-circuit test plants came the realisation that no one of these factors alone or two or more in combination was necessarily decisive, and certainly mere magnitude was not proof of interrupting ability. It has been shown, for example, that circuit-breakers having an exceedingly small oil volume can match the interrupting ability of those containing much greater quantity.

While it is obviously desirable that the moving contacts, opening to clear a fault, should reach the point at which the arc is interrupted as quickly as possible, it is known that high-speed operation can result in long arcs because of the greater distance the moving contacts travel between current zeros and at which interruption occurs. On the other hand, if the speed of break is too low at contact separation, there is the possibility that welding of the fixed and moving contacts may occur with disastrous consequences.

This problem of speed of break is one which is affected by a number of factors, some concerned with the design (e.g. double or single-break and, if the latter, whether the break is horizontal or vertical) and others inherent in a.c. systems, as for example, contact 'grip' and the electromagnetic forces set up in the loop formed by the terminal stems and the moving contact bar. In addition, where the 'break' is vertical, gravity assists in opening the breaker once the contacts have parted.

The energy for initiating the opening movement once the latching-in mechanism has been upset is derived from accelerating springs which have been compressed by the closing of the circuit-breaker. These springs are opposed in the first movement not only by the frictional resistance of the engaging contacts but by contact 'grip'. This is shown typically in Fig. 12.2 noting that when current flows from the fixed contacts to the moving contact, electromagnetic fields are set up which tend to force the fixed contacts on to the moving contact as shown by the arrows. These forces can be quite considerable when the current reaches short-circuit magnitude.

On the other hand, the accelerating springs get some help in their task by loop forces as shown in Fig. 12.3, and thus offset the opposition due to 'grip'.

Another factor affecting the speed of break is that the oil must present some resistance to the moving contact system, and this becomes particularly important where the circuit-breaker may be used in cold climates resulting in the oil becoming very viscous.

High speed of break can lead to other problems, not the least among them being that of arresting the motion at the end of the stroke. Many designs accomplish this by a dashpot which is filled with oil from the breaker tank, and by this means bouncing at the end of the stroke is minimised. Excessive bounce can be dangerous in that it may so reduce the contact gap that it cannot withstand the system voltage.

Oil dashpot buffering has the disadvantage that when the breaker is taken out of the tank for maintenance, the dashpot may empty itself and the breaker may be opened on check operations without means of arresting the moving parts. In very small circuit-breakers, the desired result can be achieved by buffer springs.

Having fitted powerful accelerating springs to get the moving contacts away, it now has to be remembered that the circuit-breaker has to be closed against them. Furthermore, as noted earlier, it is essential that a circuit-breaker is capable of being closed on to a fault, and in such an operation the electromagnetic

CURRENT

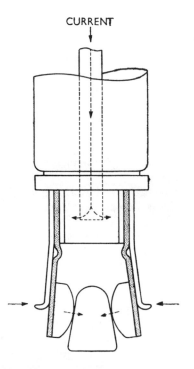

Figure 12.2.   Contact 'grip'

forces set up as soon as the contacts touch (or just before should pre-arcing occur) tend to oppose closure at a point in time when the throw-off (accelerating) springs are reaching maximum compression. This leads to the need for a powerful closing mechanism, which, for high values of peak making current, must be of a type which removes the closing operation from the hands of an operator. Such closing mechanisms may be of the spring, solenoid, compressed air or hydraulic types, the first of these being practically standard for bulk-oil circuit-breakers over a wide range of ratings and voltages.

Pre-arcing referred to above, is a condition arising out of a breakdown of the oil in the contact gap as the moving contact approaches the fixed contacts, the breakdown being due to the high voltage across the gap. It is a condition which can cause high impulsive pressures to be set up within the arc-control devices.

The speed of opening can also be seriously retarded by the pressure set up inside the oil tank, this pressure acting on the moving crossbar carrying the contacts. Cases are on record where reclosure has occurred owing to the difference of pressure between the inside and outside of the tank, this being most likely to occur in designs (if they still exist) where the contact lift-rod passes through the top plate to atmosphere (as shown in Fig. 1.3). The majority of

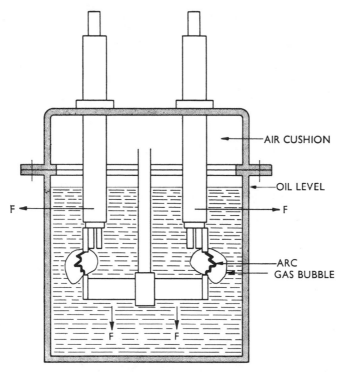

Figure 12.3.   Schematic diagram to illustrate a plain-break oil circuit-breaker and the electromagnetic loop forces in the direction of arrows F

modern oil circuit-breakers, however, have the whole of the operating mechanism, except the final link to the handle gear, within the breaker dome or top plate, thus equalising the pressure on all moving parts.

The gap between the fixed and moving contacts with the breaker fully open must be such that it will withstand the circuit-voltage and must be greater than any foreseeable length of arc which can be drawn when interrupting fault current. This gap is the measure of the length of break which in turn is related to the number of breaks in series per pole.

The head of oil above the contacts in a plain-break design affects gas bubble formation, must be sufficient to ensure ample pressure at the arc and prevent the occurrence of a chimney of gas from the arc to the oil surface. A small volume of air above oil level means a higher pressure for a given volume of gas, a condition, however, which results in a desirable reduction of arcing time. The correct values are determined by test and it is important in service that the manufacturers' indicated oil level and, in consequence, the air cushion, is maintained. It is interesting to note that in certain proving tests, circuit-breaker performance has been improved by the apparently simple expedient of increasing or decreasing the head of oil by a fraction and thereby modifying the air cushion by a similar amount.

Both tank and top plate must be capable of withstanding the internal gas pressures generated. These are considerably less in arc-controlled breakers, but in plain-break types the general tendency is for the oil above the contacts to be thrown, *en masse*, upwards into the air space, violently striking the top plate and tending to cause the breaker to jump. There is a danger that the top plate may be distorted or that an opening between this and the oil tank may be caused through which oil can be forced, and thus if nothing worse ensues, may reduce the oil content to a dangerous level. It is a requirement of design that, after fault clearance, there shall be no permanent distortion of the tank or top plate and this is the subject of check during short-circuit proving tests. As the pressures transmitted to the structure are impulsive, a certain flexibility in the structure is not a disadvantage, provided permanent distortion is not caused. For this reason, cast iron or similar material is rarely used in modern breaker construction.

Both rectangular and circular-tank constructions are used with equal success. Some designers favour the circular construction because of its greater strength for a given weight of material and the need for a single-welded seam only, whilst others favour a rectangular tank which can be made equally strong, but requires more material. Those who favour this construction point to a greater volume of oil at or near the two outer-phase arcing areas in plain-break circuit-breakers. In the light of present-day testing, either form can be accepted with confidence.

Steps must be taken in circuit-breaker design to prevent a build-up of pressure within the enclosure by operations in close succession. A vent is therefore located in the expansion chamber above oil level and is so designed that it restricts the emission of oil and yet allows a free passage for gas. This is usually accomplished by an arrangement of baffle plates, clay pebbles or steel marbles.

The vent should, in general, be connected to a vent pipe which discharges clear of live parts, preferably right outside the switch cubicle or housing at a point away from an operator who may be in close proximity at the moment of discharge. In medium-sized switch houses it is usual practice to allow venting into the switch room. For higher powers, the vent pipes may be taken out through the walls of the room, either separately or via a common header pipe, and exhausted to atmosphere. In the latter case, a non-return valve must be fitted at each junction of vent pipe and header to prevent the discharge from one breaker passing into another.

There are several constructional features in the design of tank and top-plate structures which are important. Among these are tank linings and phase barriers, avoidance of obstructions within the top plate, magnetic break-up of top plates for the heavier currents, tank to top-plate joint and the provision of adequate bolting between tank and top plate.

In a three-phase tank, phase barriers are always provided. In some designs, these barriers are continuous, while in others they are in two parts with a central slot. In the former, the contact-lifting crossbar is at the upper end of the moving system, while in the latter, the crossbar is placed at the lower end. It is common practice to line the inside of the tank and the phase barriers with an insulating material.

The design of the top plate in most modern circuit-breakers is in the form of a box or dome, rectangular or circular to suit the tank design and of welded-steel construction. This formation provides the expansion chamber above oil level and houses the operating link mechanism for connection to the external operating gear. As far as it is possible, the top plate should have a uniform section, avoiding the introduction of pockets or projections which may set up unequal distribution of oil flow and tending to restrict the mass return of the oil after its first movement. For current ratings of 800 A and above it is necessary to break up the magnetic circuits to prevent local heating. In many cases it is usual to weld non-magnetic inserts in between the poles for the sake of economy, but this demands careful workmanship in order not to introduce weak points in the top plate. In other designs the box-type top plate has been cast in aluminium (this is the material used in the design shown in Fig. 12.1) or aluminium alloy, while in one for heavy current at medium voltage, the top plate has been formed out of a block of densified wood (see Fig. 12.4).

Considerable importance must be attached to the tank to top-plate joint, and to the number and size of the bolts securing the joint. Two forms of joint are evident, (a) in which there are two machined surfaces butting or (b) in which there is a gasket or packed joint. But, whatever the form, it must be capable of preventing the emission of flame, oil or gas. The number and size of the fixing bolts (usually high-tensile steel) must be related to the stresses set up during

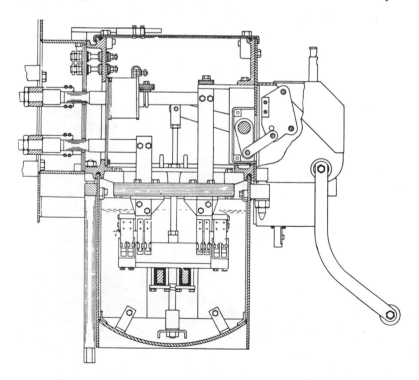

Figure 12.4.   Medium-voltage plain-break circuit-breaker with wedge and finger-type contacts

fault clearance when there is a tendency for the tank and top plate to part company and for the bolts to become elongated, rendering the joint useless. As this elongation may be so slight as to be undetected by ordinary observation it is important that attention is given to this aspect of the design.

Up to this stage no mention has been made of contact design, except to note the problem of contact 'grip'. It is convenient for our purpose to segregate contacts into two groups, i.e. those used in 'plain-break' oil circuit-breakers and those which are associated with arc-controlled breakers. The former is a type which, very largely, is used only in the voltage range 400–600 V and although designs do exist for voltages up to 11 kV, most oil circuit-breakers for voltages of 3·3 kV and upwards now employ means of arc control. Here it will be assumed that the division is on this basis and each type will be considered in turn.

The processes involved when interrupting current in a plain-break circuit-breaker have been considered in Chapter 2 where it was noted that performances can be quite erratic, and in practice it is often found that many more proving tests in the design stages are necessary than in the case of controlled-arc designs. In some cases, it will be found that performance can be dependent on the profile of the contacting faces and that only experimental work can determine the final shape.

Figure 12.5. Close-up view of wedge and finger-type contacts in plain-break circuit-breaker (courtesy George Ellison Ltd.)

Figure 12.4 shows in cross-section a low-voltage plain-break oil circuit-breaker employing contacts of the wedge and finger type, which are perhaps the most popular form. This type of contact is shown in more detail in Fig. 12.5 and from this it is seen that the moving contact comprises a main crossbar which is wedge-shaped on both its upper and lower edges and carrying, at its extremities, removable arcing contacts of the same general shape but of such size that the arcing contacts break last and make first. The double wedge shape has, in this design, been adopted so that both the crossbar and the arcing contacts can be reversed thus effectively doubling the contact life. The fixed contacts comprise a group of self-aligning spring-loaded fingers, the number used being related to the normal current rating of the circuit-breaker.

This form of contact has several advantages. It is easy to assemble, is of unit construction, lends itself to self-alignment, and the contact pressure of the fingers is relatively constant over a range of wedge positions. Contact pressure is further assisted by mutual attraction of the fingers under electromagnetic influence, i.e. contact 'grip'.

In early designs of the wedge and finger type of contact, both the wedge and the fingers had plain flat surfaces because it was assumed that the normal current to be carried would be more easily achieved by having the components in contact over the face area. It is now known, however, that unless exceptional care is taken in the preparation of flat surfaces, contact will not be made over the whole area but, more likely, only at a number of high spots, thus leading to contact chatter and overheating. The practice has been adopted, therefore, of making one or both of the contacting surfaces slightly curved to provide a 'line pressure' contact, and under proper conditions of pressure, this enables more than 100 A to be carried per 0·5 in of line contact.

A form of contact in which the problem of 'grip' is eliminated is the rolling butt type, one example of which is shown in Fig. 12.6. This type of contact has another advantage in that spring loading of the fixed contacts gives valuable assistance at contact separation, but it must be remembered that the closing mechanism has to overcome this pressure when closing the breaker. Examples will be mentioned later of how butt contacts are used as arcing contacts, etc.

While the wedge and finger type of contacts can readily be used for normal current ratings of up to 2 000/2 400 A, an alternative but rarely used design is based on the use of laminated brushes forming the main current-carrying element with arcing contacts of the butt type, typically as shown in Fig. 12.7 Here the brushes form the fixed contacts while the moving contact is a solid copper plate carried on a copper channel base. Both the brush contacts and the plate contact are silver plated. Separate arcing contacts are provided, these comprising a solid copper block (carried on the channel crossbar) mating with a spring-loaded brass plunger to give butt contact.

Whatever form of contact is used, it is important to ensure that low contact resistance is obtained and maintained, bearing in mind that resistance varies inversely as the pressure. Further, it is equally important to remember that copper oxidises when working at reasonably high temperatures and that copper oxide has a very high resistance. Once this oxidation has started a vicious circle ensues; the increase in contact resistance causes further heating which, in turn, causes further oxidation, leading to more heat, and so on. These effects are particularly important in heavy current circuit-breakers which usually operate for long periods in a closed state at temperatures somewhere near the design

Figure 12.6.   Butt-type contacts

Figure 12.7.   Laminated brush-type main contacts with butt-type arcing contacts

384

limit. It emphasises the importance of maintaining contacts in a clean condition, a condition which can be helped by the simple expedient of opening and closing a circuit-breaker a few times at regular intervals. This process is further assisted where line pressure or rolling butt contacts are used as these are self-cleaning to a high degree.

In order to lessen contact resistance, silver plating or facing may be resorted to. This is generally done for the heavier currents but only on the main contacts because any silver applied to arcing contacts would soon be destroyed under arcing conditions.

As noted earlier, the plain-break bulk-oil circuit-breaker is today mainly used in the medium-voltage range (400–600 V) and, subject to limitations imposed by series overload coils when these are below a certain current rating, plain-break circuit-breakers such as the one shown in Fig. 12.5 have been successfully proved to BS 116 at ratings up to 45 MVA at 600 V, equivalent to 31 MVA at 415 V.

For higher voltages, the plain-break design has been completely superseded by designs of the controlled-arc type, the basic principles of which have been

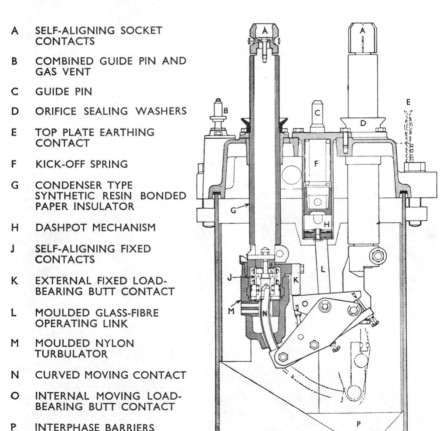

A	SELF-ALIGNING SOCKET CONTACTS
B	COMBINED GUIDE PIN AND GAS VENT
C	GUIDE PIN
D	ORIFICE SEALING WASHERS
E	TOP PLATE EARTHING CONTACT
F	KICK-OFF SPRING
G	CONDENSER TYPE SYNTHETIC RESIN BONDED PAPER INSULATOR
H	DASHPOT MECHANISM
J	SELF-ALIGNING FIXED CONTACTS
K	EXTERNAL FIXED LOAD-BEARING BUTT CONTACT
L	MOULDED GLASS-FIBRE OPERATING LINK
M	MOULDED NYLON TURBULATOR
N	CURVED MOVING CONTACT
O	INTERNAL MOVING LOAD-BEARING BUTT CONTACT
P	INTERPHASE BARRIERS

Figure 12.8. Cross-section of a 1 200A single-break oil circuit-breaker, 250 MVA up to 11 kV (courtesy A. Reyrolle & Co. Ltd.)

385

noted in relation to Fig. 1.12. Arc-control devices based on the E.R.A. invention have been and continue to be used in bulk-oil circuit-breakers of both single and double-break types and, incidentally, in small-oil-volume circuit-breakers as will be noted in Chapter 13. The circuit-breaker shown in Fig. 12.1 is typical of a single-break bulk-oil design with arc-control and it will be of interest at this point to note part of the reasoning behind its use.

Early research into the problem of circuit-breaking revealed that in some circumstances (as for example when interrupting an earth fault) the recovery voltage at current zero in a double-break design was divided in the ratio of 85% on one break and only 15% on the other. It was argued, therefore, that as the greater part of the interrupting duty fell on one break, why not dispense with the other and let a single-break perform 100%? It has been claimed that the second break is in fact something of a handicap in that it draws an arc equal in length to that of the more effective break thereby generating an unnecessary volume of gas. This investigation was studied by Davis and Flurscheim[1] as long ago as 1936 and in an article related to arc-control devices by

Figure 12.9.   Single-break 1 200A contact system and arc-control devices as in Figure 12.8. Note the load-bearing butt contacts external to the arc-control device (courtesy A. Reyrolle & Co. Ltd.)

McNeill and Crane[2] in 1954, while Crane has also considered the relative merits of double and single breaks in his book[3].

When considering a single-break design, it is important to bear in mind that the moving-contact arm is hinged and that current has to be carried by or across the hinge.

A sectional view of the circuit-breaker under discussion is given in Fig. 12.8, from which many of the general design features considered earlier can be noted,

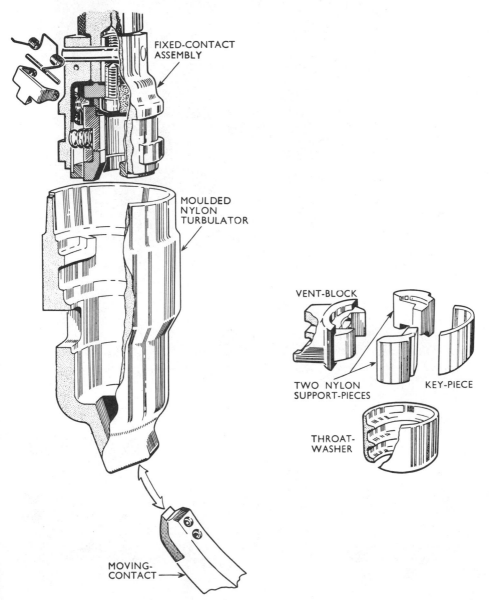

FIXED-CONTACT ASSEMBLY

MOULDED NYLON TURBULATOR

VENT-BLOCK

TWO NYLON SUPPORT-PIECES

KEY-PIECE

THROAT-WASHER

MOVING-CONTACT

Figure 12.10. Exploded view of contact system and 'Turbulator' arc-control device (courtesy A. Reyrolle & Co. Ltd.)

387

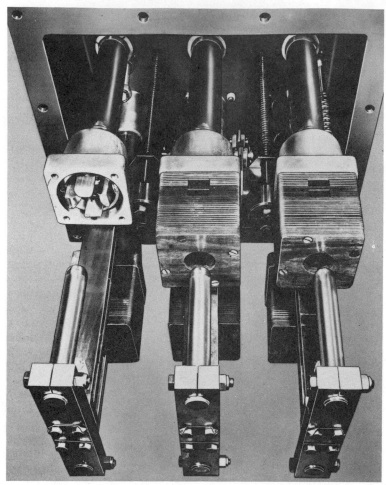

Figure 12.11. 11/13·8 kV bulk-oil circuit-breaker of the double-break type, one arc-control device removed. An example using a rectangular tank (courtesy Brush Switchgear Ltd.)

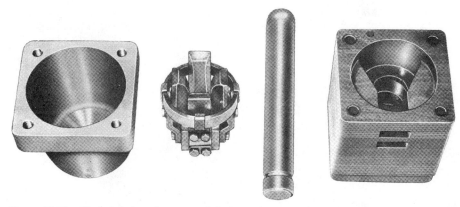

Figure 12.12. Exploded view of arc-control device and contacts (courtesy Brush Switchgear Ltd.)

388

Figure 12.13. 11 kV bulk-oil circuit-breaker (A.E.I.) with one arc-control device and moving contact removed. An example employing a circular tank (courtesy G.E.C. Switchgear Ltd.)

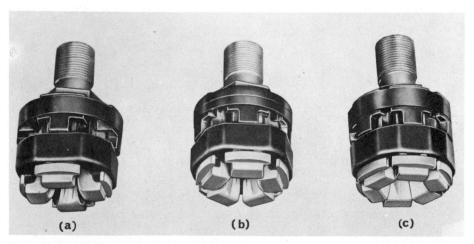

(a)   (b)   (c)

Figure 12.14. The detail of fixed-contact assemblies used in the A.E.I. breaker shown in Figure 12.13. (a) 400A, (b) 800A and (c) 1 200A (courtesy G.E.C. Switchgear Ltd.)

e.g. the top-plate construction, the kick-off (accelerating) springs, the dashpot buffering mechanism and the gas venting arrangements.

The contact system is quite different to that which has been noted in relation to plain-break circuit-breakers. Here, due to the fact that the moving contact arm has to move in the relatively close-fitting throat at the base of the arc-control device, the arm is either rectangular or circular. In Fig. 12.8 a rectangular arm is used which is curved to match the movement from the closed-to-open positions and at the point where arcing occurs it is fitted with copper/tungsten tips. The fixed contacts, located within the arc-control device, comprise a

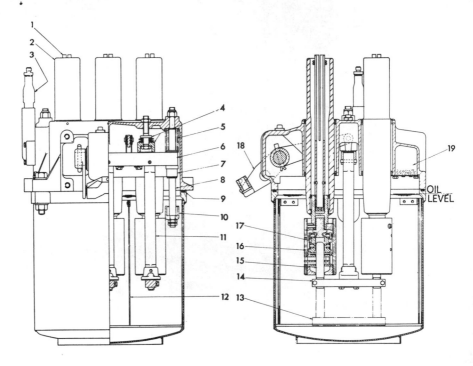

LEGEND

1. ISOLATING SOCKET
2. TERMINAL INSULATOR
3. COMBINED OIL CIRCUIT-BREAKER VENT AND TOP-PLATE EARTHING CONTACT
4. BUFFER OR OVERRIDE STOP ASSEMBLY
5. ACCELERATING SPRINGS
6. CROSSHEAD
7. GUIDE SLIDER FOR '10'
8. GUIDE ROD FOR '6'
9. TANK GASKET
10. DASH-POT CUP
11. LIFTING ROD
12. PHASE BARRIER
13. CONTACT BAR IN OPEN POSITION
14. CONTACT BAR IN CLOSED POSITION
15. MOVING CONTACT
16. ARC-CONTROL DEVICE
17. FIXED-CONTACT ASSEMBLY
18. EXTERNAL DRIVE LEVER
19. VENT CHAMBER

Figure 12.15.   Sectional arrangement of type BVRP 17 (A.E.I.) bulk-oil circuit-breaker shown in Figure 12.13 (courtesy G.E.C. Switchgear Ltd.)

cluster of four spring-loaded segments with retaining ring. Current transfer from the moving contact arm to the fixed hinge blocks is effected by means of spring-hinge contacts.

For normal current ratings of 1 200 A and above, additional load-bearing contacts of the spring-loaded butt-type are located outside the arc-control device and these additional contacts are arranged to open before the arcing contact in the arc-control device, so that no arcing occurs outside that device. In Fig. 12.8, the load-bearing contacts are those marked K and O and they can also be seen in Fig. 12.9, a close-up view of the main moving contacts and arc-control devices. The latter, designated *Turbulators* by this manufacturer, are made in moulded nylon with fibre inserts forming the vent block. Shown in exploded form in Fig. 12.10, the device has a breech-block fitting for easy removal and inspection.

In a double-break design, arc-control devices are fitted at each break as seen in Fig. 12.11. In this, and for ratings up to 150 MVA at 6·6 kV and 250 MVA at 11 kV, the moving contacts comprise brass rods clamped into brass crossbars, the rods being tipped with steel at the point of arcing. The fixed contacts consist of a cluster of four individually spring-loaded brass contacts, one of the

Figure 12.16.   Contact system using 'Caton Arc-Trap' on moving contact of circuit-breaker (courtesy Yorkshire Switchgear & Engineering Co. Ltd.)

four being extended to form an arcing contact. For higher ratings the moving-contact rods are made of copper with sintered copper/tungsten arcing tips while the fixed contacts comprise, in each set, six brass segments again with one extended as the arcing contact and tipped with sintered copper/tungsten.

In Fig. 12.11, one arc-control stack has been removed to show the fixed contact cluster while Fig. 12.12 shows, in exploded form, the fixed and moving contacts and the two parts of the arc-control device. The latter comprises a metal body in cast brass or copper which is threaded and clamped to the bottom of each bushing stem; the fixed contact cluster fitting into this body as seen in Fig. 12.11 where the control stack has been removed. The rectangular arc-control device is side vented with two vents and is built up in synthetic-resin-bonded wood

391

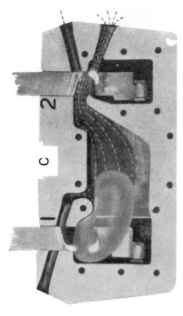

No. 1 Electrode leads by ¼ cycle producing
constricting pressure around No. 2

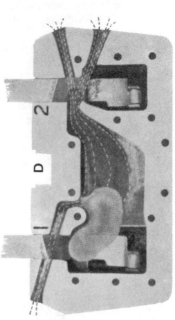

Arc severed at current zero by high
pressure clean oil

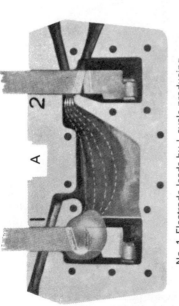

No.2 Electrode parts contact.
Arcing restricted and displaced by pressure

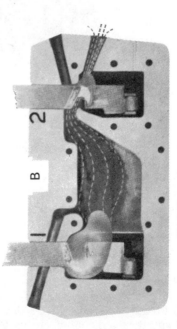

Arc Trap scoured by exhausting pressure and
rapidly refilled with clean oil

Figure 12.17. Operating sequence of the 'Caton Arc-Trap' (courtesy Yorkshire Switchgear & Engineering Co. Ltd.)

laminate. When assembled in the breaker, the extended arcing finger in the fixed contact cluster is located such that it is in line with the side vents so that the arc is drawn in close proximity to the vents.

In the double-break design shown in Fig. 12.13, one arc-control device has again been removed to show the fixed contacts, examples of which are given in more detail in Fig. 12.14. This is a design using circular arc-control devices as opposed to rectangular and for ratings up to 800 A; they are compression-moulded from phenolic resin with injection-moulded baffle plates. For higher current ratings glass-fibre alkyd material is used but retaining the same geometrical shape of those for lower ratings.

Figure 12.15 shows this breaker in cross-section and is an example of a design in which the crossbar carrying the moving contacts is above oil level so that the tank phase barriers (12) completely segregate the phases in the tank. This

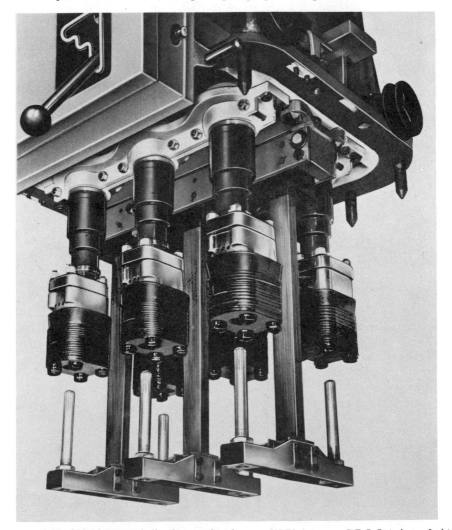

Figure 12.18   22/33 kV A.E.I. bulk-oil circuit-breaker type VLP9 (courtesy G.E.C. Switchgear Ltd.)

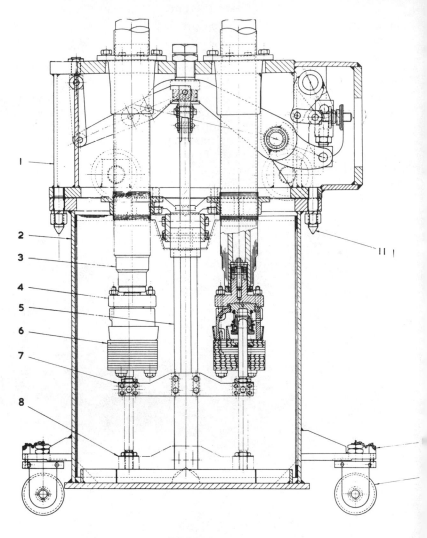

LEGEND

1. CIRCUIT-BREAKER TOP-PLATE
2. TANK
3. TERMINAL BUSHING
4. CONTACT-ADAPTER PLATE
5. MOVING-CONTACTS 'LIFTING' ROD
6. ARC-CONTROL DEVICE
7. MOVING-CONTACT BAR IN THE 'CLOSED' POSITION
8. MOVING-CONTACT BAR IN THE 'OPEN' POSITION
9. TANK WHEEL
10. STOP-PIN FOR LOCKING THE TANK WHEEL IN POSITION
11. TANK HOLDING BOLT

Figure 12.19.   Sectional view of 33 kV type VLP9 (A.

394

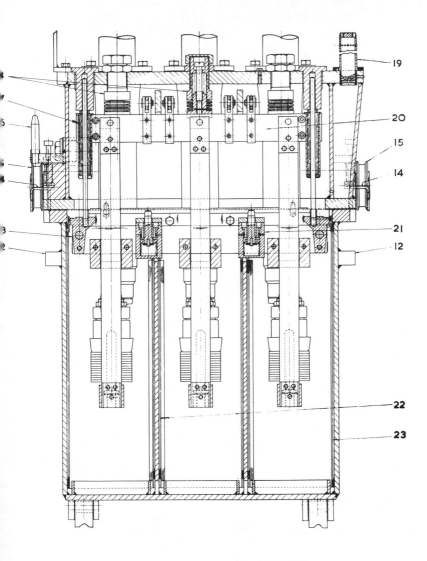

12. TANK LIFTING BLOCKS WHICH
    ENGAGE WITH THE LIFTING RAIL
13. GUIDE BEAM
14. SPRING CLIP INTERLOCK
15. GUIDE ROLLERS
16. DOWEL FOR LOCATING THE
    POSITION OF THE CIRCUIT-
    BREAKER WHEN INSIDE THE
    HOUSING
17. ACCELERATING SPRINGS
18. BUFFERS
19. VENT
20. CROSSHEAD
21. DASH-POT
22. PHASE BARRIERS
23. TANK LINING

-oil circuit-breaker (courtesy G.E.C. Switchgear Ltd.)

illustration is of a circuit-breaker for use in a vertical-isolation switchgear unit but is made available for use as a fixed breaker in cubicle or cellular-type switchgear with separate isolating switches. This is also an example of a design using a cylindrical tank and top plate as opposed to the rectangular types in earlier illustrations, and the top plate is a die-casting in aluminium.

When a circuit-breaker is used in a switchgear unit employing the principle of vertical or horizontal isolation, it is necessary to ensure that when the breaker is plugged-in (i.e. in the service position) the top plate and tank are adequately earthed. This is usually achieved through a pair of mating contacts, one fixed to the top plate itself and one in the switchgear housing, the latter contact being permanently connected to the main earth bar. By this means, earth continuity is maintained between the circuit-breaker frame and housing. In the design in

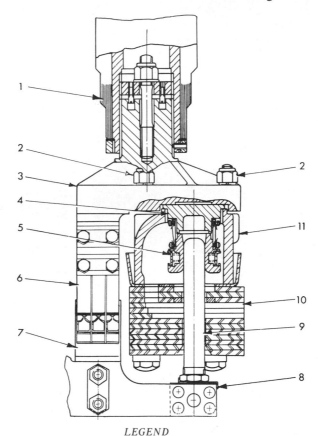

LEGEND

1. TERMINAL BUSHING
2. NUTS FOR CONTACT-ADAPTER BLOCK
3. CONTACT-ADAPTER BLOCK
4. CARRIER PLATE FOR FIXED SOCKET CONTACTS
5. SOCKET CONTACT ASSEMBLY
6. FIXED FINGER CONTACTS
7. MOVING WEDGE CONTACTS
8. MOVING-CONTACT BAR
9. MOVING-CONTACT PLUG
10. BLAST CHAMBER OF ARC-CONTROL DEVICE
11. METAL BODY OF ARC-CONTROL DEVICE

Figure 12.20. Detail of arc-control device used in type VLP15 (A.E.I.) bulk-oil circuit-breaker, 33 kV (courtesy G.E.C. Switchgear Ltd.)

Fig. 12.15 the top plate earthing contact is combined with the circuit-breaker vent (marked 3 in the illustration) and this engages with a socket contact in the housing.

In the designs so far noted, and others which we shall note later for higher voltages, the arc-control devices are fixed to the circuit-breaker bushings and the moving contact is withdrawn on opening. There is, however, a design in which the arc-control devices form part of the moving contact system, as shown

Figure 12.21.   33 kV outdoor oil circuit-breaker of the single-tank type and frame mounted (courtesy Brush Switchgear Ltd.)

in Fig. 12.16 and with the breaker in the open position, the devices are isolated from the system.

This illustration shows that only the arcing contacts are operating within the arc-control device (designated 'Caton Arc-Trap') and that the main current-carrying contacts are placed outside so that burning on the arcing contact surfaces has no effect on the main contacts.

The principle on which this arrangement functions is demonstrated in Fig. 12.17, it being noted that there are two sets of interconnected arcing contacts within the oil reservoir formed by the device and these co-operate with electrodes on the fixed contact system. Electrode 1 is foreshortened so that the initial arc

Figure 12.22. Interior view of 33 kV outdoor-type oil circuit-breaker shown in Figure 12.21 (courtesy Brush Switchgear Ltd.)

398

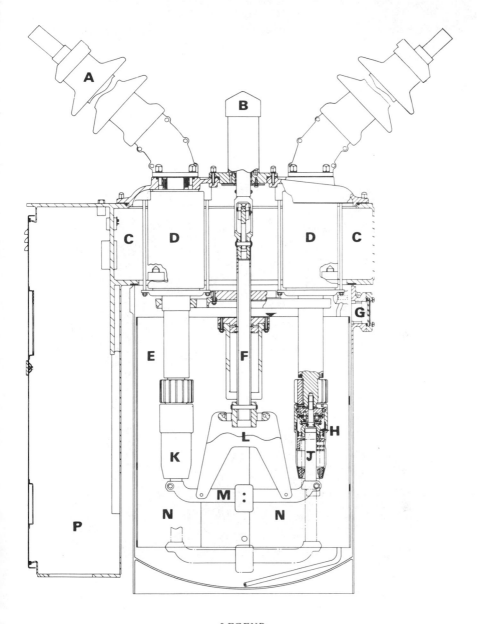

LEGEND

A	GLAZED-SHEDDED INSULATOR	H	FIXED-CONTACT CLUSTER
B	GAS-VENT	J	MOVING CONTACT
C	CIRCUIT-BREAKER TOP PLATE	K	TURBULATOR
D	CURRENT TRANSFORMERS	L	GLASS-FIBRE OPERATING SADDLE
E	BENT-THROUGH INSULATOR	M	CAST-ALUMINIUM CARRIER
F	PLUNGER ROD	N	PHASE CARRIERS
G	OIL-LEVEL INDICATOR	P	CONTROL CUBICLE

Figure 12.23. Cross-section of 33 kV outdoor circuit-breaker for pedestal mounting (courtesy A. Reyrolle & Co. Ltd.)

is drawn here in advance of that at electrode 2. These electrodes operate through very limited apertures which develop and control the point where a concentration of high-pressure oil is allowed to constrict the arc at 2. At a natural current zero, the oil is forced at high velocity into the arc path and in sweeping away the conducting vapour, interposes a barrier of high dielectric strength. The ideal condition for interruption in this device is that the arc at electrode 1 should commence immediately following a current zero, in which case extinction usually occurs at the next zero. If arcing commences at or about current maximum,

Figure 12.24.   Interior view of the 33 kV oil circuit-breaker shown in Figure 12.23 (courtesy A. Reyrolle & Co. Ltd.)

another loop of current might be necessary to develop the necessary pressure for extinction.

The circuit-breakers so far discussed are those for system voltages up to about 11 kV but apart from changes essential for the service voltage, circuit-breakers for 22/33 kV do not differ radically.

Figure 12.18 for example shows the interior of one design for this voltage range while Fig. 12.19 shows the complete breaker in cross-section. The tank and top plate are rectangular, the latter in this case being a fabricated structure, and the ratings assigned are 500/1 000 MVA at 22 kV and 750/1 500 MVA at 33 kV. The arc-control devices are rectangular assemblies of insulating plates with suitable passages incorporated in the blast chamber which direct an oil flow between the separating contacts to achieve arc extinction. These devices are shown in detail in Fig. 12.20, a view which also shows the separate load-carrying wedge and finger contacts located outside the arc-control device, these being used for normal current ratings above 1 600 A.

The outdoor bulk-oil circuit-breaker differs little from its indoor counterpart, the major difference arising out of the need to make the unit completely weather-proof and to ensure that moving linkages associated with the closing mechanism

Figure 12.25.   33 kV outdoor oil circuit-breaker, A.E.I. type JB424 (courtesy G.E.C. Switchgear Ltd.)

401

arc adequately protected so that any tendency to stick due to weathering is eliminated. The exposed end of each circuit-breaker bushing will have a porcelain weather shield with rain sheds which also give an extended creepage path from the live terminal at the upper end to the earthed flange at the circuit-breaker top plate. The shape of these sheds may vary depending on the atmospheric conditions anticipated, a popular form being that known as *anti-fog*. The bushings themselves are generally of the bakelised paper-condenser type and are often oil-filled.

Outdoor breakers are available for most voltages in the range 6·6 to 380 kV and, up to about 88 kV, they are generally arranged as frame-supported units,

Figure 12.26. Interior view of 33 kV circuit-breaker shown in Figure 12.25, single-break type (courtesy G.E.C. Switchgear Ltd.)

Figure 12.27.   66 kV outdoor bulk-oil circuit-breaker, A.E.I. type JB428 (courtesy G.E.C. Switchgear Ltd.)

the frame also carrying the operating mechanism. At higher voltages, the breaker becomes too large for this form of mounting and it is necessary to stand the tank directly on the ground. In the frame-mounted arrangement, access to the contact system for inspection and maintenance is obtained by lowering the tank by means of a self-contained mechanism. To gain access to a floor-mounted breaker, a manhole or access port must be provided, but before entry can be made, the oil must be drained off or pumped away. Access by this means will be noted in a later illustration.

A typical 33 kV outdoor frame-mounted circuit-breaker is seen in Fig. 12.21, the interior of which, with the oil tank lowered, is noted in Fig. 12.22. Apart from the angled bushings, the general similarity with the indoor types is obvious although there is one other difference of importance, viz. that ring-type current-transformer cores and secondary windings can be accommodated on each bushing, the latter being the primary insulation, and the breaker terminal conductor stems being the primary for the current transformers. These transformers are accommodated in the circular pockets forming part of the top-plate and this facility is a common feature in all bulk-oil outdoor circuit-breakers for high-voltage service. It represents an advantage over other types, e.g. small-oil-volume or air-blast, as with these separate current transformers must be used.

Figure 12.28. Interior view of 66 kV circuit-breaker shown in Figure 12.27. Note the exceptionally large accommodation for bushing-type current transformers (courtesy G.E.C. Switchgear Ltd.)

The arc-control devices seen in Fig. 12.22 are of the conventional side-vented type, but in this design there is an auxiliary oil reservoir at the lower end designed to facilitate the interruption of low values of current by the generation of extra pressure.

In the 33 kV breaker shown in cross-section in Fig. 12.23, the interesting feature is the bushing design, which uses bent conductor stems in cast epoxy-resin mounting flanges. By this means the necessary clearances at outer terminals

Figure 12.29.   132 kV outdoor oil circuit-breaker of the three-tank type with compressed-air closing mechanism. NOTE: Although this A.E.I. design is no longer in production it is included here so that it may be compared with Figure 12.30 (courtesy G.E.C. Switchgear Ltd.)

are provided while keeping a vertical bushing formation within the tank, so reducing the dimensions of the latter with consequent reduction in the quantity of oil. In this design also, accommodation for ring-type current transformers is provided in the top plate (marked *D* in the illustration). An interior view of this circuit-breaker is given in Fig. 12.24, one arc-control device having been removed. These devices, given the name '*Turbulators*', are accommodated in circular resin-bonded glass-fibre casings.

The 33 kV designs of outdoor breakers so far noted have employed the double-break per pole principle, but, as with indoor types, single-break designs exist. One such design is that shown in Fig. 12.25, the contact system being noted in more detail in Fig. 12.26. Removal of an arcing chamber has been made particularly easy in this design; the large thread and only one locking screw making the operation both simple and quick without involving the contacts.

At the next higher voltage rating, i.e. 66 kV, a typical frame-mounted circuit-breaker is that shown in Fig. 12.27. This is a double-break unit, the contact system and arc-control device being illustrated in Fig. 12.28. This latter view shows particularly well the accommodation over the bushings for ring-type current transformers, each bushing being able to accommodate several cores

Figure 12.30. 110/132 kV outdoor-type bulk-oil circuit-breaker with all poles in one tank (A.E.I. type JB431). Installed at Kawerau substation, Poverty Bay, New Zealand (courtesy G.E.C. Switchgear Ltd.)

406

with secondary windings as may be required for instrumentation and protection. The arc-control casings in both Figs. 12.26 and 12.28 are filament-wound glass-fibre.

The short-circuit ratings of bulk-oil circuit-breakers in the voltage range 22–66 kV are generally of the order of 350/750 MVA at 22 kV, 500/1 000 MVA at 33 kV and 1 500 MVA at 66 kV.

It was, for many years, the standard practice to build bulk-oil circuit-breakers for 110/132 kV service as single-pole units, three units being coupled to form a three-phase breaker. Examples of these were noted in earlier editions of this book and although no longer in production, one of these is repeated here as Fig. 12.29 to enable the reader to compare this with the present-day single-tank

Figure 12.31.   The contact-system arc-control devices with shunt resistors of the 110/132 kV circuit-breaker shown in Figure 12.30 (courtesy G.E.C. Switchgear Ltd.)

design shown in Fig. 12.30. The major advantage of the latter is of course the greatly reduced quantity of oil employed, the single-tank containing only about 50% of the total in the three separate tanks. Thus the total weight is reduced with resulting savings in foundation costs. For breakers of this size, floor mounting is essential and this means that access to the contact system for inspection and/or maintenance is only possible through a manhole in the tank wall (visible in Fig. 12.30 above the oil-drain valve). After the oil has been pumped away to storage, a maintenance engineer can readily enter the tank via the manhole and work conveniently inside.

The circuit-breaker incorporates resistance switching applied to side-vented arc-control chambers and has two breaks per pole. The contact system is shown in Figs. 12.31 and 12.32, the latter being a dismantled view of the elements at each break. The resistors used are of the linear non-inductive type and are automatically switched into circuit across the fixed and moving contacts after contact separation, the process being illustrated in Fig. 12.33. By this means, as discussed in earlier chapters, control of restriking voltage and overvoltages caused by switching operations or current chopping is achieved, in addition to providing equal voltage division between breaks.

For voltages from 220 kV up to 380 kV, the oil circuit-breaker takes on a different appearance as will be judged from Fig. 12.34.

This shows a typical installation of 275 kV circuit-breakers known by the name 'Shuntarc' and employing tanks of lenticular shape, each tank together

Figure 12.32. From left to right: the arc-control chamber body; the baffle stack and resistor contacts; the head casting with fixed contact and resistor, with the moving contact rod shown below the fixed contact system. All of these are used on each pole of the A.E.I. circuit-breaker shown in Figures 12.30 and 12.31 (courtesy G.E.C. Switchgear Ltd.)

with the operating mechanism housing, bushing seatings and support structure, being a one-piece steel fabrication.

Dependent on the rating, four or six breaks are employed per pole, the breaks being divided between the two terminals. Fig. 12.35 shows one phase of a four-break breaker with a half-sectional view of the arc-control chambers and switching resistors fitted to one terminal.

A study of this shows that one break (the outer) is of the conventional pattern with the moving contact mounted directly on the cross bar. The other break

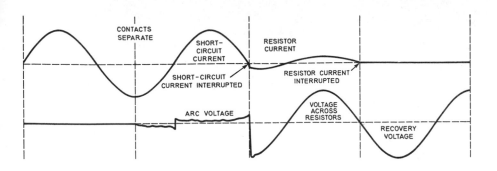

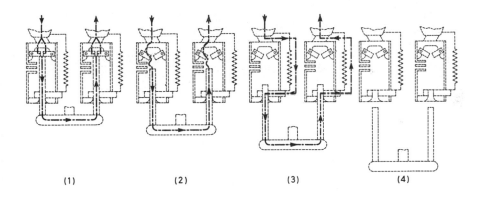

LEGEND

Stage 1 THE BREAKER IS IN THE CLOSED POSITION (CURRENT PATH SHOWN BY DOTTED LINE)

Stage 2 THE CONTACTS SEPARATE AND ARCS ARE DRAWN BETWEEN THE FIXED AND MOVING CONTACTS. AT AN EARLY CURRENT ZERO, THE ARCS ARE EXTINGUISHED BY THE ACTION OF THE SELF-COMPENSATED ARC-CONTROL CHAMBERS

Stage 3 IMMEDIATELY FOLLOWING THE INTERRUPTION OF THE MAIN ARCS, A CURRENT FLOWS THROUGH THE RESISTORS AND THE RE-STRIKING VOLTAGE TRANSIENT APPEARING ACROSS THE MAIN CONTACT GAP IS DAMPED. THE PRESENCE OF THE SHUNTING RESISTORS THEREFORE REDUCES THE VOLTAGE SURGES WHEN OPENING THE CIRCUIT, AN IMPROVEMENT THAT ALSO APPLIES WHEN CLOSING THE CIRCUIT. (IT SHOULD BE NOTED THAT IN THE ABOVE OSCILLOGRAM THE AMPLITUDE OF THE RESISTOR CURRENT HAS BEEN EXAGGERATED FOR CLARITY)

Stage 4 THE CURRENT IN THE RESISTORS IS EASILY INTERRUPTED BY THE SEPARATION OF THE MOVING CONTACTS FROM THE RESISTOR CONTACT PLATES

Figure 12.33. Process of current interruption by means of resistance switching on the 110/132 kV oil circuit-breaker (A.E.I. JB431) shown in Figures 12.30, 12.31 and 12.32 (courtesy G.E.C. Switchgear Ltd.)

Figure 12.34. 275 kV, 7 500 MVA A.E.I. 'Shuntarc' outdoor oil circuit-breakers installed at Castle Donnington, C.E.G.B., East Midland Division (courtesy G.E.C. Switchgear Ltd.)

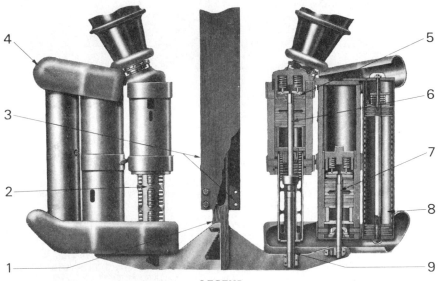

LEGEND

1. TENSION ROD
2. STRIKER ROD REMOVED TO SHOW SPRING AND TRAPPED MOVING CONTACT IN OPEN POSITION
3. V-GUIDES AND GUIDE BLOCKS
4. UPPER STRESS SHIELD
5. FIXED CONTACTS
6. TRAPPED MOVING CONTACT
7. MOVING CONTACT ROD
8. NON-INDUCTIVE SHUNT RESISTOR
9. INSULATION STRIKER ROD

Figure 12.35. The arc-control chambers, resistor and controls on one pole of a four-break A.E.I. 'Shuntarc' circuit-breaker (courtesy G.E.C. Switchgear Ltd.)

410

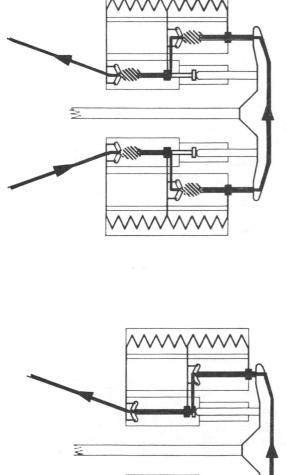

STAGE 1 THE BREAKER IN THE CLOSED POSITION (CURRENT PATH SHOWN BY THICK BLACK LINE)

STAGE 2 THE CONTACTS SEPARATE AND ARCS ARE DRAWN SIMULTANEOUSLY BETWEEN EACH SET OF FIXED AND MOVING CONTACTS. AT AN EARLY CURRENT ZERO, THE ARCS ARE EXTINGUISHED BY THE ACTION OF THE SIDE-VENTED ARC-CONTROL CHAMBERS

Figure 12.36. Process of current interruption by means of resistance switching in an A.E.I. four-break 'Shuntarc' oil circuit-breaker (courtesy G.E.C. Switchgear Ltd.)

411

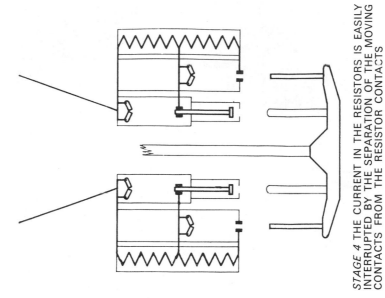

STAGE 4 THE CURRENT IN THE RESISTORS IS EASILY INTERRUPTED BY THE SEPARATION OF THE MOVING CONTACTS FROM THE RESISTOR CONTACTS

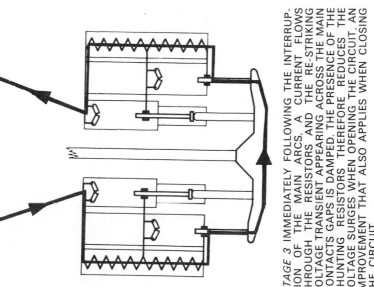

STAGE 3 IMMEDIATELY FOLLOWING THE INTERRUPTION OF THE MAIN ARCS, A CURRENT FLOWS THROUGH THE RESISTORS AND THE RE-STRIKING VOLTAGE TRANSIENT APPEARING ACROSS THE MAIN CONTACTS GAPS IS DAMPED. THE PRESENCE OF THE SHUNTING RESISTORS THEREFORE REDUCES THE VOLTAGE SURGES WHEN OPENING THE CIRCUIT, AN IMPROVEMENT THAT ALSO APPLIES WHEN CLOSING THE CIRCUIT

Figure 12.36 (continued)

412

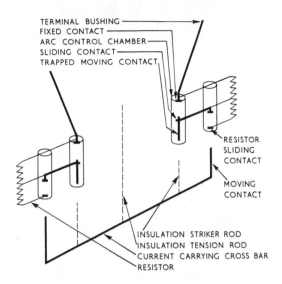

TERMINAL BUSHING
FIXED CONTACT
ARC CONTROL CHAMBER
SLIDING CONTACT
TRAPPED MOVING CONTACT

RESISTOR
SLIDING
CONTACT

MOVING
CONTACT

INSULATION STRIKER ROD
INSULATION TENSION ROD
CURRENT CARRYING CROSS BAR
RESISTOR

Figure 12.37. Schematic diagram of a four-break 'Shuntarc' (A.E.I.) circuit-breaker showing the current path (courtesy G.E.C. Switchgear Ltd.)

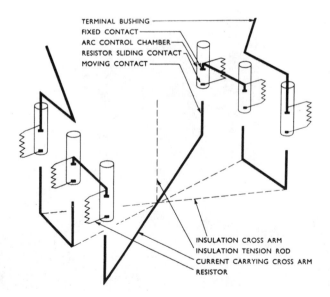

TERMINAL BUSHING
FIXED CONTACT
ARC CONTROL CHAMBER
RESISTOR SLIDING CONTACT
MOVING CONTACT

INSULATION CROSS ARM
INSULATION TENSION ROD
CURRENT CARRYING CROSS ARM
RESISTOR

Figure 12.38. Schematic diagram of a six-break 'Shuntarc' (A.E.I.) circuit-breaker showing the current path (courtesy G.E.C. Switchgear Ltd.)

413

incorporates a 'trapped' moving contact which is normally held in the open position by springs but which is pushed upwards to engage with its fixed contact by an insulation striker-rod carried on the cross bar, so that the two breaks, which are in series electrically, are operated simultaneously. The process of current interruption in such an arrangement, how the switching resistors are utilised and how the resistor current is interrupted, are shown diagrammatically in Fig. 12.36.

Figure 12.39.   Compressed-air equipment associated with the pneumatic operating mechanism on the A.E.I. type JW 220/380 kV 'Shuntarc' bulk-oil circuit-breaker (courtesy G.E.C. Switchgear Ltd.)

The current paths for the four-break and six-break arrangements are shown schematically in Figs. 12.37 and 12.38 respectively. With six breaks per pole, each terminal has to carry three breaks mounted across the width of the tank and the moving contacts are carried on a cross bar assembly comprising insulated and current-carrying cross arms as indicated by the dotted and full lines in Fig. 12.38. These cross arms are strapped together at the centre, at which point they are picked-up by the lift rod connected to the closing mechanism.

For operating a breaker of this size, a pneumatic mechanism is used, the nominal air pressure being 320 lbf/in^2 (2·2 MN/m^2) fed from a receiver (or

Figure 12.40. The pneumatic operating mechanism for a 220/380 kV 'Shuntarc' (A.E.I.) oil circuit-breaker (courtesy G.E.C. Switchgear Ltd.)

415

Figure 12.41.   380 kV 'Shuntarc' (A.E.I.) oil circuit-breaker installed at Kitwe substation, Zambia (courtesy G.E.C. Switchgear Ltd.)

reservoir) mounted below the mechanism housing, as shown in Fig. 12.39. This receiver is supplied either from a central air storage plant (e.g. in large installations) or from unit compressors at each breaker. The pneumatic operating mechanism is shown in Fig. 12.40. It can be arranged to incorporate a high-speed single-shot auto-reclose feature and if single-phase auto-reclose is required, separate mechanisms are fitted to each breaker pole to permit independent operation.

An example of this design of circuit-breaker in service at 330 kV is shown in Fig. 12.41.

REFERENCES
1. DAVIES, D.R. and FLURSCHEIM, C.H., 'The Development of the Single-break Oil Circuit-breaker for Metal-clad Switchgear', *J.I.E.E.*, **79** (1936)
2. MCNEILL, W.A. and CRANE, P.H.G., 'Arc-control Devices', *Elect. Rev.*, July (1954)
3. CRANE, P.H.G., *Switchgear Principles*, Macmillan (1957)

BIBLIOGRAPHY
AMER, D.F., 'Modern Developments in Heavy Electrical Plant Switchgear', *Reyrolle Rev.*, No. 180 (1962)
COX, H.E. and WILCOX, T.W., 'The Performance of High-voltage Oil Circuit-breakers Incorporating Resistance Switching, *J.I.E.E.*, **94** Part 2 (1947)

BULK-OIL CIRCUIT-BREAKERS

GARRARD, C.J.O., 'High-voltage Switchgear—a Review of Progress', *Proc. I.E.E.*, **113** No. 9, Sept. (1966)

GARRARD, C.J.O., 'High-voltage Distribution Switchgear—a Review of Progress', *Proc. I.E.E.*, **116** No. 6, June (1969)

TRENCHAM, H., *Circuit Breaking*, Butterworths (1953)

Oil Circuit-breakers for Alternating Current Systems, BS 116:1952

Oil Circuit-breakers for Medium-voltage a.c. Systems, BS 936:1960

417

Chapter 13

Small-oil-volume circuit-breakers

Having noted in the preceding chapter some of the design features of the bulk-oil circuit-breaker based very largely on the advances made possible by the invention of the side-blast arc-control device, attention can now be directed towards circuit-breakers which, while using that same device, operate in a 'tank' containing a relatively small quantity of oil, hence the designation *small-oil-volume**, or S.O.V. for brevity.

As noted in our historical introduction (Chapter 1) this idea is far from new and many articles in the technical press in the 1930s also bear witness to this, although almost always these articles related to continental designs. In the U.K., users and designers alike have maintained a general preference for the bulk-oil type for voltages up to 33 kV, but excluding the 400–600 V range where the air-break type finds greatest favour. In other European countries however, the bulk-oil type is the least popular and in an article Towill[1] states:

'Apart from some air-blast circuit-breakers at 120 kV, the use of oil-minimum circuit-breakers is almost universal. Bulk-oil circuit-breakers are never encountered.'

In a report[2] on the 50th Swiss Industries Fair (1966) it is noted that:

'New designs of small-oil-volume circuit-breakers were prominent among the electrical exhibits. They ranged from 6 kV 250 MVA up to 420 kV 25 000 MVA.'

Small-oil-volume circuit-breakers for use on the lower range of distribution voltages, i.e. up to 22/24 kV, have not been enthusiastically taken up in the U.K., largely because of the high performance and degree of reliability achieved with bulk-oil designs. On the continent of Europe however, this range has been extensively developed and in recent years S.O.V. breakers for voltages up to 36 kV have been adapted for use in metal-clad units with draw-out facilities to give horizontal isolation.

Against this, British designs have concentrated on circuit-breakers in the voltage range 33–230 kV, suitable primarily for outdoor use but finding useful application indoors where necessary, original developments going back to 1938. Over the past 10–15 years extensive research and testing in all manufacturing countries has resulted in major advances in design, particularly due to the use of modern high-strength insulating materials such as glass-fibre. This

---

*Variously designated *low-oil-content* or *oil-minimum* and at one time as *oil-poor*.

has led to significant reductions in size and improved ratings and performance. In this respect, Brown Boveri[3] have noted that a present-day design for 12 kV service, while taking only 60% of the space required by an earlier design, has a current rating and interrupting capacity 100% higher. Figure 13.1, which has been taken from a paper by Amer and Gray[4], demonstrates the relative sizes of an arcing chamber for a 66 kV S.O.V. breaker with an interrupting capacity

OLD   NEW

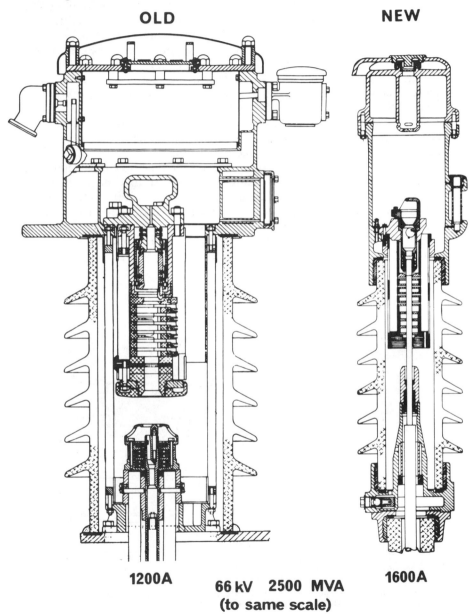

1200A   66 kV   2500 MVA   1600A
(to same scale)

Figure 13.1.   Comparison between old and new circuit-breaking chambers in S.O.V. 66 kV circuit-breakers (courtesy A. Reyrolle & Co. Ltd.)

of 2 500 MVA, that on the left being the chamber in use ten years or so ago, and that on the right being a present day chamber. It is noted also that the normal current rating of the smaller chamber is one-third greater than the larger one.

Before noting some typical examples of S.O.V. breakers it is appropriate to take note of some design features.

In the bulk-oil circuit-breaker the tank is 'dead', i.e. it is at earth potential and the necessary clearances for the system voltage must be obtained in oil between the 'live' contacting elements within the tank and between these and the tank itself. In the S.O.V. breaker, the 'tank' is a tube of insulating material held between metal end caps, and as these caps are the terminal points for the external circuit, the 'tank,' in normal circumstances, is live at line voltage. This assembly, which can be designated the circuit-breaking compartment or interrupter head, has therefore to be supported on one or more insulators (depending on the design) suitable for the system voltage and impulse level.

This arrangement results in a tank of small dimensions, circular in shape and in relatively close proximity to a circular arc-control device of the side-blast type located inside and at the upper end of the tank.

In most high-voltage designs the oil used in the circuit-breaking compartment is segregated from that used for insulation purposes, so that the latter is never contaminated by the former. This ensures a high degree of insulation security in that part of the circuit-breaker which is electrically stressed to earth, irrespective of the condition of the oil in the arcing chamber and whether the breaker is open or closed. Figure 13.2 gives a comparison of the conditions between a small-oil-volume design and a bulk-oil alternative.

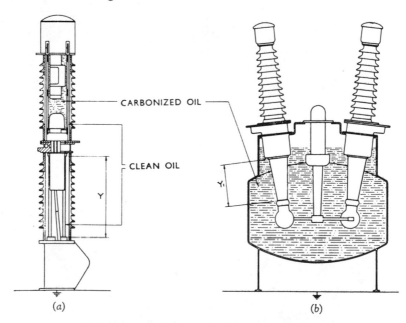

STRESSED PATH TO EARTH SHOWN AT Y (THROUGH CLEAN OIL)
AND Y_1 (THROUGH CARBONISED OIL)

Figure 13.2. Comparison of stressed paths to earth in (a) a small-oil-volume circuit-breaker and (b) a bulk-oil circuit-breaker (courtesy A. Reyrolle & Co. Ltd.)

Arcing under oil causes carbonisation and sludging, and in any oil circuit-breaker changing or conditioning of the oil is essential from time to time. How often this is necessary will depend on the frequency of switching, and when this is high the smaller volume of oil in an S.O.V. breaker may demand more frequent changes. In this respect Brown Boveri have recorded that no change of oil was necessary during a series of twelve full-power short-circuit tests.

Apart from the need to change the oil occasionally, routine maintenance requires that carbon and sludge deposited in the arc-control device must be removed, and here again this may be more frequently required in S.O.V.

Figure 13.3. Small-oil-volume circuit-breaker, 11 kV 500 MVA on withdrawal carriage for horizontal isolation in a metal-clad unit (courtesy Brown Boveri & Co. Ltd.)

breakers than in the bulk-oil type. In data published originally by English Electric it is noted that the frequency of maintenance depends upon a random mixture of duties, but as a guide it recommends that it should be given after:

    4 interruptions at 1 000 MVA (full rating), or
    6 interruptions at 750 MVA, or
    14 interruptions at 500 MVA, or
    50 interruptions at 250 MVA, or
    500/700 interruptions at full-load current.

In his review of progress in high-voltage switchgear, Garrard[5] notes the problem of maintenance and in addition remarks on the fact that the S.O.V. breaker, like the bulk-oil type, can be sensitive to evolving faults and to the effects of restrikes, but against this he sets good performance when breaking low inductive currents and when interrupting short-line faults (see Chapter 2 for discussion on evolving and short-line faults).

Making allowances for the foregoing, the S.O.V. circuit-breaker is a valuable alternative to other types, particularly for locations where switching operations are not too frequent. At the higher voltages it is an economical alternative to the air-blast type in that it avoids the cost and complexities of an air compressor installation with its associated pipe lines, etc. Like the air-blast circuit-breaker, two or more interrupting chambers can be connected in series per pole to achieve the required overall interrupting capacity, and, unlike the air-blast type, it is silent in operation and therefore does not require the use of costly silencers.

Like all other types of circuit-breakers, the S.O.V. type has to be proved on test to national and/or international standards, British designs complying with BS 116 and I.E.C. 56.

Typical of designs intended for service on system voltages in the range 7·2—36 kV is the breaker seen in Fig. 13.3, an illustration which also shows its withdrawable carriage for horizontal isolation in a metal-clad unit. The range of circuit-breakers of this type have breaking capacity ratings of 350 MVA at 7·2 kV, 350/500 MVA at 12 kV, 500/1 000 MVA at 24 kV and 1 000/1 500 MVA at 36 kV. It is also available for fixed installation in cells or cubicles when separate means of isolation are provided. Normal current ratings through the range vary with different breaking capacity ratings and voltage, the lowest being 630 A and the highest 2 500 A.

Figure 13.4 is a cut-away view of one pole of this type of breaker, from which it is seen that an insulated cylindrical chamber (glass-fibre reinforced epoxy resin) acts as the oil tank and contains the fixed and moving contacts and the arc-control device, the latter being of the classical side-blast type. The whole of this assembly is carried between upper and lower end flanges, the former designed to provide a pressure-balancing chamber with oil separator, gas vent and oil-level indicator, the lower flange serving to house the operating linkage to the moving contact rod. A dashpot at the base of the lower flange is provided to buffer the opening stroke at the end of contact travel and at the same time afford facility for draining-off the oil. These flanges serve as incoming and outgoing terminals for the circuit conductors and form brackets to pick-up on the support insulators fixed to the carriage, as seen in Fig. 13.3.

The fixed contacts comprise a cluster of spring-loaded fingers while the moving contact is a rod of silver-plated copper. As in all single-break designs of this form, a second set of fixed contacts in sliding and permanent contact with the moving rod is essential. These are located opposite the lower terminal flange and comprise a system of multiple rollers, which, while ensuring adequate contact for current transfer, offer minimum friction with the sliding rod.

At the lower breaking capacities, the arc-control device has two in-line vents, similar to devices noted and discussed in earlier chapters. At the highest ratings, four vents are provided and these are disposed so that they face alternately in opposite directions. The arc is therefore forced into a zig-zag path, effectively lengthening it at an early stage in the opening operation, thus assisting in the extinction process and keeping the arc duration short. Published test data indicate arcing times of 14–20 ms when interrupting rated fault currents, while the total break-time* does not exceed 70 ms.

* Total break-time is the time from a tripping command through to final arc extinction. On a 50 Hz system, 1 cycle occupies 20 ms.

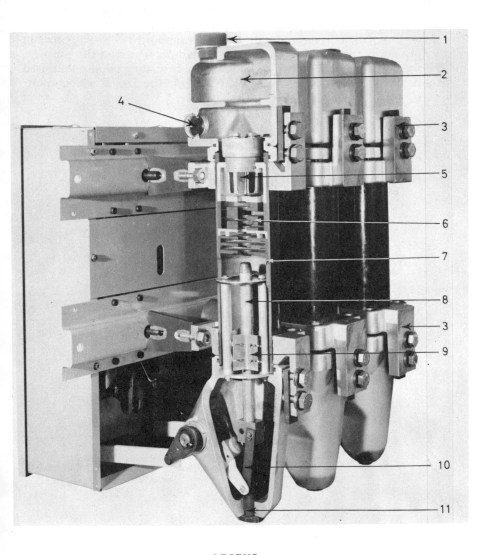

LEGEND

1. VENT
2. PRESSURE EQUALISING CHAMBER
3. TERMINAL FLANGES
4. OIL-LEVEL GAUGE
5. FIXED CONTACT CLUSTER
6. INTERRUPTING CHAMBER

7. INSULATING TUBE
8. MOVING CONTACT ROD WITH ARCING TIP
9. SLIDING CONTACT
10. OPERATING LINKS TO CLOSING MECHANISM
11. BUFFER AND OIL DRAIN

Figure 13.4.   Small-oil-volume circuit-breaker 12 kV, 500 MVA and 1 250A with one pole cut away (courtesy Brown Boveri & Co. Ltd.)

423

Operation of the breaker is by a spring mechanism in which the springs are either manually charged or are charged by a motor and the energy stored in the springs is utilised for *both* the closing and tripping operation.

Because the circuit-breaker under discussion is supported on solid porcelain or other insulators none of the oil in the arcing chamber is used for this purpose, and the segregation described earlier between the insulating oil and that used in the interrupting process, does not arise. A study of the designs which follow

Figure 13.5. 33 kV 1 000 MVA S.O.V. circuit-breaker for outdoor installation (courtesy G.E.C. Switchgear Ltd.)

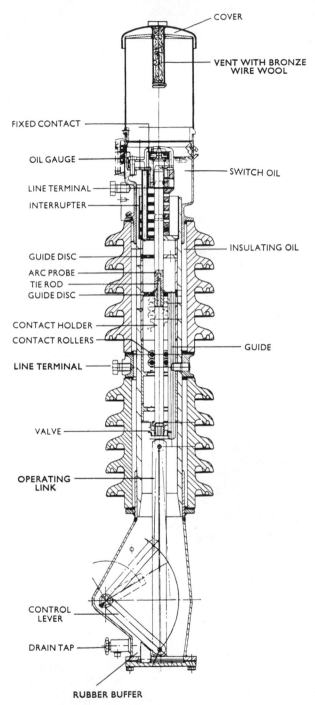

COVER

VENT WITH BRONZE
WIRE WOOL

FIXED CONTACT

OIL GAUGE

SWITCH OIL

LINE TERMINAL

INTERRUPTER

INSULATING OIL

GUIDE DISC

ARC PROBE
TIE ROD
GUIDE DISC

CONTACT HOLDER
CONTACT ROLLERS

GUIDE

LINE TERMINAL

VALVE

OPERATING
LINK

CONTROL
LEVER

DRAIN TAP

RUBBER BUFFER

Figure 13.6. Sectional view of one pole of 33 kV S.O.V. circuit-breaker (courtesy G.E.C. Switchgear Ltd.)

425

show that a different construction is used, i.e. the arcing chamber is mounted vertically above a supporting insulator which is oil filled and provides the main insulation to earth. Although different means are adopted in different designs, each ensures that contaminated oil in the interrupting chamber does not invade the oil used for insulating purposes.

As in the designs so far discussed, metal flanges at the upper and lower ends of the interrupting chamber form the terminal points for the external circuit connections, the topmost flange providing an expansion chamber, gas and oil

Figure 13.7.   Small-oil-volume circuit-breaker of 38–72·5 kV 1 500–2 500 MVA breaking capacity (courtesy A. Reyrolle & Co. Ltd.)

separator, and a gas vent. A metal housing below the support insulator contains the link mechanism to the moving contact, and at this point too there is facility to drain-off the oil.

An outdoor S.O.V. breaker rated at 1 000 MVA 33 kV is shown in Fig. 13.5, and it should be noted that in this illustration the three poles of the circuit-breaker are in the rear of three current transformers carried on an extension framework. A sectional view of one pole of this breaker is shown in Fig. 13.6 from which it may be seen that a synthetic resin-bonded paper tube is centralised inside the upper and lower insulators, running the full length of these. There is an annular space between the outside of the tube and the inside of the porcelains, this space being filled with thick insulating oil. The inside of the synthetic resin-bonded paper tube is filled with switch oil from the base flange up to the sight gauge on the upper housing, the arrangement ensuring complete separation of the insulating and switch oils.

The multi-vented side-blast arc-control device is located at the upper end of the resin-bonded paper tube along with tulip-type fixed contacts which are

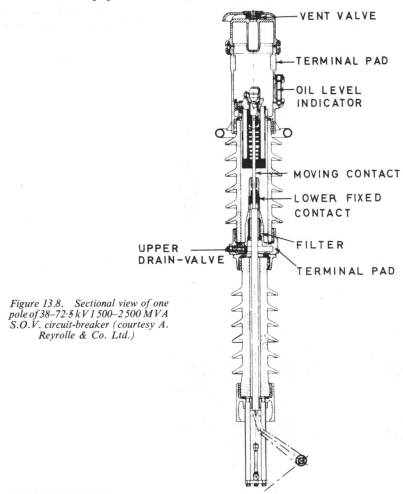

VENT VALVE

TERMINAL PAD

OIL LEVEL INDICATOR

MOVING CONTACT

LOWER FIXED CONTACT

UPPER DRAIN-VALVE

FILTER

TERMINAL PAD

Figure 13.8. Sectional view of one pole of 38–72·5 kV 1 500–2 500 MVA S.O.V. circuit-breaker (courtesy A. Reyrolle & Co. Ltd.)

tipped with arc-resisting metal. The lower set of fixed contacts which remain in permanent contact with the moving contact rod are of the roller-type.

Tension springs are used both for closing and opening the breaker, the tensioning of the closing spring and circuit-breaker operations all being either electrical or mechanical. On units where the closing spring is motor wound, automatic recharging of the spring is provided after a closing operation, thus allowing 3-phase auto-reclosure if required.

For the next higher range of voltages, the S.O.V. circuit-breaker shown in Fig. 13.7 is for service in the range 33–69 kV with interrupting capacities of 1 250–2 500 MVA. A sectional view of one pole is given in Fig. 13.8 from which it is seen that in this design the operating linkage at the base is external to the pole column and is picked-up for connection to the three-pole closing mechanism within the steel enclosure which, as seen in Fig. 13.7, also supports the three poles. Also in this design, both the upper (circuit-breaking) compartment and the lower (insulating) compartment are oil filled, separation of the two bodies of oil being achieved by a sintered-metal filter. This arrangement allows an exchange of oil between compartments during the travel of the moving contact but prevents contamination of the insulating oil in the supporting compartment.

Figure 13.9.   Small-oil-volume cir-cuit-breaker, 88–170 kV 1 500–7 500 MVA breaking capacity (courtesy A. Reyrolle & Co. Ltd.)

For service in the voltage range 88–150 kV, the circuit-breaker shown in Figs. 13.9 and 13.10 has an interrupting capacity of 2 500–3 500 MVA. Apart from obvious differences to meet the voltage conditions, this breaker generally follows the pattern of that just discussed, but in this case separation of the two bodies of oil is by means of a free piston which again permits displacement of oil during the movement of the moving contact but, as before, prevents contamination of the insulating oil.

In both designs (Figs. 13.7 and 13.9) the arc-control device is built up of fibre plates shaped and arranged to form a series of throats and radial vents. The plates are located by glass-fibre tube spacers and are held in compression in an outer glass-fibre cylinder between a throat washer at the base and the upper

428

fixed contact bracket. A ball valve at the top of the device allows rapid displacement of the residual gases by clean oil after the arc is extinguished.

Operating mechanisms are of the spring-closed spring-opened type, the closing spring being charged by a hydraulic pump driven by an a.c. or d.c. motor. Automatic recharging of the closing spring after a breaker closing operation is provided, thus allowing 3-phase auto-reclosing if required. With the 132 kV design, a special arrangement allows each pole to be equipped with a separate operating mechanism thus permitting single-phase auto-reclosing. Should failure occur in the auxiliary supply, a means is provided so that the

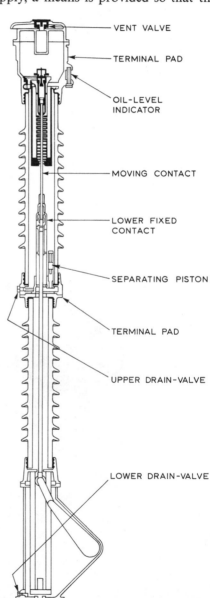

Figure 13.10. Sectional view of one pole of S.O.V. circuit-breaker, 88–170 kV 1 500–3 500 MVA (courtesy A. Reyrolle & Co. Ltd.)

VENT VALVE

TERMINAL PAD

OIL-LEVEL INDICATOR

MOVING CONTACT

LOWER FIXED CONTACT

SEPARATING PISTON

TERMINAL PAD

UPPER DRAIN-VALVE

LOWER DRAIN-VALVE

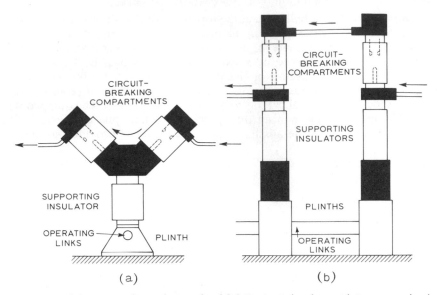

Figure 13.11. Schematic outlines of one pole of S.O.V. circuit-breakers with interrupter heads in series (see Figures 13.12 and 13.13)

CIRCUIT-
BREAKING
COMPARTMENTS

SUPPORTING
INSULATOR

OPERATING
LINKS

PLINTH

(a)

CIRCUIT-
BREAKING
COMPARTMENTS

SUPPORTING
INSULATORS

PLINTHS

OPERATING
LINKS

(b)

Figure 13.12. 132 kV 5 000 MVA S.O.V. circuit-breaker (courtesy South Wales Switchgear Ltd.)

430

closing spring can be charged manually, while for the purpose of operational checks following maintenance the breakers can be closed and opened slowly by hand, a procedure which does not entail the charging of either the closing or opening springs.

In each of the designs so far illustrated, interruption is achieved at a single break, i.e. in one interrupter unit per pole. As the required interrupting capacity increases, and bearing in mind what has been said in earlier chapters concerning the power limitations in short-circuit test plants for direct testing, multiple breaks in series can be employed so that unit testing can be used.

When two breaks in series are used per pole, the two interrupter heads may be assembled in 'V'-formation as indicated at (a) in Fig. 13.11, or alternatively each interrupter head could be mounted on its own support column as indicated

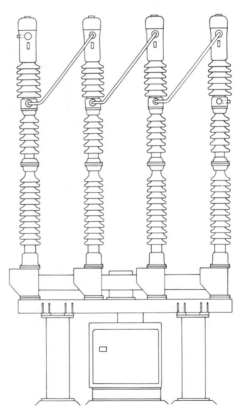

Figure 13.13. Arrangement of one pole of a 220 kV 7 500 MVA S.O.V. circuit-breaker with four interrupter heads in series (courtesy A. Reyrolle & Co. Ltd.)

at (b). As will be noted later, the latter arrangement is basic in a design with four breaks in series per pole. As with all designs of breaker employing multiple breaks in series, identical interrupter heads will be used for each break and provision made to ensure equal voltage distribution across each break, i.e. using either resistors or capacitors connected in shunt.

Figure 13.12 illustrates a design where two interrupter heads are arranged in 'V'-formation and supported on a single central-support insulator which provides the main insulation to earth. Each interrupter head comprises a tube of filament-wound glass-fibre to house the arc-control device, fixed and moving contacts and the voltage grading resistor. This tube is filled with switch oil and the assembly is contained in the protective porcelain insulator with an annular space between them, the space being filled with insulating oil.

The vertical supporting insulator houses a torsion drive tube of epoxy-resin-bonded glass-fibre for actuating the two moving contacts. This insulator is also oil filled, the oil being in communication with that in the annular space surrounding the interrupter units. This ensures a balance of oil pressure where the mechanical drive passes from the support insulator to the 'V'-shaped mechanism housing below the interrupter units. In this design, the sliding contact assembly in permanent contact with the moving contact rod is a multi-point construction designed to ensure freedom from burning and pitting which might arise due to high values of peak-making-current and to heavy through-fault currents. This breaker has an interrupting capacity of 5 000 MVA maximum at 132 kV. It can be operated either by a solenoid or a compressed-air unit, the individual operating elements for each pole being linked to the main operating mechanism by interphase drives between the supporting plinths.

In a design for use on the next higher range of voltages, four breaks in series per pole are employed, each interrupter head being mounted on its own insulating support column as shown in Fig. 13.13. Suitable for use on 220/230 kV systems (ultimately 245 kV), this breaker has a 3-phase rating of 7 500 MVA at 220 kV, and uses the same interrupter heads as in the 66 kV design noted earlier in Fig. 13.8. Similarly, the operating mechanism is of the type noted in relation to Figs. 13.7 and 13.9, but in this case, a separate mechanism for each phase is standard giving the facility of single-phase auto-reclosure if required.

REFERENCES

1. TOWILL, S., 'Electricity Supply in Sweden', *Electronics and Power*, **11**, Aug. (1965)
2. ANON., *Elect. Rev.*, 29 April (1966)
3. SCHNEIDER, J., 'New Low-oil-volume Circuit-breakers for 500 and 1 000 MVA at 12 and 24 kV', *Brown Boveri Rev.*, **52** No. 4, April (1965)
4. GRAY, W. and AMER, D.F., 'Some Recent Developments in Switchgear', Paper presented to South African I.E.E. Available from A. Reyrolle & Co. Ltd. as reprint No. RR 122
5. GARRARD, C.J.O., 'High-voltage Switchgear—a Review of Progress', *Proc. I.E.E.*, **113** No. 9, Sept. (1966)

BIBLIOGRAPHY

ANON., 'New e.h.v. Switchgear Developed for World Markets', *Elect. Rev.*, **186** No. 8, 20 Feb. (1970)
CAULLET, P., 'Small-oil-volume Circuit-breakers of Modern Design', *Elect. Eng. (Australia)*, 10 Sept. (1964)
CRANE, P.H.G., *Switchgear Principles*, Macmillan (1957)
DAVIES, D.R. and FLURSCHEIM, C.H., 'The Development of the Single-break Oil Circuit-breaker for Metal-clad Switchgear', *J.I.E.E.*, **79**, 129 (1936)
GANZ, A. and BERGER, E., 'Type T Minimum-oil Circuit-breakers for 170 kV', *Brown Boveri Rev.*, **57**, Dec. (1970)
LYTHALL, R.T., 'Small-oil-volume Circuit-breakers', *Elect. Rev.*, 19 Aug. (1966)
MAYER, A., 'New l.o.v. Breakers for 36 kV 1 500 MVA', *Brown Boveri Rev.*, **55** No. 12, Dec. (1968)
SZENTA-VARGA, S.P. and HOFMANN, W., 'New Indoor Low-oil-volume Circuit-breakers', *Brown Boveri Rev.*, **51** No. 4, April (1964)
WIDMER, H. and LATAL, W., 'Type F Outdoor Minimum-oil Circuit-breakers', *Brown Boveri Rev.*, **57**, Dec. (1970)

Chapter 14

Heavy-duty air-break circuit-breakers

The air-break circuit-breaker is now extensively used on heavy-duty power circuits operating in the medium-voltage range up to 650 V in all kinds of installations. For similar circuits in the high-voltage range, i.e. 3·3–11 kV in the U.K. and up to 17·5 kV elsewhere, their use is generally confined to particular types of installations where they have many advantages over other types.

British designs will, in particular, comply with BS 3659:1963, a specification which covers all voltages up to 11 kV. For medium voltages, designs having interrupting capacities of 15·6, 26 and 31 MVA at 415 V are assumed to comprise the 'heavy-duty' class with normal current ratings up to 3 000 A. In the high-voltage range, breakers rated 50/250 MVA at 3·3 kV, 150/500 MVA at 6·6 kV, and 150/750 MVA at 11 kV come within the scope of the specification. Apart from compliance with the latter, many designs at all voltages will meet the requirements of the appropriate specifications of the International Electro-technical Commission (I.E.C.). Continental and American designs will naturally comply with the national specifications of the country of origin, while continental designs in particular will almost invariably comply with I.E.C.

The very considerable swing towards the air-break circuit-breaker in the medium-voltage range has been largely due to the relative ease with which multi-tier assemblies of withdrawable units can be achieved, two and three-tier arrangements being commonplace with consequent saving in floor space. Such arrangements too can readily be lined up with fuse switches and motor control units, both of which have progressed extensively in multi-tier assembly, thus facilitating the building of composite switchboards in which all the apparatus is air-break. This type of board is in fact the basis of the packaged substation (see Chapter 19) in which the power transformers form an integral part, the transformer being either of the dry-type or Pyroclor filled.

All this does not mean that the bulk-oil circuit-breaker has disappeared in current practice, as we have noted earlier and will note again in Chapter 19, but where the oil hazard, no matter how small, must be completely eliminated the air-break design is an obvious solution.

On high-voltage systems in the U.K., air-break circuit-breakers find their major application in modern power stations for the control of high-voltage auxiliary services and in large industrial plants such as steel works, cement and paper mills, the oil and chemical industries, etc. and for the control of electric furnaces. In most of these, motors of considerable horsepower have to be controlled, and the switching operations may be very frequent. This latter condition arises in furnace operation, and in all of these the high-voltage air-break circuit-breaker is an ideal but costly choice. In power station work particularly, the increasing size of the main power unit led automatically to the need for higher-powered auxiliaries, with motors well beyond the practical limit for medium-voltage operation.

In a power distribution system, the loads are, with few exceptions, spread over wide areas and the voltage chosen will be related to the condition of minimum cable losses. In a power station (and large industrial plants) the loads are concentrated, with short cable runs, and cable losses are not important. These loads are mostly motor drives of large size requiring good system voltage regulation, and hence the auxiliary transformers must be large units of moderate impedance, leading to high fault levels at the system busbars. Thus, as a first step, 3·3 kV was chosen for certain auxiliaries with a system fault level of 150 MVA, but with further increases in the size of auxiliary drives, 6·6 kV became necessary, the fault level moving up to 250/350 MVA. This in turn proved insufficient as the size of power stations increased still further so that the auxiliary services voltage quickly moved to 11 kV and 750 MVA fault level.

While the bulk-oil circuit-breaker in British practice and the small-oil-volume breaker elsewhere, can satisfy these voltage and fault level demands, they are not ideal where the frequent stopping and starting of motors is an operational requirement, due to (a) the arcing being rooted in a very localised area with consequent high-contact erosion and (b) the rapid build-up of oil contamination. In noting the design of modern air-break circuit-breakers later, we shall see how the arc is rapidly transferred clear of both the main and arcing contacts to the tips of arc runners so that contact erosion is reduced to negligible proportions. As there is no oil to contaminate, the condition (b) above does not arise.

In the U.S.A. and Europe, the high-voltage air-break circuit-breaker has been used over a wider field of application, including in many cases distribution networks up to 17·5 kV, a voltage which would appear to be the economic design limit. Its use in America goes back many decades, the forerunners of the successful designs of today being noted in learned papers of the 1920s, e.g. the 'De-ion' and 'Magneblast' types.

Both medium and high-voltage designs, used as they generally are at locations close to power sources, must be capable of performing no less efficiently than the bulk-oil or small-oil-volume counterparts and the proving tests demanded are indeed equal for all types.

MEDIUM-VOLTAGE DESIGNS

In its simplest form, the air-break circuit-breaker has been used on d.c. systems for over 50 years and, when fault levels were very low, a similar design was used on a.c. systems. Such breakers would be mounted on the front and at the top of slate or marble panels, i.e. the flat-back switchboard discussed in Chapter 1. These designs were relatively slow acting and arcing times would be long. Arc chutes in the modern sense were not fitted, the arc being free to 'balloon' upwards without restriction, hence the need to mount the breaker at the top of the supporting panel, phase barriers being used to prevent the arc wandering to adjacent phases. To assist and hasten the process of lengthening the arc, suitably located series coils with an associated magnetic circuit might be fitted, i.e. a magnetic blow-out as indicated typically in Fig. 14.1.

Breakers of this type are quite inadequate for use on high fault-level systems. Normally hand-closed they would be even more inadequate for the onerous task of 'making' on to a fault and all modern designs are found to have power-operated closing devices, e.g. spring or solenoid.

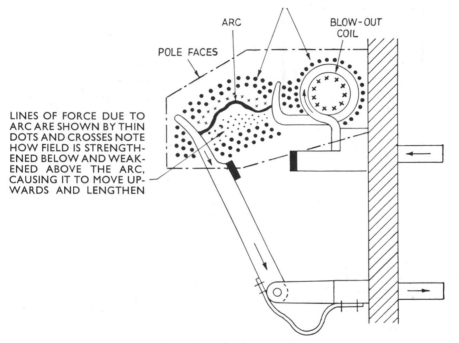

LINES OF FORCE IN BLOW-OUT FIELD TRAVELLING TOWARDS OBSERVER AS SHOWN BY THICK DOTS AND AWAY BY THICK CROSSES

ARC

BLOW-OUT COIL

POLE FACES

LINES OF FORCE DUE TO ARC ARE SHOWN BY THIN DOTS AND CROSSES NOTE HOW FIELD IS STRENGTH-ENED BELOW AND WEAK-ENED ABOVE THE ARC, CAUSING IT TO MOVE UP-WARDS AND LENGTHEN

Figure 14.1.   Principle of magnetic blow-out

Basically, present day breakers (often described as the 'chute' type) follow the elementary arrangement shown in Fig. 14.2. Here the contact system comprises separate main and arcing contacts, the latter fitted with arc runners to assist the upward movement of the arc into the arc chute. The arc, initiated across the arcing contacts, is forced upwards by the electromagnetic forces and by thermal action, the roots of the arc travelling rapidly along the arc runners until it is forced into the arc chute. Here its length is rapidly and considerably extended by the splitter plates and, if the latter are of metal, divided into a number of very short arcs formed between adjacent plates. These splitter plates also serve to cool the arc, thus assisting the all important process of de-ionisation, and at the same time they reduce the velocity of the arc products expelled above the chute.

While designs based on these principles are extremely efficient when called upon to interrupt high values of fault current, they are not always so good when

435

interrupting low values of current, as with these the electromagnetic forces are so much less. This means that arc movement towards and into the chute is slow, and to offset this some assistance may be given by fitting magnetic blow-out plates on the outside faces of the chutes at points opposite the arcing area, thus intensifying the magnetic field.

The elementary arrangement in Fig. 14.2 indicates a single-break design and this is the basis of many actual breakers. With a hinged-contact system of this type, the same problem arises which we noted in single-break bulk-oil circuit-breakers, viz. that continuity of the current path across the hinge must be

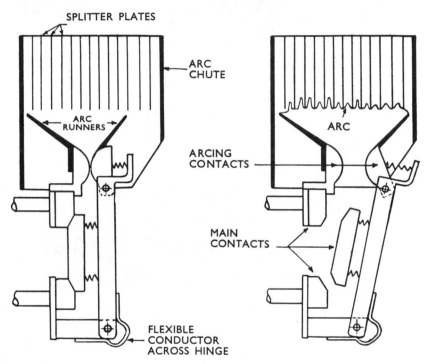

Figure 14.2.   Elementary arrangement of air-break circuit-breaker

ensured, either by a flexible conductor as shown or by the use of a special hinge bolt which maintains good contact under pressure.

In practical designs, some of which we shall note, numerous variations occur such as a single or double break at the main contacts, an arcing-contact system separated from the main contacting elements, fixed or moving arc runners associated with the moving contact arm, insulated or metal splitter plates, etc. In recent years, designs designated as *current limiting* have been developed, i.e. circuit-breakers which exhibit the cut-off characteristic of the h.r.c. fuse, so that the current interrupted is some value less than the prospective peak current with interruption taking place in the first half-cycle of short-circuit. The use of such types would appear to depend to some extent on the point of application on a network in relation to other interrupting devices.

This is because, in a series network, a breaker nearer to the power source must carry the full short-circuit current until such time as it is interrupted by a

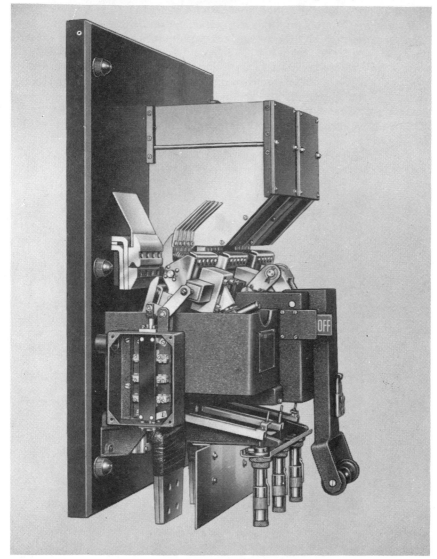

Figure 14.3. Air-break circuit-breaker in closed position with one arc chute removed (courtesy W. Lucy & Co. Ltd.)

circuit-breaker (or fuse) at a location nearer the point of fault. It may be noted in passing that the current-limiting principle has been used also in a design of moulded-case circuit-breaker* rated 100 A at 500 V and for use on systems where the prospective fault level is 50 kA r.m.s. symmetrical (110 kA peak) equivalent to about 36 MVA at 415 V. Used, as it no doubt will be, at remote distribution points, any of the problems just noted would be unlikely to arise, providing discrimination with any h.r.c. fuses at sub-distribution points is carefully studied.

*S.p.A. Costruzioni Elettromechaniche (S.A.C.E.), Bergamo, Italy.

High fault levels in medium-voltage systems mean that the possible through-fault current will be high, and if as is often demanded, the breaker must have a 3 s short-time rating, then there will be a minimum normal-current rating for the breaker, probably about 800 A or even 1 200 A. Normally, direct-acting series-overcurrent trip coils will be used and when the rating of these is less than that of the breaker, e.g. 400 A, it may be necessary to limit the short-time rating to 1 s (see clause 9 of BS 3659).

With very-low-rated coils, the interrupting capacity of the breaker may be limited by the ability of the coils to withstand high fault current. This problem

Figure 14.4. Air-break circuit-breaker in open position with one arc chute removed (courtesy W. Lucy & Co. Ltd.)

is of course not peculiar to the air-break circuit-breaker; it applies equally to any design employing series trip coils, but a solution can be found by using current-transformer operated protective coils or relays, in which case the short-time factor of the current transformers must be considered (see Chapters 11 and 23).

With some designs, alternatives are made available, one being a withdrawable unit for horizontal isolation and another being a fixed type for use in open or cellular switchgear where separate means of isolation are provided. The latter arrangement is quite common on the continent but less frequent in British practice.

A breaker designed in these alternative ways is shown in Figs. 14.3 and 14.4, these photographs showing the fixed version, panel mounted. The contact system used here is a three-part assembly comprising main, secondary and

Figure 14.5. 800A solenoid-operated medium-voltage air-break circuit-breaker in withdrawn position with front plate and arc chutes removed (courtesy George Ellison Ltd.)

arcing contacts which, on opening, break in that order. This introduction of secondary contacts between the main and arcing contacts is adopted in several designs, the purpose being to eliminate any possibility of even slight arcing and burning on the main contact surfaces. The illustrations also show that one set of arc runners form an extension to the arcing contacts and therefore move with the latter.

When a circuit-breaker is of the withdrawable type, some form of slide rails or runners must be provided to enable the breaker to be moved from its service position to (a) its isolated position and (b) its fully withdrawn position. In Fig. 14.5 an example is shown where telescopic slide rails are used, the rails being completely within the cubicle when the breaker is in service. The movement necessary for isolation is relatively small and in most cubicle assemblies this takes place within the cubicle depth without the need to open the enclosing door, an operation only necessary when full withdrawal for inspection or maintenance is required. The design in Fig. 14.5 however is one in which the front enclosing panel is carried in unit with the breaker, and so that no opening is left when in the isolated position, a skirt on the rear of the panel is provided, its depth being equal to the movement between the service and isolated positions.

Figure 14.6. Circuit-breaker carriage adapted to provide a 2 100A off-load isolator, front plate removed (courtesy George Ellison Ltd.)

In Chapter 19, an illustration will be given of a switchboard comprising units of this type with several circuit-breakers in the isolated position. In passing, it is of interest to note that the designers of the circuit-breaker shown in Fig. 14.5 have used the breaker carriage with the upper and lower isolating plugs directly connected by copper straps to form an off-load isolator uniform in size and style with circuit-breaker units. A typical example of such an isolator is shown in Fig. 14.6 and is a useful method of providing complete isolation of a switchboard at the point of supply.

In the design shown in Fig. 14.7, the breaker is again withdrawn on telescopic slide rails, but here a hinged door is used to enclose the breaker in its service and isolated positions. This requires that the operating mechanism be carried on a control facia forming part of the breaker unit and framed by a rectangular opening in the door panel. The circuit-breaker itself is shown in more detail in

Fig. 14.8 where one arc chute has been removed. The latter comprise moulded asbestos-cement boxes containing steel splitter plates above which are cooling sections of Sindanyo*. Butt-type contacts are employed in a single-break arrangement so designed that the electromagnetic forces set up by fault current tend to increase the contact pressure, a valuable feature when called upon to carry a through-fault.

In our earlier discussion note was taken of the need to ensure efficient current-carrying ability at the hinge point in single-break designs, either by flexible conductors bridging the hinge or by spring loading of the mating surfaces of

Figure 14.7. 1 600A medium-voltage air-break circuit-breaker in withdrawn position (courtesy A. Reyrolle & Co. Ltd.)

the pivots. The latter method is adopted in this design, the surfaces being silver plated.

To move the breaker from the service position to the isolated position a worm and wheel mechanism is provided which is operated at the control facia with the door closed. When the breaker is in its service position, this mechanism holds it firmly in that position under all fault conditions. As in all withdrawable-type circuit-breakers, interlocks prevent movement out of or in to the service position unless the breaker is open, and the door can only be opened with the breaker in the isolated position.

* Trademark of insulating material made by Turner Bros. Asbestos Cement Co. Ltd. (Turner Newall Group).

The existence has been noted earlier of a design designated as 'current-limiting,' and in Chapter 11 details have been given of the protective characteristics of such a design. This circuit-breaker is shown in Figs. 14.9 and 14.10 and from the sectional view it is seen that two sets of protection are provided, one being an overcurrent thermal/magnetic device (marked 1) which operates through the closing mechanism and incorporates an inherent time delay, and secondly an ultra-rapid short-circuit trip device (marked 13) which, on initiation, immediately trips out the faulty phase and almost simultaneously trips the healthy phase(s) by collapsing the closing mechanism.

To ensure rapid operation of the ultra-rapid trip, the three devices in a three-phase breaker are uni-polar in construction and are not interconnected. Operation of a single-trip, e.g. on an earth fault, will cause the mechanism associated with the faulty phase to collapse, whereupon an activating rocker (20) operates the trip bar (21) to collapse the mechanisms of the other phases to completely isolate the circuit, the time interval being a matter of a few milliseconds.

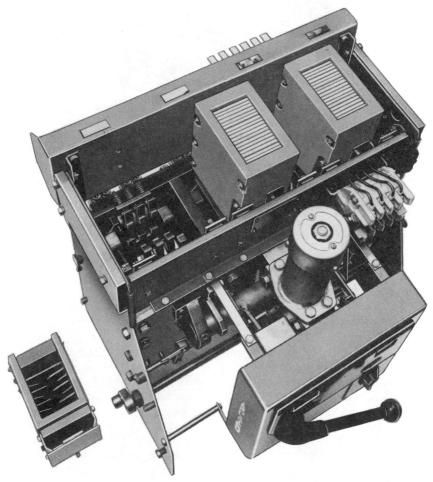

Figure 14.8. Circuit-breaker shown in Figure 14.7 viewed from above. One arc chute is removed (courtesy A. Reyrolle & Co. Ltd.)

442

When heavy (e.g. fault) currents are conducted via a loop, the electromagnetic forces will tend to expand the loop, and when, as in this breaker design, the main contacts form part of the loop, the tendency will be for those contacts to separate, i.e. the moving contact will, by repulsion, be 'lifted' off the fixed contact. As no mechanism is involved in this, partial contact separation occurs rapidly, i.e. before the first peak of fault current. An arc is therefore struck at a very early stage, introducing resistance in the fault-current circuit and tending to reduce its magnitude.

Figure 14.9. 'Brush-Delle' current-limiting medium-voltage air-break circuit-breaker (courtesy Brush Switchgear Ltd.)

Unless prevented however, the slightly opened contacts would, as the current reached its first natural zero, reclose and then immediately re-open as the current rose again, a process which could be repeated at subsequent zeros with unfortunate consequences. To avoid this, the ultra-rapid magnetic trip is fitted. This is a hinged armature which is rapidly attracted to a pole piece on the current carrying conductor, the armature movement causing the release of the holding-in mechanism via a trip-pawl (15). The setting of the magnetic trip is such that

443

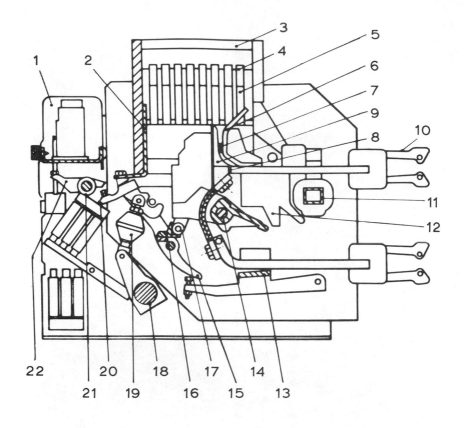

Figure 14.10. Sectional view of 'Brush-Delle' current-limiting air-break circuit-breaker (courtesy Brush Switchgear Ltd.)

it operates very slightly in advance of the current level at which self-repulsion at the contact occurs. Once the operation is initiated therefore, the contacts are free to accelerate to the fully open position, the arc transferring to the arc runners, lengthening as it travels upwards to the arc chute where it is split, cooled and extinguished. The interrupting capacity of a breaker of this type is high because of its current-limiting feature and is given as 65 MVA at 415 V, i.e. it can be used on systems where the prospective fault current may be as high as 90 000 A r.m.s. symmetrical.

The illustrations given here are of a withdrawable type for horizontal isolation, but fixed designs are available. In an alternative design, the ultra-rapid

Figure 14.11. 1 600A English Electric air-break circuit-breaker with arc chutes removed to show butt-type contacts with arcing horns (courtesy G.E.C. Switchgear Ltd.)

trip is omitted and the breaker becomes a conventional non-current-limiting type.

Figures 14.11 and 14.12 show, in some detail, the contact system and the cluster-type isolating contacts respectively in an English Electric (G.E.C. Switchgear Ltd.) design.

At this point, particular attention may be drawn to the fact that in all withdrawable types of circuit-breaker (air or oil) the fault current has to be carried by the isolating contacts. This demands not only good contact under pressure between the fixed and moving elements, but also that they cannot be forced apart. The cluster formation shown in Fig. 14.12 is typical of good design in this respect, a cluster comprising several contacts in parallel, and when carrying fault current the already high pressure tends to be increased.

We have noted in Chapter 11 the existence of specially designed direct-acting series overcurrent tripping devices having various characteristics to meet particular conditions. These are fitted to the breaker shown in Figs. 14.11 and 14.12 and to another range by the same manufacturer. The contact system (butt-type) of this other range is shown in Fig. 14.13 and at the base of this unit can be seen the magnetic circuit of the overcurrent tripping devices.

It is of interest now to look at a continental design of conventional (i.e. non-current-limiting) breaker by Brown Boveri & Co. Ltd., which has a number of

Figure 14.12.   Rear view of the English Electric circuit-breaker shown in Figure 14.11, with arc chutes fitted. This view also shows the 'cluster'-type isolating contacts and the auxiliary contacts (courtesy G.E.C. Switchgear Ltd.)

interesting features. Some of these can best be studied by reference to the schematic diagrams in Fig. 14.14 from which it is seen that entirely separate main and arcing-contact systems are employed, the former being of the double-break type and the latter connected electrically in parallel with the main contacts. The main moving contact (comprising multiple spring-loaded fingers) is 'V'-shaped and, as seen from the front of the breaker, is located *behind* the fixed main contact bars, this being generally opposite to contemporary designs. Thus the

446

current loop formed by the contact bars, the terminal stems (not shown) and the moving contact itself is such as to ensure that under short-circuit conditions the electromagnetic forces tending to expand the loop will augment the pressure at the main contacts.

As is usual, spring-closing mechanisms are used, but in this design each pole has its own springs, and when, as noted later, each pole is built-up of multiple elements, each element has its own springs. From Fig. 14.14 it is seen that the springs are loaded to maximum tension by rollers riding on the shaped edges of cams. This condition is that shown at (a) in the illustration, and further anti-clockwise movement results in the rollers passing over the lobe of the cam to take up the position at (b) so that the energy stored in the springs closes the circuit-breaker, which is latched by C. Only part of the stored energy is used on closing, that remaining in the springs being used to open the breaker on receipt of a tripping command. This unlatches the operating shaft which is now

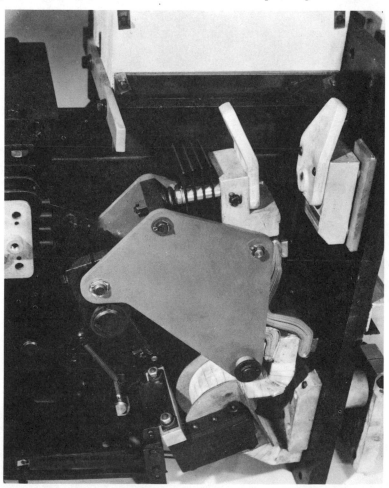

Figure 14.13. Contact system (arc chute removed) in the English Electric 'Trimpact' medium-voltage air-break circuit-breaker. The magnetic circuit at the base is part of the direct-acting overcurrent devices discussed in Chapter 11 (courtesy G.E.C. Switchgear Ltd.)

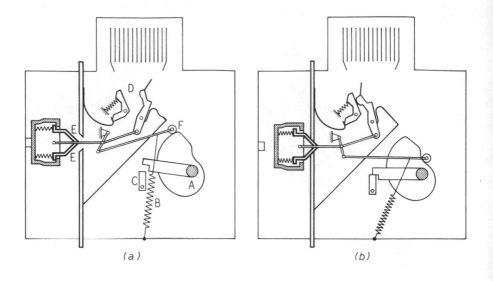

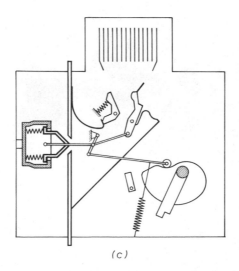

(c)

LEGEND

A   OPERATING SHAFT AND CAM
B   OPENING AND CLOSING SPRING
C   LATCH TO LOCK OPERATING
    SHAFT
D   ARCING CONTACTS
E   MAIN CONTACTS
F   ROLLER ON CAM

Figure 14.14.   Schematic diagram of circuit-breaker contacting elements and cam-operated opening and closing mechanism in three positions. (a) Spring B at maximum tension ready to close, (b) breaker closed, latch C closed and spring B loaded and (c) breaker open, latch C released and spring B unloaded (courtesy Brown Boveri & Co. Ltd.)

free to continue its anti-clockwise rotation to open the breaker as shown at (*c*). A free-wheel device in a chain drive between the means adopted for charging the springs (hand lever or motor) and the operating shaft ensures that the former is completely disengaged during the opening sequence. It is claimed for this cam operated mechanism that it has the advantage of eliminating highly stressed latches during the charging operation and that there is no reversed rotation to trip the breaker.

Two illustrations of this design are noted in Figs. 14.15 and 14.16, the former being a rear view showing the isolating contacts and, behind the lower 'electric flashes', the main contact assemblies.

Figure 14.15.   1 600/2 000A air-break circuit-breaker with one switching element per pole. This rear view shows the isolating contacts and the main contact enclosures as at (c) *in Figure 14.14 (courtesy Brown Boveri & Co. Ltd.)*

This breaker uses one switching element per pole but Fig. 14.16, which is a front view, shows how two switching elements are used per pole to produce a higher normal current rating. This feature is extended to a unit having three elements per pole to give a rating of 4 500 A and will have two operating springs per element, i.e. a total of six per pole. Because of proximity effects, with switching elements in parallel, current ratings cannot be in the proportion 1:2:3 but will be of the order 1:1·52:1·95. By this method of modular construction the same components, including the actuating and tripping devices, are identical, each rating of breaker being of common height and depth and varying only in width. A further feature of the construction is that any one of the identical poles can be removed and, if necessary, replaced by a spare pre-adjusted pole, typically as shown in Fig. 14.17.

In the arc chute assembly, metal splitter plates are used, and because it is generally found that those directly above the initial arc suffer the heaviest erosion by burning, the chutes are made so that they can be reversed through 180° so that by reversal the erosion can be equalised.

Earlier, we have noted the general use of telescopic slide rails for breaker withdrawal. In the Brown Boveri design, rails are fitted on the inside face of the

Figure 14.16.   2 400/3 200A air-break circuit-breaker with two identical switching elements per pole. The closing and opening [(a) in Figure 14.14] can be seen along with the motor for charging the springs via the cams (courtesy Brown Boveri & Co. Ltd.)

front cover, which, as shown in Fig. 14.18, hinges down to provide a platform on which the breaker rests when fully withdrawn, the breaker itself being fitted with wheels as seen in Figs. 14.15 and 14.16. As in other designs, the cover remains closed when it is required to move the breaker from the service to the isolated position, a racking mechanism with external means of operation being provided.

The medium-voltage air-break circuit-breaker, for heavy-duty applications, must often have normal current ratings higher than those generally available in bulk-oil designs and as noted above, can be rated up to 4 500 A, and several designs with ratings of 3 000 A are available. These high ratings are not normally employed in other than single-tier formation because of heating problems. When multi-tier construction is used, most manufacturers place a limit on the *total* full-load current which can be tolerated in the bank, e.g. if one unit in a

Figure 14.17. Individual pole assembly in Brown Boveri air-break circuit-breaker. Any pole can be removed and replaced by another (courtesy Brown Boveri & Co. Ltd.)

three-tier bank is rated at say 1 600 A, the normal full load of other units in that bank must be such as not to exceed the limit specified.

HIGH-VOLTAGE DESIGNS

In terms of current, the interrupting capacity required of the high-voltage air-break circuit-breaker is of the same order as that required of the medium-voltage breakers we have just studied, i.e. up to 43·6 kA r.m.s. symmetrical. To interrupt currents of this magnitude at say 415 V is one thing; to do so at 3·3–11 kV (or even 17·5 kV) is a much more formidable problem. The success of any design in achieving this duty lies very largely with the steps taken to control the arc prior to and after its entry into the arc chute. This has demanded very considerable research and development requiring the use of high-speed ciné

451

Figure 14.18. How a Brown Boveri air-break circuit-breaker is withdrawn on a platform formed by front cover (courtesy the former Belmos Peebles Switchgear Ltd.)

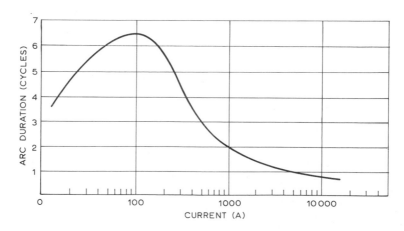

Figure 14.19. Typical arc duration/current curve for a high-voltage air-break circuit-breaker

photography by means of which the behaviour of the arc can be judged. This has naturally required a study of contact and arc-runner design with some emphasis on the transfer of the arc from the arcing contacts to the arc runners.

Lengthening of the arc being essential for successful interruption, it is clear that an arc chute of the relatively simple type associated with medium-voltage circuit-breakers would, if it was to achieve results, have to be of such physical size as to be prohibitive in any compact design of switchgear equipment. Thus, to achieve the necessary lengthening, an arc chute has to be used in which the arc path follows a zig-zag, spiral or other form, so that the chute is kept down to a reasonable height.

In high-voltage designs, the natural tendency for the arc to balloon upwards by convection and electromagnetic force is aided by other means, e.g. blow-out coils with an associated magnetic circuit or by the use of insulated steel splitter plates which intensify and direct the magnetic field, driving the arc rapidly into the chute. The lengthening arc results in a rapid build up of arc voltage which results in a modification of the waveform of the currents.

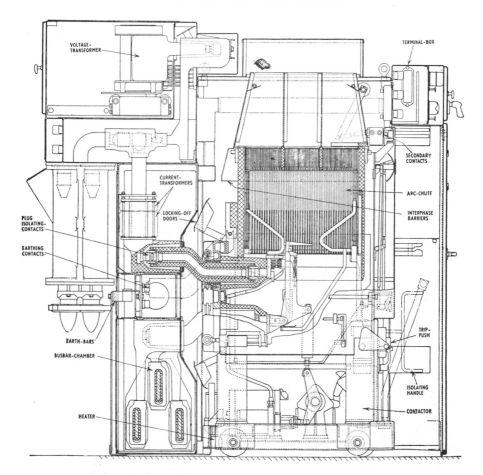

Figure 14.20.   Section of a 6·6/11/15 kV 500 MVA air-break circuit-breaker (courtesy A. Reyrolle & Co. Ltd.)

The oil circuit-breakers which we have discussed earlier and the air-blast types to be noted later, have been defined as *low-arc-resistance* interrupters because here the arc resistance remains low until current zero when it is transformed into or replaced by a high-resistance dielectric, i.e. oil or compressed air. We have noted how, in some breakers, external resistors are shunted in parallel with the contact breaks for the purpose of easing the interrupting duty.

The air-break circuit-breaker on the other hand has been defined as a *high-arc-resistance* interrupter because here, as the arc lengthens so the arc resistance increases, so that at current zero it will be high enough to prevent the reestablishment of the arc.

Since the magnetic blow-out field is weak when low inductive currents have to be interrupted, it is fairly general practice to assist the arc into the chute by means of an air puffer, which is a mechanically-operated device which directs a blast of air into the arc zone from below the contacts as they part. A typical curve of arc duration as a function of current interrupted is given in Fig. 14.19 from which it is seen that there is a critical value of current which is associated

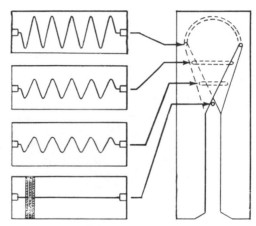

Figure 14.21. How the arc is lengthened in alternately inclined slots in the arc chute (courtesy A. Reyrolle & Co. Ltd.)

with the maximum arcing time and which is of the order of 50–100 A. It is at this point that the air-puffer has been most successful in reducing the arcing times to the values noted in the curve, from values twice or even three times as long.

In general, horizontal withdrawal for isolation is employed with high-voltage air-break circuit-breakers on account of size and weight, particularly at the highest current and MVA ratings. A sectional view of a metal-clad unit of this type is shown in Fig. 14.20, a view which shows in some detail the circuit-breaker construction and the size of the arc chute with its cooler and roof barriers above.

Magnetic blow-out coils are not used with this design; instead the chute plates are of a sandwich type in which iron 'sucker-loops' are moulded between plates of refractory material to produce a self-excited magnetic field, and they are generally called *coil-less magnetic blow-out* chutes. Initially, the arc moves in a very restricted tunnel and is lengthened by being forced to follow a zig-zag path via alternately inclined slots as indicated in Fig. 14.21. If the arc reaches

454

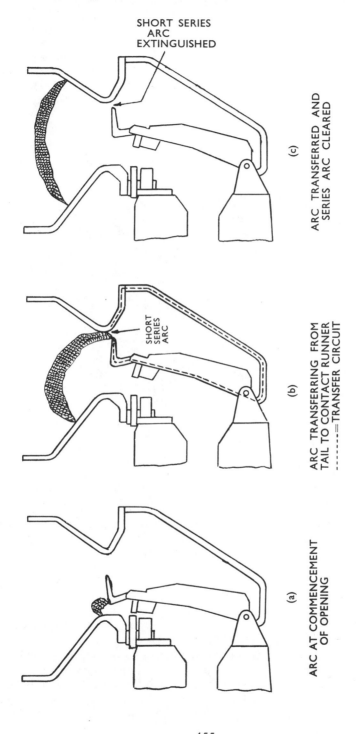

SHORT SERIES
ARC
EXTINGUISHED

(c)

ARC TRANSFERRED AND
SERIES ARC CLEARED

SHORT
SERIES
ARC

(b)

ARC TRANSFERRING FROM
TAIL TO CONTACT RUNNER
------=TRANSFER CIRCUIT

(a)

ARC AT COMMENCEMENT
OF OPENING

Figure 14.22. Stages in the opening of the air-break circuit-breaker shown in Figure 14.21 (courtesy A. Reyrolle & Co. Ltd.)

the top of the slots, it will be further lengthened by bowing between adjacent plates beyond the slots.

From Fig. 14.20 it is seen that both arc runners are fixed and lie in the bottom zone of the arc chute plates, i.e. in the parallel-sided portion of the slot in Fig. 14.21. As the arcing contacts also move in this slot, the arc will be initiated above the bottom of the slots so that a magnetic field will be created before the arc is drawn. The contact system is shown in more detail in Fig. 14.22 and it comprises main contacts of the wedge and finger high-pressure type, an intermediate set of current-transfer contacts and arcing contacts of the butt blow-off type. The tail forming part of the moving arcing contact assists the transfer to the arc runner as shown at (b) and acts as a shield to prevent the arc moving down the back edge of the moving contact to a position below the chute. As the arc

Figure 14.23. 11 kV 500 MVA air-break circuit-breaker withdrawn from its housing and with arc chutes raised (courtesy A. Reyrolle & Co. Ltd.)

travels back along the tail of the moving contact faster than the latter opens, the time from arc initiation to transfer to the runner is kept to a minimum. The link which is seen to connect the right hand arc runner to the hinged point of the moving-contact arm is provided to act as a shunt to ensure that, with the breaker open, a short series arc does not persist between the tip of the tail and the runner at a point low down in the arc chute.

For inspection and maintenance purposes, the arc chutes are hinged to lift and swing clear of the circuit-breaker elements as illustrated in Fig. 14.23.

As noted earlier, weight and size alone generally requires that breakers of the type discussed above be arranged for horizontal isolation. With a more limited range of normal current and short circuit ratings however, vertically isolated designs are possible and one is shown in Fig. 14.24. This breaker is designed for the same range of voltages (3·3–11 kV) but its current rating is limited to 1 200 A and its interrupting capacity to 13·1 kA r.m.s. symmetrical, equivalent to 250

MVA at 11 kV. It has also been designed so that it can be housed in a metal-clad unit which is similar in all essential dimensions, etc. to that which is used for a comparable range of bulk-oil circuit-breakers so that a composite board can be provided. An example of such a use would be an installation where oil circuit-breakers could be used for the control of incoming feeders, local transformers and a bus-section with air-break circuit-breakers used for the control of motors, arc furnaces or other circuits where repeated switching occurs.

A cross-section of a typical unit is shown in Fig. 14.25 from which it is seen that the arc chute now has its splitter plates lying horizontally, but its design

Figure 14.24.   3·3/11 kV air-break circuit-breaker designed for vertical isolation. One arc-chute and two insulating shrouds removed (courtesy A. Reyrolle & Co. Ltd.)

follows that previously described, i.e. with the arc forced to follow a zig-zag path and self-excited magnetic field. As seen on the right-hand phase in Fig. 14.24, an insulating shroud is fitted over each arc chute to give protection between phases and to separate expelled gases which are ultimately released to atmosphere via a ventilator.

Figure 14.26 shows the contact system used, the right-hand schematic diagram indicating the position with an arc initiated between the butt-arcing contact on the upper runner and the moving-arcing contact on the articulated transfer runner and thence to the lower arc runner. The left-hand illustration shows the breaker fully open with the arc lengthened inside the arc chute.

The fixed main contacts comprise two sets of four-point self-aligning contacts while the main moving contacts are parallel-sided finger-type carried on the moving blade. The moving-arcing contact is spring biased and connected through a spring-loaded hinge to the articulated transfer-runner. The location of the air nozzle is noted in this illustration, the air being provided by air cylinders the pistons of which are driven from the moving blades.

From a range of English Electric designs covering the voltage range 3·3–11 kV and with interrupting capacities of 150–750 MVA, Fig. 14.27 is included here to show a breaker of the highest rating, viz. 3 000 A, 11 kV and 750 MVA. This illustration, as with others in this section, shows the very considerable part of the total size taken up by the arc chute structure, an indication of its importance in the interrupting process. In the design shown, magnetic blow-out coils (encapsulated in epoxy resin) in series with arc runners provide the necessary transverse magnetic field to force the arc into the chute, where it is lengthened in a labyrinth of ceramic splitter-plate assemblies.

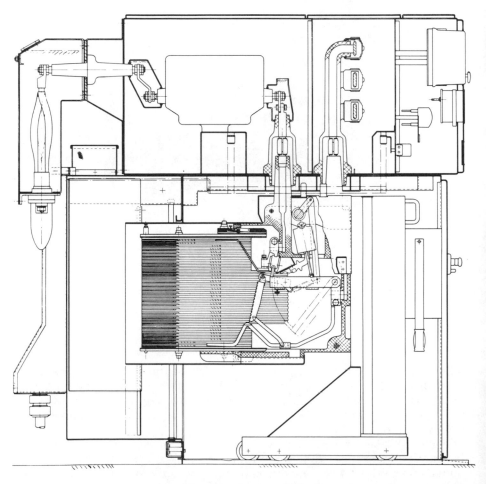

Figure 14.25. Cross-section of a metal-clad unit incorporating a high-voltage air-break circuit-breaker arranged for horizontal isolation (courtesy A. Reyrolle & Co. Ltd.)

The blow-out coils and the magnetic cheeks are integral with the arc chute, the complete assembly being plugged into cluster contacts on the breaker to connect the coils electrically with the circuit. Assistance when interrupting low values of current is given by twin-jet air puffers. The hot gases arising from the process of interruption are cooled in the top of the chute and are then vented into a glass-fibre expansion chamber in the top of the cubicle housing the circuit-breaker.

For circuit-breakers of these high ratings, the contact systems must be highly efficient. The moving and fixed elements of the system employed are seen in

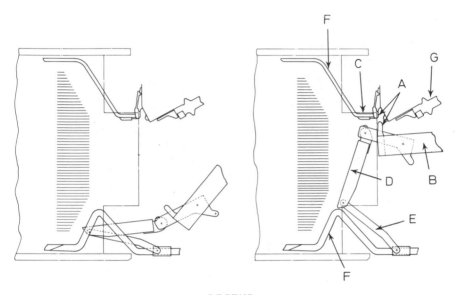

LEGEND

A	MAIN CONTACTS	E	GLASS-REINFORCED RESIN-
B	BREAKER BLADE		CONTROL LINK FOR D
C	ARC CONTACTS (ARC INITIATED)	F	ARC RUNNERS IN CHUTE
D	ARC TRANSFER RUNNER	G	AIR PUFFER NOZZLES

Figure 14.26. The contact systems at arc initiation (right) and fully open (left) of the circuit-breaker shown in Figure 14.25 (courtesy A. Reyrolle & Co. Ltd.)

Figs. 14.28 and 14.29 respectively. Alloy-tipped faces are used and each pair of contacts consists of a rigid flat surface mating with spring-loaded radiused fingers to provide high-pressure line contact with a wiping action on opening and closing. A three-part system comprising main, intermediate and arcing contacts is arranged to open in that order and in the reverse order on closing. To assist in carrying the high normal-load current in the 3 000 A design, auxiliary (load bearing) contacts are fitted on each side of the main contacts and are arranged to open before the latter. These illustrations of the contact systems show, incidentally, the cluster contacts into which the arc chute is plugged to connect the blow-out coils in circuit.

Another design employing magnetic blow-out coils with magnetic side cheeks is shown in Fig. 14.30. This shows how the arc, at initiation, exists at position I across the arcing contacts and moving rapidly to positions II and III. At stage

459

II the blow-out coil (5) is automatically connected in series in the arc circuit, the intensified field now forcing the arc into the chute where it is divided into a number of partial arcs by the connecting horns (7). As the arcs continue their upward movement they are twisted by the shape of the connecting horns so that the arcs are now parallel to one another and are perpendicular to the original plane of the arc. The connecting horns are in series and the arc current follows a helical path of considerable length, the inherent magnetic field of which drives

Figure 14.27. English Electric type E8 air-break circuit-breaker, 3 000 A, 11 kV and 750 MVA (courtesy G.E.C. Switchgear Ltd.)

the partial arcs further upwards into the region of the splitter plates (8), i.e. into the extinguishing region IV, where they are divided yet again into very small arcs, all in series.

As in other designs assistance is given when interrupting very low values of current by directing a self-generated blast of air across the arc, as shown in Fig. 14.30. A circuit-breaker of this type is shown in Figs. 14.31 and 14.32, the former with one arc chute and a phase barrier removed, the latter showing how an arc chute can be tilted to give access to the breaker for inspection and maintenance.

460

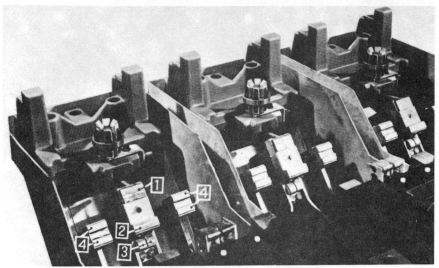

LEGEND
1. RIGID FLAT ARCING CONTACT AND ARCING HORN
2. RIGID FLAT INTERMEDIATE CONTACT INTEGRAL WITH THE ARCING CONTACT
3. PAIRED SPRING-LOADED RADIUSED MAIN CONTACTS
4. ON 3 000A BREAKERS ONLY: AUXILIARY MAIN CONTACTS (LOAD BEARING) COMPRISING A RIGID BLOCK WITH TWIN FLAT CONTACTS CARRIED ON OUTER MOVING ARMS, ONE ON EACH SIDE OF THE MAIN ARM

Figure 14.28. The moving contact system of the 11 kV air-break circuit-breaker used in English Electric type E7 & E8 switchgear (courtesy G.E.C. Switchgear Ltd.)

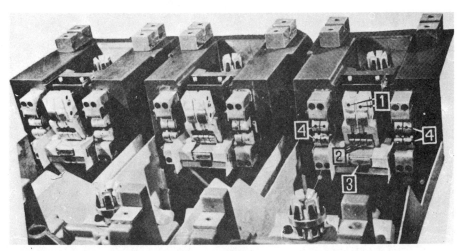

LEGEND
1. PAIRED SPRING-LOADED RADIUSED ARCING FINGERS
2. FOUR SPRING-LOADED RADIUSED INTERMEDIATE CONTACT FINGERS
3. RIGID FLAT MAIN CONTACT
4. ON 3 000A BREAKERS ONLY: ADDITIONAL BLOCKS ON EACH SIDE OF MAIN BLOCK AND EACH CARRYING FOUR SPRING-LOADED RADIUSED CONTACT FINGERS (LOAD BEARING)

Figure 14.29. The fixed contact system of the 11 kV air-break circuit-breaker used in English Electric type E7 & E8 switchgear (courtesy G.E.C. Switchgear Ltd.)

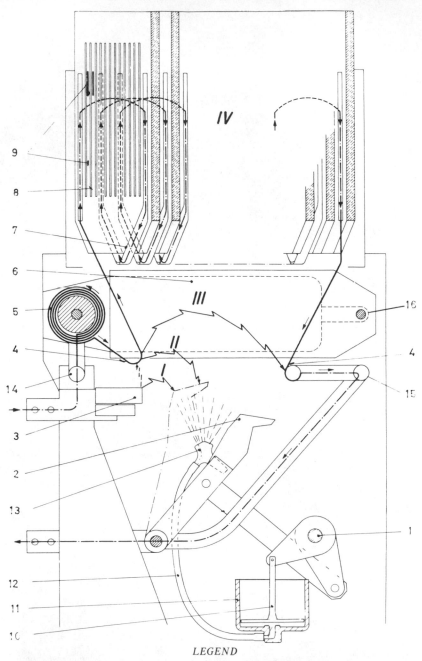

LEGEND

1. OPERATING SHAFT
2. MOVING CONTACT BLADES
3. FIXED MAIN AND ARCING CONTACTS
4. ARCING HORNS
5. MAGNETIC BLOW-OUT COIL
6. MAGNETIC SIDE CHECKS
7. CONNECTING HORNS
8. SPLITTER PLATES
9. INSULATING CARRIERS
10. AIR PUFFER PISTON
11. AIR PUFFER CYLINDER
12. AIR TUBE
13. AIR NOZZLES
14. BLOW-OUT COIL CONNECTION
15. SHUNT LINK
16. SECOND BLOW-OUT COIL MAY BE FITTED HERE

Figure 14.30. Schematic diagram of high-voltage air-break circuit-breaker showing control and lengthening of the arc in the arc chute (courtesy Brown Boveri & Co. Ltd.)

Figure 14.31. Brown Boveri type T *high-voltage air-break circuit-breaker with one arc chute, phase barriers and front cover removed (courtesy Brown Boveri & Co. Ltd.)*

Figure 14.32. How the arc chute can be tilted to give access to the contact system of a high-voltage air-break circuit-breaker (courtesy Brown Boveri & Co. Ltd.)

These illustrations are typical of breakers for voltages from 3·6–7·2 kV. In a design for voltages up to 17·5 kV, similar principles apply although some design changes are made, including the fitting of a second magnetic blow-out coil at point 16 in Fig. 14.30.

For closing circuit-breakers of the types described, power mechanisms of the spring or solenoid types are essential. By this means high-speed operation is achieved, but for maintenance checks, and particularly when adjustment of the contact settings is necessary, it must be possible to close and open a circuit-breaker slowly. For this purpose provision will be made for hand operation but the use of a slow closing/opening device must be only possible when the circuit-breaker is *completely withdrawn*, i.e. its use must be impossible in the service or isolated positions.

BIBLIOGRAPHY

BARDORF, O., 'The New G.B. Range of Low-voltage Air-break Circuit-breaker', *Brown Boveri Rev.*, No. 7, July (1967)

FAY, F.S., THOMAS, J.A., LEGG, D. and MORTON, J.S., 'Development of High-voltage Air-break Circuit-breakers with Insulated Steel-plate Arc Chutes', *Proc. I.E.E.*, **106** No. 29, Oct. (1959)

GARRARD, C.J.O., 'High-voltage Distribution Switchgear—a Review of Progress', *Proc. I.E.E.*, **116** No. 6, June (1969)

LLOYD, L.J., 'Switchgear for Auxiliaries in Power Stations', *Elect. Times*, 12 June (1969)

MAYER, A., 'Magnetic Circuit-breakers with High Breaking Capacities for Medium Voltages', *Brown Boveri Rev.*, No. 9/10, Sept./Oct. (1962)

SCHNEIDER, J., 'Design and Development of Magnetic Circuit-breakers', *Brown Boveri Rev.*, No. 3, March (1959)

TABB, R.P.E. and NEWMAN, S.E., 'Switchgear Trends in British Stations', *Elec. Times*, 21 June (1962)

THOMAS, J.A., ROBERTS, F.A. and LEGG, D., 'The Application of High-speed Ciné Photography to Switchgear Research and Design', *B.E.A.M.A. Journal*, Feb. (1958)

WRIGHT, A., 'Report Upon Fuses in Series with Circuit-breakers', *Reyrolle Rev.*, No. 189 (1966)

Heavy-duty Air-break Circuit-breakers for a.c. Systems, BS 3659:1963

Chapter 15

Air-blast circuit-breakers

Some of the historical background to the development of the air-blast circuit-breaker has been related in Chapter 1, while the general principle of current interruption by directing a powerful blast of air at high pressure and velocity into the arcing region has been noted in Chapter 2. In earlier editions of this book, examples of British designs for voltages in the range 3·3–66 kV were included, but now these have largely been abandoned, mainly because for a majority of applications other well established types of circuit-breaker can meet requirements, and at less cost. In this respect, it has to be remembered that with bulk-oil, small-oil-volume and air-break circuit-breakers no external aid is required for current interruption, whereas for air-blast designs a supply of clean, dry air at the correct pressure and in sufficient volume must be available at all times. For this a compressed-air plant is essential, probably with duplicate compressors for security, along with air storage facilities and a network of feed pipes, valves and safety devices. At 33 and 66 kV, new designs of small-oil-volume circuit-breakers (see Chapter 13) provide a much less costly alternative for medium powers.

European countries, on the other hand, have retained air-blast designs in this voltage range and have indeed extended one design, i.e. for very heavy current applications. These designs are intended for indoor use, and apart from the heavy-current type, exist in competition with the small-oil-volume breaker at voltages up to 36 kV and air-break types up to 15/17·5 kV. More recently the sulphur hexafluoride (SF_6) breaker up to 30 kV has made its challenge (see Chapter 16).

For voltages of 100 kV and upwards and for high fault powers particularly, the air-blast circuit-breaker has established a predominant position and will probably do so for many years, although the SF_6 breaker is challenging this. As we shall see in the next chapter, this latter type has the advantage that it lends itself to incorporation in compact metal-clad high-voltage switchgear units which go a long way to solving the problem of siting high-voltage switchgear indoors where the conditions are against the use of open-type outdoor sub-stations. Among the many features which have led to the predominant use of air-blast designs are (a) high-speed operation, (b) short and consistent arcing and total break times, (c) the relative ease with which single or three-phase auto-reclosing can be applied, (d) the facility of assembling multiple identical interrupter heads in series to provide a design rating, (e) suitability for frequent

466

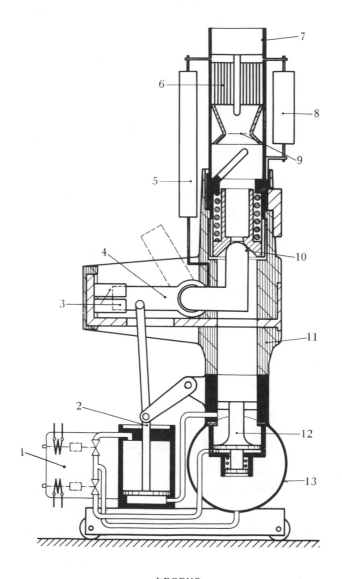

LEGEND

1. CONTROL UNIT	8. HIGH RESISTOR
2. OPERATING MECHANISM	9. AUXILIARY SPARK GAP
3. BRUSH CONTACTS	10. EXTINCTION CHAMBER
4. ISOLATOR BLADE	11. LOWER PART OF POLE IN
5. LOW RESISTOR	MOULDED RESIN
6. EXHAUST COOLER	12. MAIN VALVE
7. EXHAUST PIPE	13. AIR RECEIVER

Figure 15.1. Sectional arrangement of 12 kV, 1 500A and 1 000 MVA air-blast circuit-breaker type DE (courtesy Brown Boveri & Co. Ltd.)

switching duties and (f) minimum maintenance. Most, if not all of these however, can now be offered in SF$_6$ types while for medium-power applications up to 220 kV, the small-oil-volume breaker can satisfy many requirements.

INDOOR DESIGNS OF 3 kV TO 33 kV

In this range, two designs by Brown Boveri may be noted in which a number of common components are used, and both are built on unit construction principles from building blocks.

The first design is for current ratings of 1 600 and 2 500 A and for use on service voltages of 3–12 kV. These are three-phase units, i.e. the three poles are carried on a common air receiver and by adding certain elements to a basic unit, e.g. high and/or low value resistors (the latter with an auxiliary spark gap) the breaker can be supplied to meet a variety of switching duties with breaking capacities of 200/300 MVA at 3·6 kV or 500/1 000 MVA at 12 kV. They can also be supplied as draw-out units in metal-clad or open-type switchgear or as fixed units, i.e. with bolted external connections.

Figure 15.1 shows in section the general arrangement of one pole of a 12 kV 1 000 MVA breaker with both high and low-value resistors. It is shown in the closed (service) position and an opening sequence is initiated by the opening of the lower valve in the control unit (1). This allows high-pressure air at 370 lbf/in^2 (2·55 MN/m^2) to flow from the receiver (13) to the underside of the blast valve (12) which opens allowing air to pass to the extinction chamber. Under the pressure of this air, the spring-loaded moving contact moves away from the fixed contact and the arc which strikes between the contacts is quenched by the blast of air flowing through the nozzle. The recovery voltage now causes the auxiliary spark gap to strike, thereby connecting the low value resistance in parallel with the extinction chamber, the resistance damping the transient produced by the natural frequency of the network. The current which flows through this resistor ceases at the first natural zero whereupon the high value non-linear resistor in parallel with the main current path comes into circuit. These resistors are used to prevent inadmissible switching surges being produced when interrupting small inductive currents, e.g. no-load switching of transformers. Finally the isolator blades are opened, thus interrupting the current through the high value resistors. The isolator operating mechanism (2) is actuated by admitting air below the piston to open it and above it to close. With the isolator open at the end of the opening sequence, the blast valve closes and the moving contact is returned to the closed position under the influence of the spring. This sequence is noted diagrammatically in Fig. 15.2.

To restore the breaker to service, all that is necessary is to close the isolator. It may be noted that only one blast valve is fitted on a three-phase breaker, a distributor channel above the valve allowing air to pass to all three poles simultaneously. Figure 15.3 shows a typical breaker and it should be noted that here a silencer is fitted at the upper end of the exhaust pipe effectively reducing the noise to an acceptable level, as the air passes to the atmosphere.

When the rating of a generator is such that the full-load current does not exceed 2 500/3 000 A, switchgear of suitable rating is generally available in various types so that the machine can be connected to its own circuit-breaker and be protected as a unit. The steady increase in generator ratings in major

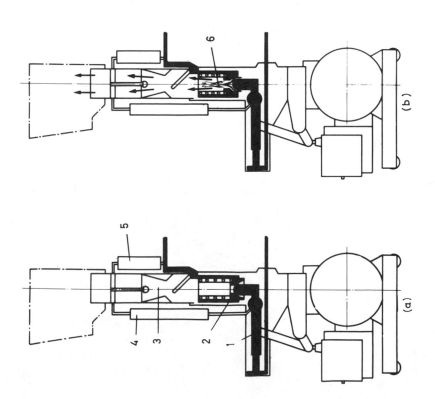

LEGEND

1. ISOLATOR BLADES
2. EXTINCTION CHAMBER
3. AUXILIARY SPARK GAP
4. LOW RESISTANCE
5. HIGH RESISTANCE
6. ARC

Figure 15.2. Various stages in the breaking operation of the air-blast circuit-breaker shown in Figure 15.1. (a) breaker closed and trip command given at time t = 0. (b) main current interrupted in the extinction chamber at t = 20–40 ms after the tripping command is given. (c) auxiliary spark gap cuts-in low damping resistor when main current has been interrupted. (d) auxiliary spark is quenched and high resistance is cut-in to limit over-voltages. (e) breaker open; isolator has opened to switch off high resistance (courtesy Brown Boveri & Co. Ltd.)

469

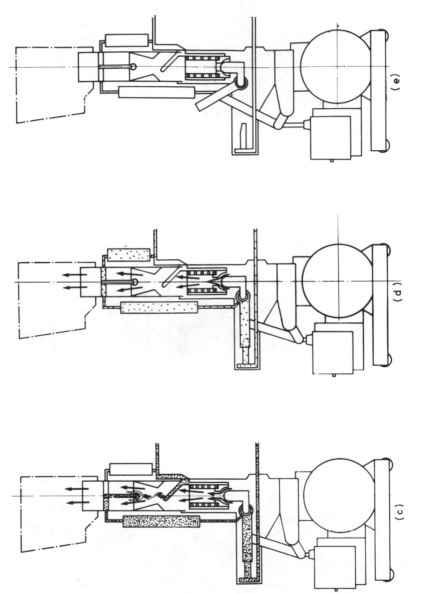

Figure 15.2 (continued)

(e)

(d)

(c)

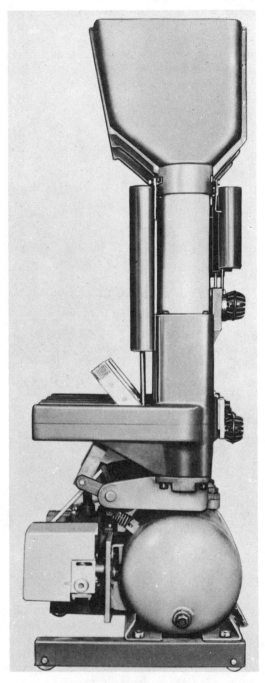

Figure 15.3. Side view of the air-blast circuit-breaker of Figure 15.1, shown here fitted with a silencer (courtesy Brown Boveri & Co. Ltd.)

471

power stations over the past 20 years or so has, in spite of elevated generation voltages, meant that the normal currents have risen well above the value noted, so that it has become common practice to omit switchgear at generation voltage and to connect the machine solidly to an associated step-up power transformer with switchgear on the high-voltage side of the latter. Thus the two items of plant are, in effect, one unit and we have seen in Chapter 11 how such a combination can be protected overall without difficulty.

Figure 15.4.   One pole of a 12 000 A, 20 kV and 3 000 MVA air-blast circuit-breaker (courtesy Brown Boveri & Co. Ltd.)

There is however some loss of operational flexibility with this arrangement, a fault in one part of the combination resulting in both being out of service, and in recent years the tendency has been to revert to the practice of providing separate switchgear for each element. This can only be done if equipment of very high current rating is available, some idea of the magnitude involved being given by noting that a 660 MW set, generating at 23 kV, results in a full-load current of 19 500 A. Larger sets in the range of 1 100/1 300 MW will be in service before 1975, while by 1980 ratings of 2 000 MW are predicted.

472

To meet this situation and other heavy-current applications, Brown Boveri have developed a special purpose range of air-blast circuit-breakers, along with associated apparatus such as isolators, current transformers, etc. for normal current ratings up to 24 000 A, a range ultimately planned to extend to 36 000 A.

These breakers are built as single pole units, one such pole rated 12 000 A 20 kV being noted in Fig. 15.4, with a three-phase breaking capacity of 3 000 MVA. To carry the high normal current continuously, each pole has three current paths in parallel, typically as shown in the schematic diagram in Fig. 15.5. From this it is seen that each of the outer paths comprises a pair of parallel current-chambers (S), the additional contact system here being comparable to the load-bearing contacts we have already noted in some designs of bulk-oil and air-break circuit-breakers. In the centre path, four identical power chambers

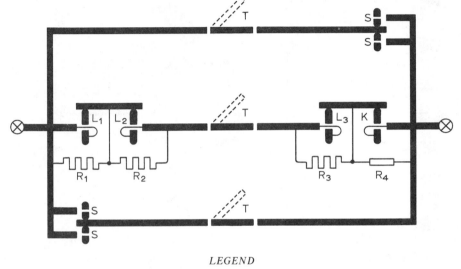

LEGEND

L_1, L_2, L_3	POWER CHAMBERS	T	ISOLATOR
S	CURRENT CHAMBERS	R_1, R_2, R_3	RESISTORS OF LOW OHMIC
K	RESIDUAL CURRENT		VALUE
	CHAMBER	R_4	NON-LINEAR RESISTOR

Figure 15.5.   Schematic diagram of the single-pole heavy-current circuit-breaker shown in Figure 15.4 (courtesy Brown Boveri & Co. Ltd.)

(interrupter units) are connected in series. Three of these (L_1, L_2 and L_3) are shunted by resistors R_1, R_2 and R_3 of equal ohmic value whose purpose it is to ensure equal voltage distribution between the three breaks. The fourth interrupter K is shunted by a non-linear resistor R_4, this interrupter being used to break the residual current which flows through R_1, R_2 and R_3, the non-linear resistor R_4 effectively reducing any switching surges which may result from the interruption of low inductive currents. Finally, each path has it own isolator blade.

On receipt of a trip signal, the opening sequence is that the four load-bearing contacts open first, leaving the full current carried by the centre path. The contacts at L_1, L_2 and L_3 now open to interrupt the current in a blast of air at 218 lbf/in² (1·50 MN/m²). This is followed by contacts K opening to interrupt

473

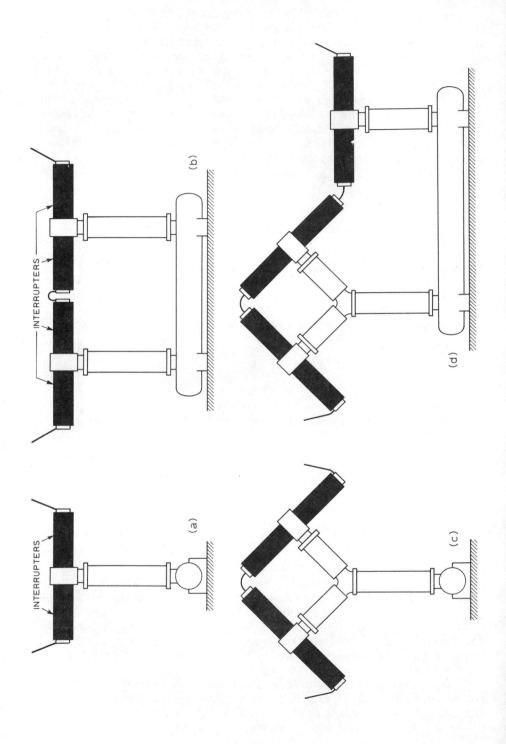

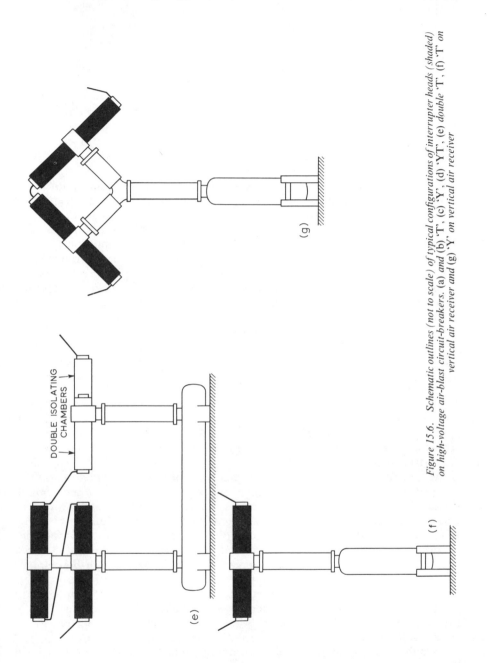

DOUBLE ISOLATING CHAMBERS

(e)

(f)

(g)

Figure 15.6. Schematic outlines (not to scale) of typical configurations of interrupter heads (shaded) on high-voltage air-blast circuit-breakers. (a) and (b) 'T', (c) 'Y', (d) 'YT', (e) double 'T', (f) 'T' on vertical air receiver and (g) 'Y' on vertical air receiver

the resistor current and then by the opening of the isolator blades to complete the operation.

At this stage the load-bearing and interrupter contacts reclose so that the breaker can be restored to service simply by closing the isolator.

OUTDOOR DESIGNS ABOVE 60 kV

The constructional features of modern high-voltage air-blast circuit-breakers have undergone numerous changes over the past 10/15 years. It was, for example, a practice where multiple interrupter heads had to be employed to stack these in a single vertical column at the top of a supporting insulator, typically as noted in the 6th edition of this book in Figs. 8.22 and 18.64, among others. With this construction, the blast of air to each head would be non-uniform, the distance between the lowest and the uppermost heads resulting in a significant drop in pressure at successive heads while the blast would reach each at different instants in time, these factors tending to affect the interrupting ability overall.

Today, symmetrical arrangements are adopted to ensure uniformity of air supply to each break, both as regards pressure and time. These arrangements may take various forms based on the use of even numbers of interrupter heads, i.e. two, four, six, etc. the most frequently used base being two heads supported on a single insulating column in 'T' formation. An alternative is an arrangement of four interrupter heads using two units mounted at both ends of the branches of a 'Y' assembly. In one continental design, four interrupters are mounted in pairs one above another on a single column. From this same source an arrangement is also used in which 'T' or 'Y' formations are carried on individual local air receivers mounted vertically.

These module or building block principles are now universally adopted, each pole of a circuit-breaker comprising one or more columns as required to achieve a desired rating, the multiple breaks all being connected in series and, except in the case noted above, all the columns making up the pole supported on a common base, which may be the local air receiver. This discussion is summarised schematically in Fig. 15.6.

Perhaps the most significant change has been the almost complete abandonment of high-voltage designs in which, prior to the initiation of an opening operation, the air in the interrupter heads is at atmospheric pressure, the high-pressure air only reaching the contact system during the operation and reverting to atmospheric after interruption is completed. Figure 15.7 illustrates the condition prior to a trip signal being received, from which it is seen that the blast valve (closed) is at the base of the support column, i.e. at the high-pressure air receiver. On receipt of a trip signal, the valve opens but the air has to traverse the full height of the support column before it reaches the interrupter head from which it exhausts to atmosphere. This introduces delay and some loss of pressure which, in very tall columns (the height increases in proportion to the system voltage), may be such as to affect the interrupting ability adversely.

In many designs, operation of the moving contact from the closed to open position was dependent on the high-pressure air acting on it (as for example in the lower voltage design in Fig. 15.1) so that contact separation would be similarly delayed, adding to the total break time of the breaker. After interruption, the blast valve closes and the air in the interrupter heads and the feed pipe reverts to atmospheric pressure so that the contacts reclose under spring pressure, hence the need for the external isolator which had to be sequenced to open *before* the breaker contacts reclose. At the higher voltages, such isolators present many problems and at the very highest voltages become virtually impossible on account of the length of break in atmospheric air to withstand the system voltage. This long break adds to the difficulties of reclosure as restoration of the circuit-breaker to service is achieved by closing the isolator, if necessary on to a fault.

Present day designs avoid most of these problems, including the need for an external isolator, by employing a permanently pressurised system, shown in

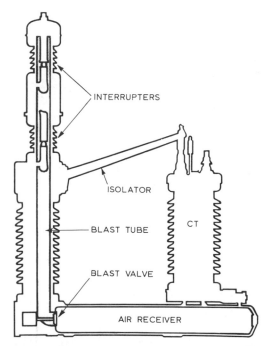

Figure 15.7. The early principle where the interrupters are pressurised during operation only. English Electric frame G (courtesy G.E.C. Switchgear Ltd.)

principle in Fig. 15.8. From this it is noted that the blast (exhaust) valve is now located at the top of the column *beyond* the interrupter heads so that air at full pressure constantly fills the receiver, the feed pipe through the support column and the interrupter heads right up to the blast valve. Coupled with this, the movement of the contacts is controlled through a system of mechanical linkages from an operating mechanism at the base of the breaker, the contacts held closed by a latch. When a trip signal is given, this latch is released so that the contacts are free to part, either mechanically or pneumatically by the opening of local trip valves, or a combination of both, the movement also initiating the opening of the blast valve to release high-pressure air to atmosphere, its flow passing into and through the arcing region to extinguish the arc.

The blast valve remains open long enough for interruption to be complete and when it closes, the complete circuit-breaker remains filled with air at full pressure. In most designs, the contacts remain open, the dielectric strength of the air ensuring ability to withstand the voltage across the gap so that an external isolator is not needed. This does mean however that the main contact system must now be capable, if called upon, to close on to a fault and it also means that a separate means of interrupting the residual current through the switching resistors must be provided.

Because of the dual duty of both breaking and making fault current at the main contact, one continental design[1] separates them by employing interrupting and isolating heads, both permanently pressurised with the isolating head now performing the duties hitherto undertaken by the external isolator. For convenience, this design will be noted in Chapter 18 (Fig. 18.15) as it is these isolating heads which form the basis of a design of load-breaking switch with which that chapter deals. With this design, the number of isolating heads is always less than

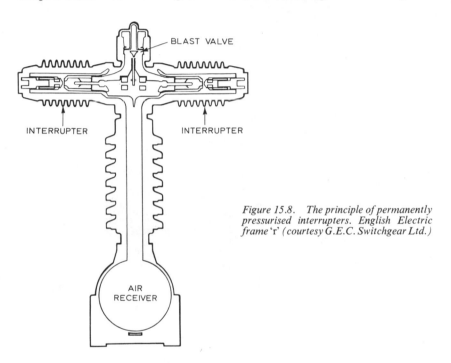

Figure 15.8.   The principle of permanently pressurised interrupters. English Electric frame 'r' (courtesy G.E.C. Switchgear Ltd.)

the number of interrupter heads, e.g. for a 275 kV design, two isolating and four interrupting. It allows for the main contacts to reclose after interruption and isolation is complete, so that the closing operation involves only the isolating heads. The latter, on opening, will also interrupt the residual current through the switching resistors.

With the increased powers now available in short-circuit test plants for the proving of interrupting ratings and the acceptance of synthetic testing (see Chapter 5), coupled with, in some instances, an increase in air pressures (one design now uses air at 900 lbf/in^2, i.e. 6·2 MN/m^2), it has been proved possible to use fewer interrupter heads than hitherto for a given (or even increased) rating. Reference to page 213 in the sixth edition of this book shows that at that time a 275 kV breaker rated 10 000 MVA had six breaks in series per pole or eight breaks for a rating of 15 000 MVA. Today, a 275 kV breaker with a rating of 25 000 MVA can be obtained with only four breaks in series per pole, this design using air at the high pressure noted above.

Because the electrical conditions differ widely between systems, many designs of high-voltage air-blast breaker can be fitted with alternative types of switching resistors*. The choice is between resistors of high ohmic value which are usually fitted where the interrupting duty is relatively light, i.e. up to about 35 kA short-circuit current and resistors of low ohmic value for heavy duties above 35 kA and up to 60/70 kA short-circuit current. This is a problem associated with the interruption of short-line faults (these are discussed in Chapter 2) as when these occur on systems with particularly high fault current levels, the rate of rise of restriking voltage may well be such as to be beyond the capabilities of the interrupters, and it is therefore essential that the switching resistors effectively damp

Figure 15.9. Interrupter head in 'T' formation for English Electric frame 'r' air-blast circuit-breakers (courtesy G.E.C. Switchgear Ltd.)

this transient (which appears at the line side terminals of the breaker) to a rate of rise within the capability of the interrupters.

These conditions of maximum severity are generally found only in areas of concentrated and high-load density with fully interconnected transmission systems. The British grid systems are a typical example, but systems of this type are in a minority and for this reason it has been the practice of some manufacturers to have two designs on offer, one which, as outlined above, can be adapted to meet all conditions and another, with smaller and simplified interrupters and one range of switching resistors, designed specifically for use on systems of relatively low circuit severity. It is also the practice to allot a lower normal current rating to the latter type, e.g. 2 500/3 000 A as against 4 000 A.

The current English Electric (G.E.C. Switchgear Ltd.) designs follow this pattern, a range known as frame 'r' being of the first type with alternative switching resistors for fault currents up to 35 kA or 60 kA respectively and a second

* More specifically 'opening resistors' which are inserted in parallel with the interrupter during an *opening* sequence. When a circuit-breaker is closed to energise a very long extra-high-voltage transmission line, and particularly under the condition of rapid automatic reclosure, high overvoltages may build up under unfavourable system conditions. The overvoltages can however be limited by fitting 'closure resistors' which are automatically inserted across the interrupter contacts for a few milliseconds during the *closing* sequence [2,3,4].

range, frame 's' specifically for use on systems of lower severity where the fault currents do not exceed 41 kA. Both types are permanently pressurised and are available for system voltages from 110 kV up to 765 kV.

In the frame 'r' range, the interrupters are used either in 'T' configurations, i.e. two interrupters per support column as in Fig. 15.9, or in 'Y' configurations with four interrupters per column as in Fig. 15.10. These illustrations show how the switching resistors (with associated interrupters) and the voltage grading capacitors are disposed about each main interrupter.

Apart from their function in relation to short line faults, the resistors ensure that the breaker will not cause excessive overvoltages when switching small inductive currents. (Also discussed in Chapter 2.)

The mode of operation is that with the breaker closed, the resistor interrupters are open so that the resistors are open-circuited, i.e. conditions as shown in

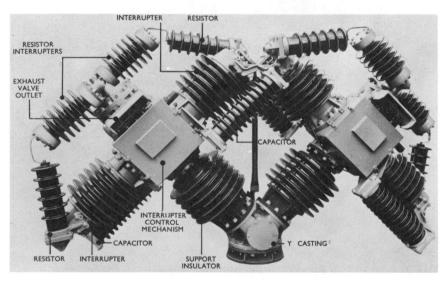

Figure 15.10.   Interrupter head in 'Y' formation for English Electric frame 'r' air-blast circuit-breakers (courtesy G.E.C. Switchgear Ltd.)

the sectional view of a 'T' configuration (Fig. 15.11). When the breaker is tripped, the resistor interrupters are closed first before the main contacts separate, thus inserting resistance in parallel with each main gap before an arc is struck. After the latter has been extinguished, the blast valve closes and the resistor interrupters open automatically (under spring pressure) to break the residual current flowing through the resistors.

The function of the capacitors connected across each main break is to ensure equal voltage division across the interrupters when the breaker is open and, in conjunction with the resistors, when it is breaking load.

Figure 15.11 shows that one exhaust valve *H* is used for a pair of interrupters and in this illustration it is in the closed position. When a trip command is received, a trip solenoid in the main operating mechanism is energised to release a latch which holds the contacts (in both interrupters) closed. A pull-rod from the mechanism, passing up through the hollow support column, is then free to move upwards under spring pressure to cause a master operating beam to

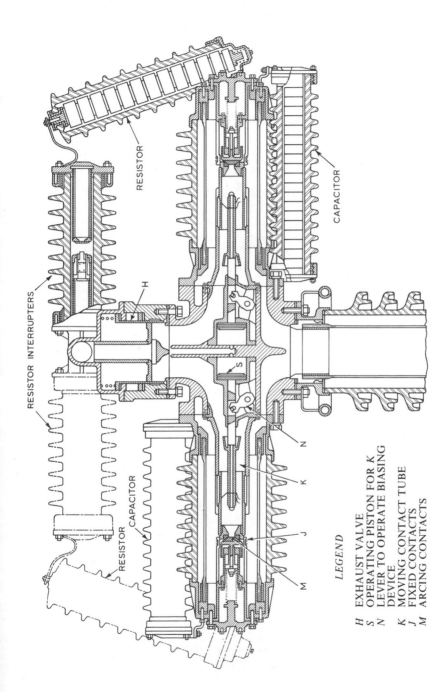

LEGEND

H EXHAUST VALVE
S OPERATING PISTON FOR K
N LEVER TO OPERATE BIASING
   DEVICE
K MOVING CONTACT TUBE
J FIXED CONTACTS
M ARCING CONTACTS

Figure 15.11.   Sectional view of English Electric frame 'T' interrupter head in 'T' formation (courtesy G.E.C. Switchgear Ltd.)

481

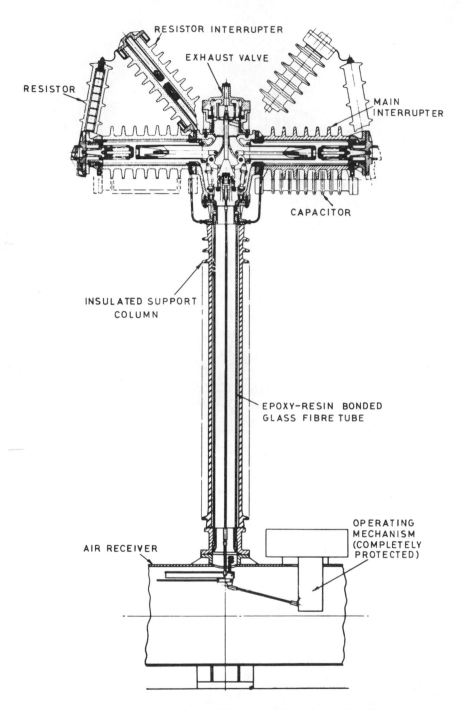

RESISTOR INTERRUPTER

EXHAUST VALVE

RESISTOR

MAIN INTERRUPTER

CAPACITOR

INSULATED SUPPORT COLUMN

EPOXY-RESIN BONDED GLASS FIBRE TUBE

OPERATING MECHANISM (COMPLETELY PROTECTED)

AIR RECEIVER

Figure 15.12.   Sectional view of one column of the English Electric frame 's' air-blast circuit-breaker (courtesy G.E.C. Switchgear Ltd.)

482

move from a neutral position and in so doing, open a local trip valve. This apparatus is located in a control box (not shown) between the two interrupters. Opening of the local trip valve releases a supply of air to the piston of the exhaust valve, which opens to exhaust the air from the tube K and the back of its operating piston S. Thus an air pressure differential is created causing the combined piston, moving tube and the contact throat to retract. On its initial movement, contact is first broken at the fixed contacts J, the latter now closing into contact with the central arcing contacts M. These latter contacts are spring loaded so that they follow the movement of the contact tube and its throat.

The follow-up travel of M is halted after a short distance by a stop, by which time the tube is moving at speed and contact separation occurs at high velocity. At contact separation, the arc which is struck is subjected to a blast of air which is now free to flow from the body of the interrupter chamber through the nozzle and to atmosphere via the open exhaust valve. Movement of the contact piston S causes the lever N to move through about 30°, a movement which operates a spring biasing device which (a) retains the moving contact positively in the open position and (b) returns the master operating beam to the neutral position so that the local trip valve resets and the exhaust valve closes under spring pressure. The breaker is now fully pressurised again.

In a closing sequence, the main operating mechanism pulls the latch into a reset position and recharges the tripping spring via the pull rods. This action now causes the master operating beam to move from neutral to open a local close valve in the control box. This exhausts the air from the front of the piston S creating a pressure differential to drive the piston and the moving contact tube into contact, first with the central arcing contacts and then the main fixed contacts. The return travel of piston S moves lever N back to operate the biasing device to retain the contacts closed, reset the master beam to neutral and to reset the local close valve. Compressed air for this design is stored in a main receiver common to an installation at 600 lbf/in² (4·1 MN/m²) for 132 and 275 kV breakers and at 3 000 lbf/in² (20·7 MN/m²) for 400 kV designs from which air is supplied through reducing valves to the local receivers at the circuit-breakers. The pressure here and in the complete breaker is at 350 lbf/in² (2·4 MN/m²). The breaker operating mechanism, located in a cabinet mounted close to the air receiver, is also pneumatic and is suitable for high-speed reclosing via suitable relays which initiate the reclose operation. If single-phase auto-reclosing is required, each pole has its own operating mechanism, as against a common mechanism for three-phase operation.

The frame 's' design, one column of which is shown in Fig. 15.12, differs in several respects, one being that a 'T' configuration only is used, the range extending from a single column per pole with two interrupters in series through to six columns per pole with 12 interrupters in series. The interrupter units, shown in more detail in Fig. 15.13, are considerably reduced by comparison and instead of each moving contact having its own operating piston (S in Fig. 15.11), a single operating piston is coupled to the pair of moving contacts through a system of rods and cranks with overcentre biasing springs to retain positively the contacts closed or open. The contact system follows the principle of that used in frame 'r' with a spring-loaded arcing contact following the movement of the moving contact for a short distance on opening.

Tripping is initiated as in frame 'r' by electromagnetic release of the mechanism allowing a spring-loaded rod to operate a trip valve. This allows the exhaust

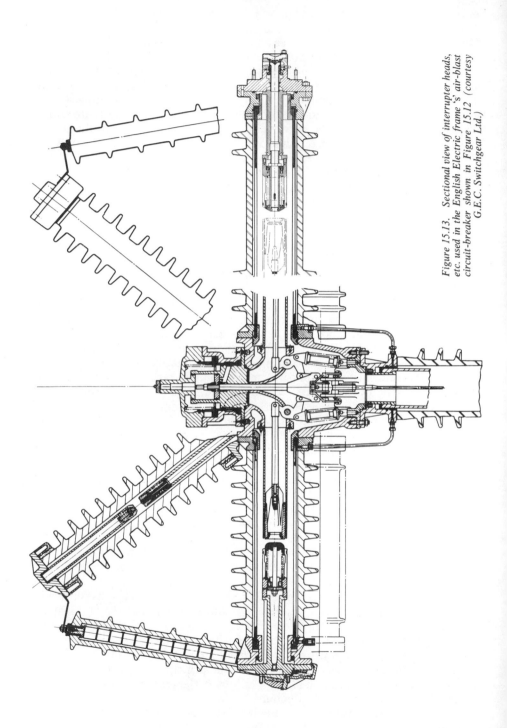

Figure 15.13. Sectional view of interrupter heads, etc. used in the English Electric frame's air-blast circuit-breaker shown in Figure 15.12 (courtesy G.E.C. Switchgear Ltd.)

valve to open releasing air to cause a pressure differential across the throats and the operating piston. This moves to drive the pair of moving contacts via the linkage just described, movement of the contacts causing the trip valve to reset and the exhaust valve to close.

Closing is initiated by the main operating mechanism causing a close valve to open and admit air to the other side of the main operating piston to close the contacts via the mechanical linkage, the exhaust valve remaining closed during this operation. As seen in Fig. 15.12, the operating mechanisms for the frame 's' breaker are contained within the air-receiver, a separate mechanism being used for each phase, thus facilitating either single or three-phase auto-reclosing to be carried out.

The switching resistors and capacitors connected across each break serve the same purpose as in the frame 'r' design, the sequence of switching the

Figure 15.14.   400 kV 35 000 MVA English Electric frame 'r' air-blast circuit-breaker, fitted with silencers and installed in the C.E.G.B. 275/400 kV switching station at Swindon (courtesy G.E.C. Switchgear Ltd.)

resistors in and out being similar. Typical examples of the two designs of breaker described are noted in Figs. 15.14, 15.15 and 15.16.

In a new Reyrolle range of heavy-duty permanently-pressurised breakers, several features are noteworthy. These include the use of high-pressure air at 900 lbf/in^2 (6·2 MN/m^2) as against 500 lbf/in^2 (3·4 MN/m^2) in earlier designs, the interrupter units serve as the local air receiver, the switching resistors are enclosed in the interrupter heads thus reducing the external insulation with a

Figure 15.15.   English Electric frame 's' air-blast circuit-breaker, 330 kV 10 000 MVA in course of erection at the Jabba substation forming part of an installation for the Niger Dam Authority, Nigeria (courtesy G.E.C. Switchgear Ltd.)

Figure 15.16.   English Electric frame 's' 400 kV 20 000 MVA air-blast circuit-breaker being prepared for tests (courtesy G.E.C. Switchgear Ltd.)

consequent easing of pollution problems and silencers are built-in as integral elements.

The range, covering voltages 132 kV up to 750 kV and normal currents up to 4 000 A, is based on three interrupter modules, mechanically similar with variations in normal current rating and unit voltage being obtained by a range of bushings. The possible arrangements are noted in Fig. 15.17, which shows that each phase consists of a number of two-break interrupter units mounted on insulating support columns using a 'T' configuration. The several columns are carried on a bedplate which accommodates the operating mechanism, the latter being connected to the moving contacts by pull rods.

A cross-section of a two-break interrupter module is shown in Fig. 15.18. For descriptive purposes this is designed to show a main contact system in the

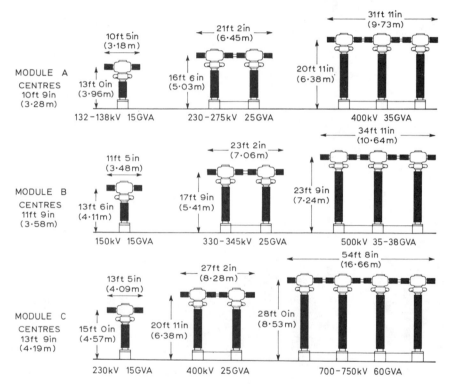

Figure 15.17. The Reyrolle range of heavy-duty modular air-blast circuit-breakers (courtesy A. Reyrolle & Co. Ltd.)

right-hand half and the resistor with its switching-contact system in the left-hand half. In practice, both halves are identical and include both sets of contact systems as shown in the schematic circuit diagram shown in Fig. 15.19. Contact travel is, for both the main and resistor elements, vertical, the blast valve being located below the contacts and exhausting directly to the silencer, the air supply to the local air receivers (the interrupter chamber) being carried through a feed pipe inside the support columns, as shown in Fig. 15.20. The sequence of the closing and tripping operations is briefly as follows: to close the circuit-breaker, air is fed to the main operating piston in the base mechanism. This pulls the

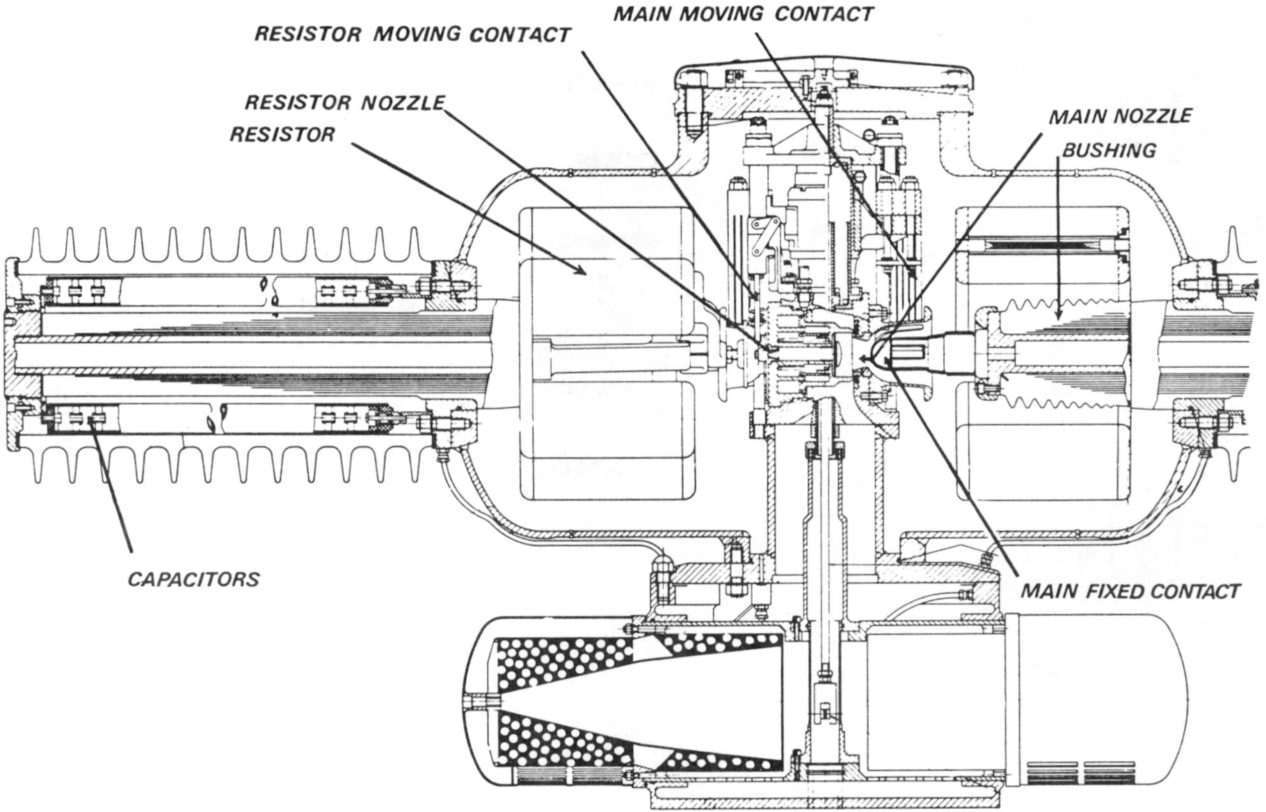

MAIN NOZZLE BUSHING

MAIN FIXED CONTACT

MAIN MOVING CONTACT

RESISTOR MOVING CONTACT

RESISTOR NOZZLE

RESISTOR

CAPACITORS

Figure 15.18. The high-duty interrupter module used in the Reyrolle range of air-blast circuit-breakers, as in Figure 15.17 (courtesy A. Reyrolle & Co. Ltd.)

488

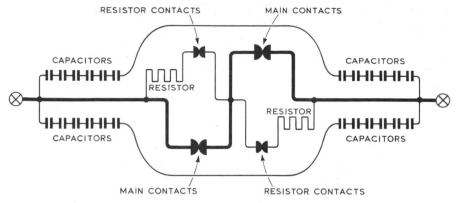

Figure 15.19. *Schematic plan view of the circuit in a two-break interrupter module for the range shown in Figure 15.17 (courtesy A. Reyrolle & Co. Ltd.)*

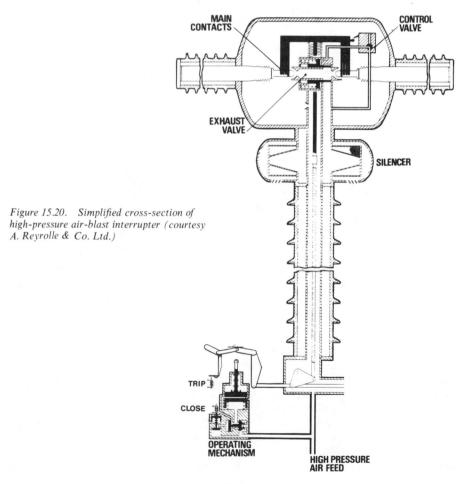

Figure 15.20. *Simplified cross-section of high-pressure air-blast interrupter (courtesy A. Reyrolle & Co. Ltd.)*

489

operating links downwards, first closing the resistor contacts and then the main contacts, so compressing the opening springs. The circuit-breaker is held in the closed position by a tripping latch in the base mechanism. To trip the circuit-breaker, the trip latch is released and the opening springs, housed in each interrupter unit, start to open the main contacts. As the contacts move, a cam is rotated which operates both the pilot and time-delay valves, whilst at the same time the resistor contacts are locked in the closed position. Exhausting air from the pilot valve causes the control valves and then the blast valve to open to establish a flow of air through the main and resistor nozzles, and when the main contacts separate, an arc is drawn and is cleared by the air blast. The

Figure 15.21.   One pole of a 275 kV 25 000 MVA high-duty air-blast circuit-breaker, as module A *in Figure 15.17 (courtesy A. Reyrolle & Co. Ltd.)*

exhaust air passes through a silencer mounted on the underside of the interrupter. On the operation of the time-delay valve, the locking linkage is disengaged from the resistor contact carrier, the resistor contacts are opened by a spring to interrupt the resistor current and simultaneously the pilot valve is released and resets causing the control and blast valves to close. Figure 15.21 shows one pole of a 275 kV circuit-breaker.

In the Brown Boveri ranges of high-voltage air-blast circuit-breakers, the modular or building block principle is followed in two design series, both permanently pressurised. One series (type *DLF*) is specifically a medium-capacity design for use on systems where the currents to be interrupted are of

490

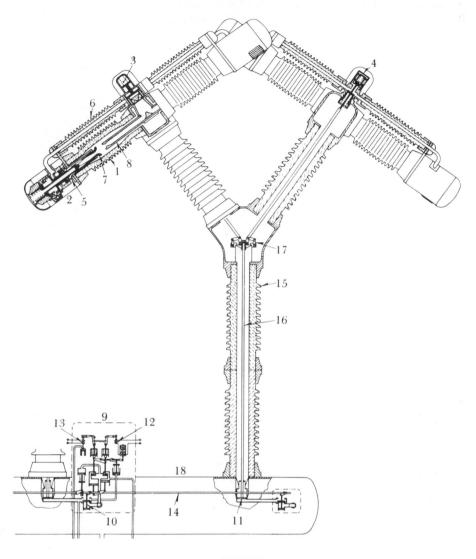

Figure 15.22. Functional diagram of Brown Boveri air-blast circuit-breaker (courtesy Brown Boveri & Co. Ltd.)

the order 20/40 kA symmetrical and for voltages in the range of 72·5–1 100 kV. Both 'T' and 'Y' configurations (alone or in combination) are used, and throughout the air receiver can be a horizontal component on which the appropriate number of support columns per pole are mounted, or alternatively each column in each pole can be carried on individual receivers mounted vertically. This latter arrangement is advantageous when the breakers are installed indoors as the space requirements are more modest.

As we have noted in earlier discussions, progress in design and testing techniques has significantly reduced the number of interrupters used in present day breakers compared with those of two decades ago. This is noted in an article by Leibold and Keinert[5] in which they illustrate the dimensions of a 420 kV breaker supplied in 1952 which, for a breaking capacity of 12 000 MVA, had 10 interrupters in series per pole and compare this with a *DLF* design for the same voltage which has a breaking capacity of 20 000 MVA using only four interrupters. The latter, in 'Y' configuration requires only one support column whereas the earlier design used 'T' configurations demanding five support columns per pole.

Figure 15.22 illustrates the functional details of a typical 'Y' assembly from which it is seen that the control system comprises pneumatic and mechanical elements, the transmission of closing and tripping commands from the control unit (9) being via an insulated rod (16) to the control valves, etc. at the interrupter heads. As in other designs we have noted, the moving contact is fitted with a follow-up system which, when the breaker is tripped, ensures that the contacts separate at speed.

The second series (type *DMF*) is one designed specifically to meet the most severe circuit conditions and capable of interrupting very high fault currents, e.g. up to 92 kA (symmetrical) and for service voltages of 60–765 kV. In this design, the separate isolating chambers which we have discussed earlier are used, this necessitating a further insulating support column on the air receiver, as will be noted by reference to Fig. 18.15 in Chapter 18 which illustrates the *DMF* design for 245 kV.

For voltages up to 400/500 kV, the breakers can be fitted with the alternatives of high or medium-value switching resistors, but for 765 kV it is normally only necessary to fit high-value elements. One unit of a pole of a 765 kV design is shown in Fig. 15.23, three such units being used for one complete pole as seen in Fig. 15.24 showing that each pole comprises 12 interrupters in series along with six isolating chambers, the three-phase breaking capacity being 60 000 MVA.

As noted in earlier discussion, the main contacts reclose after interruption of the arc while the separate isolating contacts remain open, so that a closing operation involves reclosure of the isolating contacts only, the command (from 16) being pneumatically carried through the hollow support insulators (4). Voltage distribution across the isolating chambers is controlled by the capacitors (14).

A tripping operation is initiated at the control block (2), the command being transmitted to the interrupter chamber control valves (13) via the insulated rods (15) inside the support insulators (3). The upper air vessels (7) surrounding the main contacts (8 and 11) contain sufficient air for one interruption and are immediately refilled with air from the main receiver (1). The fixed contacts (8) consist of fixed nozzles through which the air flows when current is being

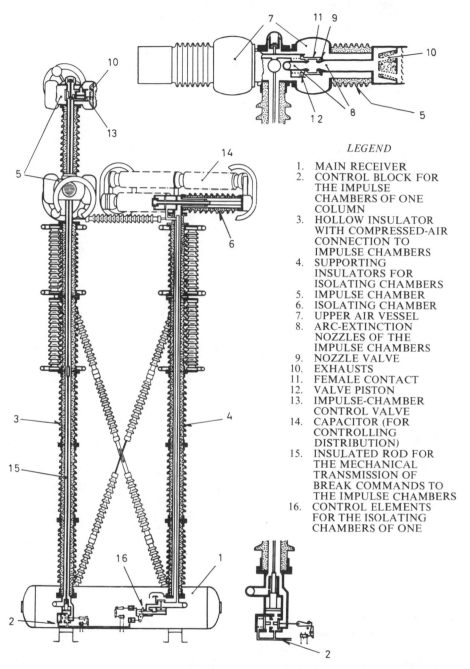

LEGEND

1. MAIN RECEIVER
2. CONTROL BLOCK FOR THE IMPULSE CHAMBERS OF ONE COLUMN
3. HOLLOW INSULATOR WITH COMPRESSED-AIR CONNECTION TO IMPULSE CHAMBERS
4. SUPPORTING INSULATORS FOR ISOLATING CHAMBERS
5. IMPULSE CHAMBER
6. ISOLATING CHAMBER
7. UPPER AIR VESSEL
8. ARC-EXTINCTION NOZZLES OF THE IMPULSE CHAMBERS
9. NOZZLE VALVE
10. EXHAUSTS
11. FEMALE CONTACT
12. VALVE PISTON
13. IMPULSE-CHAMBER CONTROL VALVE
14. CAPACITOR (FOR CONTROLLING DISTRIBUTION)
15. INSULATED ROD FOR THE MECHANICAL TRANSMISSION OF BREAK COMMANDS TO THE IMPULSE CHAMBERS
16. CONTROL ELEMENTS FOR THE ISOLATING CHAMBERS OF ONE

Figure 15.23. Schematic diagram of one unit of a Brown Boveri 750 kV type DMF air-blast circuit-breaker pole. A complete pole comprises three such units giving a total of 12 impulse (interrupting) chambers [(see Figure 15.24) courtesy Brown Boveri & Co. Ltd.] NOTE: the top right part of the diagram shows a double impulse chamber, and the 12 impulse chambers are fitted at right angles to the plane of the diagram

493

Figure 15.24. One pole of Brown Boveri type DMF 750 kV 60 000 MVA *air-blast circuit-breaker comprising three units as in Figure 15.23 (courtesy Brown Boveri & Co. Ltd.)*

interrupted, the air passing through the contact zone from valve (9) in the immediate vicinity of the nozzles, and then passes to atmosphere through the exhaust vents (10). Valve (9) is connected to the moving contacts (11) which move during the opening operation with the valve piston (12).

SILENCERS

When compressed air is released suddenly in the form of high velocity jets into a relatively still atmosphere, the resulting interaction produces sound which is explosive in nature. When an air-blast circuit-breaker opens, such a release of air occurs at the exhaust point of each interrupter, and as these multiply with the size of the breaker the noise emanating can be such as to be startling at close quarters and very annoying at some distance.

This problem is one of considerable importance as it becomes necessary to locate substations in residential areas, particularly at the higher voltages and where high air pressures are employed. It is a subject which all manufacturers have had to study in considerable detail[6,7] and all have developed suitable devices which can be fitted to a circuit-breaker or are a part of the basic design to reduce the noise to acceptable levels.

While it is impossible to consider the design of silencers here in any detail, it can be noted that a primary aim is to reduce the velocity of the jet of air by passing it through intermediate expansion chambers before being exhausted to atmosphere. A silencer based on this principle is that shown in Fig. 15.25, designed to be fitted at the top of each interrupter column at the point of exhaust as seen on the English Electric frame 'r' 400 kV breaker shown in Fig. 15.14.

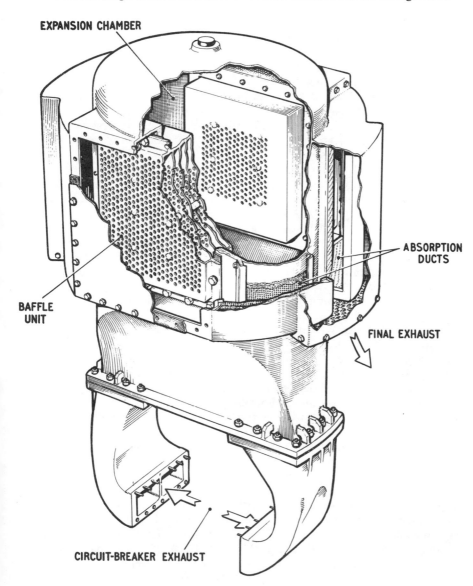

EXPANSION CHAMBER

ABSORPTION DUCTS

BAFFLE UNIT

FINAL EXHAUST

CIRCUIT-BREAKER EXHAUST

Figure 15.25.   Silencer fitted to the English Electric frame 'r' air-blast circuit-breaker—see Figure 15.14 (courtesy G.E.C. Switchgear Ltd.)

Whatever form a silencer takes, various conditions must be satisfied in so far as the breaker itself is concerned, i.e. the electrical clearance necessary must not be impaired, the electrical and mechanical performance must not be adversely affected by back pressure developed within the silencer and the normal rate of air flow at the blast nozzles must be maintained.

As we have seen in Fig. 15.18, the silencer used in the new Reyrolle range is an integral part of the two-break interrupter assembly and is fitted below the interrupters.

COMPRESSED-AIR EQUIPMENT

As the operation and performance of an air-blast circuit-breaker is entirely dependent on an air supply at the right pressure and in sufficient quantity at all times, it is very essential that the most careful and detailed consideration be given to the equipment provided for this purpose. Such equipment is normally supplied by the manufacturer of the circuit-breakers thus ensuring an installation tailored to the special requirements. Briefly, the conditions which must be satisfied may be related as follows:

1. The air delivered to the circuit-breaker must be clean and dry, otherwise abrasion and corrosion of the operating mechanism will result. When air is used as an insulating medium or to condition solid insulation this need for freedom from dirt and moisture is even more imperative.

2. The supply of air must be constantly available. This necessitates a system whose performance is unimpaired by component failure or routine maintenance.

3. Sufficient stored air should be available to supplement and replenish the air in the local air-receivers, so that a predetermined number of circuit-breaker operations can be made without any dependence on the compressors. These should be capable of making-good normal leakage and air used for conditioning purposes without excessive running.

4. The compressed-air system should be suitable for installing in unattended or partially-attended stations.

The problem of ensuring freedom from moisture is one which can be solved by refrigeration or dehydration, but they both require complicated changeover arrangements to allow for defrosting of the cooling vessels in the first case and regeneration of the dessicant in the second. To avoid these complications, it is usual to employ a two-pressure system in which the compressed air is stored at a pressure much greater than that required for operating the circuit-breaker. The stored air is contained in a main air receiver at a central point, from which it will be fed to the distribution system through a reducing valve where the air expands to the required operating pressure.

As no component can be regarded as infallible and as it cannot function indefinitely without maintenance, all vital components are normally duplicated and so placed in the system that they can be isolated while the air supply is maintained by an alternative route. This duplication extends to the air-compressors themselves, which are arranged for automatic operation so that they cut-in and cut-out in response to pressure fluctuation in the main air receivers.

An alarm system, also fully automatic, is essential to give early warning of abnormal leakage or compressor failure. To guard against complete loss of air or the passage of wet air to the switchgear, automatic isolating valves (known

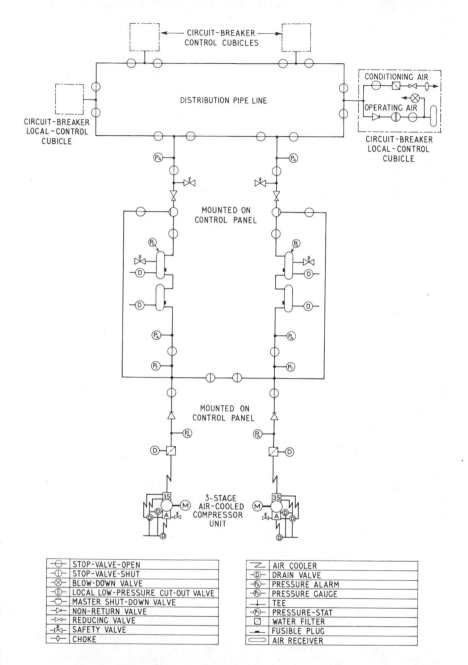

–⊖–	STOP-VALVE-OPEN
–⊕–	STOP-VALVE-SHUT
–⊗–	BLOW-DOWN VALVE
–⊕–	LOCAL LOW-PRESSURE CUT-OUT VALVE
–⊖–	MASTER SHUT-DOWN VALVE
–▷–	NON-RETURN VALVE
–⋈–	REDUCING VALVE
–⧖–	SAFETY VALVE
–◇–	CHOKE

◀	AIR COOLER
–Ⓓ–	DRAIN VALVE
–Ⓟ ₐ–	PRESSURE ALARM
–Ⓟ_G–	PRESSURE GAUGE
⊥	TEE
–Ⓟ–	PRESSURE-STAT
▢	WATER FILTER
▬	FUSIBLE PLUG
⬭	AIR RECEIVER

Figure 15.26. Schematic diagram of a central compressed-air system for air-blast circuit-breakers (courtesy A. Reyrolle & Co. Ltd.)

as master shut-down valves) will be installed in the outlet pipes from the main receivers. When the pressure falls to a predetermined value these valves close, thus limiting the extent of the failure and conserving some of the stored air, the conservation being aided by strategically placed non-return valves. Valves similar in design to the master shut-down valves will be fitted in the supply pipes to the circuit-breakers to provide automatic isolation of any circuit-breaker which develops a leak.

A schematic diagram of a central compressed-air system is shown in Fig. 15.26. It consists of two identical branches, each branch consisting of one or more compressors delivering air via after coolers, filters, non-return valves and stop valves into one or more main air receivers. From the latter the air passes through a stop valve and a master shut-down valve to a reducing valve where the air is expanded to the circuit-breaker operating pressure and then fed into the distribution system. The latter is in the form of a ring-main system with sectionalising valves at each tee-off point. By this means, alternative routes are available to any circuit-breaker and, in the event of a leak developing in a section of pipe, it may be isolated for maintenance without loss of supply. Safety valves and fusible plugs give protection from excess pressure and excess heat respectively, and pressure gauges with pointer contacts for pressure control and alarms are located as shown.

A connection is provided between the two branches so that one branch may feed the other should the need arise. The stop-valves in the connecting pipeline are normally closed for the following reasons. Firstly, with the two branches working independently, a leak in the high-pressure section of the one cannot affect the other. Secondly, if the system was operating with the stop valves open thus commoning the two sets of air receivers, one compressor would take all the load (since it is practically impossible to synchronise the pressure-stats) and the other compressor would not operate unless a large demand for air occurred. It is undesirable that one compressor should remain idle for long periods, and to ensure that both compressors shared the load by paralleling them electrically would defeat the object of duplication.

The operation of the system with the stop-valves closed is thus a practical and reliable way of ensuring that each compressor takes a share of the load, since each cuts in and out in response to pressure fluctuations in the associated set of main air receivers. The compressors do not, necessarily, take equal shares of the load; consequently there is less likelihood of their requiring maintenance at the same time.

REFERENCES

1. EIDINGER, A., 'Outdoor Air-blast Circuit-breakers type *DMF* for Extremely High Breaking Capacities', *Brown Boveri Rev.*, **54** No. 12, Dec. (1967)
2. BATTISSON, M.J. *et al.*, 'Calculation of Transients on Transmission Lines with Sequential Switching', *Proc. I.E.E.*, **117** No. 3, March (1970)
3. ALTHAMMER, P. and PETITPIERRE, R., 'Switching Operations and Switching Surges in Systems Employing Extremely High Voltages', *Brown Boveri Rev.*, **51** No. 1/2, Jan./Feb. (1964)
4. DORSCH, H., 'Voltage Stresses and Insulation Co-ordination in a.c. Extra-high-voltage Systems', *Extra-high-voltage a.c. Transmission*, Siemens AG, W. Germany
5. LEIBOLD, A. and KEINERT, L., 'The Versatile and Economical *DLF* Range of Outdoor Air-blast Circuit-breakers', *Brown Boveri Rev.*, **56** No. 7, July (1969)

6. SCHUBERT, H. and MEINZINGER, W., 'Silencing of Air-blast Circuit-breakers', *Brown Boveri Rev.*, **52** No. 8, Aug. (1965)
7. FAWDRAY, C.A. *et al.*, 'Suppression of Noise in Air-blast Circuit-breakers', *Proc. I.E.E.*, **117** No. 5, May (1970)

BIBLIOGRAPHY

ANON., 'Brown Boveri Design Circuit-breakers for 1 000 MW Generators', *Elect. Rev.*, 14 June (1968)
ANON., 'Designing Air-blast Circuit-breakers for Export', *Elect. Rev.*, 18 March (1966)
ANON., 'New e.h.v. Switchgear Developed for World Markets', *Elect. Rev.*, 20 Feb. (1970)
ANON., '400 kV Switchgear', *Elect. Rev.*, 13 Oct. (1966)
ANON., 'Silent 400 kV Circuit-breakers', *Elect. Times*, 15 Feb. (1968)
ANON., 'Noise Reduction in Air-blast Circuit-breakers', *Elect. Rev.*, 10 Dec. (1965)
ANON., 'Circuit-breakers Well Silenced', *Elect. Rev.*, 16 Feb. (1968)
BALTENSPERGER, P. and SCHNEIDER, J., 'Circuit-breakers for 750 kV', *Brown Boveri Rev.*, **51** No. 1/2, Jan./Feb. (1964)
BURCKHARDT, P. and KNECHT, H., 'Type *DR 36* Generator Circuit-breakers Rated 12–36 kA', *Brown Boveri Rev.*, **57**, Dec. (1970)
EIDINGER, A. and CUK, N., 'Type *DMF* Air-blast Circuit-breakers for Extreme Conditions and Special Requirements', *Brown Boveri Rev.*, **57**, Dec. (1970)
EIDINGER, A. and KOPPL, G., 'Type *DLF* Air-blast Circuit-breakers, a New Range of Medium-capacity Outdoor High-voltage Breakers', *Brown Boveri Rev.*, **54** No. 12, Dec. (1967)
GARRARD, C.J.O., 'A Return to Generator Switching', *Elect. Rev.*, 9 Jan. (1970)
GARRARD, C.J.O., 'High-voltage Distribution Switchgear—A Review of Progress, *Proc. I.E.E.*, **116** No. 6, June (1969)
GARRARD, C.J.O., 'High-voltage Switchgear—A Review of Progress', *Proc. I.E.E.*, **113** No. 9, Sept. (1966)
GARRARD, C.J.O., 'Some Recent Developments in High-voltage Switchgear', *Electronics and Power*, June (1966)
GARRARD, C.J.O., 'Trends in Switchgear Design', *Elect. Rev.*, 26 Sept. (1969)
GRAY, W. and AMER, D.F., 'Some Recent Developments in Switchgear', South African Institute of Electrical Engineers (1966). Available as Reyrolle reprint No. RR 122
LEIBOLD, A. and KEINERT, L., 'Outdoor Air-blast Circuit-breakers type *DLF* for 245 kV with Two Extinction Chambers', *Brown Boveri Rev.*, **57**, Dec. (1970)
MOSELE, J. and ROHR, R., 'Indoor Air-blast Circuit-breakers type *DB* and Switchgear Cubicles for Very-high Capacities', *Brown Boveri Rev.*, **54** No. 12, Dec. (1967)
MOSELE, J. and VADASZI, J., 'The New Range of Indoor Air-blast Breakers type *DE* for Voltages from 3–12 kV', *Brown Boveri Rev.*, **54** No. 12, Dec. (1967)
ROHR, R. and RUCKSTUHL, H., 'Metal-clad Heavy Current Switchgear', *Brown Boveri Rev.*, **51** No. 4, April (1964)
SCHNEIDER, J. and PETITPIERRE, R., 'A New Range of Air-blast Circuit-breakers for Extremely-high Voltages and Capacities', *Brown Boveri Rev.*, **53** No. 4/5, April/May (1966)
TRENCHAM, H., *Circuit-Breaking*, Butterworths, London (1953)
VADASZI, J. and KNACHT, H., 'Development of Indoor Air-blast Circuit-breakers for Current Ratings up to 12 000 A', *Brown Boveri Rev.*, **52** No. 8, Aug. (1965)
WHITNEY, W.B., 'The Early History of the h.v. Air-blast Circuit-breaker', *Electronics and Power*, Jan. and Sept. (1968)
WOOD, B. and WHITNEY, W.B., 'Origin of the Air-blast Circuit-breaker', *Electronics and Power Correspondence*, 126–127, March (1968)

Chapter 16

Sulphur hexafluoride (SF$_6$) circuit-breakers and metal-clad switchgear

SF$_6$ is a heavy chemically-inert non-toxic non-inflammable gas, and is odourless and colourless. Although first produced as long ago as 1904, it was not until some 30 years later that American investigators found that it had considerable possibilities for use as an insulant. It was determined that at atmospheric pressure its dielectric strength was between two to three times that of air, while at a pressure of about three atmospheres it equalled the dielectric strength of good insulating oil. As we shall note in Chapter 23, one example of its present day use as an insulant is to be found in extra-high-voltage current transformers, an example which, it has been estimated, can result in a 40–50% reduction in weight as compared with an oil-filled equivalent.

In a device which has to interrupt current however, we are concerned not only with the insulating properties of a liquid or gas but, very much more important, its arc-quenching ability. In this connection, further research in the U.S.A. revealed that SF$_6$ not only had this ability but that it exceeded that of air many times.

With this combination of superior insulating and arc-quenching properties, it became apparent that a breakthrough in circuit-breaker technique was at hand and, today, numerous designs of SF$_6$ circuit-breakers have been developed and put into commercial production over a range of voltages from 6·6 kV through to 765 kV. As we shall note in Chapter 18, it has also been used in high-voltage load-breaking switches.

The stability of the gas is such that it shows no sign of chemical change at temperatures well above those at which switch oil begins to oxidise and decompose. Some decomposition does occur on exposure to an electric arc, the dissociation products being the lower order fluoride gases SF$_2$ and SF$_4$ (these largely recombine on cooling) plus some metallic fluoride in the form of an insulating powder. This and any remaining gases can be readily absorbed by activated alumina in suitably placed filters.

The superior arc-quenching ability of the gas is attributable to the fact that it is electronegative, which means that its molecules rapidly absorb the free electrons in the arc path between the breaker contacts to form negatively-charged ions, which are ineffective as current carriers. This electron-trapping action results in a rapid build up of insulation strength after a current zero. For

500

effective arc extinction however, it is necessary to force the gas into the arc, but the properties of SF$_6$ are such that the gas-flow speed does not need to be high as in air-blast breakers and for dealing with currents up to about 10 kA at 33 kV sufficient movement can be obtained by a piston which moves with the contact system on opening. In such designs, the breaker is contained in a pressure-tight casing and filled with SF$_6$ at a pressure of say 3 atmospheres, at 20°C.

Alternatively, and this is essential for interrupting high values of current, the breaker is normally sealed in a housing filled with gas at low pressure (again at about 3 atmospheres) but this housing is connected via a normally-closed valve to a high-pressure reservoir containing gas at about 16 atmospheres at 20°C. On receipt of a trip command, the valve opens releasing the high-pressure gas to flow through and past the breaker contacts as they open. After current interruption, a pressure switch on the high-pressure system switches on a compressor motor and excess gas is pumped back from the low-pressure side, through a filter to the high-pressure reservoir. The blast valve meanwhile will have closed and the double-pressure system will be restored to the normal condition.

Among the advantages claimed for the SF$_6$ circuit-breaker are:
1. The low gas velocity and the pressures employed minimise any tendency towards current chopping and capacitive currents can be interrupted without restriking.
2. The closed-circuit gas cycle coupled with low gas velocity gives quiet operation as there is no exhaust to atmosphere as in air-blast breakers.
3. The closed gas circuit keeps the interior dry so that there is no moisture problem.
4. The arc-extinguishing properties of SF$_6$ result in very short arcing times so that contact erosion is only slight. The contacts can be run at higher temperatures without deterioration.
5. There are no carbon deposits so that tracking or insulation breakdown is eliminated.
6. Electrical clearances can be reduced due to the insulating properties of the gas.
7. As the circuit-breaker is totally enclosed and sealed from the atmosphere, it is particularly suitable for use in coal mines or in any industry where an explosion hazard exists.
8. As we shall note later, it lends itself to incorporation in designs of high-voltage metal-clad switchgear where the problem of pollution or the need to locate a substation in an urban or built-up area precludes an open-type outdoor installation.

In spite of many of these advantages, only relatively few designs of SF$_6$ circuit-breaker have been introduced for voltages up to 33 kV. Of the possible reasons for this, that of cost in competition with existing types is important. Coupled with this is the fact that the other possible alternative, i.e. the vacuum interrupter, will see considerable developments leading to commercial production within the next 5–10 years, and it is this type of breaker which would appear to be most likely to challenge the present-day bulk-oil, small-oil-volume and air-break types in this voltage range. One step in this direction will be noted in the Appendix.

We can, nevertheless, consider two designs of SF$_6$ circuit-breaker, one for service at 6·6 or 11 kV in a flameproof switchgear unit for use in coal mines or

501

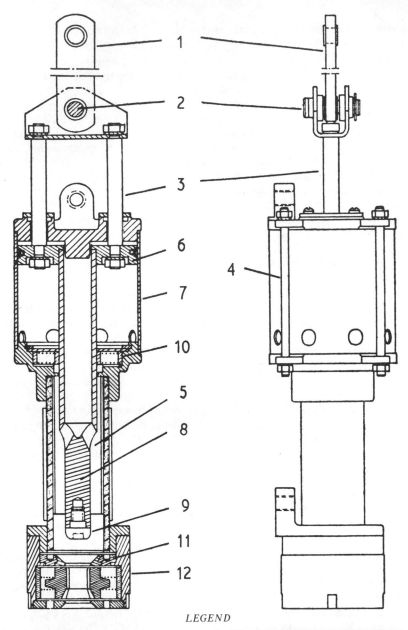

LEGEND

1. INSULATED MOVING-CONTACT
   ACTUATOR
2. STEEL CONNECTING PIN
3. GUIDES
4. SF$_6$ COMPRESSION CYLINDER
   SUPPORTS
5. GLASS-FIBRE REINFORCED
   EPOXY-RESIN ARCING CHAMBER

6. SF$_6$ COMPRESSION PISTON TO
   ASSIST RAPID ARC EXTINCTION
7. SF$_6$ COMPRESSION CYLINDER
8. MOVING CONTACT ATTACHED TO 6
9. TUNGSTEN-TIPPED MOVING CONTACT
10. MOVING-CONTACT CURRENT-
    COLLECTOR RING
11. FIXED-CONTACT ARCING RING
12. FIXED-CONTACT HOLDER

Figure 16.1. The fixed and moving-contact system and arc-control chamber of the 6·6/11 kV Delle Alstham SF$_6$ circuit-breaker as incorporated in FLP mining switchgear (courtesy Brush Switchgear Ltd.)

other hazardous locations, the second for normal industrial or distribution systems operating at voltages up to 30 kV.

Of these, the first is a breaker developed and manufactured by the Delle-Alsthom Co. in France and which has been incorporated by the Brush Electrical Engineering Co.* in the U.K. in a flameproof unit complying with appropriate British Standard and National Coal Board Specifications. The three-phase circuit-breaker is contained in a gas-tight steel case subdivided by steel phase barriers into three compartments, the whole being filled with SF$_6$ gas at a pressure of 48 lbf/in^2 (0·33 MN/m^2).

Each compartment accommodates a single-pole single-break interrupter assembly as shown in Fig. 16.1, the three moving-contact actuators being coupled and brought out to a spring-close spring-trip operating mechanism externally mounted on the case, or, when remote or automatic control is required, a motor-operated closing mechanism.

Figure 16.2.   *A 500 kVA mining-type power transformer fitted with an F.L.P. switchgear unit incorporating an SF$_6$ circuit-breaker (courtesy Brush Switchgear Ltd.)*

This breaker is one in which movement of the gas into the arcing region is caused by a piston attached to the moving contact assembly. In Fig. 16.1 the contacts are in the open position, and when closed the piston (6) attached to the tubular extension of the moving contact (8) will be at the bottom of the compression chamber (7). On receipt of a trip command, the piston and moving contact will move vertically, compressing the gas in (7) above the piston and forcing it to flow through the tube and into the arc formed between the contacts (9 and 11) as they part. The gas so moved passes back to the main body of gas via a filter of activated alumina in the base of the interrupter unit, the filter purifying the gas of the products of arcing described earlier. Fresh gas is admitted to the compression chamber behind the piston through a ring of holes in the base of the chamber walls. A pressure-sensitive relay in communication with the main body of gas monitors the pressure and is arranged to trip the breaker should this fall below about 40 lbf/in^2 (0·28 MN/m^2). Two valves fitted to the main case

* A Hawker Siddeley Company.

Figure 16.3.   Switchboard comprising F.L.P. units incorporating SF$_6$ circuit-breakers as in Figure 16.1 (courtesy Brush Switchgear Ltd.)

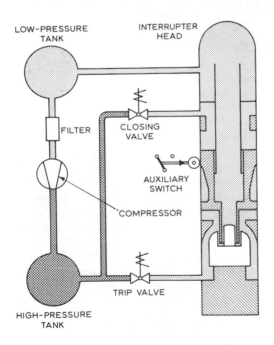

LOW-PRESSURE
TANK

INTERRUPTER
HEAD

FILTER

CLOSING
VALVE

AUXILIARY
SWITCH

COMPRESSOR

TRIP VALVE

HIGH-PRESSURE
TANK

Figure 16.4.   The closed gas system in the Siemens 'F' circuit-breaker, 10/30 kV. Contacts in closed position (courtesy Siemens (UK) Ltd.)

provide facilities for periodic checks on the gas pressure and for recharging with SF$_6$. Rated at 400 A, this breaker has a breaking capacity of 150 MVA at 6·6 or 11 kV.

Figures 16.2 and 16.3 show two arrangements for this unit, the first a special application for coal mining where a single breaker is mounted on a 500 kVA flameproof power transformer of the dry-type, and the other showing a number of units arranged in switchboard form. It is of passing interest to note that the circuit-breaker and its operating mechanism can, after opening the front cover, be withdrawn horizontally, disengaging at plug and socket contacts. This, as we have seen elsewhere, is a method of isolation in other types of switchgear, but here, to meet regulations and specifications, separate manually-operated isolating switches are also included and which are interlocked so that they can only be opened with the breaker open. With both the isolators and the breaker open, the door to the flameproof enclosure can be opened giving access so that the breaker can be withdrawn for inspection, checking of the gas pressure or recharging with gas. Depending on the type of circuit (outgoing or incoming), either one or two sets of isolators can be provided, and where two are used, both are operated simultaneously from a single handle. It is further required that it must be possible to make a visual check on the position of the isolator blades through an observation window, the blades having 'on', 'off' and 'earth' positions.

The other SF$_6$ circuit-breaker in the voltage range up to 33 kV which we may note is one by Siemens of Germany. This is a breaker using a double-pressure gas system (closed circuit) as shown typically in Fig. 16.4, noting that while this illustrates a single pole, a common gas circuit is used for all three poles of a three-phase breaker. This shows the condition with the contacts closed, low-pressure gas at 43 lbf/in^2 (0·30 MN/m^2) being lightly stippled and high-pressure gas at 214 lbf/in^2 (1·5 MN/m^2) heavily stippled. It is to be noted that not only is the gas used as the insulating and arc-quenching medium but also as the drive medium for opening and closing the contacts.

From Fig. 16.4 it is seen that when a trip command is received, the electro-magnetically-operated trip valve will open so that high-pressure gas flows into the bottom part of the interrupter unit forcing a piston carrying the moving contact upwards to the open position shown in Fig. 16.5. The gas flows through nozzles of moulded plastic inset in the fixed contact so that the gas is directed against the arc almost at right angles, de-ionising the break at current zero and establishing a high dielectric strength at the break. The gas passes into the upper part of the interrupter unit and is discharged into the low-pressure tank. This causes a rise in pressure in this tank which, through a pressure switch, starts up the compressor to return the excess gas to the high-pressure tank via the filter, thus restoring the normal condition of the double-pressure system. To close the breaker, the closing valve is opened, admitting high-pressure gas above the piston.

The interrupter units are made of cast resin, the mounting flanges containing the intake and discharge gas ducts. In a three-phase assembly, the separate interrupter units are mounted at the rear of a cubicle (with phase barriers at the highest voltages), the cubicle accommodating the three interconnected two-stage gas tanks along with the control and auxiliary equipment for operating the breaker. Current ratings for this breaker are 1 250 and 2 500 A with breaking capacity ratings ranging from 500 MVA at the lowest service voltage through to 1 500 MVA at 30 kV.

For system voltages of 100 kV upwards, the SF$_6$ circuit-breaker has been developed to a much greater extent. Here, as in air-blast designs, multiple breaks in series per pole are used, present day designs employing two, four, six or eight interrupter heads.

In circuit-breakers with two or four breaks in series, two types are to be noted based on a dead or live-tank principle respectively. In the former, the interrupter units are enclosed in an earthed steel tank with bushing insulators for current

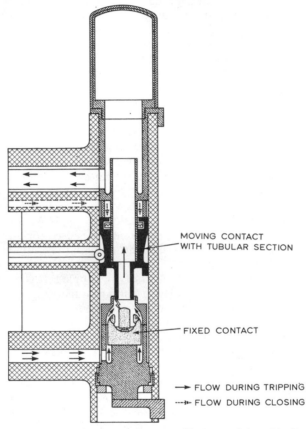

MOVING CONTACT
WITH TUBULAR SECTION

FIXED CONTACT

→ FLOW DURING TRIPPING
---⇥- FLOW DURING CLOSING

Figure 16.5. Interrupter unit with arc-quenching assembly (one pole) used in Siemens 'F' circuit-breaker. Contacts opening with an arc striking at the gap (courtesy Siemens (UK) Ltd.)

entry and exit, the tank and bushings being filled with SF$_6$ and constituting the low-pressure part of a double-pressure closed-circuit gas system.

In live-tank designs, which may be used for any number of interrupter heads and always for six or eight per pole, the heads are mounted in pairs in 'V' or 'T'-formation at the top of a hollow insulating support column, multiple columns being used as required to cover the total number of interrupters, again as in air-blast designs. In this arrangement, the interrupter heads and the hollow support columns are filled with low-pressure SF$_6$ and thus constitute the low-pressure part of the double-pressure system.

A dead-tank SF$_6$ circuit-breaker rated 132 kV 5 000 MVA with two breaks in series is illustrated in Fig. 16.6. This shows the three poles each with its own low-pressure tank containing two interrupter units in series and the insulating bushings for connections to the external circuit. The circular pockets at the base of each bushing can each accommodate up to three ring-type current transformers, i.e. a total of six per phase. Below the low-pressure tanks and at right angles to them is the high-pressure reservoir common to the three phases. At the remote end of the breaker, a cubicle houses a pneumatic closing mechanism, an air receiver for which is located outside the cubicle and which can be supplied either by a station compressor or (in single circuit-breaker installations) by a unit compressor in the cubicle. The gas equipment comprising a compressor

Figure 16.6. A 132 kV 5 000 MVA SF$_6$ circuit-breaker, dead tank design (courtesy G.E.C. Switch-geat Ltd.)

and driving motor, filters, control valves and instruments is housed in another cubicle (not visible in the illustration) mounted on the steel underframe between two of the breaker poles.

A sectional view of one pole is shown in Fig. 16.7. From this it is seen that the external high-pressure gas receiver is connected via feed pipes to a local high-pressure reservoir inside the low-pressure tank containing the interrupter units. When the circuit-breaker is tripped, the contacts part under the influence of the accelerating spring and in so doing open a mechanically-operated blast valve on the local high-pressure reservoir to release the gas therein. This flows via tubes into the arcing region, passing through and past the contacts into the low-pressure tank, the arc being extinguished by this high to low pressure gas flow. Immediately after interruption, the blast valve closes.

507

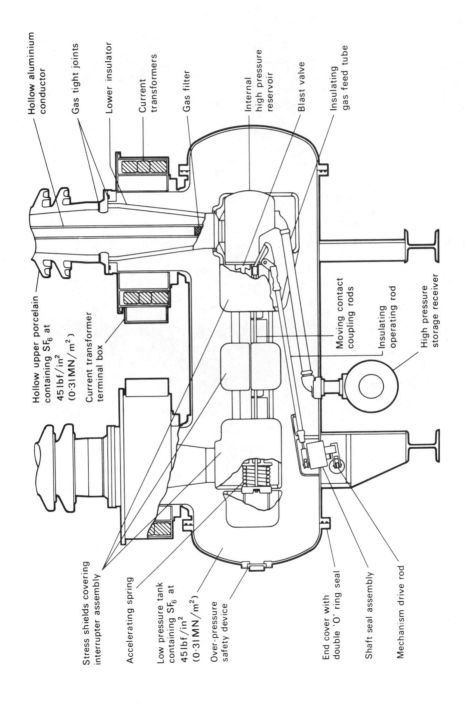

Hollow aluminium conductor

Gas tight joints

Lower insulator

Current transformers

Gas filter

Internal high pressure reservoir

Blast valve

Insulating gas feed tube

Hollow upper porcelain containing SF_6 at $45\,lbf/in^2$ $(0.31\,MN/m^2)$

Current transformer terminal box

Moving contact coupling rods

Insulating operating rod

High pressure storage receiver

Stress shields covering interrupter assembly

Accelerating spring

Low pressure tank containing SF_6 at $45\,lbf/in^2$ $(0.31\,MN/m^2)$

Over-pressure safety device

End cover with double 'O' ring seal

Shaft seal assembly

Mechanism drive rod

Figure 16.7. Sectional view of one pole of a 132 kV 5 000 MVA dead-tank SF_6 circuit-breaker (courtesy G.E.C. Switchgear Ltd.)

The discharge of high-pressure gas into the general volume of the low-pressure tank causes a rise of pressure in the latter, and to restore the original differential pressure a pressure switch is arranged to start the compressor to pump an appropriate amount of gas back into the high-pressure reservoir. In the process, the gas passes through filters which remove the products of arcing.

Figure 16.8 shows in more detail the construction of an interrupter unit. The fixed contacts comprise a set of current-carrying fingers and an arcing probe. With the breaker closed, the fingers make contact round the circumference of

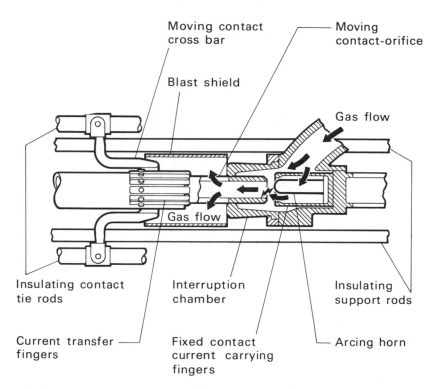

Figure 16.8.   Part detail of interrupter unit used in SF$_6$ circuit-breaker shown in Figures 16.6 and 16.7 (courtesy G.E.C. Switchgear Ltd.)

the moving contact with the arcing probe inside the hollow end of the moving contact. The contacts are surrounded by interrupting nozzles and a blast shield which control arc displacement and hot gas movement.

The moving contact takes the form of hollow nozzles sliding in a second set of spring-loaded fingers. Side vents in the moving contact permit the passage of the high-pressure gas into the main tank.

On opening and as soon as the moving contact is withdrawn from the fixed finger contacts, an arc is drawn between the arcing probe and the inside of the moving nozzle. It is extended and attenuated as the contacts move further apart, controlled by the nozzle and blast shield and finally extinguished by the high to low pressure gas flow.

The two interrupter units are designed to operate in unison, the two moving contacts being joined together in a 'ladder' formation of insulating rods, the

509

ladder moving as one unit during opening and closing. The sets of fixed contacts are supported rigidly by insulating bars extending the full length of the assembly.

From Fig. 16.7 it is seen that the bushing comprises two parts, the shedded portion beyond the current transformer pocket and the plain portion projecting into the tank. The two parts are held together by an aluminium tube fitted with a cap at either end, the lower porcelain being coated with an air-drying epoxy resin on its outer surface. This resin is highly resistant to the products of arced SF$_6$. The aluminium tube also serves as the conductor through the bushing, the complete interior of which is filled with SF$_6$ from the low-pressure tank. To ensure that the gas in the bushing is uncontaminated, it enters the bushing through a filter inside the bottom end of the tube and then out into the bushing via holes near the top of the tube.

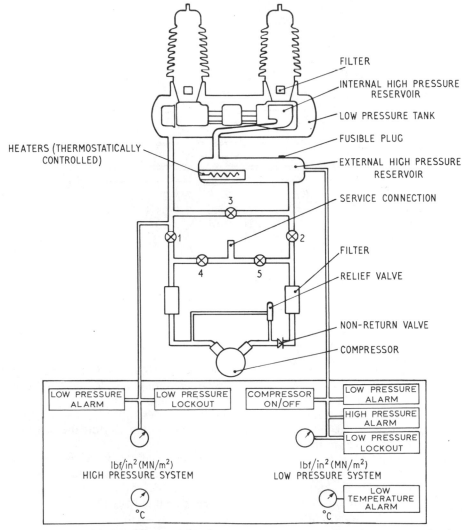

Figure 16.9. Schematic diagram of the closed-circuit gas system used in the SF$_6$ circuit-breaker shown in Figures 16.6 and 16.10 (courtesy G.E.C. Switchgear Ltd.)

As in all designs where gas is under pressure, considerable care has to be taken to prevent leakage at joints, etc. and perfect sealing is essential. Both the high and low-pressure systems are fitted with low-pressure alarm and lock-out switches to give warning of pressure drops which could reduce the dielectric strength and endanger the arc-quenching ability. If a danger limit is reached, the safety devices immobilise the breaker. Overriding safety devices ensure that a control-circuit fault cannot permit the compressor to build up excessive pressure in the high-pressure reservoir or continue to pump gas into the atmosphere in the event of a major leak.

In the design under discussion, the high-pressure gas is at 235 lbf/in^2 (1·62 MN/m^2) while the low-pressure gas is at 45 lbf/in^2 (0·31 MN/m^2), both at 20°C. Gas at 235 lbf/in^2 will liquefy at temperatures below 10°C, and to safeguard against this a heater is fitted in the high-pressure reservoir, thermostatically controlled to switch on when the ambient temperature falls below

Figure 16.10.   A 275 kV 15 000 MVA SF$_6$ circuit-breaker—dead tank design (courtesy G.E.C. Switchgear Ltd.)

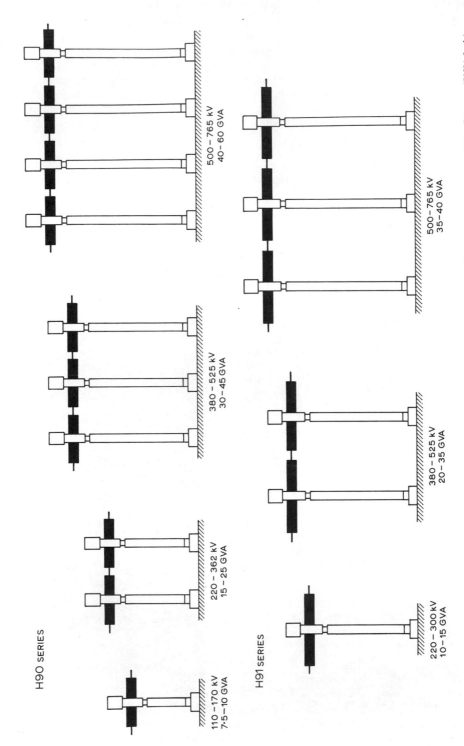

H90 SERIES

500 – 765 kV
40 – 60 GVA

380 – 525 kV
30 – 45 GVA

220 – 362 kV
15 – 25 GVA

110 –170 kV
7·5 –10 GVA

H91 SERIES

500 – 765 kV
35 – 40 GVA

380 – 525 kV
20 – 35 GVA

220 – 300 kV
10 – 15 GVA

Figure 16.11. Schematic block diagram showing the range of Siemens high and extra-high-voltage SF₆ circuit-breakers (courtesy Siemens (UK) Ltd.)

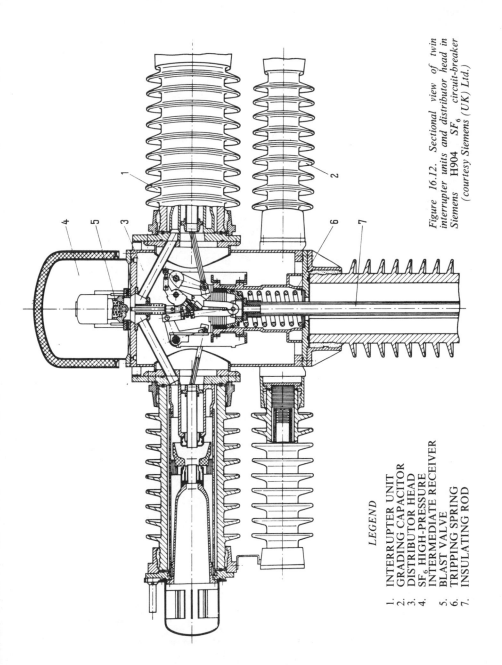

Figure 16.12. Sectional view of twin interrupter units and distributor head in Siemens H904 SF$_6$ circuit-breaker (courtesy Siemens (UK) Ltd.)

16°C. To minimise heat loss, the reservoir is lagged. Figure 16.9 is a schematic diagram of the gas system.

In a generally similar design for 275 kV 15 000 MVA shown in Fig. 16.10, four making and breaking units in series per pole are used as against two in the 132 kV design, the four units being enclosed in the low-pressure tank. Another difference is that instead of a common high-pressure reservoir for the three phases, each phase has its own reservoir located along the axis of the phases.

In both designs, equal voltage distribution across the breaks is achieved by a number of ceramic capacitor packs slung below the interrupting elements and in shunt with each break. Also in both designs, synchronous operation of all three phases is ensured by mechanical pull-rods which transmit the movement of the pneumatic closing mechanism simultaneously to the moving contacts at each break. Normal current ratings for these circuit-breakers are 800, 1 200 and 2 000 A at 132 kV and 2 000 A at 275 kV.

The live-tank principle is used by Siemens (Germany) in two series of SF$_6$ circuit-breakers covering a range of voltages from 110 kV through to 765 kV and illustrated diagrammatically in Fig. 16.11. Two breaks per support column are employed, the required ratings being obtained using one or multiple columns with all the breaks per pole connected in series, i.e. using the modular arrangements we have discussed in relation to air-blast designs in Chapter 15.

A part sectional view of a typical two-break assembly at the top of a support column is shown in Fig. 16.12. From this it is seen that in this design an SF$_6$

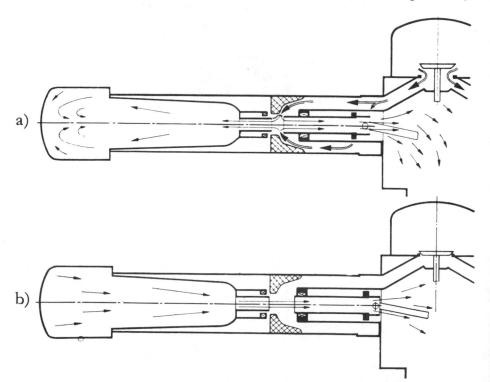

Figure 16.13. Schematic diagram of gas flow in the interrupter unit in the Siemens H904 SF$_6$ circuit-breaker. (a) During arc-quenching and (b) with arc extinguished (courtesy Siemens (UK) Ltd.)

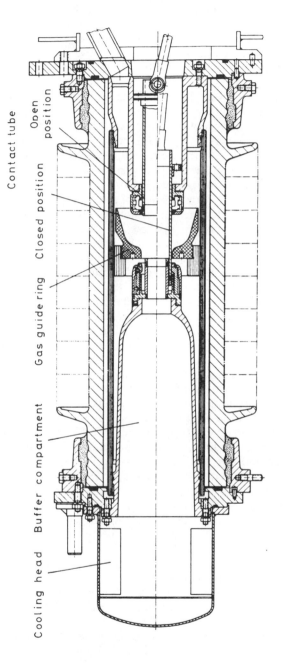

Contact tube

Open position

Closed position

Gas guide ring

Cooling head Buffer compartment

Figure 16.14. Design detail of a typical interrupter unit used in Siemens H904 SF_6 circuit-breaker (courtesy Siemens (UK) Ltd.)

515

high-pressure intermediate receiver is formed by the dome above the column which is charged with gas from a main high-pressure storage tank at the base of the breaker through feed pipes (not shown) which pass through the hollow support insulator. The low-pressure system is constituted by the interrupter units, the distributor head and the hollow insulator support insulators, the pressures employed being 18 kgf/cm^2 (1·8 MN/m^2) and 2 kgf/cm^2 (0·2 MN/m^2) high and low respectively.

The blast valve is located in the base of the intermediate receiver and is opened as the breaker is tripped through the mechanical linkage seen in the distributor head, releasing a blast of high-pressure gas into the arc in both interrupter units via the blast tubes. The flow of gas during and after arcing is shown schematically in Fig. 16.13. It can be noted from (a) that a part of the gas, after passing through the arc region, flows to the right into the low-pressure system direct, the remainder passing to a buffer compartment on the left where it cools and returns to the low-pressure system shown at (b).

As in other designs discussed, restoration of the differential between the low and high-pressure systems after each operation is achieved by pumping excess gas from the low to high-pressure systems via filters and a compressor. A heater system in the high-pressure storage tank prevents the gas from liquefying at low temperatures, the heater being thermostatically controlled and both this tank and the intermediate receiver are lagged to minimise heat loss.

Design details of an interrupter unit are given in Fig. 16.14, the contact system being closed and opened mechanically. The closing mechanism is an electrohydraulic system, the breaker being latched in the closed position. The action of closing the breaker automatically charges the tripping spring so that when the hold-in latch is released by a trip coil, the energy stored in the spring is released to open the breaker. A schematic diagram of the operating mechanism is given in Fig. 16.15. Pressure monitoring of the hydraulic system as well as that of the SF$_6$ system ensures safe operation of the circuit-breaker, closure of the latter being blocked under certain conditions.

Voltage grading across the multiple breaks is controlled by capacitor units mounted below each interrupter as shown in Fig. 16.12. On very long overhead lines surges occur when the line is switched in and these can be reflected at either end of the line and thus lead to serious overvoltages, possibly exceeding 2·5 times the line-to-neutral voltage (see article by Dorsch[1]). These can however be limited by fitting closing resistors with an associated resistor interrupter connected in parallel with the main interrupters. In the Siemens design the resistors, comprising cylindrical discs of ceramically bonded carbon arranged in stacks, are combined with the resistor interrupter unit and its drive gear in porcelain bushings which are bolted to the distributor head. The contacts in the interrupter are driven from the mechanism controlling the main interrupters, but an interposed cam drive ensures that the resistors are only switched in when the main interrupters close and not when they open. The resistors are cut in and loaded for about 10 ms during the closing stroke (see article by Einsele[2]).

Whereas in the dead-tank types current transformers can be accommodated in the circuit-breaker, this is not possible with live-tank types and separate transformers of types to be noted later in Chapter 23 must be used.

High-voltage SF$_6$ circuit-breakers of the types just mentioned are those intended for installation in open switchyards, as in the examples which will be

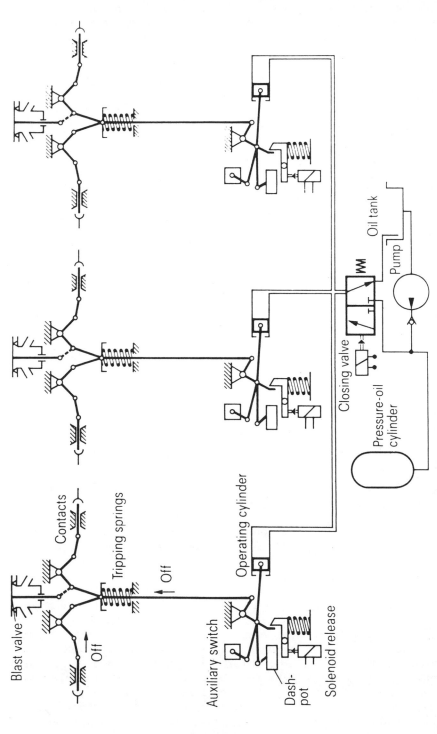

Figure 16.15. Schematic diagram of the electrohydraulic operating mechanism used in the Siemens SF$_6$ circuit-breakers. This shows a 3-pole breaker with two interrupter units per pole (courtesy Siemens (UK) Ltd.)

Blast valve

Contacts

Tripping springs

Off

Off

Auxiliary switch

Operating cylinder

Dash-pot

Solenoid release

Closing valve

Pressure-oil cylinder

Oil tank

Pump

517

shown later in Chapter 21. The space occupied by these, along with associated isolating switches, busbars and other apparatus, is often considerable and is determined largely by the insulating distances essential under normal atmospheric conditions.

As it becomes more and more necessary to bring the higher voltages into densely populated and/or industrial areas, so it becomes extremely difficult to find locations with sufficient space for an open installation. Even if such space can be found, objections to its use on account of noise or amenity may be formidable. In addition, the problem of pollution of the many insulators which is always present in outdoor installations, can be much greater in built-up areas and particularly in industrial areas. In Chapter 20 it will be noted how normal

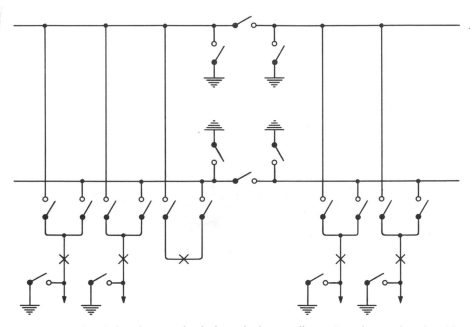

Figure 16.16. Single line diagram of a duplicate busbar installation. How this is achieved in SF$_6$ metal-clad switchgear is shown in Figure 16.17 (courtesy Merlin & Gerin Ltd.)

outdoor switchgear, i.e. with air-blast circuit-breakers, etc. has been installed indoors in relatively simple buildings, but while this solves some of the problems, it does not greatly reduce the space required, even if insulation levels are reduced to a minimum. There is a limit to the extent of such reduction because all clearance distances are still in air at atmospheric pressure.

To achieve really significant savings in space it is clear that an alternative to air as a dielectric must be used. Here the superior properties of SF$_6$ gas have led to a solution, but as this must be contained, a metal-clad form of switchgear has evolved. In this, all components (circuit-breaker, isolating and selector switches, earth switches, busbars, etc.) are each separately enclosed in gas-tight chambers and filled with SF$_6$ at a pressure of two to three atmospheres, all the individual chambers being integrated into a single mechanical unit. This building block principle enables the various components to be assembled in a variety of ways to meet a desired electrical layout and because the circuit-breaker can be mounted either vertically or horizontally to suit conditions of restricted area or restricted height, e.g. in basements below ground.

Designs based on this concept have been put into service by various continental manufacturers for voltages of 150–245 kV while their use at higher voltages is contemplated. In most cases, complete phase segregation is employed, i.e. each phase of each component is separately enclosed in gas-tight compartments although in some designs, a three-phase busbar assembly is used. In the literature relating to this development it has been stated that substations with metal-clad switchgear can be as much as 20 times smaller in area and 30 times smaller

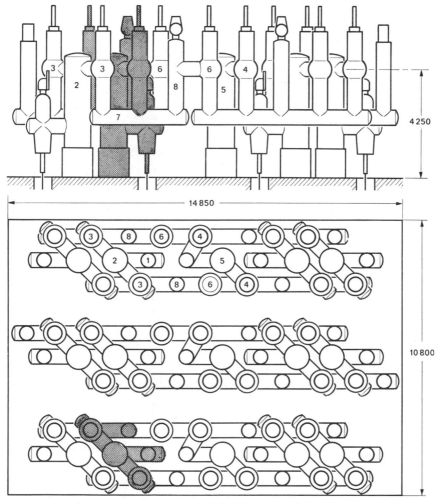

LEGEND

1. CABLE BOX
2. CIRCUIT-BREAKER (FEEDER)
3. BUSBAR SELECTOR SWITCHES
4. BUS-COUPLER ISOLATING
   SWITCHES

5. BUS-COUPLER CIRCUIT-BREAKER
6. BUS-SECTION ISOLATORS
7. BUSBARS
8. EARTHING SWITCHES

Figure 16.17.   Layout of a 5-bay duplicate busbar installation of a 245 kV metal-clad SF$_6$ switchgear. Diagram as Figure 16.16 (courtesy Merlin & Gerin Ltd.)

519

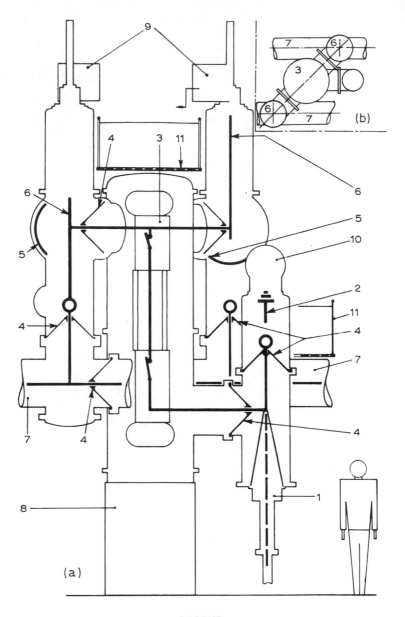

(b)

(a)

LEGEND

1. CABLE BOX
2. EARTHING SWITCH
3. CIRCUIT-BREAKER
4. INSULATING CONES
5. SAFETY SCREEN
6. SELECTOR SWITCHES
7. BUSBARS
8. PEDESTAL CONTAINING
   BREAKER AUXILIARIES
9. SELECTOR SWITCH ELECTRICAL
   MECHANISM
10. EARTHING SWITCH MECHANISM
11. PLATFORMS

Figure 16.18.   Diagrammatic cross-section (a) and plan view (b) of a 245 kV bay of SF_6 metal-clad switchgear and duplicate busbars and selector switches (courtesy Merlin & Gerin Ltd.)

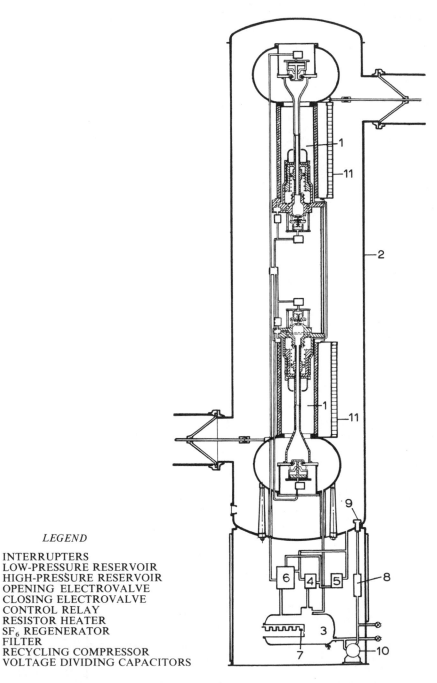

Figure 16.19.   Cross-section of the 245 kV SF₆ circuit-breakers (item 3 in Figure 16.18) (courtesy Merlin & Gerin Ltd.)

in volume than a similar substation with conventional outdoor switchgear. Alongside this, the use of metal-clad switchgear completely eliminates the problem of insulator pollution, adds to the safety of operating personnel as all live parts are enclosed in earthed metal and reduces civil engineering costs, erection time on site and maintenance.

For the purpose of illustrating the foregoing discussion, we may take as an example a 245 kV design by Merlin & Gerin of France, based on an article by Pariselle[3]. Figure 16.16 is a single-line diagram of a duplicate busbar switchgear installation comprising four feeder circuit-breaker units, a bus-coupling circuit-breaker unit, two bus-sectioning isolators and various earthing switches. Using

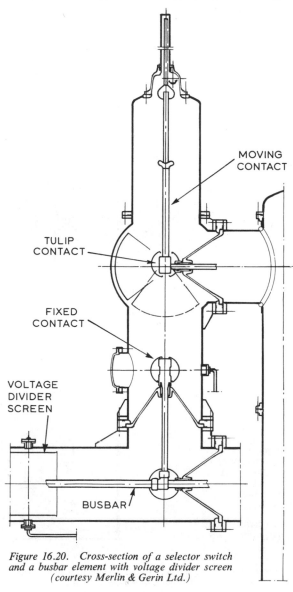

Figure 16.20. Cross-section of a selector switch and a busbar element with voltage divider screen (courtesy Merlin & Gerin Ltd.)

SF$_6$ metal-clad switchgear, the whole of this primary system can be laid out in an area of 16·2 yd × 11·77 yd (14·95 m × 10·8 m) as shown in the plan view in Fig. 16.17, the phases being segregated throughout.

Constructionally, Fig. 16.18(a) gives a diagrammatic cross-section of one pole of a feeder unit, noting from the small·scale plan in Fig. 16.18(b) how, to conserve space, the circuit-breaker is connected diagonally between the dupli-cate busbars. Note also that one selector switch is shown closed with the other open, and that between the contacts of the latter a safety screen has been moved into position. The segregation into compartments is obtained by epoxy-resin conical insulators (4) designed to withstand differential pressures as high as the absolute rated pressure as it is necessary to evacuate the air from a compart-ment after a maintenance operation before it can be refilled with SF$_6$, the adjacent compartment(s) being still pressurised. The cones have a further function of equal importance, viz. to support live conductors, thus forming a part of the phase-to-earth insulation and having a dielectric strength not less than the gas alone. From this illustration it is seen that there are five basic elements each constituting a sealed individual compartment and each filled with SF$_6$ at 36·75 lbf/in^2 (0·25 MN/m^2), for insulating purposes.

The circuit-breaker, shown in more detail in Fig. 16.19, comprises two inter-rupter units in series contained in a vertical cylinder supported on a pedestal base housing the high-pressure SF$_6$ reservoir, a recycling compressor controlled by a pressure switch and the controls for opening and closing the circuit-breaker. Operation is on the double-pressure principle with a closed gas circuit as previously noted, the gas for arc-quenching purposes being at a pressure of 191 lbf/in^2 (1·32 MN/m^2). Each interrupter is permanently pressurised at this value and when a trip signal is applied, blast valves at both ends of each inter-rupter open simultaneously with the contacts, the high-pressure gas flowing through the arcing region and out to the low-pressure cylinder. After inter-ruption, the blast valves reclose and the interrupters refill with high-pressure gas which ensures the insulation across the open contacts. Restoration of the pressure differential is achieved by the compressor operating in the manner discussed earlier.

The selector switches (6) are in compartments supported by the circuit-breaker body, one switch being noted in Fig. 16.20. While used in our example as duplicate busbar selectors, this switch can also be used as a cable or busbar isolator. The moving contact (shown in the open position) slides vertically through a tulip contact mounted on the connection to the circuit-breaker. The fixed contact at the bottom of the compartment is supported on an insulating cone and is directly connected to the busbar below. The upper end of the moving contact is terminated by an epoxy-resin insulator attached to an earthed toothed rack which is operated by a motor-driven mechanism.

The safety screen is provided as a substitute for a visible break, a lever attached to the spindle of the screen giving personnel an unmistakable indication of the switch position. It can be padlocked closed and mechanical and electrical interlocks prevent mal-operation.

This illustration also serves to show a portion of a busbar compartment, the busbar being supported by cast epoxy-resin conical insulators. At the left of the busbar a capacitive voltage divider is shown. This comprises a small co-axial insulated screen fitted over a section of busbar and, combined with a series capa-citor, it provides a capacitive voltage divider of very high impedance. A co-axial cable connection enables the output to be taken to a transistorised amplifier; an arrangement which can meet power output requirements up to 25 VA.

Figure 16.21 shows the cable box and earthing-switch elements. The former is based on a cable end similar to those used with oil-filled cable ends elsewhere on 245 kV cable systems. This is possible as the dielectric strength of SF$_6$ at 2·5 atmospheres in the connection chamber is very close to that of oil.

The earthing switch is capable of closing on to a short-circuit and is operated by a quick-make stored-energy operating mechanism, of the manual or electrical type. With the latter, the earthing switch can be used as a short-circuiter.

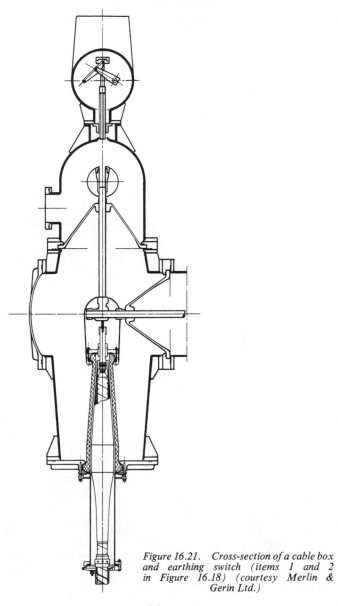

Figure 16.21. Cross-section of a cable box and earthing switch (items 1 and 2 in Figure 16.18) (courtesy Merlin & Gerin Ltd.)

Figure 16.22 serves to illustrate typically some of the constructional details, this being a prototype single-pole assembled for laboratory tests and comprising, from left to right, a cable box, a section of busbar (horizontal) the circuit-breaker, a selector (isolating) switch and a second cable box. Equipment of the type described has a normal current rating of 2 000 A and a breaking capacity rating of 12 000 MVA.

Developed on similar building block principles, Brown Boveri of Switzerland have commissioned metal-clad switchgear using SF$_6$ gas for insulation, arc-quenching and circuit-breaker operation. One such installation is completely underground in the centre of the city of Zurich, the substation including not only the extra-high-voltage metal-clad switchgear (insulation level 245 kV but operating initially at 150 kV) but also the 11 kV switchgear, two 30 MVA 150/11 kV power transformers along with auxiliary and control apparatus, as described by Acker and Szenta-Varga[4].

Figure 16.22.   A single-phase bay of 245 kV SF$_6$ metal-clad switchgear assembled for laboratory tests (courtesy Merlin & Gerin Ltd.)

Installations of metal-clad SF$_6$ switchgear may have the circuit-breaker and some other components assembled vertically or horizontally, the former occupying a minimum floor area, the latter giving a low overall height which is of advantage in basement or underground installations. A comparison between the two arrangements is noted in the Brown Boveri proposals reproduced here as Figs. 16.23 and 16.24, both illustrating single-bus circuits with the busbars contained in a common enclosure as opposed to the segregated design previously noted.

Figure 16.25 shows, in outline, a typical arrangement of a 300 kV (highest system voltage) design due to collaboration between the British manufacturers

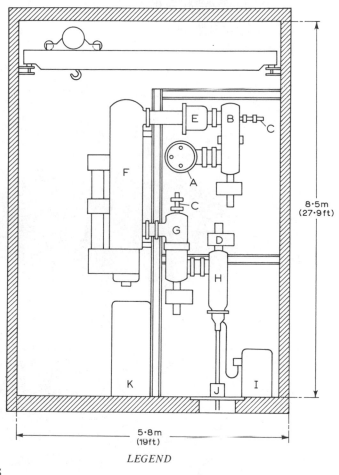

LEGEND

A	BUSBARS
B	BUSBAR ISOLATOR
C	MANUAL EARTHING SWITCH
D	RAPID EARTHING SWITCH
E	CURRENT TRANSFORMER
F	CIRCUIT-BREAKER
G	FEEDER ISOLATOR

H	CABLE AND BOX
I	ADAPTOR FOR CABLE VOLTAGE TRANSFORMER
J	CABLE CURRENT TRANSFORMER
K	SWITCHGEAR CABINET (CONTROL)

Figure 16.23.   Arrangement of 245 kV SF$_6$ metal-clad switchgear (single busbar) to give small floor area, i.e. with circuit-breaker and other components mounted vertically (courtesy Brown Boveri & Co. Ltd.)

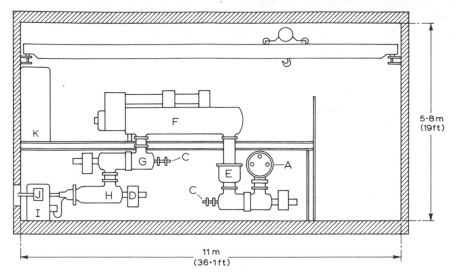

Figure 16.24. *Arrangement of 245 kV SF₆ metal-clad switchgear (single busbar) to give low overall height, i.e. with circuit-breaker and other components horizontal. Legend as for Figure 16.23 (courtesy Brown Boveri & Co. Ltd.)*

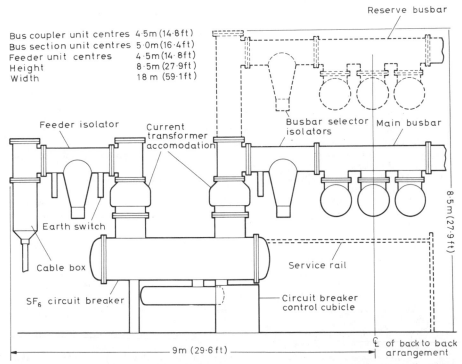

Bus coupler unit centres 4·5m (14·8 ft)
Bus section unit centres 5·0m (16·4 ft)
Feeder unit centres 4·5m (14·8 ft)
Height 8·5m (27·9 ft)
Width 18 m (59·1 ft)

Figure 16.25. *Outline of back-to-back arrangement of single or double-bus metal-clad switchgear, 300 kV (highest voltage). Equipment is repeated to the right of the centre line (courtesy G.E.C. Switchgear Ltd. and A. Reyrolle & Co. Ltd.)*

527

SULPHUR HEXAFLUORIDE (SF_6) CIRCUIT-BREAKERS AND METAL-CLAD SWITCHGEAR

G.E.C. Switchgear and A. Reyrolle. In this joint development, the 275 kV circuit-breaker is the G.E.C. Switchgear design described earlier, while the associated isolators, busbars, earth switches, etc. are of Reyrolle design, the component items being designed to provide a degree of flexibility of assembly to meet particular requirements. The whole equipment is filled with SF_6 gas at a pressure of 4 bars absolute but with gas-tight barriers between components to localise any leakage and to provide facilities for maintenance without having to remove large quantities of gas. Gas pressure is continuously monitored to provide an alarm in the event of a leak developing.

The equipment shown is that on one side of the centre line and is repeated on the other side thus giving two circuits back-to-back, either single or double-bus, in an area of 59 × 14·4 ft (18 × 4·4 m). This area includes a service area down the centre which gives access to the circuit-breaker and isolator operating controls and permits withdrawal of the circuit-breaker interrupter units for inspection and maintenance. The area saved by such an arrangement is demonstrated by comparing the relative areas of a 275 kV double-busbar station for which, in a conventional outdoor layout, the area required *per circuit* is of the order of 11 000 ft^2 (1 000 m^2) whereas the equivalent area for the metal-clad layout is 430 ft^2 (40 m^2).

The first installation of this kind in the U.K. comprises a seven-circuit double-bus equipment in a 275 kV substation at Neepsend, Sheffield.

Extra-high-voltage SF_6 metal-clad switchgear is necessarily more expensive than open equipment but the extra cost can be more than recovered by the saving in land costs, particularly where these are high as in densely populated residential or industrial areas, or by savings on difficult sites where considerable excavation or levelling is required.

REFERENCES
1. DORSCH, H., 'Voltage Stresses and Insulation Co-ordination in a.c. Extra-high-voltage Systems', special issue on Extra-high-voltage a.c. Transmission, Siemens AG, 60–66
2. EINSELE, A., 'EHV Circuit-breakers', special issue on Extra-high-voltage a.c. Transmission, Siemens AG, 60–66
3. PARISELLE, R., 'Le Poste Blindé 245 kV à Encombrement Reduit', *Techniques M.G.*, No. 55 (revue Merlin Gerin)
4. ACKER, J. and SZENTA-VARGA, H.P., 'Sempersteig Substation of the Zurich Electricity Authority', *Neue Zürcher Zeitung*, supplement 'Technik' No. 639, 15 Feb. (1967). Available as Brown Boveri Reprint No. 3521–E

BIBLIOGRAPHY
ANN, H. and NOACK, D., 'New SF_6 Circuit-breakers with Electrohydraulic Operating Mechanisms', *Siemens Rev.*, XXXVI No. 9 (1969)
ANON., 'SF$_6$ Switchgear for Transmission and Industrial Applications', *Elect. Rev.*, 4 June (1965)
ANON., 'Prototype French EHV Metal-clad Substation Equipment', *Elect. Rev.*, 23 Aug. (1968)
ANON., 'First British SF_6 Circuit-breakers Commissioned by the C.E.G.B.', *Elect. Rev.*, 11 March (1966)
BATTISSON, M.J. *et al.*, 'Calculation of Transients on Transmission Lines with Sequential Switching', *Proc. I.E.E.*, 117 No. 3, March (1970)
BECKER, K. and PFLANM, E., 'Testing a 220/245 kV Gas-blast Circuit-breaker Under Short-line Fault Conditions in a New Synthetic Test Circuit', *Siemens Rev.*, XXXV No. 6 (1968)
EASTWOOD, D.G., 'SF_6 Switchgear for Use in Coal Mines at Voltages of 6·6 kV and 11 kV', *Elect. Rev.*, 9 July (1965)

SULPHUR HEXAFLUORIDE (SF$_6$) CIRCUIT-BREAKERS AND METAL-CLAD SWITCHGEAR

EINSELE, A., 'The New Siemens F Circuit-breaker for 220 kV 15 GVA', *Siemens Rev.*, XXXI No. 7 (1964)

FROWEIN, E.A. and SZENTA-VARGA, H.P., 'Metal-clad High-voltage Installations with SF$_6$ Insulation', *Brown Boveri Rev.*, **53** No. 4/5, April/May (1966)

GARRARD, C.J.O., 'High-voltage Distribution Switchgear: A Review of Progress', *Proc. I.E.E.*, **116** No. 6, June (1969)

GARRARD, C.J.O., 'Some Recent Developments in High-voltage Switchgear', *Electronics and Power*, June (1966)

GARRARD, C.J.O., 'High-voltage Switchgear: A Review of Progress', *Proc. I.E.E.*, **113** No. 9, Sept. (1966)

KEHLER, W. and MOEBIUS, M., 'Siemens F Breakers with Sulphur Hexafluoride for 10 to 30 kV', *Siemens Rev.*, XXXII No. 10, Oct. (1965)

LEEDS, W.M., 'SF$_6$ Switchgear Comes of Age', *Elect. Rev.*, 14 Aug. (1970)

MAUTHE, G. *et al.*, 'Metalclad SF$_6$ Circuit-breakers Type *BCK*', *Brown Boveri Rev.*, **57**, Dec. (1970)

RIEDER, W., 'Vacuum and SF$_6$ Circuit-breakers', *Elect. Rev.*, 10 June (1966)

SZENTA-VARGA, H.P. and KRAFFT, N., 'Metal-clad High-voltage Switchgear with SF$_6$ Insulation', *Brown Boveri Rev.*, **54** No. 12, Dec. (1967)

SZENTA-VARGA, H.P., 'Metal-clad Switchgear with SF$_6$ Insulation for 72 to 525 kV', *Brown Boveri Rev.*, **56** No. 11/12, Nov./Dec. (1969)

SZENTA-VARGA, H.P., '170 kV Metalclad Switchgear for Sempersteig Substation', *Brown Boveri Rev.*, **57**, Dec. (1970)

Chapter 17

Oil switches and ring-main units

Some consideration has been given in Chapter 9 to the use of oil switches on certain types of circuit, notably ring main distribution, the switches being used in place of the more costly oil circuit-breaker equipment. It was noted that an oil switch is a device which is *not* called upon to interrupt currents beyond its normal continuous rating, eg. 400/630 A, but which must nevertheless be capable of carrying through-fault currents and of being closed on to a short-circuit.

These requirements can be met in designs which can, additionally, provide other desirable features, such as integral facilities for circuit earthing and cable testing, and it is with these designs that we are concerned here.

In British practice, the minimum requirements are given in BS 2631[1], a specification which covers apparatus for use on system voltages of 3·3–33 kV and which requires the units to comply at least with the following ratings at *each* voltage:

Current rating	400 A
Breaking capacity	400 A
Making capacity	33·4 kA peak

Rated short-time current 13·1 kA r.m.s. symmetrical for 3 s

These values envisage use on systems where the fault levels are:

75 MVA at   3·3 kV
150 MVA at   6·6 kV
250 MVA at 11·0 kV
500 MVA at 22·0 kV
750 MVA at 33·0 kV

but with fault levels at 6·6 kV and 11 kV often exceeding the values given, designs are available for use on 250 MVA systems at 6·6 kV and 350 MVA at 11 kV, with appropriately higher making capacities (58·0 and 46·9 kA peak respectively) and rated short-time currents (21·9 and 18·4 kA respectively). Additionally, many designs now have the higher normal current and breaking capacity rating of 630 A in accordance with I.E.C. ratings*, while in one design the rating is up to 800 A.

To ensure the ability to close on to fault currents of the magnitude noted, all designs have power closing mechanisms of the spring or spring-assisted type. The method adopted for circuit earthing varies with different designs, some

---

* It is anticipated that in due course, BS 2631 will be brought into line with I.E.C.

using a common switch blade which moves between the 'on', 'off' and 'earth' positions, while in others, separate blades may be used for line switching and for earthing. It is usual to design the unit such that the switch or switches can 'make' on to the specified fault current both when closing on to the line or to earth.

The facility whereby applied high-voltage or injected current tests can be carried out on the cable connected to the switch, again differs with designs, some requiring the insertion of a set of test bushings through an aperture normally covered by an interlocked door, while in others built-in facilities are provided.

An adequate system of interlocks is an essential with all designs. These are necessary, e.g. to prevent the inadvertent operation of the switch from 'on' to 'earth', so that an earthing action must be deliberately required. This is often achieved by requiring that a single operating handle must be relocated in the 'off' position, or two operating handles may be provided which are interlocked so that incorrect operation is impossible. Similarly, access for the insertion of test plugs or the preparatory action for testing when the devices are self contained, can only be undertaken when the switch is in the 'earth' position and movement of the switch to the 'on' position prevented with a test access cover open.

The present-day oil switch appears in two general forms. The first is a self-contained unit with busbars, etc. designed in many cases to line up with and form part of a switchboard in which other units are or may be of the metal-clad oil circuit-breaker type or with fuse-switch units also with busbars. By using two oil switch units and an oil circuit-breaker unit, with the latter controlling a tee-off feed, an *extensible* ring main unit is provided. Alternatively, any number of oil switches may be arranged in switchboard form where the circuits to be controlled are suitable for this application.

The second type is one which has no busbars and is therefore *non-extensible*. It is a form used exclusively in ring main units comprising three circuits, i.e. the ring main circuit in and out and a tee-off feed to a distribution transformer. Oil switches are used in the ring main, while in the tee-off, control may be via another oil switch, a fuse switch or an oil circuit-breaker. In these arrangements, the oil switches are contained within a common enclosure which can also accommodate, when appropriate, the fuses associated with the tee-off circuit. When the latter is controlled by a circuit-breaker, the enclosures for the two oil switches in the ring main surmount the metal-clad breaker enclosure.

Considering first the individual type of oil switch unit with busbars, Fig. 17.1 shows one such design (left) which has a range of normal currents up to 800 A and is for use on systems up to 13·8 kV, lined up with a metal-clad circuit-breaker unit of the vertical isolation type (right). As noted earlier, a second oil switch coupled to the busbars of the assembly shown would provide a ring main unit which could be extended if necessary to allow for the control of other tee-off feeds.

Constructionally, the oil switch is as shown in Fig. 17.2 which shows that the design employs a single blade which can be in the 'on', 'off' or 'earth' positions as indicated at (a), (b) and (c) respectively. With the switch in the 'earth' position, the test access cover can be opened as shown and this operation causes a one-piece epoxy-resin moulding carrying test contacts to be automatically inserted into engagement with the feeder conductors. Before testing can commence

Figure 17.1. High-voltage oil switch (A.E.I.) lined up with an air-insulated metal-clad unit (right) with an oil circuit-breaker of the vertical isolation type (courtesy G.E.C. Switchgear Ltd.)

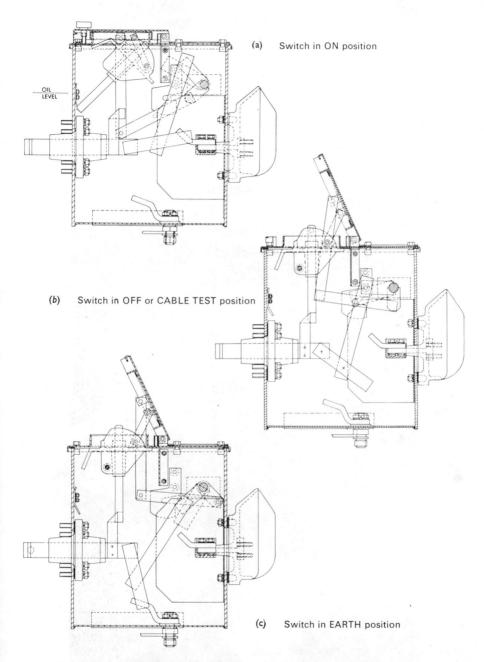

(a)   Switch in ON position

OIL
LEVEL

(b)   Switch in OFF or CABLE TEST position

(c)   Switch in EARTH position

Figure 17.2.   The three positions of the oil switch shown in Figure 17.1 (left) (courtesy G.E.C. Switchgear Ltd.)

however, the switch must be moved back to the 'off' position (b) and when testing is completed, the switch must be returned to the 'earth' position before the access cover can be closed to automatically withdraw the test contacts. With the access cover open, an interlock prevents the switch being moved to 'on'. To prevent the switch being inadvertently moved from 'on' to 'earth', the operating handle has to be removed in the 'off' position and relocated, at the same time actuating a manually-operated interlock, as in Fig. 17.3.

In another design for 11 kV service and again for lining up with a range of metal-clad circuit-breakers or with similar oil switches, the line and earth switch blades are separate elements, operated by a common mechanism but with a single detachable handle which has to be located on an appropriate

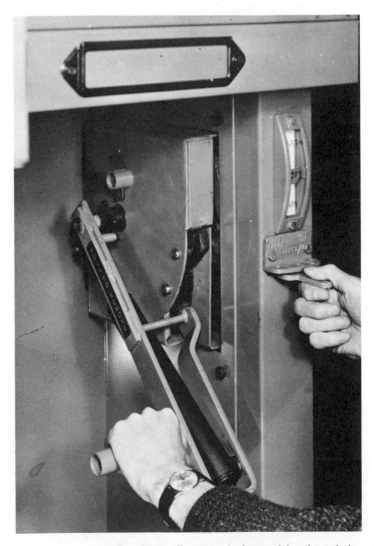

Figure 17.3. The operating handle and manually operated selector of the oil switch shown in Figure 17.1 (left) (courtesy G.E.C. Switchgear Ltd.)

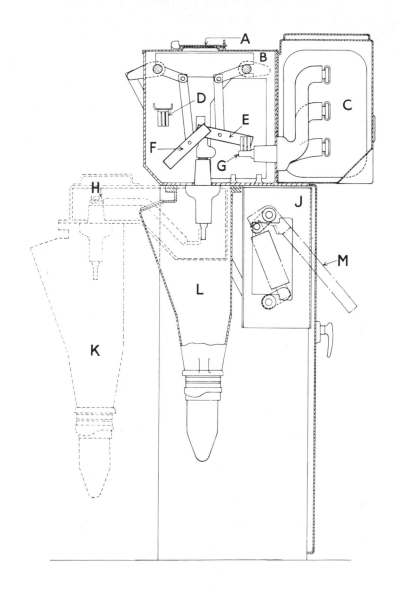

LEGEND

A	TEST ORIFICE COVER	H	ADAPTER CHAMBER FOR REAR CABLE BOX
B	SWITCH CHAMBER	J	OPERATING MECHANISM
C	BUSBAR CHAMBER	K	CABLE BOX WHEN ADAPTER
D	FIXED EARTH CONTACT		CHAMBER FITTED
E	LINE SWITCH BLADE	L	CABLE BOX
F	EARTH SWITCH BLADE	M	DETACHABLE OPERATING
G	FIXED LINE CONTACT		HANDLE

Figure 17.4.   *Sectional view of an 11 kV oil switch unit (courtesy A. Reyrolle & Co. Ltd.)*

operating shaft depending on the required operation, i.e. 'off' to 'on' or 'off' to 'earth'. The design is shown in Fig. 17.4, the operating handle *M* being shown on the upper shaft with the line switch closed. To operate the earth switch, the handle will be relocated on the lower shaft.

With the switch in the 'earth' position, the test orifice cover *A* can be opened so that a three-phase assembly of test plugs can be inserted to make contact at the hinge point to which the feeder cable is connected. Full insertion of the test plugs allow the earth switch to be moved to the 'off' position as shown in Fig.

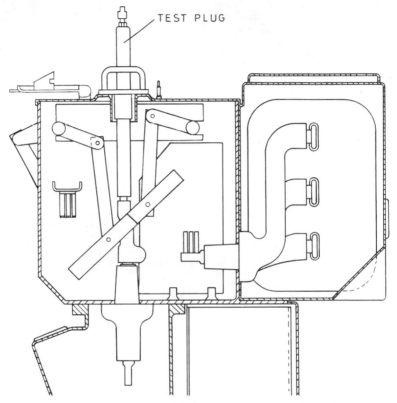

TEST PLUG

Figure 17.5.   Sectional view of the oil switch shown in Figure 17.4 with test plugs fitted (courtesy A. Reyrolle & Co. Ltd.)

17.5, and cable testing can proceed. On completion of testing, the earth switch must be reclosed before the test plugs can be removed.

An oil switch unit designed for use on 33 kV systems is shown in Fig. 17.6. The busbars in this unit are in a compound-filled chamber and are designed for lining up with metal-clad circuit-breaker equipments of the vertical isolation type. All the facilities noted in earlier discussion are provided, but a somewhat different switching procedure is used. This is based on the use of two separate switches, one of these being a selector switch, the position of which determines the function of the second switch, i.e. for 'service' or 'earth'. Separate operating mechanisms and handles are used with interlocks to prevent incorrect operation.

The selector switch is designed for off-load operation but can carry through-fault current for the specified time. No part of the switching duty falls on this

switch, this being the sole function of the line switch which is closed via a spring
assisted mechanism.

A sectional view of this unit is given in Fig. 17.7, the selector switch being seen
in chamber *F* in the 'service' position and the oil switch proper in chamber *E*
in the closed position. An arc-control device is fitted at the fixed contacts of the
oil switch.

Cable testing is carried out via the test bushings *C* inserted through the
orifices as shown to make contact with the cable side of the switch. The cover
over the test orifices is interlocked so that it can only be opened with the selector
switch in the earth position and the oil switch closed. The selector switch cannot
now be moved to the busbars and can only be moved to this position when the
test orifice cover is closed and the oil switch has been opened.

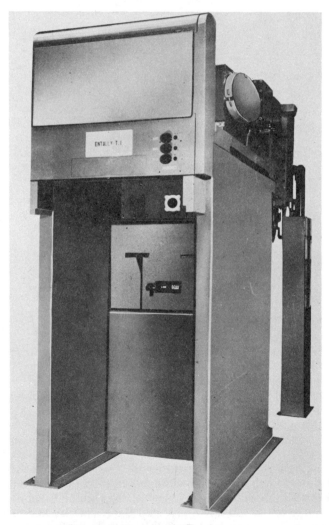

*Figure 17.6.   33 kV oil switch with busbars for lining-up with circuit-breaker units or further oil
switches. The front cover has been removed (courtesy A. Reyrolle & Co. Ltd.)*

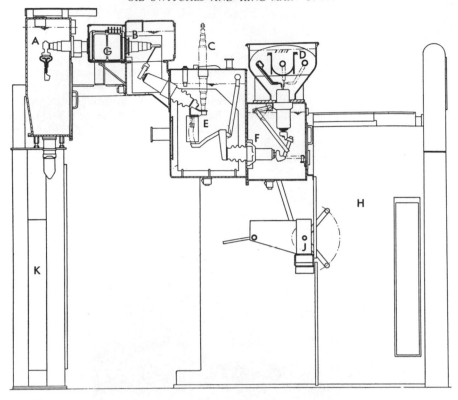

LEGEND

A	CABLE BOX	*F*	SELECTOR CHAMBER
B	ADAPTER CHAMBER	*G*	CURRENT TRANSFORMERS
C	TEST BUSHINGS	*H*	FRAME STANDARD
D	BUSBAR CHAMBER	*J*	OPERATING MECHANISM
E	OIL SWITCH CHAMBER	*K*	CABLE BOX PEDESTAL

Figure 17.7.   Sectional view of the 33 kV unit shown in Figure 17.4 (courtesy A. Reyrolle & Co. Ltd.)

The sectional view shows that current transformers can be fitted in this unit should these be required for indicating, or other instruments.

A number of oil switch units are designed specifically to line up with fuse-switch or switch and fuse units, instead of with circuit-breaker equipments. One such design is that shown in Fig. 17.8 in which separate line and earth switches are employed, each with its own operating handle, but suitably interlocked. Cable testing is via bushings inserted as previously described, through an interlocked access cover.

Considering now the 11 kV non-extensible ring main unit, these normally comprise a three-switch assembly, two being in the ring main and one in the tee-off. The latter in most cases will be associated with high-voltage h.r.c. fuses with ratings up to about 150 A at 6·6 kV and 100 A at 11 kV and of appropriate breaking capacity to suit the system's fault level. These fuses in some designs will be oil insulated, i.e. immersed in oil, and in others will be air insulated.

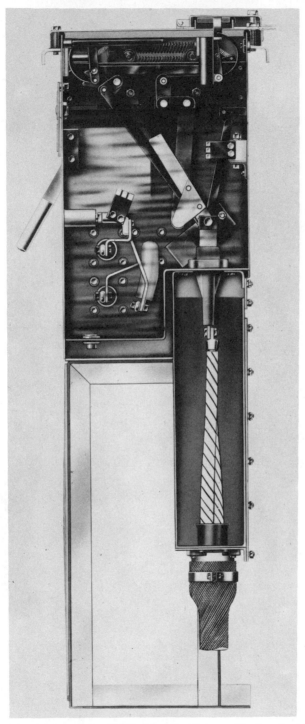

Figure 17.8.   Sectional view of an 11 kV oil switch with integral busbars (courtesy Long & Crawford Ltd.)

539

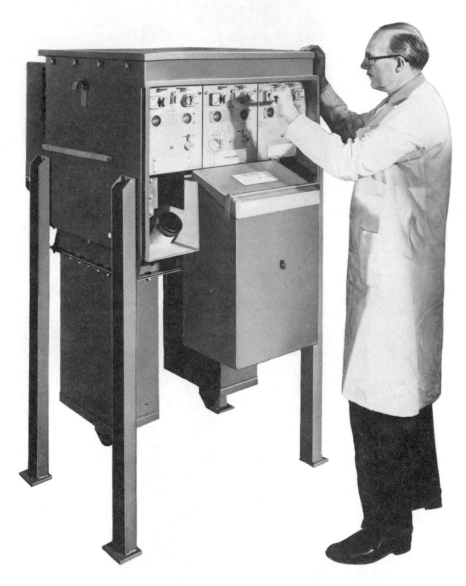

Figure 17.9. English Electric ring main of oil switch unit with oil-insulated fuses in tee-off, weather cover removed (courtesy G.E.C. Switchgear Ltd.)

There are differences of opinion as to the merits of oil or air insulation for the fuses. One advantage of the former is that they can form an integral element of the switch although this is not always so in practice. A disadvantage is that fuse replacement involves messy handling, but as this is an infrequent task it can be tolerated. The most important consideration is to ensure that the fuses used are proved to be oil-tight and with considerably increased reliability in this respect, oil-immersion would appear to be most favoured. If air-insulated

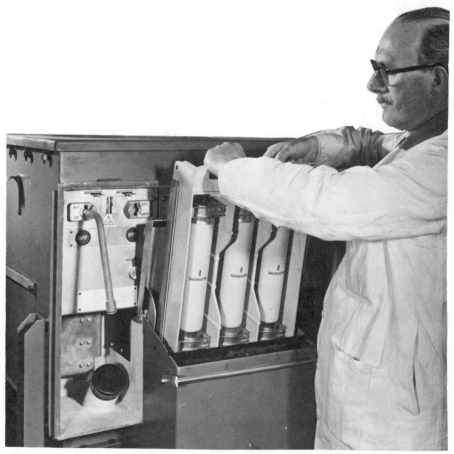

Figure 17.10. The h.r.c. fuse carriage used in the English Electric ring-main unit of Figure 17.9 being withdrawn from its oil tank (courtesy G.E.C. Switchgear Ltd.)

fuses are used, these have to be accommodated in a separate chamber and cannot form any part of the controlling switch.

Ring main units of the non-extensible type are extensively used by the British Electricity Boards on distribution networks and they have prepared and published a standard specification (B.E.B.S.-S16:1968) with which units used by them must comply.

One such unit is that shown in Fig. 17.9, which is a design that uses oil immersed fuses*. In this unit, the three oil switches are contained in a common tank of

* An alternative design with air-insulated fuses is available.

oil, seen in the illustration immediately behind the operating facias. The fuses are in a separate oil filled compartment seen as a forward projection below the operating panel.

Each switch has 'on', 'off' and 'earth' positions and has an independent manual (spring) closing mechanism with a relocatable handle for 'off-on' and 'off-earth' operations. A spring-biased sliding interlock gate ensures access only to one of the two operating shafts.

The three fuses are carried on a removable carriage which can be taken bodily from its compartment as shown in Fig. 17.10. This operation requires first that the associated switch be in the 'off' position and that an interlock be operated to free the carriage. The latter has two positions, 'service' and 'isolated'. The

Figure 17.11. 11 kV ring-main unit with oil-insulated fuses in tee-off (courtesy Long & Crawford Ltd.)

isolated condition is brought about by opening the cover of the chamber which disconnects the carriage by tilting it forward through 10°, thus providing double disconnection of the fuses. It is not necessary to remove the carriage completely to change a fuse as the carriage can be latched partly lifted but giving ample access. The operating mechanism for the associated switch is locked 'off' until the fuse carriage is returned to the 'service' position and the access cover reclosed.

The fuses are of the striker-pin type so that operation of any one or more fuses automatically trips open the three-phase oil switch and locks it in that position until the fuse or fuses have been replaced. If the switch should be closed on to a

Figure 17.12. Fuse carriage assembly used in the unit shown in Figure 17.11, alternative 10in and 14in fuses illustrated (courtesy Long & Crawford Ltd.)

fault, the mechanism gives full closure to ensure that the fault is interrupted by the fuses before the switch trips open. Facilities for testing the cables or the transformer are provided by means of integral three-phase bushings located beneath the associated mechanisms.

In another design, shown in Fig. 17.11, the two ring-main oil switches and an oil fuse-switch are contained in a common tank. The three fuses here are mounted on a carriage as in Fig. 17.12 which surmounts the tee-off switch, the fuses being accessible via an interlocked top cover, which, when opened, gives visible indication that the fuses are isolated.

543

Each ring-main oil switch has its own power (spring) closing mechanism with separate handle locations for the 'off' to 'on' and 'off' to 'earth' operations. The tee-off fuse-switch mechanism is again spring assisted, and is located, as seen in Fig. 17.11, to the left of the unit.

Testing of cables is by means of a three-phase bushing assembly inserted through an interlocked cover, generally as described earlier for other designs.

It is of interest in passing to note that in both of the designs just described, earth fault indicators can be provided along with the necessary current transformers. When fitted, these are accommodated in a special cable-gland assembly

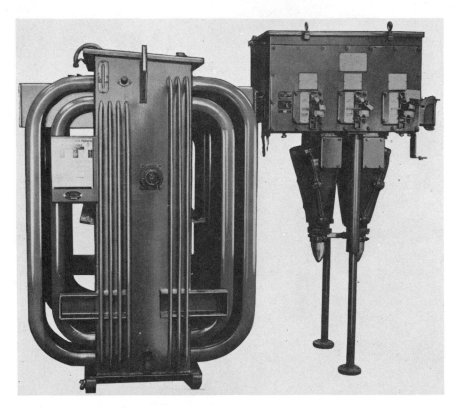

Figure 17.13. 11 kV ring-main unit with three oil switches. Tee-off, with direct connection to power transformer (courtesy A. Reyrolle & Co. Ltd.)

fitted in place of the normal gland on the cable box, the current transformer being a ring-type core-balance design through which the cable cores pass. Both designs can also be assembled for direct connection to a power transformer in the tee-off.

An arrangement of the latter type is shown in Fig. 17.13, but here there are no fuses in the tee-off, the transformer being controlled by an oil switch only. As shown in the sectional view in Fig. 17.14, the three switches are contained in a common tank. As in other designs each switch is of the three position type with spring assisted operating mechanisms and separate operating shafts for 'off' to 'on' and 'off' to 'earth' switching.

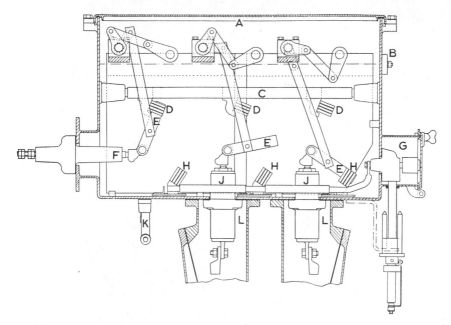

A TOP COVER
B OIL-LEVEL INDICATOR
C INTERCONNECTING BARS
D FIXED LOAD CONTACTS
E MOVING-CONTACT BLADES
F TEE-OFF INSULATOR

G TESTING CHAMBER
H FIXED EARTHING-CONTACTS
J CABLE-BOX INSULATOR
K DRAIN PIPE
L CABLE BOXES

Figure 17.14. Sectional view of the triple oil-switch ring-main unit shown in Figure 17.13 (courtesy A. Reyrolle & Co. Ltd.)

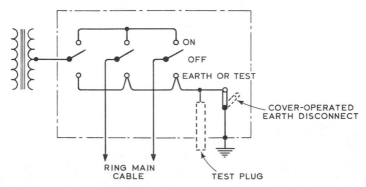

Figure 17.15. Connection diagram for the ring-main unit shown in Figures 17.13 and 17.14, for direct connection to a power transformer. Alternatively, the tee-off can be a cable feed (courtesy A. Reyrolle & Co. Ltd.)

In this design it is seen that a common cable testing chamber G permits testing on any selected circuit, via a three-phase set of test plugs inserted in the base of the chamber. The procedure requires that the circuit to be tested is first earthed at its oil switch, then a padlock is removed from the chamber front cover, and a sliding cover on the underside is moved to expose the testing orifices for the plugs to be inserted as shown. The front cover of the testing chamber is then opened to remove automatically the earth, and the cable test can now be applied. After testing, the cable is discharged by earthing in an approved manner and

Figure 17.16. 6·6/11 kV ring-main unit with oil switches in ring main and a.c. circuit-breaker in the tee-off. The circuit-breaker is shown withdrawn from the housing (courtesy A. Reyrolle & Co. Ltd.)

the switch is restored to normal. Figure 17.15 is a diagrammatic arrangement for this unit and illustrates how the connection to earth is via a hinged link operated from closed to open by the testing chamber cover as described above.

Most of the non-extensible arrangements shown are suitable for both indoor and outdoor use and represent only a few of the many available.

For indoor use only, and where it is required to use a circuit-breaker in the tee-off, an arrangement such as that shown in Fig. 17.16 is typical. Here a circuit-breaker of the vertical isolation type is surmounted by an oil-filled chamber containing the two ring-main oil switches each comprising separate line and earth switching elements with independently-operated mechanisms using re-locatable and reversible handles as previously discussed. Testing is normally by means of test-plugs as in other designs, but if required, built-in test bushings can be provided. This arrangement is of course non-extensible, as is that shown in Figs. 17.17 and 17.18. Here again the tee-off is controlled by a circuit-breaker of the vertical isolation type with facilities for earthing either the cable or the busbars by the transfer breaker method (see Chapter 20). Figure 17.18, showing a rear view, also shows the access cover being opened preparatory for cable testing on one side of the ring main.

Figure 17.17.   11 kV ring-main unit (Switchgear & Cowans) with oil switches in the ring main and an oil circuit-breaker in the tee-off (courtesy G.E.C. Switchgear Ltd.)

Figure 17.18.   Rear view of the ring-main unit shown in Figure 17.17 showing test access cover (courtesy G.E.C. Switchgear Ltd.)

REFERENCE
1. *Oil Switches for Alternating Current Systems*, BS 2631:1955

BIBLIOGRAPHY
ARMSTRONG, T.V., 'Portable Weatherproof Switchgear', *Elect. Rev.*, 3 April (1970)

Chapter 18

High-voltage load-breaking switches

In suitable circumstances, a load-breaking fault-making switch can be used as a substitute for the more costly circuit-breaker, and at the same time provide switching facilities not possible with the normal off-load isolating switch. This has been considered in Chapter 9 and some examples of situations where they can profitably be used have been noted. In that chapter also, the switching and through-fault capabilities required of such switches have been summarised, while in Chapter 17 we have seen that these requirements can be met by designs of oil switch up to 33 kV.

Oil, however, is not essential to this performance, and numerous air-break designs have been proved successful up to 15 kV in the U.K. and up to 36 kV on the continent. At higher voltages, recent developments have shown that designs right up to 765 kV are possible, but using other techniques for circuit interruption, e.g. compressed air or SF_6 gas, developments which arise directly from circuit-breaker designs using these techniques.

In the air-break range, the switches can be used either with or without h.r.c. fuses. When they are used with these, most designs are based on fuses with striker pins arranged to trip open the three-phase switch when any fuse operates. In both forms, however, the making ability of the switch is the same, so that proving tests in this respect are made on unfused switches. If required, other automatic features can be added, e.g. shunt or no-volt trip coils, a facility which enables remote tripping to be arranged or intertripping with other apparatus such as a circuit-breaker on the secondary side of a power transformer, the opening of which simultaneously trips the load-breaking switch on the primary side.

The combination of the switch with h.r.c. fuses is especially advantageous when used to control the infeed to a high-voltage distribution or motor control board in that not only can the complete board be isolated on-load, but the h.r.c. fuses also provide ideal short-circuit protection against busbar faults.

While load-breaking switches in general need not have a breaking capacity in excess of their normal current rating, those employed on motor circuits should preferably be capable of interrupting the stalled current of the motor with which they are associated. Thus, the 3·3 kV switch shown in Fig. 18.1 with normal current ratings of 630/1 250 A can interrupt currents up to about 3 000 A at 0·3 p.f. In another design shown in Fig. 18.2, and alternatively available for use on 3·3, 6·6 or 11 kV systems, the normal current rating is 630 A but the switch can safely interrupt 3 150 A at the appropriate voltage and 0·2 p.f.

The switch shown in Fig. 18.1 is one in which arc extinction is achieved within an arc chute, the material of which produces a hard gas under the influence of the arc and which quenches the arc. It can be seen that separate main and auxiliary switch blades are used, the former closing into contacts outside the arc chute, and the latter inside the chute. The design is such that on closing, the main blades close first and thus the duty of fault-making falls on them. The auxiliary blade then automatically closes. On opening, the reverse operation

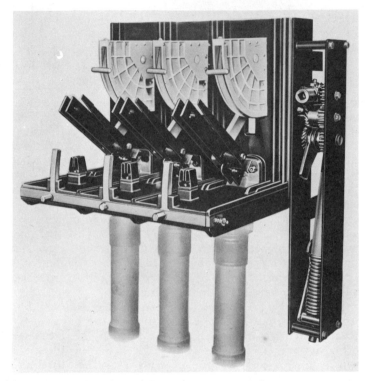

Figure 18.1. 3·3 kV load-breaking fault-making switch with cover and phase barriers removed (courtesy E.M.P. Electric Ltd.)

takes place, i.e. the auxiliary blade opens last so that all arcing takes place within the chute.

To achieve the high making and breaking capacity, high-speed closure and opening is essential, and this is obtained by a spring-toggle operating mechanism which gives closing and opening times of the order of 0·025 s.

The contacts seen on the horizontal platform of the chassis afford a means of earthing, the movement of the main blades from the normal open position to earth being made by the switch-operating handle, but to prevent inadvertent operation to earth the operation is only possible after passing through a gated device. It is of interest to note that the chassis is an all-insulated construction in cast resin, designed with integral slots to locate interphase barriers and an outer case.

In the switch shown in Fig. 18.2, each switch pole comprises two hinged blades carrying main and arcing moving contacts, the latter mating with fixed contacts in an arcing nozzle. The interrupting ability of this switch is ensured by (a) a self-generated jet of air directed into the arc through the fixed arcing contact, and (b) by the generation of an extinguishing gas by the action of the arc on the material from which the arcing nozzle is made. The jet of air is a constant quantity regardless of the current to be interrupted and is particularly useful when the switch has to interrupt small inductive and capacitive currents when

Figure 18.2.   3·3/11 kV load-breaking fault-making switch with striker pin and h.r.c. fuses (courtesy N.E.B.B., Skien, Norway and the former Belmos Peebles Switchgear Ltd.)

gas generation is small. At higher currents, the jet of air augments the greater gas generation to give successful interruption. High-speed closing and opening of the switch is obtained through a spring mechanism independent of the operator.

Switches of the types noted are intended for use, without fuses, on systems where the fault level is 150 MVA at 3·3 kV. At 6·6 kV and 11 kV the system fault levels are 250 and 350 MVA, with fault-making and through-fault ratings appropriate to these levels.

Figure 18.3 illustrates a switch suitable for higher voltage systems up to 66 kV. This is available in single and double-break types, the illustration showing the latter form. It is, basically, a rotating pillar isolator to which an interrupter head has been added at each break, the arcing contact system within the heads being operated by the main isolator blade as it opens and timed to ensure that current is interrupted within the head and not at the main contacts. On reclosure the circuit is made at the main contacts, and when these are in full contact the arcing contact system is reset ready for a subsequent operation, but not forming part of the circuit.

A detail of a typical interrupter head is given in Fig. 18.4 from which it is seen that the moving-contact spindle is driven (from external levers) by an internal

Figure 18.3. 'SafetibrakE' interrupter switch, one pole only shown (courtesy Switchgear & Equipment Ltd.)

linkage designed to give an approximately straight-line motion. This linkage is spring loaded so that it remains in the open or closed positions and must be positively driven in each direction by strikers attached to the main blades.

At the trailing end of the moving-contact spindle, there is a gas-producing plastic follower, the purpose of which is to confine the arc between the contacts and in close proximity to the horn-fibre bore lining. As in all devices using gas-generating materials, gradual erosion will occur and in due course such parts must be replaced.

Transfer of current from the main switch blades to the interrupter heads during the opening sequence is effected by a bow-shaped contact which slides across the serrated face of the interrupter mechanism housing (see Fig. 18.4) as the isolator blade swings open. This opening sequence and also that of closing

552

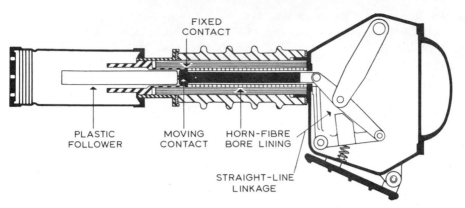

FIXED
CONTACT

PLASTIC
FOLLOWER

MOVING
CONTACT

HORN-FIBRE
BORE LINING

STRAIGHT-LINE
LINKAGE

Figure 18.4.   Sectional view of an interrupter head used on the switch shown in Figure 18.3 (courtesy Switchgear & Equipment Ltd.)

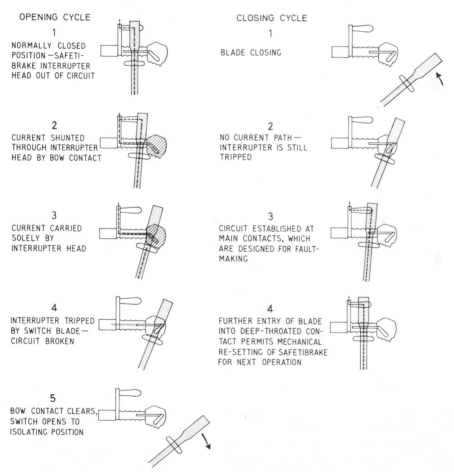

OPENING CYCLE

1
NORMALLY CLOSED
POSITION —SAFETI-
BRAKE INTERRUPTER
HEAD OUT OF CIRCUIT

2
CURRENT SHUNTED
THROUGH INTERRUPTER
HEAD BY BOW CONTACT

3
CURRENT CARRIED
SOLELY BY
INTERRUPTER HEAD

4
INTERRUPTER TRIPPED
BY SWITCH BLADE—
CIRCUIT BROKEN

5
BOW CONTACT CLEARS,
SWITCH OPENS TO
ISOLATING POSITION

CLOSING CYCLE

1
BLADE CLOSING

2
NO CURRENT PATH—
INTERRUPTER IS STILL
TRIPPED

3
CIRCUIT ESTABLISHED AT
MAIN CONTACTS, WHICH
ARE DESIGNED FOR FAULT-
MAKING

4
FURTHER ENTRY OF BLADE
INTO DEEP-THROATED CON-
TACT PERMITS MECHANICAL
RE-SETTING OF SAFETIBRAKE
FOR NEXT OPERATION

Figure 18.5.   Interrupting and isolating sequence on opening and the making sequence on closing of a 'SafetibrakE' load switch (courtesy Switchgear & Equipment Ltd.)

553

is shown diagrammatically in Fig. 18.5, with the bow contact on the main blade below the interrupter head. While giving adequate contact pressure the bow contact ensures minimum friction while the serrations help to clear its surface of deposits of dirt or ice.

Designed with a fault-making capacity and a 3 s through-fault capacity of 18·1 kA, the load interrupting ability is as follows:

Switch type	Interrupting ability
single break	600 A at 11 kV and
	400 A at 33 kV
double break	600 A at 33 kV and
	400 A at 66 kV

and the switch can deal with inductive and capacitive currents in the range of 10–40 A depending on type and voltage.

In our discussion on switching systems in Chapter 9, note was taken of the practice of using fault-throwing switches in transformer circuits teed-off a main feeder and where no circuit-breaker is used in the tee-off. It was indicated further how such an arrangement would be improved by installing a load-breaking switch of the type under consideration in the tee-off.

This scheme has been shown in Chapter 9, Fig. 9.23(c), and although the fault-throwing switch is not load-breaking (only fault-making), its association with such switches makes it convenient to note the design here. This can be either of the double-make type which can be used to throw a fault across two lines or one line to earth, or of the single-make type which can only be used to fault one line to earth.

Typical of a double-make type is the 11 kV unit shown in Fig. 18.6. When used for line to earth fault-throwing, *one* of the pedestal insulators carrying the fixed contacts can be replaced by a fabricated steel pedestal subject to there being no objection to the steelwork becoming live. This saves cost and can, if required, be taken further using a steel pedestal for the centre-rotating element.

Figure 18.7 shows a single-make fault-throwing switch for 132 kV service. With this the line is earthed through the top contact, the blade and a heavy flexible conductor to ground. With the double-make design, two arrangements can be provided for operating the switch, i.e. spring-close hand-reset or spring-close spring-open, while for single-make types, only the former is used.

Switches fitted with the hand-reset type are normally arranged for 'instantaneous' closure, the inherent operating time from initiation of the trip mechanism to complete closure being of the order of 0·2 s for 11 kV and 66 kV switches and 0·4 s for 132 kV, but if required, a time-delay device can be added. A command to close can be initiated either by hand at the switch, by a solenoid actuated from a remote point, or automatically, typically as in Fig. 9.23(c). The mechanism has to be reset by hand ready for subsequent operation.

With the alternative mechanism the switch can be both closed and opened, via motor-charged springs, from a remote-control point or linked with an automatic installation. An inherent delay of 7 s from initiation to full closure is included, making the switch suitable for short-circuiting a 'Petersen' (arc-suppression) coil as discussed in Chapter 7 in relation to Fig. 7.5. Additional delay can be provided if operational requirements make this desirable.

A load-breaking fault-making switch for use in the service voltage range of 110–150 kV is illustrated in Fig. 18.8. It shows the isolator blades open (vertical).

In series with the latter, interrupter heads with double-break main and arcing contacts are provided. These heads are sealed chambers filled with the gas SF_6 under pressure.

Figure 18.9 illustrates the sequence of operation on opening, from which it is seen that when the isolator is closed both the main and arcing contact systems (in parallel) are closed and carry current. When an opening operation is initiated, the two current paths operate in conjunction and consecutively, the main contacts opening first leaving the current carried by the arcing contacts. When the main contacts are fully open, they cause the release of a latch holding the arcing contacts and these now open to break the current. This sequence is completed *before* the isolator blade leaves its contacts so that no current is broken on the isolator.

Figure 18.6. 11 kV double-make fault-throwing switch (courtesy Switchgear & Equipment Ltd.)

Operation of the two sets of contacts in the interrupter is from outside that unit via push-rods driven from a sequencing device associated with the isolator blade operating mechanism. The contacts are closed against spring pressure and latched, i.e. as in circuit-breaker practice. The main contact system in the interrupter is a low-impedance system designed to carry the normal current rating of the switch continuously and with a short-time rating for through-fault conditions appropriate to fault levels of 3 500 MVA in an 800 A switch and 5 000 MVA in a 1 200 A switch, both at 132 kV.

From sketch 5 in Fig. 18.9 it is seen that when the isolator blade is fully open, the main and arcing contacts in the interrupter automatically reclose ready for the circuit to be restored by closing the isolator blade. It is the latter therefore

Figure 18.7.   132 kV single-make fault-throwing switch (courtesy Switchgear & Equipment Ltd.)

which must be capable of closing on to a fault and this requires that a power-operated mechanism is employed to ensure high-speed closure. For the switch described, this mechanism comprises an electrically-driven hydraulic pump, a hydro-pneumatic accumulator, hydraulic ram, reservoir and valve system. With the switch in service, a charge is stored at high pressure in the accumulator ready to be released. When an operating command is given, the pump motor starts up and the resultant movement of the hydraulic fluid operates the valve system to release the stored charge to the ram. After operation, the motor continues to run to restore the charge in the accumulator ready for a subsequent operation.

Figure 18.10 shows one pole of a 275 kV load-breaking fault-making switch, again using SF_6 in the interrupter heads as the insulating and arc-quenching

Figure 18.8.   132 kV SF₆ load-breaking fault-making switching isolator with isolator blades open; installed at the C.E.G.B. Addington substation (courtesy Switchgear & Equipment Ltd.)

medium. In this design, double-break interrupter heads are fitted on each side of a rotating centre-post insulator, the heads rotating with the post so that isolation is achieved at contacts at each extremity and on the outer post insulators as shown in Fig. 18.11. Operation of the rotating post is normally by compressed air using standard industrial equipment, but a motor-driven hydraulic equipment similar to that noted earlier can be used.

Within the interrupter heads, concentric contacts are used, the outer contacts for main current-carrying and fault making, the inner ones for load breaking. To ensure correct voltage division across the four breaks, external resistors are

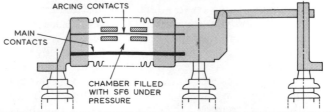

ARCING CONTACTS

MAIN CONTACTS

CHAMBER FILLED WITH SF6 UNDER PRESSURE

1 SWITCHING ISOLATOR IN THE NORMALLY CLOSED POSITION. CURRENT IS CARRIED THROUGH THE INTERRUPTER UNIT BY THE MAIN CURRENT PATH AND THE INTERRUPTER PATH IN PARALLEL

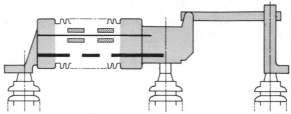

2 FIRST MOVEMENT OF CENTRE-ROTATING PEDESTAL TRIPS THE MAIN CURRENT CONTACTS, LEAVING THE FULL LOAD MOMENTARILY CARRIED BY THE INTERRUPTER CONTACTS

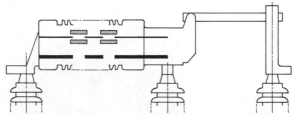

3 THE FULL OPENING OF THE MAIN CURRENT PATH AUTOMATICALLY TRIPS THE INTERRUPTER MECHANISM AND THE CIRCUIT IS BROKEN

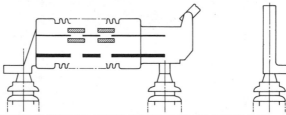

4 FURTHER MOVEMENT OF THE CENTRE ROTATING PEDESTAL OPENS THE ISOLATOR BLADE

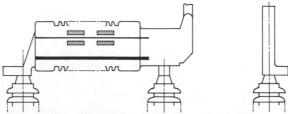

5 DURING THE LATTER PART OF THE STROKE OF THE ISOLATOR BLADE THE INTERRUPTER UNIT IS RE-SET, THE TWO CURRENT PATHS BEING RECLOSED

Figure 18.9.   Operating sequence on opening of the 132 kV switching isolator shown in Figure 18.8 (courtesy Switchgear & Equipment Ltd.)

connected across the breaks. With the switch in the open position, full conventional air clearances are provided. When a closing sequence is initiated, the first movement rotates the centre post until the external contacts are closed, thus connecting the voltage equalising resistors across the supply. During the second part of the closing operation, the four main contacts in the interrupter heads are closed independently of the initial movement of the assembly. Concurrently the arcing contacts are closed in readiness for a subsequent opening operation and all contacts are held closed by a latch in the operating mechanism.

Figure 18.10. One pole of a 275 kV SF$_6$ load-breaking switch exhibited at the 1969 Hanover Fair (courtesy Switchgear & Equipment Ltd.)

The opening sequence is in three stages. First, the trip coil releases the holding latch to allow push-off springs to open the main contacts in the interrupter, the current now being carried by the arcing contacts. During this stage, 'puffer' pistons come into action to increase the gas pressure around the arcing contacts, which now open at high speed. The final stage is reached when a latch is released to allow the centre posts to rotate to the isolated position.

With this switch and that noted in Fig. 18.8, fully-rated earthing switches can be provided at either or both sides of the unit. Rated at 2 000 A this switch can interrupt load currents up to this value, transformer magnetising currents up to 100 A, line charging currents up to 200 A and capacitor-bank switching up to 400 A. Its making capacity is 97 kA peak and it has a short-time rating of 37·8 kA for 1 s.

The SF$_6$ gas interrupter unit is also the basic element in a switch for use on systems up to 400 kV, using, at this voltage, four interrupter units per pole in series and disposed in pairs on each side of a rotating centre post isolator as shown in Fig. 18.12. In passing it can be noted that the two parts of this arrangement, i.e. the circuit interrupters on the one hand and the isolator on the other, can be installed as separate units with individual operating mechanisms interlocked to ensure the correct sequence of operation. In such an arrangement, the two interrupter support columns each with two interrupter units would be assembled in close formation as shown schematically in Fig. 18.13, and the separate isolator could be of any type preferred by the user. It has been noted in an article by Joyce[1] that this form is to be preferred for applications involving

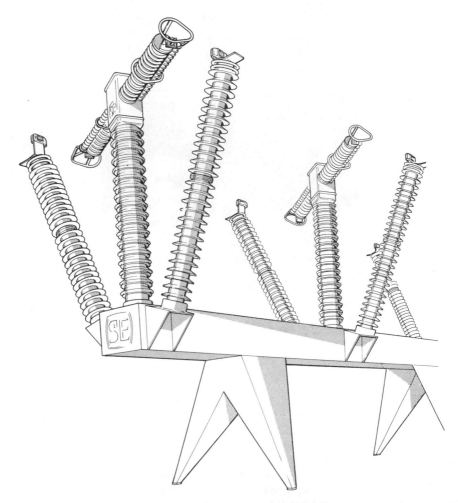

Figure 18.11. Part of the 275 kV switching isolator shown in Figure 18.10 showing interrupter heads on the rotating centre post in the isolated position (courtesy Switchgear & Equipment Ltd.)

frequent on-load switching since maintenance of the interrupter units is then helped by the fact that the isolator is separate from the switch.

Fig. 18.14 shows in some detail a pair of interrupter units and their supporting column, one unit being shown in cross-section and the column in part section. Each interrupter comprises a porcelain chamber containing main and arcing contacts and filled with SF_6 gas at a pressure of 4.5 atm ($4.6 \times 10^5 N/m^2$). Interruption is aided by the gas being caused to flow through an insulated nozzle mounted on the moving contact. This flow is obtained by means of a puffer piston mechanically coupled to the moving contact and moving in a cylinder

Figure 18.12.   A three-phase 400 kV SF_6 switching isolator (English Electric h.v. Switchgear Div.) being prepared for tests (courtesy G.E.C. Switchgear Ltd.)

formed by the tubular copper connection associated with the moving contact and mounted on the upper mechanism housing. When closed, the two tubular connectors are bridged by a tubular moving contact which makes contact with fingers formed on the ends of each connection. During an opening operation, butt-type arcing contacts stay in contact after the moving contact separates from the outer tubular connector. When the arcing contacts part, the arc is drawn between them within the nozzle, by which time the puffer piston will have caused a flow of gas through the nozzle, resulting in de-ionisation and interruption at current zero.

Operation of the interrupter contact system is from a power-operated mechanism using compressed air. This drives the moving contacts of a complete three-phase switch to both the closed and open positions via rods passing up the hollow

561

support columns to a linkage system at the junction of a pair of interrupter heads.

The rotating isolator blades are separately operated by a hydraulic mechanism, but suitably interlocked with the interrupter mechanism to ensure the correct sequence of operation.

The support column, like the interrupter heads, is gas filled at the same pressure and this gas is free to pass between the column and the interrupter heads, but only through filters designed to absorb any decomposition products caused by arcing. Similar filters are provided inside each interrupter head for the same purpose.

The 400 kV combination shown in Fig. 18.12 is designed for use on systems where the fault level can be as high as 35 000 MVA, i.e. the level on the C.E.G.B. 400 kV system in the U.K. The normal current rating is 4 000 A and load currents

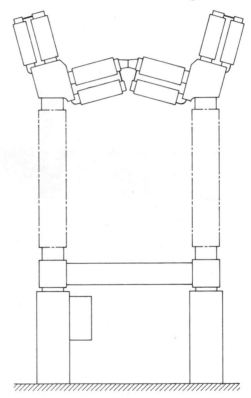

Figure 18.13. Elevation of one pole of an English Electric (h.v. Switchgear Div.) 400 kV load-breaking switch with four interrupter units in series; isolator mounted separately (courtesy G.E.C. Switchgear Ltd.)

up to this magnitude can be interrupted at 0·7 p.f., while it can make on to fault currents of 154 kA peak and has a through-fault rating of 60·6 kA r.m.s. for 3 s. Its interrupting ability for cable-charging current is 400 A r.m.s. and for reactive currents is many times in excess of the highest reactor current presently quoted at this voltage (i.e. 290 A) at 0·05 p.f.

Apart from the purely air-break types noted initially (for a limited voltage range), our study of high-voltage load-breaking fault-making switches has been

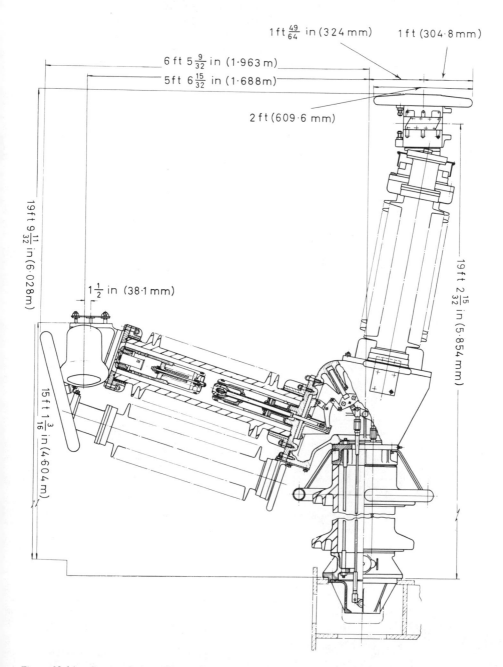

1 ft $\frac{49}{64}$ in (324 mm)   1 ft (304·8 mm)

6 ft 5 $\frac{9}{32}$ in (1·963 m)

5 ft 6 $\frac{15}{32}$ in (1·688 m)

2 ft (609·6 mm)

19 ft 9 $\frac{11}{32}$ in (6·028 m)

1 $\frac{1}{2}$ in (38·1 mm)

19 ft 2 $\frac{15}{32}$ in (5·854 mm)

15 ft 1 $\frac{3}{16}$ in (4·604 m)

Figure 18.14.   Sectional view of part of a support column with two interrupter heads used at each terminal of the switch shown in Figure 18.12 (courtesy G.E.C. Switchgear Ltd.)

563

concerned with designs in which the interrupting process takes place in chambers filled with SF_6 gas under pressure, full isolation following interruption being achieved at a sequentially operated off-load isolator connected in series with the interrupter units. This isolator also has the duty of reclosing the circuit, and, if called upon to do so, to make on to a fault current of peak magnitude.

This interrupting/isolating procedure is not very different from that used in air-blast circuit-breakers for use at the lower end of the voltage and breaking-capacity ranges (see Chapter 2, Fig. 2.10 and Chapter 15), the difference being that here currents of short-circuit magnitude in addition to load currents have

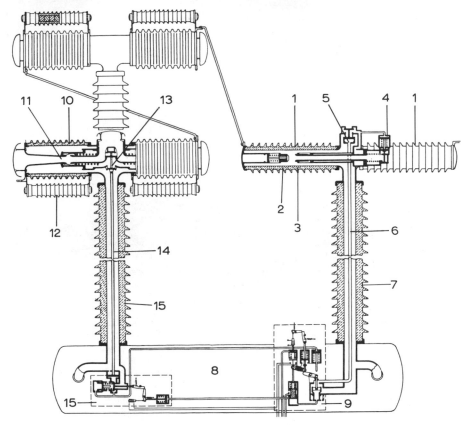

LEGEND

1. ISOLATING CHAMBERS
2. FIXED ISOLATING CONTACT (OPEN)
3. MOVING ISOLATING CONTACT (OPEN)
4. BLAST VALVE
5. ISOLATING CHAMBER VALVE
6. CONTROL TUBE
7. ISOLATING CHAMBER COLUMN
8. MAIN AIR RECEIVER
9. ISOLATING CHAMBER MAIN CONTACT UNIT
10. INTERRUPTER (IMPULSE) CHAMBER
11. INTERRUPTING CONTACTS (CLOSED)
12. HIGH RESISTANCES IN PARALLEL
13. IMPULSE CHAMBER VALVE
14. CONTROL ROD
15. IMPULSE CHAMBER COLUMN
16. IMPULSE CHAMBER CONTROL UNIT

Figure 18.15. Section through one pole of a 245 kV permanently-pressurised air-blast circuit-breaker with four interrupter chambers and two isolating chambers (courtesy Brown Boveri & Co. Ltd.)

to be interrupted and such interruption takes place in a high-velocity blast of air at high pressure.

At the highest transmission voltages, a sequentially operated isolator in air presents many design problems, and as we have seen in Chapter 15, extra-high-voltage air-blast circuit-breakers today have no such isolators. In many designs, isolation is achieved at the main breaker contacts within the interrupter heads, these contacts remaining open after interruption with air at full pressure maintained in the gap. Such designs as we have noted are designated *permanently pressurised.*

In a continental design of air-blast circuit-breaker however, and with a voltage range of 72·5–765 kV, the principle of allowing the interrupting contacts

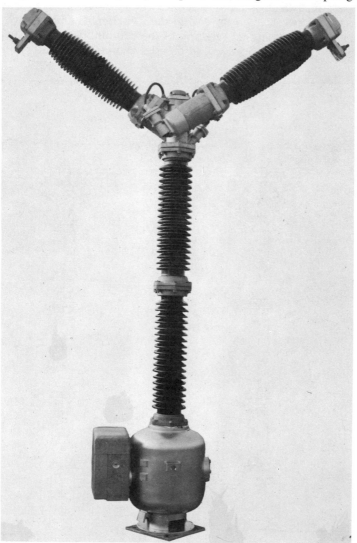

Figure 18.16. One pole of a 245 kV pneumatic load-breaking fault-making switch (courtesy Brown Boveri & Co. Ltd.)

to reclose after interruption has been maintained, and full isolation is achieved sequentially in one or more air-blast isolating heads, the contacting elements in these remaining open with air at full pressure in the head to establish the necessary electric strength in the gaps. The duty of restoring the circuit, including fault-making, resides in these isolating heads.

This design is illustrated typically in Fig. 18.15 and has been noted in this chapter because it is these isolator heads which have been used to produce a pneumatic load-breaking fault-making switch covering the same voltage range as for the circuit-breaker from which the heads are derived.

Figure 18.16 shows one pole for such a switch for a rated voltage of 245 kV. It is seen that a relatively small air receiver at the base is surmounted by an insulating column which contains the control system and forms the compressed-air connection between the receiver and the switching chambers, two in series (electrically) in 'V' formation at the top of the column. For a service voltage of 123 kV, only one isolator head would be used, mounted vertically at the top of

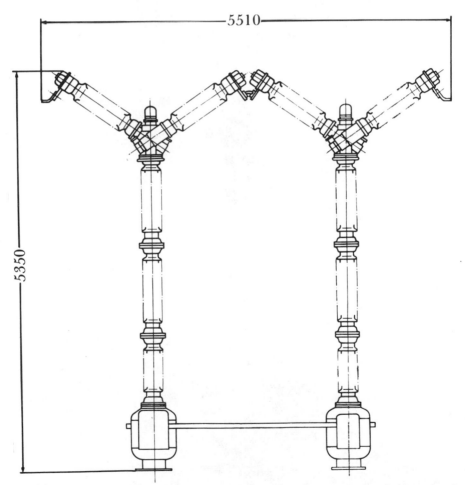

Figure 18.17.   One pole of a 420 kV pneumatic load-breaking fault-making switch (dimensions in mm, courtesy Brown Boveri & Co. Ltd.)

the supporting column, while at 420 kV, four such heads connected in series and supported on two insulating columns would be employed as indicated in Fig. 18.17.

The air used for arc quenching and insulation is also used for actuating the contacts. Such operation can be on a triple-pole or single-pole basis, the latter being required when the switch is used for earthing.

The ratings assigned to this switch indicate a normal current rating of 2 000 A which is also the current it can interrupt (at 0·7 p.f.). Its making capacity is 170 kA peak and its short-time rating is 70 kA for 1 or 3 s. The operating times achieved are extremely short, the time from a 'break' command until contacts part being 25 ms, while from a 'make' command until contacts touch the time is 55 ms.

The use of this type of switch does of course demand the existence of compressed-air plant, but as in the main it will be used at sites where such plant is available, e.g. for air-blast circuit-breakers or for pneumatic operation of other apparatus, this should rarely be an additional cost or complication.

REFERENCE

1. JOYCE, W.J., '400 kV Load-break Fault-make Switch Isolator', *Elect. Rev.*, 7 June (1968)

BIBLIOGRAPHY

ANON., 'New Designs of High-voltage Substations and Overhead Lines Cut Costs', *Elect. Rev.*, 29 Jan. (1971)

ANON., 'Switching Isolators in h.v. Substations', *Elect. Rev.*, 26 July (1968)

BARCHETTI, H., FREY, W. and KÖPPL, G., 'High-voltage Load Switches for 72·5–750 kV, *Brown Boveri Rev.*, **55** No. 4/5, April/May (1968)

COLBERT, H.J., '3·3 kV On-load Isolators', *Elect. Rev.*, 29 March (1968)

GARRARD, C.J.O., 'High-voltage Distribution Switchgear', *Proc. I.E.E.*, **116** No. 6, June (1969)

KÖPPL, G., 'Load Switches in h.v. and e.h.v. Networks: Interesting Applications for a New Type of Unit', *Brown Boveri Rev.*, **54** No. 12, Dec. (1967)

Chapter 19

Medium-voltage switchgear (up to 660 V)

The diverse nature of medium-voltage installations and of the circuits to be controlled is such as to make it impossible to suggest that any one form of switchgear is appropriate for a particular application, so much depending on what is required of the chosen type in the way of switching facilities, loading, its position on the system as a whole and on technical considerations such as protection, fault levels, etc.

The range from which a choice can be made extends from switchboards comprising full circuit-breaker units (oil or air) such as would be employed as the main switchgear at the point of supply, down to the relatively simple sub-distribution panel comprising circuit fuses only and usually found at the tail-end of the distribution system. Between these extremes, there are many applications where the moulded-case circuit-breaker can be used, while elsewhere considerable use can be made of fuse-switches in switchboard form.

In numerous applications, particularly industrial, it can be both convenient and economic to combine any or even all of the foregoing in a composite board, often including with advantage sections of motor control gear. Such composite arrangements have been made possible by the now popular modular construction, and some worthwhile saving in cable cost is possible in that a single infeed replaces multiple feeds to separate switchboards.

By accommodating, in suitable enclosures which form an integral part of the switchboard, one or more power transformers of a suitable type, a composite assembly known as a *packaged substation* is provided, a substation which can in fact be even more self-contained by the inclusion of certain high-voltage switchgear on the primary side of the transformers. Some of these possible arrangements are indicated schematically in Fig. 19.1, but in passing it must be noted that the permutations and combinations cannot all be given.

In this chapter no discussion will be offered on fuse sub-distribution boards, mainly because they are a highly standardised product and are well documented in manufacturers lists. Nor shall we consider switchboards of moulded-case circuit-breakers, the reason here being one of space not only to deal with assemblies of these breakers but also the design and technical features of them. The importance and extensive use of this class of switchgear is nevertheless acknowledged and some references to recent articles will be included in the bibliography.

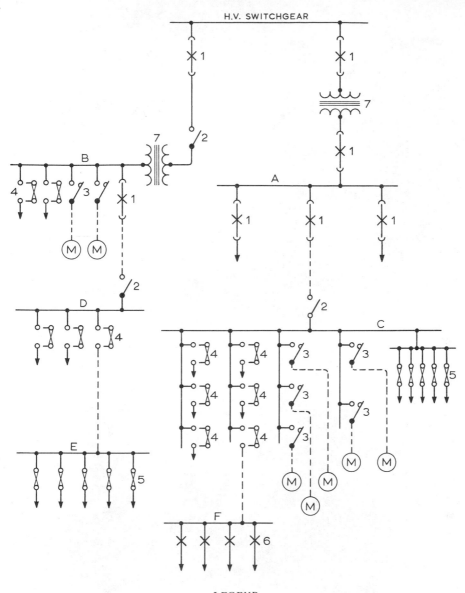

LEGEND

A MAIN SWITCHBOARD
B PACKAGED SUBSTATION
C COMPOSITE DISTRIBUTION/
   MOTOR CONTROL BOARD
D FUSE SWITCHGEAR
E FUSE SUBDISTRIBUTION PANEL
F MOULDED-CASE CIRCUIT-
   BREAKER DISTRIBUTION BOARD
M MOTOR

1. WITHDRAWABLE CIRCUIT-
   BREAKER
2. ISOLATOR OR LOAD-BREAKING
   FAULT-MAKING SWITCH
3. CONTACTOR STARTERS
4. FUSE SWITCHES
5. HANDLE-TYPE FUSES
6. MOULDED-CASE CIRCUIT-
   BREAKERS
7. STEP-DOWN POWER
   TRANSFORMER

Figure 19.1.   Some of the many possible arrangements of medium-voltage switchgear. They can all be assembled in multi-tier as shown for C

Figure 19.2. 'Combination' fuse switch (courtesy English Electric Fusegear Ltd.)

Figure 19.3. Switchgear of 'Combination' fuse switches (courtesy English Electric Fusegear Ltd.)

DISTRIBUTION FUSE SWITCHGEAR

Basically, this type of switchgear is that which, in one form or another, comprises, for each circuit to be controlled, a hand-operated switch which must be capable of interrupting load currents and some degree of overcurrent, e.g. not less than three times the normal current rating of the switch at a p.f. of 0·3. When used on motor circuits such switches will usually interrupt the stalled current of the motor. The switch will be associated with h.r.c. fuses of one or other of the types studied in Chapter 10 to provide protection against overloading and/or short-circuits. The combination may be in the form where the fuse link is an integral part of the switch, i.e. it is, in effect, the switch blade or it can be an arrangement where the switch and the fuses are separately accommodated.

A well-known and old-established fuse switch of the first type is that shown in Fig. 19.2. Used as a single unit this can be wall-mounted, the flanges above and below accepting incoming and outgoing cable boxes or glands. Used in switch-board form, any number can be carried on a central busbar chamber, either above and below or as best suited to the installation and the cabling arrange-ments. An example of such a switchboard is that shown in Fig. 19.3, which shows how metering equipment can be interposed between the fuse switches and the cable boxes.

Figure 19.4. Distribution switchboard comprising type 'HH' switches and fuses (courtesy A. Reyrolle & Co. Ltd.)

571

It is seen that this type of switch is of the double-break type, and with the switch open the fuse links are completely isolated so that they can be removed and replaced in safety, the fixed contacts being completely enclosed within insulating shrouds. An interlock ensures that the switch must be open before the cover can be opened, and conversely, the switch cannot be closed with the cover open.

In a design where the switch and fuses are in separate enclosures, the switch will be mounted on the busbar chamber with the fuses surmounting the switch, generally as shown in Fig. 19.4. Note that in this arrangement the busbar enclosure is built up of unit chambers, a feature which somewhat simplifies the addition of further circuits if required. Here again, the switches and fuses may be disposed above or below the busbars, or both. An interlock between the switch operating mechanism and the cover of the fuse box ensures that access

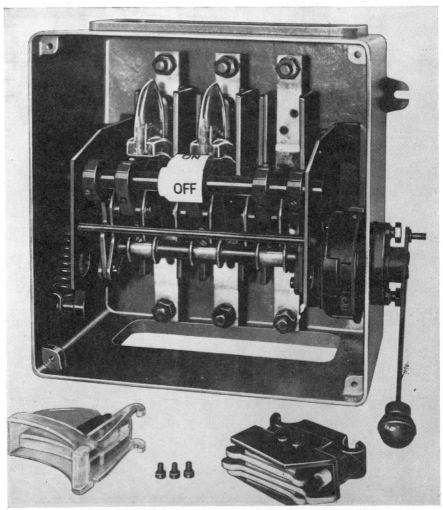

Figure 19.5. 400A air-break quick make and break switch for inductive and capacitive load switching; one arc chute removed (courtesy A. Reyrolle & Co. Ltd.)

to the latter is only possible with the switch open. A switch typical of the design is noted in Fig. 19.5. It employs a double-break and has moulded Diakon arc chutes fitted over the upper contacts.

In the separate fuse boxes, h.r.c. fuse links carried in moulded handles fit into moulded bases, the fuse links being alternatively of the bolted or non-bolted type.

As in the first design noted, separate meter or instrument chambers can be added in any circuit and in both assemblies incoming isolators or circuit-breaker units can form part of the switchboard.

These robust forms of 'ironclad' switchgear are extensively used in power stations for auxiliary services and in the heavy industries, but for many applications there has been a growing demand for distribution switchgear of a type

Figure 19.6. Type 'MM' distribution switchboard comprising fuse switches with an incoming air-break circuit-breaker (courtesy A. Reyrolle & Co. Ltd.)

which concentrates a maximum number of circuits within a minimum floor area and at the same time is of attractive appearance. This demand has been met by the development of multi-tier cubicles on the module principle, a principle which, as will be noted later, extends to air-break circuit-breakers in addition to fuse switches.

In the majority of designs, each cubicle will be a standard (common) height but will vary in width, two or perhaps three standards being used. Horizontal divisions in each cubicle provide compartments each to contain a fuse switch, or if required a switch only, the latter being obtained by replacing the fuse links by solid copper links. The number of compartments in any one cubicle is dictated by the current rating of the fuse switches to be accommodated, and it is a useful feature that spare compartments not required in the initial installation can be readily equipped later by installing suitably rated interiors, if extensions are required. Such spare provision can in many cases be purposely arranged in the initial design.

Typical examples of switchboards built on the foregoing principle are noted in Figs. 19.6 and 19.7, the former also illustrating an incoming air-break circuit-breaker unit in line with the fuse switches. To demonstrate the flexibility of arrangement, Figs. 19.8 and 19.9 are included. They are illustrations which also show the space-saving achievement of such designs.

Figure 19.7. 'Frontier'-type distribution switchboard comprising fuse switches (courtesy English Electric Fusegear Ltd.)

The ease with which maintenance can be carried out on any unit is a particular feature, perhaps the most important facility being that (a) the moving contact assembly can be removed as shown in Figs. 19.10 and 19.11, or (b) the complete fuse switch can be withdrawn and taken away, typically as shown in Fig. 19.12. These operations can be carried out while the switchboard is energised so that service on other circuits is maintained, and if spare units are held they can be fitted while that removed is serviced in a workshop. If it is necessary to work in an empty compartment, a shroud can be fitted over the fixed isolating contacts connected to the busbars.

In the two designs noted, all main cabling is made-off at the rear of the switchboard, for which purpose a gangway between the back of the board and, say, a wall is necessary. This arrangement has the advantage of keeping the width of the cubicles down, but it does require ample depth (front to back) to accommodate the cable terminations. In some designs however, provision is made whereby cables can be made-off from the front of the board, allowing it to be placed hard against a wall, but while this keeps down the depth of the cubicles, it involves additional width, thus increasing the overall length of the switchboard. This increased cubicle width is due to the fact that a cable-way has to be provided to one side of the bank of fuse switches, to which access is obtained by means of a removable front cover. This arrangement, however, introduces a problem when highly-rated circuits are involved, e.g. 800/1 200 A, and special consideration becomes necessary in such circumstances.

Figure 19.13 illustrates a switchboard of this type with front cabling facilities on two banks of fuse switches, while Fig. 19.14 is a block elevation indicating some possible combinations.

One further design may be noted in which rear cabling is adopted, but here the cable boxes are mounted externally on the rear covers of the cubicles. This arrangement is shown in Fig. 19.15, where a bank of four fuse switches is coupled to a double-tier cubicle containing air-break circuit-breakers, at the rear of which the external cable box can be seen. In this design, the fuse switches

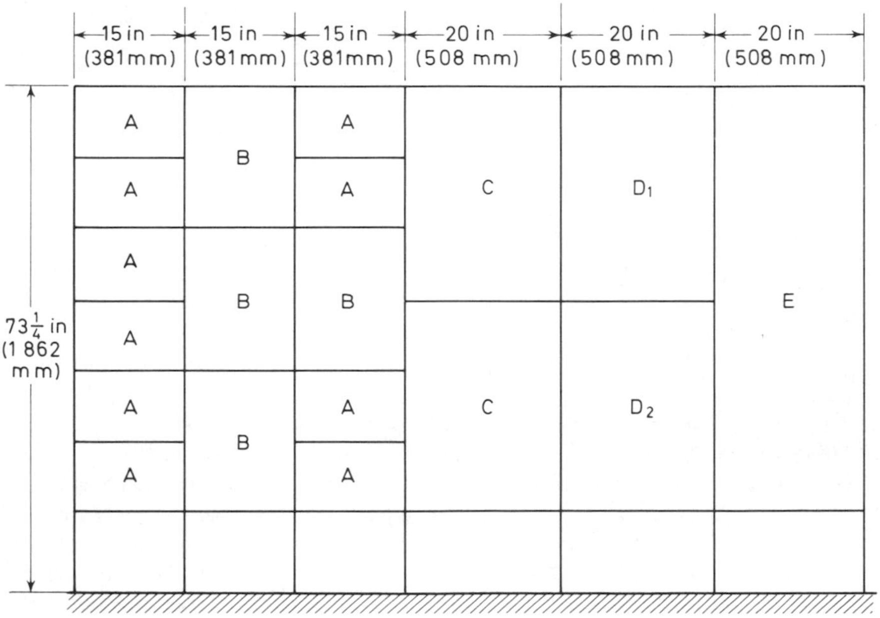

LEGEND

A	60, 100, 200 or 300A FUSE SWITCHES OR SWITCHES
B	400A FUSE SWITCH OR SWITCH
C	500A FUSE SWITCH OR 600A FUSE SWITCH OR SWITCH
D_1	800A FUSE SWITCH
D_2	800A SWITCH ONLY, e.g. BUS-SECTION UNIT
E	800 or 1 200A FUSE SWITCH OR SWITCH, OR 1 600A SWITCH ONLY

Figure 19.8. The flexibility in positioning of fuse switches in an 'MM' switchboard (courtesy A. Reyrolle & Co. Ltd.)

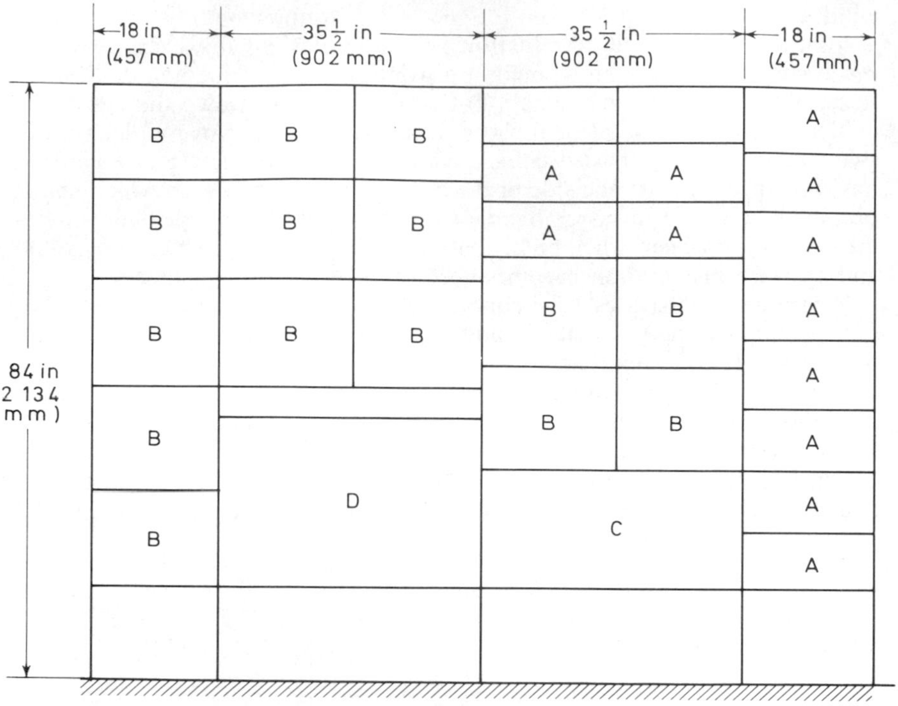

MEDIUM-VOLTAGE SWITCHGEAR (UP TO 660 v)

←18 in→ (457mm)   ←35½ in→ (902 mm)   ←35½ in→ (902 mm)   ←18 in→ (457mm)

```
┌──────┬──────┬──────┬──────────────────┬──────┐
│  B   │  B   │  B   │                   │  A   │
│      │      │      ├──────┬──────┬─────┤      │
│      │      │      │  A   │  A   │  A  │
│  B   │  B   │  B   ├──────┼──────┼─────┤
│      │      │      │  A   │  A   │  A  │
├──────┼──────┼──────┼──────┼──────┼─────┤
│      │      │      │  B   │  B   │  A  │
│  B   │  B   │  B   │      │      ├─────┤
│      │      │      │      │      │  A  │
├──────┼──────┴──────┼──────┼──────┼─────┤
│  B   │             │  B   │  B   │  A  │
│      │      D      ├──────┴──────┼─────┤
├──────┤             │      C      │  A  │
│  B   │             │             ├─────┤
│      │             │             │  A  │
└──────┴─────────────┴─────────────┴─────┘
```

84 in (2 134 mm)

LEGEND

A   60A FUSE SWITCH
B   100, 200 or 300A FUSE SWITCH
C   400, 600, 800 or 1 200A FUSE SWITCH
D   1 600A FUSE SWITCH

Figure 19.9. The flexibility in the positioning of fuse switches in a 'Frontier' switchboard (courtesy English Electric Fusegear Ltd.)

can be fixed or withdrawable, four units of ratings up to 400 A or three units of 600 A or 800 A being housed in cubicles of three standard widths.

In all the arrangements discussed, the fuse switches are of the heavy-duty type complying with BS 3185:1959, the h.r.c. fuse links complying separately with BS 88:1967. With busbars, risers and associated connections suitably proportioned and supported, these switchboards meet all the requirements essential to their use on systems where the fault level may be as high or higher than 31 MVA at 415 V.

OIL-BREAK SWITCHGEAR

Medium-voltage switchgear in this class will be based on the use of the plain-break bulk-oil circuit-breaker as discussed in Chapter 12 in relation to Fig. 12.5, etc., switchboards incorporating this being noted in Fig. 19.16.

Extremely robust, with dust and damp-proof enclosures, such switchgear is extensively used to control industrial power supplies and is particularly suitable

Figure 19.10. How the moving contact assembly can be removed from an 'MM' type of fuse-switch unit (courtesy A. Reyrolle & Co. Ltd.)

Figure 19.11. Moving-contact assembly being removed from a 'Frontier'-type fuse switch (courtesy English Electric Fusegear Ltd.)

Figure 19.12.   *The removal of an entire fuse-switch chassis (courtesy A. Reyrolle & Co. Ltd.)*

Figure 19.13.   *'Falcon 66' distribution switchboard comprising fuse switches arranged for front of panel cabling (courtesy Fluvent Electric Ltd.)*

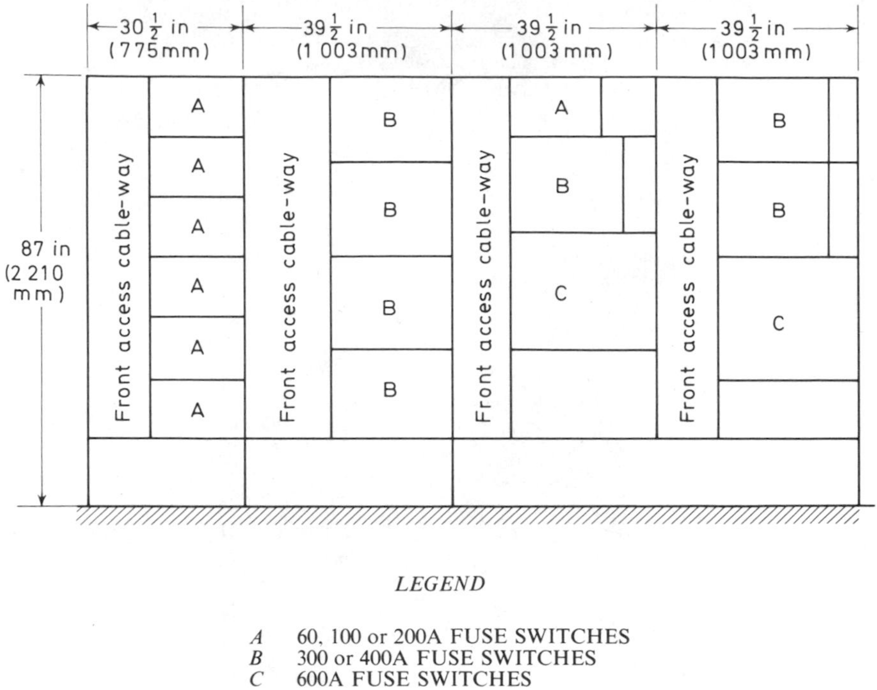

LEGEND

A	60, 100 or 200A FUSE SWITCHES
B	300 or 400A FUSE SWITCHES
C	600A FUSE SWITCHES

Figure 19.14.   The fuse switchboard designed to permit cables to be made-off from the front of the board (courtesy Fluvent Electric Ltd.) NOTE: See text regarding accommodation of 800 or 1 200A fuse switches

where poor atmospheric conditions prevail. Each circuit-breaker is isolated by horizontal withdrawal on slide-rails as seen in Figs. 19.17 and 19.18, and if a breaker is removed completely from the slide-rails, a protective cover (seen for example behind the oil tank in Fig. 19.17) can be raised by hand to cover the live fixed contacts and padlocked. Interlocks ensure that the circuit-breaker cannot be removed from the service to the isolated position (or vice versa) unless the breaker is open and the oil tank can only be lowered for contact inspection when the breaker is isolated.

Single-tier arrangements are general with this type of switchgear, but with circuit-breakers up to 400 A, a double-tier formation is possible, with valuable reduction in the overall length of a switchboard.

For many applications, the protective requirements can be met by direct-acting series-overload trip coils of the type discussed in Chapter 11, Fig. 11.1, etc. and in the designs illustrated, such coils can be included for ratings up to 1 600 A. Above this, current-transformer operated coils or a relay with a shunt trip coil must be used.

Subject only to the rating of the circuit-breakers and associated connections, etc. not being less than 600 A and the rating of series overload coils being not less than 400 A, this type of switchgear can be used on systems where the fault level is 31 MVA at 415 V. Using circuit-breakers rated up to 400 A and with series coils rated not less than 200 A, the switchgear should be used on systems where the fault level does not exceed 26 MVA at 415 V.

579

Figure 19.15. 'Delecta Mk. II' distribution switchboard comprising an air-break circuit-breaker (left) and fuse switches (courtesy Brush Electrical Engineering Co. Ltd.)

Figure 19.16. Distribution switchboards comprising draw-out type bulk-oil circuit-breakers installed in the works of I.C.I. Fibres Ltd., Doncaster (courtesy George Ellison Ltd.)

Figure 19.17.   600A withdrawable circuit-breaker of the bulk-oil type (courtesy George Ellison Ltd.)

Figure 19.18.   2 400A bulk-oil circuit-breakers, withdrawable-type, forming part of an industrial-type distribution board (courtesy George Ellison Ltd.)

AIR-BREAK SWITCHGEAR

Switchgear of the type described incorporating fuse switches, is of course entitled to come within this description, but here it is used to cover the type which uses the air-break circuit-breakers discussed in Chapter 14 for medium-voltage systems of high fault level. As we have noted in that Chapter, it is a type of increasing popularity, particularly because of its modular construction plus the ease with which it can be used in composite switchboards, as discussed earlier.

Such switchboards are designed on the flush-fronted principle with circuits variously arranged in single, double or triple-tier formations depending on the individual circuit ratings, and with, in most cases, an overriding limit as to the total load connected to a bank of breakers. We have noted in Chapter 14 how the circuit-breakers arc moved horizontally between the service, isolated and fully-withdrawn positions, isolation being achieved within the breaker compartment without exposing the interior, and full withdrawal on telescopic rails or on a platform formed by a let-down cover. When fully withdrawn, a breaker can be removed on a type of fork-lift truck and taken away for maintenance at a bench.

Our discussion on air-break circuit-breakers in Chapter 14 revealed differences in design relating to the front cover, these including designs in which it is fixed and withdrawn with the breaker, and others with side-hinged doors opening on a control facia on the breaker and one with a hinged let-down door forming

Figure 19.19. Medium-voltage distribution switchboard comprising draw-out pattern air-break circuit-breakers in double-tier formation. Breakers seen slightly withdrawn are in the isolated position (courtesy George Ellison Ltd.)

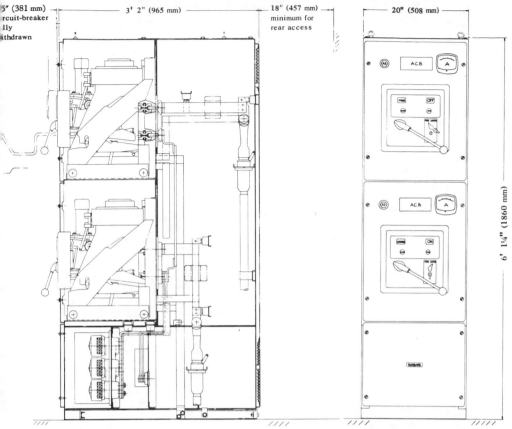

Figure 19.20. Cross-section and front elevation of a double-tier air-break circuit-breaker cubicle (courtesy A. Reyrolle & Co. Ltd.)

a platform. A breaker with a fixed cover was noted in Fig. 14.5 and mention made of a rear skirt on this cover to seal the gap when the breaker had been moved the short distance necessary for isolation. Figure 19.19 shows a switchboard using this circuit-breaker in double-tier formation from which it is seen that various circuit-breakers are in the isolated position with the skirt preventing access to the compartment.

A breaker housed in a compartment with a side-hinged door was also noted in Fig. 14.7, where isolation is achieved within the compartment without opening the door. Figure 19.20 uses this breaker, this arrangement being applicable for circuit-breakers rated up to 1 250 A. For higher rated circuit-breakers (up to 3 150 A) single-tier only is used. It is seen that the busbars are accommodated below the circuit-breakers, but where the capacity of the busbars so located is inadequate, additional busbars are installed in a compartment at the top of the switchboard.

The principle of withdrawal on rails on a platform door has been shown in Fig. 14.18 and a switchboard incorporating this design is seen in Fig. 19.21. The central circuit-breaker, shown fully withdrawn, is a bus-section unit with double-tier units on either side and a bank of fuse switches on the far right. In this arrangement it is seen how the lower compartment is used as a relay panel for the two circuits above. In a three-tier arrangement, this compartment would be occupied by a circuit-breaker, and if relays and/or meters are required with this assembly, accommodation for them demands either an adjacent panel for the purpose or a separate relay board such as we shall note in a later chapter dealing with control boards.

As a further example of our earlier discussion on composite switchboards, Fig. 19.22 shows such a board comprising an incoming air-break circuit-breaker as in Fig. 19.21, followed by a bank of fuse switches and in turn by five tiers of motor-control units, with a number of spare compartments for future use.

Figure 19.21. Medium-voltage distribution switchboard with air-break circuit-breakers in single and double-tier and a bank of fuse switches (right) (courtesy the former Belmos Peebles Switchgear Ltd.)

Figures 19.23 and 19.24 show further examples of heavy-duty air-break switchgear, the former illustrating double-tier units with circuit-breakers up to 1 600 A, the latter showing single-tier units in which the breakers are rated at 3 000 A. Figure 19.23 is another illustration showing how protective relays are mounted on the lower compartment for the two circuits above, while Fig. 19.24 shows additional panels lined up with the circuit-breaker panels on which is mounted apparatus essential for the control of the diesel driven alternators, and on a hinged panel to the left the necessary synchronising instruments. The circuit-breakers in these switchboards are shown typically in Figs. 19.25 and 19.26.

Because the cost of research and development of a range of heavy-duty air-break circuit-breakers with high interrupting capacity is considerable, many

Figure 19.22. Medium-voltage switchboard comprising incoming air-break circuit-breakers, fuse switches and motor control units (courtesy the former Belmos Peebles Switchgear Ltd.)

Figure 19.23. English Electric class M23 medium-voltage switchboard using air-break circuit-breakers (courtesy G.E.C. Switchgear Ltd.)

switchboard builders have used in their constructions loose circuit-breakers made by other manufacturers. This practice has been particularly notable where such circuit-breakers were essential to a composite switchboard comprising fuse switches and/or motor control gear.

In the majority of installations, circuit-breakers of the withdrawable type are required, so that the switchboard builder is faced with designing a cubicle structure suitable for accepting the fixed isolating contacts, withdrawal mechanism and shutter operating mechanism and to design his own shutters.

In the absence of jigs and fixtures this can be an unsatisfactory procedure, and to meet the requirements more fully, the English Electric M-pact range of

Figure 19.24. English Electric medium-voltage switchboard with three 3 000 M24 withdrawable air-break circuit-breakers, control panels and synchronising facilities for two large diesel alternator sets (courtesy G.E.C. Switchgear Ltd.)

sub-cubicle mounted circuit-breakers was introduced. A typical unit of this type is shown in Fig. 19.27, the breaker being removed to show the interior of the housing. Each such unit is complete with slide-rails, safety interlocks, automatic shutters and mechanism, a set of six jig-aligned fixed isolating contacts with cable or copper conductor terminating palms, auxiliary switches and secondary contacts. Given sub-cubicles of this type, they can readily be assembled in a simple main housing using six fixing screws only, and they can be arranged in single, double or triple-tier banks as required.

The designers of this sub-cubicle principle employ it in switchboards they build themselves, and to which the trade name 'Trimpact' is given, a typical double-tier switchboard being that shown in Fig. 19.28.

In each of the foregoing English Electric designs, access to the racking and circuit-breaker operating points is obtained via separate padlockable spring-loaded cover flaps, a detail of which is seen in Fig. 19.29. Each of the different circuit-breakers will also be provided with the sophisticated form of direct-acting series-overcurrent devices which we have noted in some detail in Chapter 11.

Current ratings up to 3 000 A per circuit can be covered in this range, three cubicle widths being employed for 1 600, 2 000 and 3 000 A circuit-breakers.

Figure 19.25. English Electric double-tier M23 unit with one circuit-breaker fully withdrawn for inspection (courtesy G.E.C. Switchgear Ltd.)

587

Figure 19.26.   English Electric M24 withdrawable air-break circuit-breaker as used in Figure 19.24
(courtesy G.E.C. Switchgear Ltd.)

Figure 19.27. English Electric M-pact sub-cubicle air-break circuit-breaker for switchboard builders. The breaker is removed to show the safety shutters (courtesy G.E.C. Switchgear Ltd.)

Figure 19.28. English Electric Trimpact switchboard using sub-cubicle air-break circuit-breakers as shown in Figure 19.27. Installed at J & S Crosfields Ltd., Chemical Manufacturers, Warrington (courtesy G.E.C. Switchgear Ltd.)

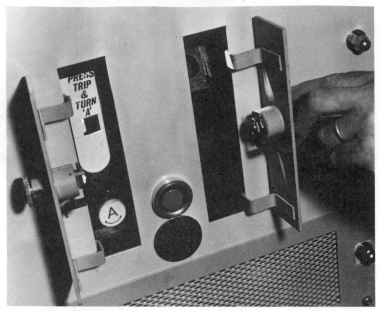

Figure 19.29. The spring-loaded flaps over, the access points to the racking and operating mechanisms for English Electric air-break circuit-breakers (courtesy G.E.C. Switchgear Ltd.)

PACKAGED SUBSTATIONS

The considerable flexibility of the modular forms of distribution switchgear described, coupled with similarly constructed motor control gear and the general acceptance in industry and elsewhere of the Class C dry-type or the Pyroclor-filled* power transformer, has led to the practice of combining all these items of apparatus into a composite assembly known as a packaged substation. The concept has two major advantages:

1. The substation can replace the more conventional brick-built (possibly remote) substation with an oil-filled transformer and maybe oil-filled switchgear, thus reducing the fire hazard to the point of elimination. This is a point of considerable importance in many industries.

2. Because of (1), the substation can be located at or very near to the centre of the electrical load, reducing the capital cost of installation by eliminating the need for a separate switch room and resulting in worthwhile savings in cable costs.

As the following illustrations will show, the power transformer is installed in a cubicle integral with the distribution switchgear and/or motor control gear, the medium-voltage output from the transformer being fed through copper links (or a switch or circuit-breaker) to the busbars in the switchgear. If it is required to be able to isolate the primary side of the transformer locally, the package can include the necessary high-voltage circuit-breaker or, as is more usual, an air-break load-breaking fault-making isolating switch.

* *Pyroclor* is a fire-resistant synthetic transformer coolant and is a Monsanto Chemicals product.

Thus it is possible in a packaged substation to assemble a wide variety of apparatus suitable for particular purposes in a multiplicity of arrangements to include:

(a) One or more power transformers up to 2 000 kVA.
(b) Air-break circuit-breakers.
(c) Moulded-case circuit-breakers.
(d) Fuse switches.
(e) Fuse sub-distribution panels.
(f) Motor control gear.
(g) Power factor improvement equipment.
(h) H.V. switches.

Depending on the available floor space, these substations can be built in a single line or divided in a back-to-back arrangement. If necessary, a right-angled formation can be made, or the substation can be in two parts joined by

Figure 19.30. Packaged substation comprising a 1 000 kVA Pyroclor-filled power transformer air-break circuit-breaker and fuse switches (courtesy George Ellison Ltd.)

Figure 19.31. Packaged substation as in Figure 19.30 with door removed to show the power transformer (courtesy George Ellison Ltd.)

Figure 19.32. Packaged substation comprising two 1 000 kVA Pyroclor-filled power transformers and air-break circuit-breakers (courtesy the former Belmos Peebles Switchgear Ltd.)

a busbar trunk, the two parts being in adjacent rooms on the same or different levels, an arrangement often adopted where it is desired to segregate the high and medium-voltage parts of the substation. When more than one transformer is included, bus sectionalising can be arranged on either or both sides, i.e. h.v. and m.v.

A typical substation is shown in Fig. 19.30, incorporating a 1 000 kVA Pyroclor-filled transformer, and medium-voltage switchgear comprising an air-break circuit-breaker and a number of fuse switches.

The transformer in its cubicle with doors removed is seen in Fig. 19.31, the transformer having tappings on the high-voltage winding to allow for deviations in supply voltage. In the unit illustrated, a tap-change selector is included, but in other designs tappings may be changed at a link board.

Figure 19.33.   How subdistribution fuse assemblies can be built into medium-voltage distribution switchboards or packaged substations (courtesy the former Belmos Peebles Switchgear Ltd.)

Figure 19.34.   Packaged substation comprising a 500 kVA Class C *dry-type transformer and fuse switches (courtesy English Electric Fusegear Ltd.)*

Figure 19.32 shows a packaged substation which includes two 1 000 kVA Pyroclor-filled transformers with a bus-section air-break circuit-breaker between them and seven feeder circuits on each section of busbar with air-break circuit-breakers.

Figure 19.33 illustrates how sub-distribution fuse panels can be included in a cubicle forming a part of the switchgear installation, arrangements being possible for single-pole and neutral, three phase, or three phase and neutral distribution.

Finally, Fig. 19.34 shows a substation which incorporates a 500 kVA Class C dry-type power transformer, with an 800 A fuse switch on the secondary side controlling the output to 16 outgoing circuits with fuse switches of various ratings.

BIBLIOGRAPHY

AGGETT, G.D., 'Applying All-insulated Techniques to Industrial Control Boards', *Elect. Rev.*, 29 Jan. (1971)

CHAPMAN, D.J., 'Moulded-case Circuit-breakers for the Economic Control of Sub-circuits', *Elect. Rev.*, Supplement, 13 Dec. (1963)

FREEMAN, C.F., 'Fusegear Has Serious Limitations in Industrial Networks', *Elect. Rev.*, Supplement, 13 Dec. (1963)

ROBBINS, J.A., 'M.C.Bs. in Modern Installations', *Elect. Times*, Parts I–IV, 22 and 29 March, 19 April and 10 May (1962)

ROBBINS, J.A., 'Economic and Technical Aspects of M.C.Bs.', *Elect. Rev.*, 26 March (1965)

Chapter 20

High-voltage indoor switchgear

For the most part, any discussion on high-voltage switchgear for use indoors will either be concerned with that associated with the smaller types of generating station where the ratings of the plant are such that switchgear at generation voltage is normal practice, or with that associated with underground-cable distribution systems. In both cases, the service voltage will be in the range of 3·3–33 kV, although it may be noted that up to about 15 kV, switchgear of normal indoor design, e.g. totally-enclosed metal-clad can be (and often is) used outdoors with a simple prefabricated enclosure such as that shown in Fig. 20.1.

At 33 kV, distribution may well be by overhead lines terminating at switchgear located either in a conventional brick-built substation or in a prefabricated housing similar to that noted in Figs. 20.2 and 20.3. The practice of installing normal outdoor-type switchgear under cover has been adopted for various reasons with switchgear for the very-high distribution and transmission voltages, and an article appeared in the *Electrical Review*[1] illustrating a design by South Wales Switchgear Ltd. incorporating 132 kV small-oil-volume circuit-breakers and other apparatus of the outdoor type. At 275 and 400 kV, outdoor-type air-blast circuit-breakers, isolators, etc. have been installed in simple buildings typically as shown in Figs. 20.4 to 20.7. At 275 kV, indoor arrangements have been used where the power transformers have been at ground level with the switchgear on a floor above.

Enclosure of extra-high-voltage switchgear in these ways is usually resorted to in areas where insulator pollution is considerable. Another reason is that it is increasingly necessary to bring these substations into urban areas so that they are located at or near load centres, but where space and other factors are against open-type outdoor installations. Such arrangements nevertheless are still space consuming and for this reason extensive research and development has been undertaken towards producing extra-high-voltage totally-enclosed metal-clad switchgear such that its space requirement is only a fraction of the equivalent open type and which, in congested areas, can if necessary be accommodated underground. How such designs have progressed in switchgear where SF_6 gas is used both for insulating and interrupting purposes has been noted in Chapter 16.

Mention has been made earlier of switchgear at generation voltage. In the modern large power station, generating sets of 300 MW upwards are in general use, and ratings of 600/660 MW are already in service and, as noted in Chapter 15

Figure 20.1. Packaged substation for voltages up to 15 kV and with five circuit-breaker units of the vertical isolation type (courtesy A. Reyrolle & Co. Ltd.)

Figure 20.2. 33 kV packaged switchgear with one circuit-breaker isolated and withdrawn from its enclosure (courtesy South Wales Switchgear Ltd.)

Figure 20.3.   33 kV packaged switchgear with rear terminations for connection to overhead lines (courtesy South Wales Switchgear Ltd.)

Figure 20.4.   Indoor installation of 275 kV air-blast circuit-breakers, etc. at the C.E.G.B. Tottenham substation; mesh connection (courtesy A. Reyrolle & Co. Ltd.)

Figure 20.5. Indoor installation of 400 kV air-blast circuit-breakers, etc. at Kingsnorth power station (courtesy A. Reyrolle & Co. Ltd.)

Figure 20.6. Indoor installation of English Electric frame 'r' air-blast circuit-breakers at the C.E.G.B. West Burton substation (courtesy G.E.C. Switchgear Ltd.)

sets of twice this rating will soon be in service, while by 1980 ratings may reach 2 000 MW. For such machines, elevated generation voltages are used, i.e. 16 kV and upwards, but even so the normal currents are extremely high, e.g. a 660 MW set generating at 23 kV results in a normal current of 19·5 kA.

Switchgear designed to meet these conditions presents many formidable problems, so that it has become common practice to tie each generator solidly to a power transformer stepping up to transmission voltage and with switchgear at this voltage only. As we have seen in Chapter 11, a protective system can be

Figure 20.7. Indoor installation of English Electric frame 'r' air-blast circuit-breakers at the C.E.G.B. No. 1 Hale-Ironbridge substation (courtesy G.E.C. Switchgear Ltd.)

applied across the generator/transformer combination, but this means that if trouble occurs on say the generator, both it and its associated transformer are disconnected.

If however, switchgear can be introduced at generation voltage, each generator and each transformer can be individually protected, the loss of one leaving all the others in service. As we have seen in Chapter 15, heavy-current circuit-breakers for use at generation voltages of the order noted have been extensively developed to cover the highest ratings presently envisaged, the breakers being of the air-blast type. Here it is of interest to look at the form of switchgear unit associated with such breakers and, although only rated at 5 000 A, the unit illustrated in Fig. 20.8 may be taken as representative*. This is a naturally-ventilated metal-clad construction with phase separation throughout and is

* But see article by Burckhardt and Knecht noted in Bibliography of Chapter 15, page 499, for more recent developments.

divided into compartments by sheet-metal barriers as indicated in the diagrammatic sketch shown in Fig. 20.9.

Because of the heavy current, aluminium is used for the structure, the main members being of special aluminium alloy with welded joints, while the enclosing panels are of ordinary aluminium sheet. The use of this metal minimises the considerable problem of local heating due to parasitic currents which could be induced in a structure employing magnetic metals.

Figure 20.8. Triple-pole metal-clad switchgear for Benmore Power Station, New Zealand, rated at 16 kV, 5 000 A with a breaking capacity of 2 500 MVA. See also Chapter 15 (courtesy Brown Boveri & Co. Ltd.)

The heavy-current isolators have been developed to match the circuit-breaker ratings, single-pole units being employed and arranged for pneumatic operation but with provision for hand operation during maintenance. The position of the isolator blades can be checked visually through windows of safety glass.

For the lower range of normal currents (typically not exceeding 3 000 A) in the distribution voltage range up to 33 kV, British practice is represented almost completely by metal-clad designs using circuit-breakers of the plug-in type, i.e. arranged for vertical isolation with bulk-oil breakers or horizontal-isolation air-break breakers.

Similar principles have now been largely adopted elsewhere, particularly on the continent of Europe where previously open-type indoor switchgear with fixed circuit-breakers and separate isolating switches found greatest favour, a difference being that the bulk-oil circuit-breaker is replaced either by the small-oil-volume or air-blast types, both arranged for horizontal isolation.

The principle of a fixed circuit-breaker with separate isolators has not however been entirely abandoned by U.K. designers, but here a metal-clad construction is retained. Figure 20.10 shows an example of a design for single-phase service at 6·25 or 25 kV, as widely used to meet present day practice in railway electrification. The busbar and cable isolating switches are contained

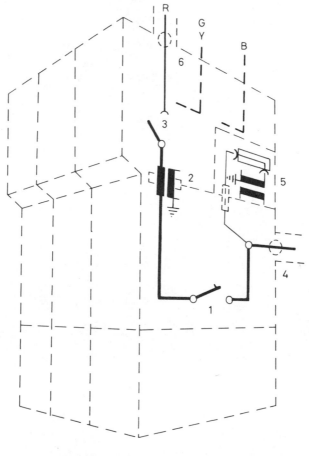

LEGEND

1. AIR-BLAST CIRCUIT-BREAKER   4. BUSHING INSULATORS
2. CURRENT TRANSFORMER   5. VOLTAGE TRANSFORMER
3. ISOLATOR   6. INCOMING PHASES

Figure 20.9. Single-pole diagram of metal-clad unit shown in Figure 20.8 (courtesy Brown Boveri & Co. Ltd.)

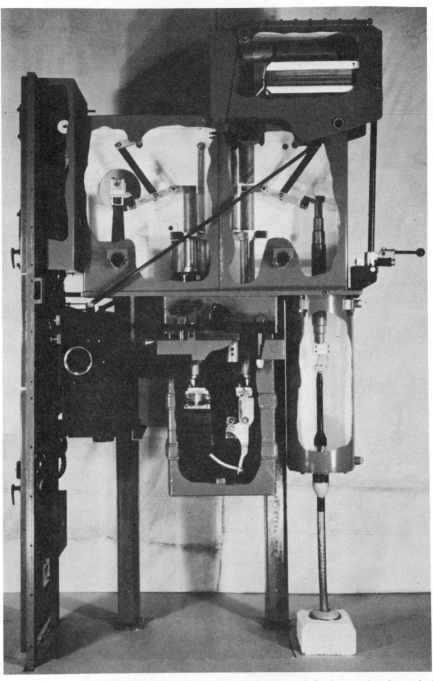

Figure 20.10.   Switchgear & Cowans single-phase metal-clad unit with fixed circuit-breaker and oil-immersed isolators (courtesy G.E.C. Switchgear Ltd.)

602

in separate oil-filled chambers surmounting the fixed circuit-breaker hood and operated from external handle gear.

A voltage transformer, mounted above the cable isolator chamber, is a hinged unit which can be isolated by rotating it from the horizontal service position to a vertical position via an isolating jack. In the isolated position, a shutter covers the orifices and the h.r.c. fuses in the tank can be withdrawn through what has now become the top of the tank.

Units of this type, designed to meet the British Transport Commission's specification, are rated 300 MVA for an 800 A unit at 25 kV single phase and 150 MVA for all units up to 1 200 A at 6·25 kV single phase. An indoor switchboard of these units is noted in Fig. 20.11, but in Chapter 21 an example will be

Figure 20.11. Switchgear & Cowans single-phase metal-clad switchgear comprising units similar to Figure 20.10 (courtesy G.E.C. Switchgear Ltd.)

given of an outdoor variation which eliminates the need for a building and with provision for direct connection to overhead lines.

Based on the foregoing, a fixed breaker unit has been developed for three-phase service at 22 or 33 kV, with ratings of up to 2 500 A and interrupting capacities in the range of 1 000–1 500 MVA. Shown in section in Fig. 20.12, it is seen that the busbar and cable-isolating switches have 'on,' 'off' and 'earth' positions coupled with the facility of cable testing by using insert bushings in the manner described in Chapter 17. Here, as in the fixed unit described earlier,

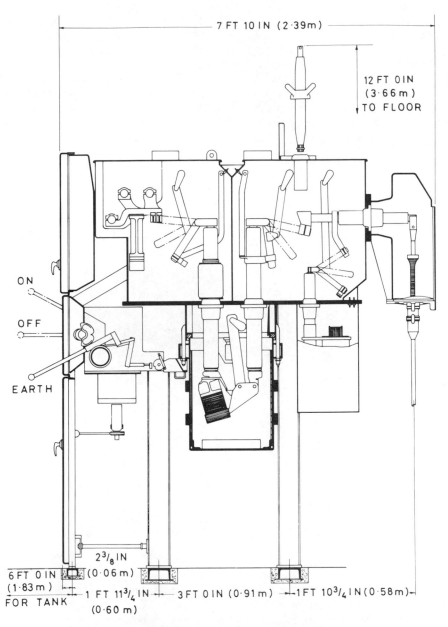

Figure 20.12. Sectional view of Switchgear & Cowans 33 kV three-phase metal-clad unit with fixed circuit-breaker and oil-immersed isolators (courtesy G.E.C. Switchgear Ltd.)

the position of the isolating switch blades can be checked visually through viewing tubes at the front of the unit, illumination in the chambers being provided by lamps carried in the top covers.

In the three-phase unit, the voltage transformer is a fixed unit in a tank of the plug-in type, behind the circuit-breaker and below an isolating switch chamber, the latter housing a separate isolator for the transformer.

VERTICALLY-ISOLATED SWITCHGEAR
(with bulk-oil circuit-breakers)

For voltages up to 33 kV, this type of metal-clad switchgear is the generally accepted standard in the U.K. for distribution purposes, and in all designs except one, isolation is achieved by *lowering* the circuit-breaker from its service position to floor level, a position at which it can be withdrawn horizontally on its carriage from the housing. The exception (noted later) is a reversed design in which the breaker is *raised* to isolate it.

Designs include those for single or duplicate-busbar systems, and for the latter, busbar selection is now generally by the transfer-breaker method described in Chapter 9. British practice requires that a means be provided for earthing either the circuit (cable) or the busbars through the circuit-breaker or a fault-making device, and whereas this was, in the past, often achieved after fitting loose parts to a chosen circuit-breaker, this is rarely the case today, many designs incorporating integral arrangements built-in to each switchgear unit. In many cases these earthing functions are carried out on the transfer-breaker principle, using additional plugging-in locations. Thus, in a single-bus unit, the breaker can be plugged-in at any one of three locations, and in a duplicate-bus unit at any one of five, as summarised in Fig. 20.13.

To ensure that the position of the circuit-breaker within the housing is in the correct location for the desired operation, some form of selector-gate mechanism is employed, the arrangement being such as to prevent the circuit-breaker being raised into any other than the preselected location. When an earthing operation is planned it will be necessary to open one or the other (but not both) of the sets of safety shutters which cover the cable and busbar spouts when the breaker is isolated, and this shutter-opening operation can often be done automatically through the location mechanism. An illustration of the external elements of one such locator mechanism is shown in Fig. 20.14, this being for a single-bus unit. For a duplicate-bus design, additional location points are necessary to meet the conditions noted in Fig. 20.13.

To avoid the need for five locations in a duplicate-bus unit, one design eliminates those for earthing by employing a fault-making earthing switch fitted in a separate chamber above the main unit. This switch is used for cable earthing only, its spring-assisted operating mechanism being interlocked with the circuit-breaker location selector so that the earthing switch cannot be closed with the breaker plugged-in to either service position, and conversely, the breaker cannot be raised into either position with the earth switch closed. When provision for busbar earthing is required, this can be arranged either by adding a similar switch or switches on busbar trunkings or at bus-section and bus-coupler breakers. It may be noted in passing that busbar-earthing facilities

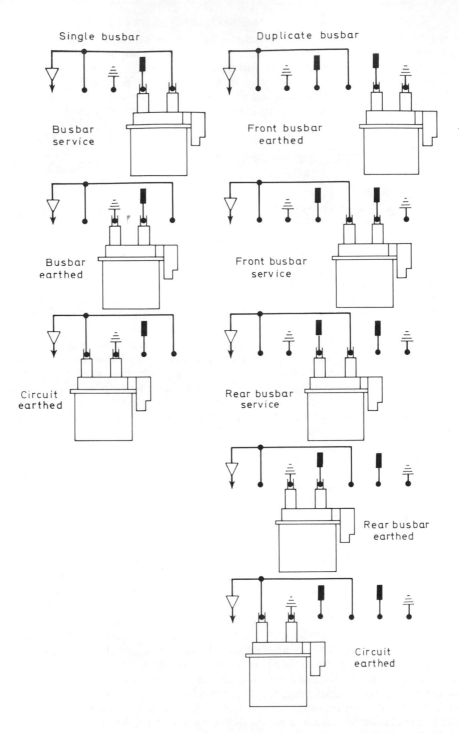

Single busbar

Duplicate busbar

Busbar
service

Front busbar
earthed

Busbar
earthed

Front busbar
service

Circuit
earthed

Rear busbar
service

Rear busbar
earthed

Circuit
earthed

Figure 20.13. Busbar and circuit earthing by the transfer-breaker method for single and duplicate busbar vertical-isolation units

606

are not essential at every unit as the requirement can be met by one or two such facilities on *each* section of busbar.

An alternative method requires the use of an earthing truck which can be used in any unit of switchgear comprising a switchboard, a typical truck being shown in Fig. 20.15. The truck itself is basically the same as that carrying the circuit-breakers, so that after isolating a circuit-breaker and withdrawing it from its housing, the earthing truck can be located at a preselected position in the housing, raised into engagement and the switch then closed to complete the earthing operation. The switch is of the air-break fault-making type with a spring-assisted closing mechanism.

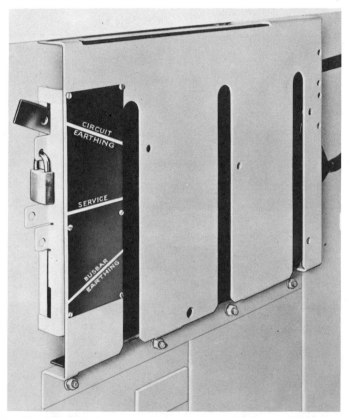

Figure 20.14.   Circuit-breaker locator mechanism used on A.E.I. single-busbar 11 kV vertical-isolation metal-clad units (courtesy G.E.C. Switchgear Ltd.)

Provision is made on this truck to allow tests to be made on a cable. For this purpose, after the switch has been engaged and closed, (i.e. cable earthed) a test-terminal cover can be opened to expose the test terminals seen in Fig. 20.16. With the earth still applied, the test connection to the terminals can be made off and then any phase can be disconnected from earth during the tests by pulling open a moving contact forming part of the test assembly. After the tests are completed, the act of closing the test-terminal cover automatically recloses any open moving contacts thus restoring the earthed condition. It should be noted that the test-terminal cover is interlocked with the switch-operating mechanism so that the earthing switch can only be operated with the cover closed.

When cable tests are required where a truck of this type is not used, i.e. units using the transfer-breaker method, these can be carried-out by means of test-injection plugs inserted into the circuit spouts, following rigidly the instructions of the manufacturer or supply authority to ensure safety to personnel and apparatus.

Relatively simple hand-closing mechanisms for circuit-breakers used in the types of switchgear under discussion have virtually been abandoned in favour of power-closing mechanisms. These are of four types (*a*) independent manual,

Figure 20.15.   A.E.I. portable earthing and testing truck for use in vertical-isolation metal-clad switchgear units; earth switch in lowered position (courtesy G.E.C. Switchgear Ltd.)

(b) hand-charged spring, (c) motor-charged spring and (d) solenoid. The mechanism (a) is a manually-charged spring-operated device in which springs are charged during the initial part of the stroke of an operating handle, and, as the movement is continued, a point is reached when the springs are released allowing the energy stored in the springs to close the circuit-breaker at high speed independently of the operator. In type (b), charging of the springs continues throughout the stroke of the handle and they are latched in a fully-charged state. To close

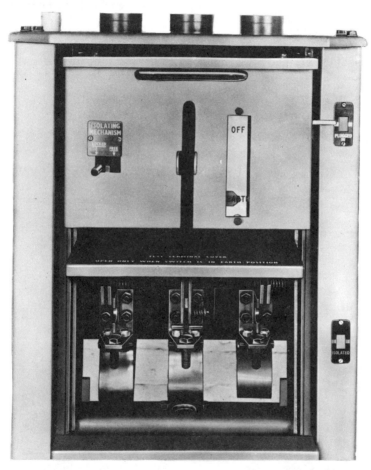

Figure 20.16. The earth switch shown in Figure 20.15 with test terminal cover open to expose test contacts for cable testing (courtesy G.E.C. Switchgear Ltd.)

the breaker, the latching device must be released, either mechanically or electrically, to allow the springs to discharge. The design is such that with the breaker closed, the springs can be recharged and latched ready for a subsequent reclosure after a trip.

Mechanism (c) is typically as (b), except that the springs are charged by a small a.c. or d.c. geared motor, an arrangement in which recharging of the springs with the breaker closed can be an automatic operation. In case of a supply failure to the motor, emergency hand-closing is provided. A solenoid mechanism (*d*) is an electrically operated device, requiring a d.c. supply which can be obtained from a station battery or a metal rectifier equipment.

For a range of voltages up to 15 kV, the type of switchgear unit under discussion is designated *air-insulated* on account of the fact that such items as busbars, connections, current transformers, etc. are accommodated in chambers which contain no oil or compound as an insulant, i.e. the chambers are air-filled at atmospheric pressure. There are, of course, many points at which other insulation in one form or another has to be used, as for example on current and voltage transformers, at the isolating spouts for the circuit-breaker and voltage transformer, in the circuit-breaker itself by way of bushings and contact lift-rods and usually some form of insulation on the busbars and connections. Varnished tape, porcelain, synthetic-resin-bonded paper, oil (in voltage transformers)

Figure 20.17. Busbar spouts and connections to busbars cast in epoxy-resin three-phase monobloc (courtesy Brush Switchgear Ltd.)

and densified wood are among the types of insulation used or are substituted by the new synthetic materials now available.

In this direction, Chapter 23 will take note of and illustrate how epoxy resins and butyl rubber have been applied as the insulant for current transformers and the epoxy resins for voltage transformers. Elsewhere in a switchgear unit there are many other points at which the epoxy resins can be used as they can be moulded (cast) into complicated shapes. These resins, transformed into hard infusible material by the addition of hardeners or catalysts in a 'curing' process have excellent mechanical and electrical properties, but the manufacturing methods for casting require specialised study[2,3,4].

The use of epoxy resins on bent conductors has already been noted in Fig. 12.23 and a further example is given later in Fig. 20.57. One of the most interesting applications is perhaps the casting of orifice insulators (spouts) such as those into which the circuit-breaker and the voltage transformer are plugged. They can, in so far as the busbar spouts are concerned, be in such a form that they also provide the busbar support posts, an example being shown in Fig. 20.17. Here it is seen that the spout conductors leading to the pick-up points for the busbars are encapsulated integrally with the spouts. Taken a stage further, the encapsulation can include the three-phase unit lengths of busbars, typically as shown in Fig. 20.18.

By shaping suitably, monobloc castings as shown in these two illustrations can ensure long creepage paths to earth, while creepage paths between phases are eliminated. When the busbars are not included in the encapsulation, the 'T'-joints between spout conductors and the busbars can be insulated by shrouding them in polystyrene boxes, the busbars between joints being covered by

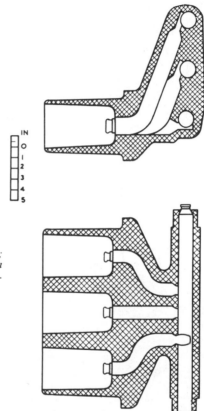

Figure 20.18. Sectional view of busbar spouts; busbars and connections cast in epoxy resin as a three-phase monobloc (courtesy A. Reyrolle & Co. Ltd.)

p.v.c. sleeving, usually shrunk-on or, as in one design, with sprayed-on epoxy resin.

In switchgear units where ring-type current transformers are used, the conductors cast in the circuit (cable) side spouts can be extended within the encapsulation to form the primary conductor over which the transformers will fit. These extended conductors can be bent at right angles to lie in a horizontal plane beyond the top of the spouts, the free ends of the conductors being directly connected to the cable-box terminals.

In some designs, depending on the fault level, the circuit-breaker bushings have been produced in epoxy resin, as have the driving rods for the moving-contact system, these rods requiring reinforcement, e.g. by glass fibres, to give them adequate strength.

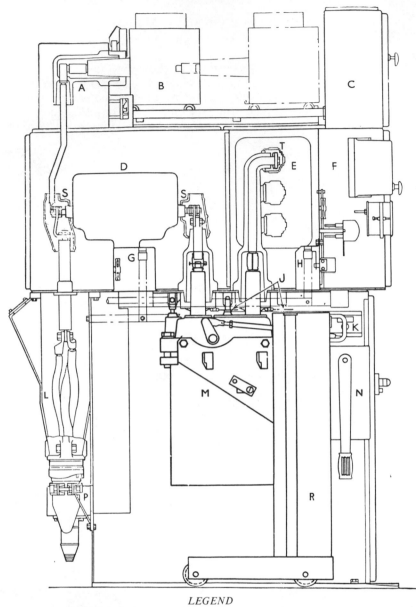

LEGEND

A	VOLTAGE-TRANSFORMER ORIFICE HOUSING	J	ORIFICE SHUTTERS
B	VOLTAGE TRANSFORMER	K	SELECTOR-GATE MECHANISM CONTROLLING CIRCUIT-BREAKER POSITION
C	EXTRA TOP UNIT FOR RELAYS, ETC.		
D	CURRENT-TRANSFORMER CHAMBER	L	CIRCUIT CABLE-BOX
		M	CIRCUIT-BREAKER
E	BUSBAR CHAMBER	N	CIRCUIT-BREAKER OPERATING MECHANISM
F	INSTRUMENT AND RELAY COMPARTMENT		
		P	PILOT CABLE-BOX
G	CIRCUIT-EARTHING CONTACTS	R	CIRCUIT-BREAKER CARRIAGE
		S	TERMINAL SHROUDS
H	BUSBAR-EARTHING CONTACTS	T	BUSBAR-JOINT SHROUDS

Figure 20.19. Sectional view of single-busbar 400A 11 kV vertical-isolation metal-clad switchgear unit with earthing by the transfer-breaker method (courtesy A. Reyrolle & Co. Ltd.)

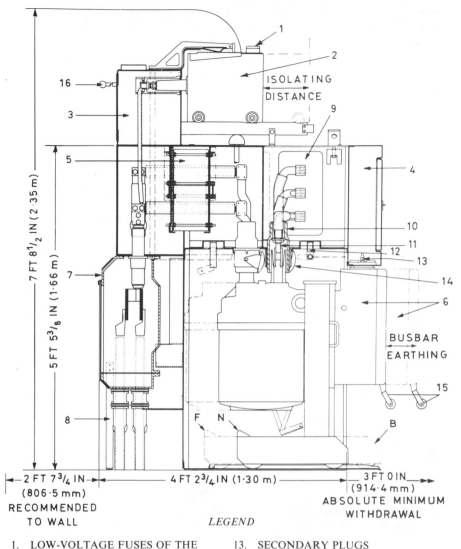

7 FT 8 1/2 IN (2·35 m)

5 FT 5 3/8 IN (1·66 m)

ISOLATING DISTANCE

BUSBAR EARTHING

|←—2 FT 7 3/4 IN—→|

(806·5 mm)

RECOMMENDED TO WALL

|←———— 4 FT 2 3/4 IN (1·30 m) ————→|

3 FT 0 IN (914·4 mm)

ABSOLUTE MINIMUM WITHDRAWAL

LEGEND

1. LOW-VOLTAGE FUSES OF THE VOLTAGE TRANSFORMER
2. VOLTAGE TRANSFORMER
3. VOLTAGE-TRANSFORMER TAPPING CHAMBER
4. INSTRUMENT PANEL
5. CURRENT TRANSFORMERS
6. CIRCUIT-BREAKER OPERATING MECHANISM
7. CABLE BOX
8. CABLE-BOX SUPPORT
9. BUSBAR CHAMBER
10. INSULATED SPOUTS FOR THE ISOLATING PLUGS
11. ISOLATING PLUG
12. EARTHING PLUG

13. SECONDARY PLUGS AND SOCKETS
14. SPOUT SAFETY SHUTTER
15. OPERATING HANDLE FOR MECHANISM
16. RACKING ARM FOR VOLTAGE TRANSFORMER
F POSITION OF THE CIRCUIT-BREAKER TRUCK FOR CIRCUIT EARTHING
N POSITION OF THE CIRCUIT-BREAKER TRUCK FOR NORMAL SERVICE
B POSITION OF THE CIRCUIT-BREAKER FOR BUSBAR EARTHING

Figure 20.20.   Sectional view of an A.E.I. 1 200A 11 kV single-busbar vertical-isolation metal-clad switchgear unit with earthing by the transfer-breaker method (courtesy G.E.C. Switchgear Ltd.)

With all the foregoing in mind, we will now take note, largely with self-explanatory illustrations, of typical air-insulated units in the 11/13·8 kV range. Considering first the single-bus design, two units are seen in cross-section in Figs. 20.19 and 20.20, both of which include facilities for earthing by the transfer-breaker method and both using the modern insulating techniques that we have discussed.

To protect the equipment and operator from the dangers of incorrect operation, units of this type and those noted later include a number of interlocks, the chief ones being that:
1. The circuit-breaker can only be closed when it is in a fully-raised or fully-lowered position.
2. The circuit-breaker cannot be raised or lowered unless its contacts are open.
3. The circuit-breaker cannot be raised and plugged in unless its tank is fixed to the top plate.
4. The circuit-breaker can only be withdrawn from, or pushed into, the housing when in the fully-isolated position.
5. The circuit-breaker can only be raised within its housing at the position determined on the locator mechanism, as mentioned in earlier discussion.
6. The top cover of the voltage transformer can only be lifted when the transformer is in its isolated position.
In addition, padlocking points will be provided where appropriate to prevent unauthorised or inadvertent operation of the equipment.

The fixed contacts within the busbar and circuit spouts are automatically covered by safety shutters when the circuit-breaker is isolated and uncovered as the breaker is raised, a typical set of shutters and associated operating mechanism being shown in Fig. 20.21. For testing and earthing, each shutter can be individually opened and latched open while either or both can be pad-locked closed.

Mention has been made earlier of a type of vertical isolation switchgear in which the circuit-breaker is *raised* to isolate as opposed to being lowered. This type, designated *inverted vertical isolation*, has been developed for use both indoors and out, the cross-sectional view in Fig. 20.22 showing the outdoor design. In the indoor version, no change in principle is involved, but here the weather-hood is omitted and instruments and relays are accommodated on a vertical panel as in other designs. Figure 20.22 shows the circuit-breaker in the service position with the breaker nearly at ground level and the breaker top-plate extended to the rear to carry the busbar and cable isolating plugs. The fixed contacts with supporting spouts are carried above the busbars and cable entry respectively.

In the service position the jacking screws used to raise the circuit-breaker hold the latter firmly against the base of the carriage at floor level, reducing the stress on the tank bolts and on the isolating components due to shock when interrupting short circuits. Whereas in designs discussed earlier the isolation of the circuit-breaker does not involve the current or voltage transformers, in the inverted type these items are contained in a chamber above the breaker and move with it when raised or lowered.

In the isolated position, the circuit-breaker assembly can be drawn forward as shown in Fig. 20.23 for inspection and maintenance. This is an illustration which shows, incidentally, a ring-main assembly comprising two load-breaking fault-making oil switches in the ring main with a breaker in the tee-off feed.

The oil switches can be isolated vertically in a manner similar to that of the circuit-breaker. Safety shutters, interlocking arrangements, etc. follow the pattern previously noted.

When a system is based on the use of duplicate busbars, the general features of appropriate switchgear are basically the same as for single-bus designs. Busbar selection will be by the transfer-breaker method which automatically determines that the two sets of busbars be located back-to-back. This deprives the designer of space used in a single-bus design for current transformers so

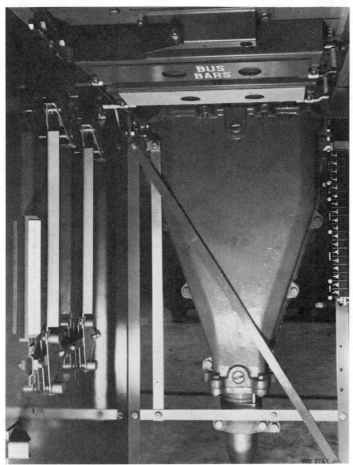

Figure 20.21. Interior of the circuit-breaker compartments of Figure 20.19 showing safety shutters and associated operating mechanism (courtesy A. Reyrolle & Co. Ltd.)

that these have to be accommodated in another chamber, two typical examples being noted in Fig. 20.24 and 20.25. The first of these illustrates the use, noted in earlier discussion, of a separate switch for cable earthing while the second illustrates an example of a unit using the transfer-breaker method for busbar selection, cable earthing or earthing either set of busbars.

Switchgear of the types so far discussed is shown in the representative illustrations of Figs. 20.26 to 20.30. Ratings in general are in a range up to 2 000 A with interrupting capacities extending from 75/150 MVA at 3·3 kV up

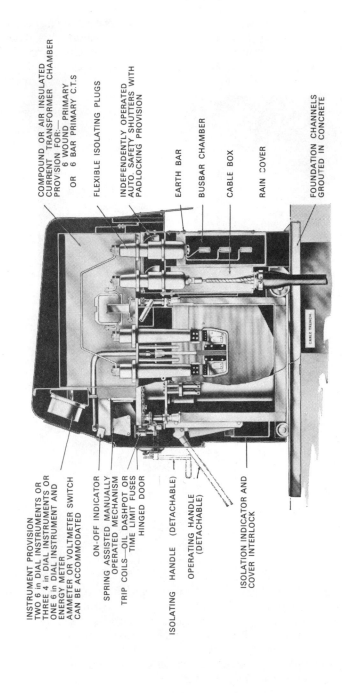

INSTRUMENT PROVISION
TWO 6 in DIAL INSTRUMENTS OR
THREE 4 in DIAL INSTRUMENTS OR
ONE 6 in DIAL INSTRUMENT AND
ENERGY METER
AMMETER OR VOLTMETER SWITCH
CAN BE ACCOMMODATED

ON-OFF INDICATOR

SPRING ASSISTED MANUALLY
OPERATED MECHANISM

TRIP COILS—OIL DASHPOT OR
TIME LIMIT FUSES

HINGED DOOR

ISOLATING HANDLE (DETACHABLE)

OPERATING HANDLE
(DETACHABLE)

ISOLATION INDICATOR AND
COVER INTERLOCK

COMPOUND OR AIR INSULATED
CURRENT TRANSFORMER CHAMBER
PROVISION FOR:—
        6 WOUND PRIMARY
OR 6 BAR PRIMARY C.T.S

FLEXIBLE ISOLATING PLUGS

INDEPENDENTLY OPERATED
AUTO. SAFETY SHUTTERS WITH
PADLOCKING PROVISION

EARTH BAR

BUSBAR CHAMBER

CABLE BOX

RAIN COVER

FOUNDATION CHANNELS
GROUTED IN CONCRETE

CABLE TRENCH

Figure 20.22.   Cross-sectional view of an inverted isolation unit for outdoor service; for indoor service the weatherproof hood is omitted (courtesy Yorkshire Switchgear & Engineering Co. Ltd.)

616

to 350/500 MVA at 11 kV, or, 750 MVA at 13·8 kV where the design includes this higher voltage rating.

For use on 22 or 33 kV systems, the basic principles of vertical isolation with integral earthing by the transfer-breaker method are retained in British designs, but there are a number of important differences in detail. For example, owing to the weight of the circuit-breaker, a power-operated raising and lowering mechanism will be used, e.g. a motor transmitting its power through a worm gear and chain drive to four lifting screws or an electrohydraulic hoist. Similarly, the voltage transformers when fitted will be heavier units demanding assistance for isolation purposes. Busbars take on various forms and may comprise copper

Figure 20.23. Outdoor-type inverted vertical isolation unit in raised and withdrawn position. Also seen is a load-breaking fault-making oil switch in its raised (isolated) position (courtesy Yorkshire Switchgear & Engineering Co. Ltd.)

rods suitably covered with insulating tape or synthetic-resin-bonded paper, or they may be in the form of synthetic-resin-bonded paper bushings with condenser layers for stress control. The chambers containing the busbars will generally be filled with bituminous compound, or in some instances with oil, and in some designs, phase separation is included. Typical busbar chambers are shown in Figs. 20.31 and 20.32, connections between the busbars of adjacent units being completed with specially designed links and enclosed after site assembly by elliptical band joints and filled with compound or oil.

For voltages above 15 kV, the use of epoxy resins has not reached a stage where it can be extensively used, largely on account of difficulties experienced in incorporating stress control layers in the material, although Rothwell[2] has noted important developments in this direction, particularly in relation to bushings both with straight or angled conductors.

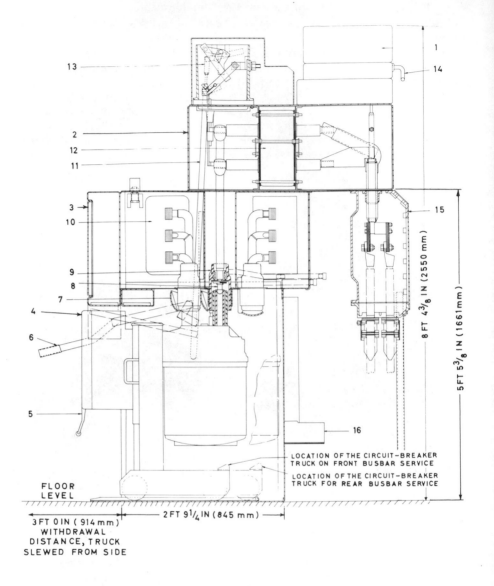

LOCATION OF THE CIRCUIT–BREAKER
TRUCK ON FRONT BUSBAR SERVICE

LOCATION OF THE CIRCUIT–BREAKER
TRUCK FOR REAR BUSBAR SERVICE

8 FT 4³/₈ IN (2550 mm)

5 FT 5³/₈ IN (1661 mm)

FLOOR
LEVEL

2 FT 9¹/₄ IN (845 mm)

3 FT 0 IN (914 mm)
WITHDRAWAL
DISTANCE, TRUCK
SLEWED FROM SIDE

LEGEND

1. VOLTAGE TRANSFORMER
2. CURRENT-TRANSFORMER
   CHAMBER
3. INSTRUMENT PANEL
4. OPERATING MECHANISM
5. OPERATING-MECHANISM
   HANDLE
6. EARTH-SWITCH HANDLE
7. SPOUT SAFETY SHUTTER
8. ISOLATING PLUG

9. INSULATED SPOUTS FOR
   ISOLATING PLUGS
10. BUSBAR CHAMBER
11. EARTH-SWITCH DRIVE
12. CURRENT TRANSFORMER
13. EARTH-SWITCH MECHANISM
14. VOLTAGE-TRANSFORMER
    ISOLATING HANDLE
15. CABLE BOX
16. MULTICORE CABLE BOX

Figure 20.24.   Sectional view of A.E.I. 1 200A 11 kV duplicate-busbar vertical-isolation metal-clad
switchgear unit with cable-earthing switch (courtesy G.E.C. Switchgear Ltd.)

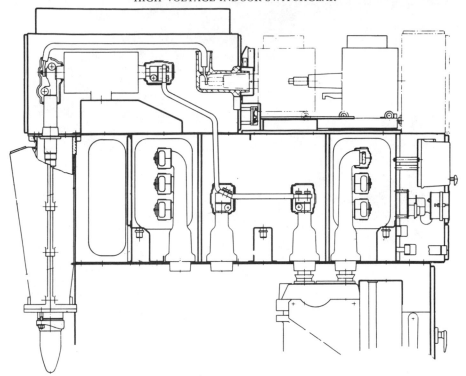

Figure 20.25. How the upper chambers of the unit in Figure 20.19 are modified to accommodate duplicate busbars, and with integral earthing by transfer breaker as in Figure 20.13 (courtesy A. Reyrolle & Co. Ltd.)

One design of 22/33 kV metal-clad unit of the type described is shown in Fig. 20.33, this being a complete sectional view of a single-bus design, while Fig. 20.34 shows the alternative part-section when duplicate busbars are included.

In this design, the voltage transformer *H* is isolated vertically, contact being made in a set of spouts similar to those used for the circuit-breaker service positions. A captive traversing carriage *O* is used for the lowering and raising operation, and this, in conjunction with a monorail *P*, enables the voltage transformer to be isolated and moved clear of the spouts while these are being used for the purpose of cable or rear-busbar earthing. This voltage transformer will be illustrated later in Chapter 23.

In another design, shown in Fig. 20.35, the voltage transformer is mounted on the top of the unit and is isolated by horizontal movement on rails. To assist this movement, a worm-gear mechanism can be operated from floor level as indicated in Fig. 20.36.

Current ratings at these higher voltages are in the range 800/2 400 A with interrupting capacities up to 1 000 MVA at 22 kV and 1 500 MVA at 33 kV. Typical switchboards are shown in Figs. 20.37 and 20.38, the former illustrating a single-busbar installation, and the latter one with duplicate-busbars, an illustration which incidentally shows the use of dividing fire walls between sections of the switchboard.

Figure 20.26. Single busbar switchboard of vertical-isolation metal-clad units up to 13·8 kV (courtesy Brush Switchgear Ltd.)

Figure 20.27. Single busbar switchboard of A.E.I. 11 kV vertical-isolation metal-clad units (courtesy G.E.C. Switchgear Ltd.)

Figure 20.28. Indoor-type switchboard of inverted vertical isolation units (courtesy Yorkshire Switchgear & Engineering Co. Ltd.)

Figure 20.29. Double busbar 11 kV switchboard of vertical-isolation metal-clad units (courtesy A. Reyrolle & Co. Ltd.)

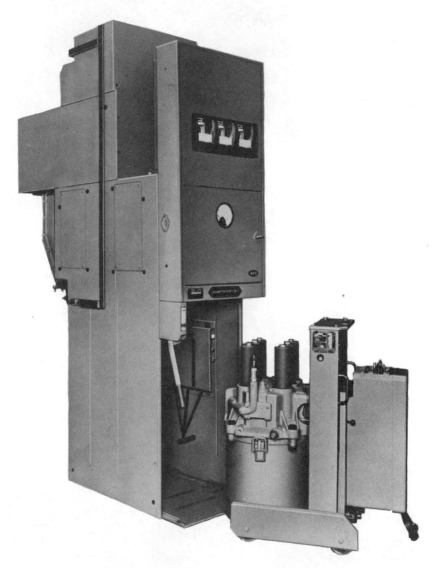

Figure 20.30. A.E.I. double-busbar 11 kV vertical-isolation metal-clad unit with circuit-breaker withdrawn (courtesy G.E.C. Switchgear Ltd.)

Figure 20.31. Typical compound-filled busbar chamber for 33 kV vertical-isolation metal-clad switchgear unit (courtesy A. Reyrolle & Co. Ltd.)

Figure 20.32. Compound-filled busbar chamber for A.E.I. 33 kV vertical-isolation metal-clad switchgear unit (courtesy G.E.C. Switchgear Ltd.)

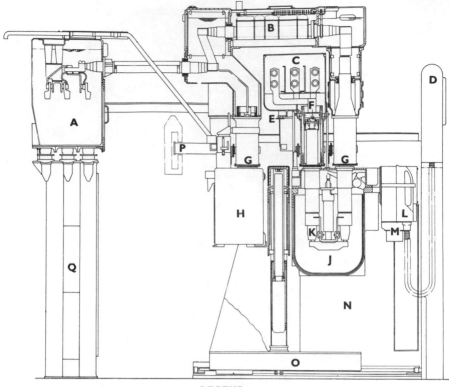

Figure 20.33.   Sectional view of 33 kV single-busbar vertical-isolation compound-filled metal-clad switchgear unit (courtesy A. Reyrolle & Co. Ltd.)

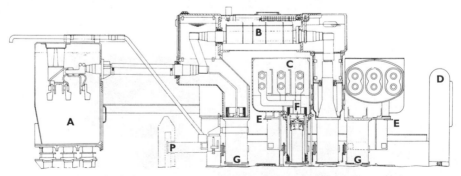

Figure 20.34.   How the upper chambers of Figure 20.33 are arranged for duplicate busbars. Legend as for Figure 20.33 (courtesy A. Reyrolle & Co. Ltd.)

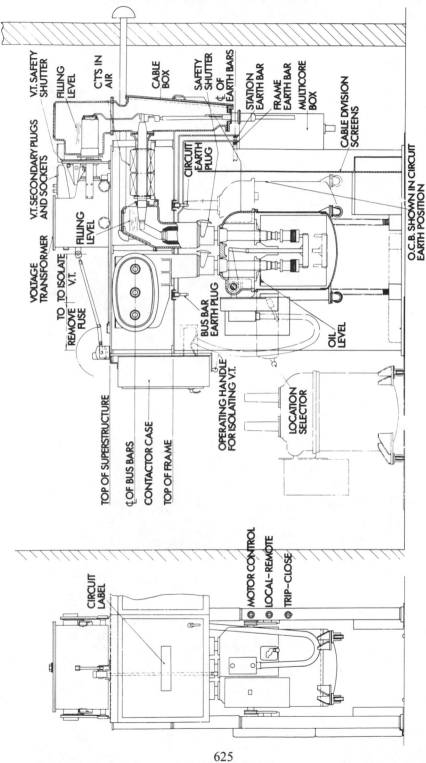

VOLTAGE TRANSFORMER

V.T. SAFETY SHUTTER

V.T. SECONDARY PLUGS AND SOCKETS

FILLING LEVEL

C'TS IN AIR

CABLE BOX

SAFETY SHUTTER

STATION EARTH BAR

FRAME EARTH BAR

$\mathbb{C}$ OF EARTH BARS

MULTICORE BOX

CABLE DIVISION SCREENS

CIRCUIT EARTH PLUG

TO ISOLATE V.T.

FILLING LEVEL

TO REMOVE FUSE

BUS BAR EARTH PLUG

OIL LEVEL

TOP OF SUPERSTRUCTURE

$\mathbb{C}$ OF BUS BARS

CONTACTOR CASE

TOP OF FRAME

OPERATING HANDLE FOR ISOLATING V.T.

LOCATION SELECTOR

O.C.B. SHOWN IN CIRCUIT EARTH POSITION

CIRCUIT LABEL

MOTOR CONTROL

LOCAL–REMOTE

TRIP–CLOSE

Figure 20.35.   Sectional view of an A.E.I. 33 kV single-busbar vertical-isolation metal-clad switchgear unit (courtesy G.E.C. Switchgear Ltd.)

625

Figure 20.36. How the voltage transformer shown in Figure 20.35 is isolated or returned to the service position from ground level (courtesy G.E.C. Switchgear Ltd.)

Figure 20.37.   A.E.I. 33 kV metal-clad switchgear at the Whalley Range substation of the North Western Electricity Board (courtesy G.E.C. Switchgear Ltd.)

Figure 20.38.   33 kV duplicate-busbar metal-clad switchboard with dividing walls between busbar sections (courtesy A. Reyrolle & Co. Ltd.)

HORIZONTALLY-ISOLATED SWITCHGEAR
(with bulk-oil circuit-breakers)

In the course of outlining some of the significant developments leading up to the present state of the art in switchgear design, note was taken in Fig. 1.12 of an armour-clad draw-out unit originated and built by Reyrolle in 1906. It is of interest here to note that the underlying principles and features of that early design are retained to this day in a range of metal-clad switchgear for use on systems up to 33 kV, although naturally many details have changed in line with modern practice.

As Fig. 20.39 suggests, the construction is extremely robust making it suitable for use under difficult conditions, and as all live parts are totally enclosed in earthed metal-casings filled with insulating compound or oil, the maximum degree of safety to personnel is achieved, while at the same time excluding dirt and vermin.

From Fig. 20.39, it is seen that the circuit-breaker is supported on two side frames, each of which carries a fixed toothed rack. The circuit-breaker carriage is fitted with pinions which engage with the rack, so that via a suitable mechanism the breaker can be racked horizontally into or out of the service position.

The circuit-breaker top-plate carries three compound-filled hoods which enclose right-angle conductors from the circuit-breaker and terminate at orifice insulators with plug contacts. The latter, in the service position, engage with fixed socket contacts within orifices forming an integral part of the busbar chamber on the one side, and of the current-transformer chamber on the cable side.

628

For duplicate-busbar units, a second busbar chamber is mounted directly above the first, and the hoods on the breaker are extended vertically to accommodate a second set of orifice insulators in line with the upper set of busbars. Only one set of plug contacts are provided, and these can be transferred by hand from the orifices corresponding to one set of busbars to those corresponding to the other set, an operation which can only be performed with the circuit-breaker fully withdrawn, i.e. it is essentially an off-load method of busbar selection as discussed in Chapter 9 and illustrated in Fig. 9.24.

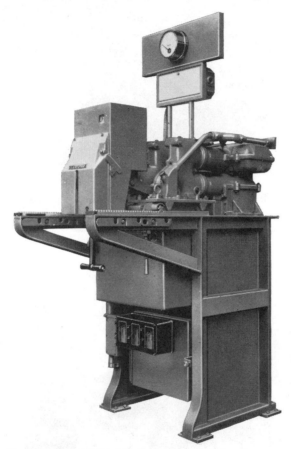

Figure 20.39. Typical compound-filled horizontal-isolation unit; 11 kV (courtesy A. Reyrolle & Co. Ltd.)

In an alternative method, a change-over switch in an oil-filled chamber can be used, the chamber replacing the hoods on the circuit-breaker top plate. Operated by hand, this switch may be of the off-load or on-load type, the latter designed to make-before-break and interlocked so that it can only be operated when an associated busbar-coupling circuit-breaker is closed. This method, in its two forms is also noted in Chapter 9, Figs. 9.25 and 9.26.

When it is required to earth either the cable or the busbars, a set of extended contacts have to be fitted to the appropriate set of circuit-breaker plug contacts and a crossbar to the opposite set of circuit-breaker plug contacts. This crossbar

Figure 20.40. 3-panel compound-filled horizontal-isolation switchboard; 11 kV (courtesy A. Reyrolle & Co. Ltd.)

Figure 20.41. 4-panel compound-filled horizontal-isolation switchboard with duplicate busbars; 22 kV (courtesy A. Reyrolle & Co. Ltd.)

is then connected to the main earth bar, the breaker racked into the test position and then closed to complete the earthing operation through the circuit-breaker.

This design of switchgear unit incorporates all the interlocks and safety features noted in the discussion on vertically-isolated types. Two typical switchboards are shown in Figs. 20.40 and 20.41.

HORIZONTALLY-ISOLATED SWITCHGEAR
(with small-oil-volume circuit-breakers)

As noted elsewhere, interest in the small-oil-volume circuit-breaker for use indoors on distribution systems up to 33 kV is almost non-existent among users in the U.K., whereas on the continent of Europe their use predominates. For the purpose of discussing the type considered in Chapter 13 a typical

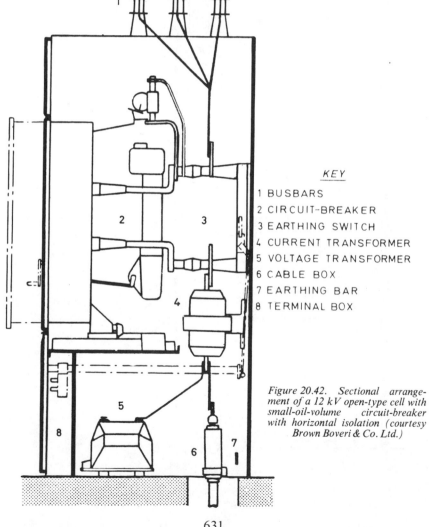

KEY

1 BUSBARS
2 CIRCUIT-BREAKER
3 EARTHING SWITCH
4 CURRENT TRANSFORMER
5 VOLTAGE TRANSFORMER
6 CABLE BOX
7 EARTHING BAR
8 TERMINAL BOX

Figure 20.42. Sectional arrangement of a 12 kV open-type cell with small-oil-volume circuit-breaker with horizontal isolation (courtesy Brown Boveri & Co. Ltd.)

continental design therefore had to be chosen, and here the various ways that the same circuit-breaker is incorporated in switchgear units will be noted.

Although made and used in a number of applications as a fixed circuit-breaker with separately-mounted isolating switches, our description will be confined to the more popular horizontal draw-out type which appears in three particular forms.

The first of these is an open-type cell shown typically in Fig. 20.42. This is a simple angle-iron structure with front access doors and rear covers, partitions between adjacent cells comprising sheets of insulating board. The busbars are quite open and are carried on top of the framework without protection, while within the cell there are no separate compartments for the various items of equipment. The circuit-breaker is supported on a shelf at a height which brings

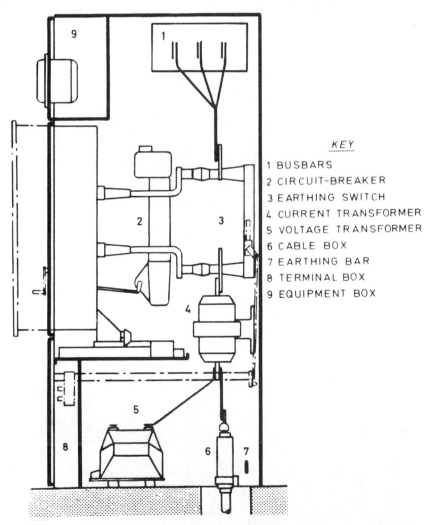

KEY

1 BUSBARS
2 CIRCUIT-BREAKER
3 EARTHING SWITCH
4 CURRENT TRANSFORMER
5 VOLTAGE TRANSFORMER
6 CABLE BOX
7 EARTHING BAR
8 TERMINAL BOX
9 EQUIPMENT BOX

Figure 20.43. Sectional arrangement of a 12 kV metal-enclosed unit with small-oil-volume circuit-breaker with horizontal isolation (courtesy Brown Boveri & Co. Ltd.)

the operating and isolating mechanisms to hand level. In the isolated position (shown dotted) the chamber containing the circuit-breaker operating mechanism projects a short distance in front of the cell, acting as a shroud over the withdrawal opening, and at the same time gives visual indication that the breaker is isolated. Because there are no compartments, there is no need for shutters over the fixed isolating contacts. Should it be necessary to remove a circuit-breaker from its cell, a wheeled bogey as shown in a later illustration must be used, a condition applying to other forms of unit in which the breaker is above floor level. It is of interest in passing to note that the circuit-breaker

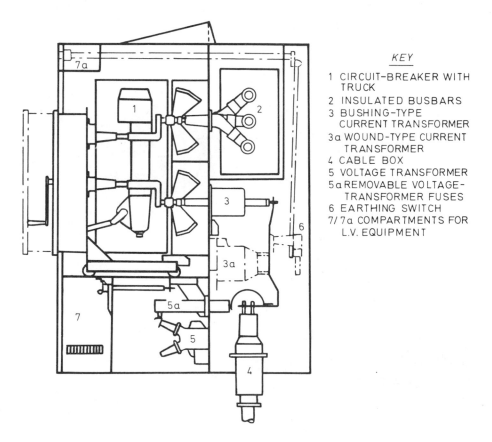

KEY

1 CIRCUIT-BREAKER WITH TRUCK
2 INSULATED BUSBARS
3 BUSHING-TYPE CURRENT TRANSFORMER
3a WOUND-TYPE CURRENT TRANSFORMER
4 CABLE BOX
5 VOLTAGE TRANSFORMER
5a REMOVABLE VOLTAGE-TRANSFORMER FUSES
6 EARTHING SWITCH
7/7a COMPARTMENTS FOR L.V. EQUIPMENT

Figure 20.44. Sectional arrangement of a metal-clad unit with small-oil-volume circuit-breaker with horizontal isolation at operating level (courtesy Brown Boveri & Co. Ltd.)

shown in Fig. 20.42 is fitted with primary overcurrent relays (above and mounted on the breaker top terminals).

The second form, shown in Fig. 20.43, is a metal-enclosed unit which is not unlike the open-type cell unit, except that the busbars are brought within the enclosure, insulated with shrunk-on sleeves of p.v.c. and are supported by insulating plates in the metal division barriers between adjacent cells.

Both these forms are intended for use in stations when only modest demands are imposed with regard to safety and ease of maintenance and for installations in rooms to which only skilled personnel have access. In other circumstances, units comparable to the British conception of metal-clad switchgear are used. Two arrangements of this allow the breaker to be accommodated in the elevated position as discussed above and shown in Fig. 20.44, or, alternatively at floor level as shown in Figs. 20.45 and 20.46. Figure 20.47 is a rear view of the circuit-breaker shown in Fig. 20.46. As these illustrations show, equipment is segregated in compartments, and the normal practice of automatic shutters to cover the live fixed terminals when the breaker is isolated or withdrawn is adopted. Tubular busbars, insulated with resin-bonded paper or p.v.c. are completely enclosed in earthed metal, and, as in British practice, are in unit lengths, the joints between adjacent units being encased in plastic mouldings.

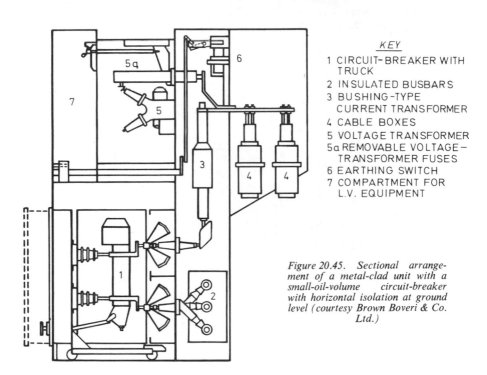

KEY

1 CIRCUIT-BREAKER WITH TRUCK
2 INSULATED BUSBARS
3 BUSHING-TYPE CURRENT TRANSFORMER
4 CABLE BOXES
5 VOLTAGE TRANSFORMER
5a REMOVABLE VOLTAGE-TRANSFORMER FUSES
6 EARTHING SWITCH
7 COMPARTMENT FOR L.V. EQUIPMENT

Figure 20.45. Sectional arrangement of a metal-clad unit with a small-oil-volume circuit-breaker with horizontal isolation at ground level (courtesy Brown Boveri & Co. Ltd.)

Basically, the foregoing illustrations relate to units suitable for service voltages up to 12 kV, but the same principles are used for 24 and 36 kV units, typical illustrations being shown in Figs. 20.48 and 20.49. From the latter it is seen that in the isolated position the circuit-breaker is within the confines of the housing, this being necessary to obtain the relatively long draw-out distance to give adequate electrical clearance between the fixed (live) and moving contacts when isolated. At 36 kV also, metal-clad designs only are employed.

For systems up to 12 kV, two interesting layouts in the metal-clad designs have been shown to be possible. In the first of these, a double-tier arrangement is employed as shown in Fig. 20.50, while in a second layout (Fig. 20.51) two sets of busbars are used.

The latter, designated 'duplex' has an application as indicated typically in

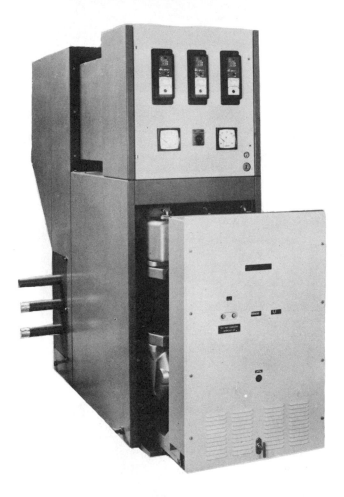

Figure 20.46. 11 kV metal-clad unit with small-oil-volume circuit-breaker at ground level (courtesy Brown Boveri & Co. Ltd.)

the schematic diagram of Fig. 20.52. In both of these layouts, space for relays, meters, mimic diagrams, control switches, etc. is provided by slightly increasing the width of the fixed cubicle as shown typically in Fig. 20.51.

Interlocks and safety measures in the various types of units are generally similar to British practice, most of the interlocks being associated with the circuit-breaker withdrawal mechanism. Earthing facilities for the cable or busbars can either be provided by a special earthing switch incorporated in the switchgear, or, as is most favoured, by the use of an earthing truck which can be plugged into any housing after completely withdrawing the circuit-breaker for cable earthing and by plugging into a separate cubicle for busbar earthing. The cubicle can, if required, be used to accommodate metering equipment. Typical switchboards of the types described are shown in Figs. 20.53, 20.54 and 20.55.

Figure 20.47. Rear view of circuit-breaker shown in Figure 20.46 on its carriage (courtesy Brown Boveri & Co. Ltd.)

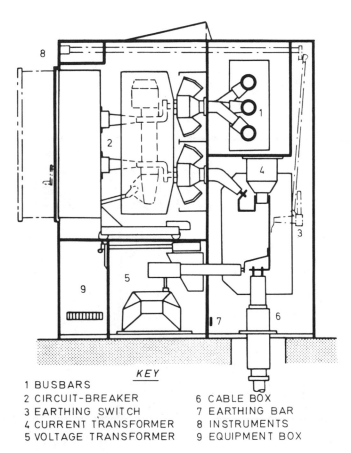

1 BUSBARS
2 CIRCUIT-BREAKER   6 CABLE BOX
3 EARTHING SWITCH   7 EARTHING BAR
4 CURRENT TRANSFORMER   8 INSTRUMENTS
5 VOLTAGE TRANSFORMER   9 EQUIPMENT BOX

Figure 20.48. Sectional arrangement of a 24 kV metal-clad unit with a small-oil-volume circuit-breaker (courtesy Brown Boveri & Co. Ltd.)

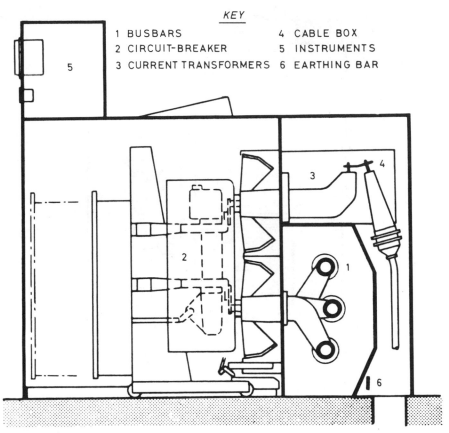

KEY

1 BUSBARS   4 CABLE BOX
2 CIRCUIT-BREAKER   5 INSTRUMENTS
3 CURRENT TRANSFORMERS 6 EARTHING BAR

Figure 20.49.   Sectional arrangement of a 36 kV metal-clad unit with small-oil-volume circuit-breaker (courtesy Brown Boveri & Co. Ltd.)

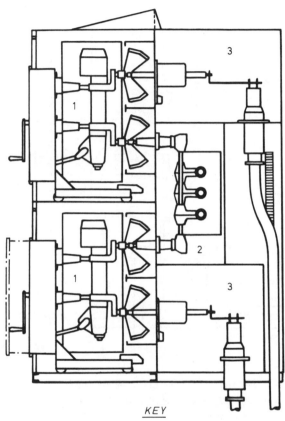

KEY
1 CIRCUIT BREAKER COMPARTMENTS
2 BUSBARS
3 CURRENT TRANSFORMERS

Figure 20.50. Metal-clad unit with small-oil-volume circuit-breakers arranged in double-tier formation (courtesy Brown Boveri & Co. Ltd.)

639

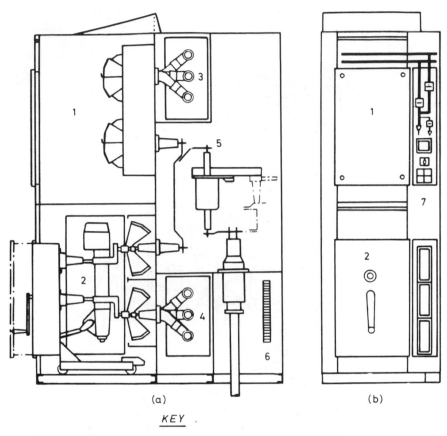

(a)   (b)

KEY .

1 BREAKER COMPARTMENT FOR BUSBAR SYSTEM NO.1
2 BREAKER COMPARTMENT FOR BUSBAR SYSTEM NO.2
3 BUSBAR SYSTEM NO. 1
4 BUSBAR SYSTEM NO. 2
5 CURRENT TRANSFORMER AND CABLE BOX WITH SPACE FOR
  EARTHING SWITCH
6 TERMINALS FOR CONTROL WIRING
7 EQUIPMENT BOX WITH TWO FLAPS FOR RELAYS, CONTROLS
  AND MIMIC DIAGRAM

Figure 20.51.   Metal-clad unit with two small-oil-volume circuit-breaker compartments in a 'duplex' arrangment. (a) Cross-section and (b) front elevation (courtesy Brown Boveri & Co. Ltd.)

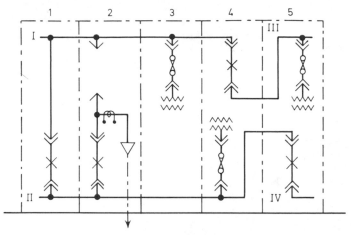

LEGEND

1. UNIT CONTAINING BUS COUPLER BETWEEN SYSTEMS I AND II
2. DUPLEX JUNCTION
3. METERING UNIT FOR BUSBAR SYSTEM I
4. UNIT WITH BUS COUPLER BETWEEN SYSTEMS I AND III WITH METERING FOR SYSTEM II
5. UNIT WITH BUS COUPLER BETWEEN SYSTEMS II AND IV WITH METERING FOR SYSTEM III

Figure 20.52. Schematic diagram of a 'duplex' unit as shown in Figure 20.51 (courtesy Brown Boveri & Co. Ltd.)

Figure 20.53. 16 kV open-cell type of switchboard with small-oil-volume circuit-breakers as shown typically in Figure 20.42 (courtesy Brown Boveri & Co. Ltd.)

641

Figure 20.54. 6 kV metal-enclosed switchboard with small-oil-volume circuit-breakers (courtesy Brown Boveri & Co. Ltd.)

Figure 20.55. 13 kV metal-clad switchboard with small-oil-volume circuit-breaker compartments as shown in Figure 20.48. Note circuit-breaker on removal bogey (courtesy Brown Boveri & Co. Ltd.)

642

HORIZONTALLY AND VERTICALLY-ISOLATED SWITCHGEAR
(with air-break circuit-breakers)

Because of the usual position of the arc-chute it is natural for the bushings on air-break circuit-breakers to be at the rear so that horizontal isolation is most widely used, but, as we have noted in Chapter 14, one design incorporating a circuit-breaker of a relatively low order of interrupting capacities has been introduced using the principle of vertical isolation.

All designs are of the metal-clad type and are designated as *air-insulated* for the reasons discussed earlier. Nevertheless, most designs allow for the busbars and connections to be insulated with either p.v.c. sleeving, resin-bonded paper or cast epoxy resin, with joints shrouded in moulded insulating boxes. Extensive use is also made of cast epoxy resin at other points in the design, using encapsulated current and voltage transformers.

Whereas in metal-clad units with bulk-oil circuit-breakers, cable or busbar earthing has been largely achieved by a common method, i.e. by transfer-breaker, no such common method is to be noted with air-break circuit-breaker units. It is of course obvious that the transfer-breaker method can only be used in units employing vertical isolation, and it is indeed the method adopted for a unit of this type noted earlier (see Fig. 14.25).

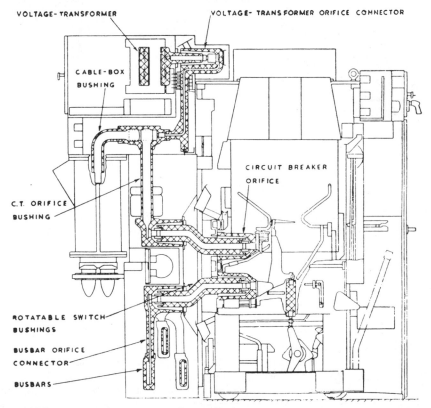

Figure 20.56. Sectional arrangement of an 11 kV horizontal-isolation switchgear unit with an air-break circuit-breaker. Cross-hatching indicates cast epoxy-resin insulation (courtesy A. Reyrolle & Co. Ltd.)

For horizontal isolation types, designers have adopted a variety of methods which will be noted in relation to some typical units to be described.

One design of horizontal draw-out unit has already been shown in the cross-sectional view in Chapter 14 (Fig. 14.20) and it is shown again in a different form in Fig. 20.56 to demonstrate the extent to which cast epoxy resin can be used. This illustration is of particular interest in showing how cast resin facilitates the use of bent and cranked bushings, e.g. cable-box bushings and rotatable switch-bushings. The latter are used with circuit-breakers whose current rating is less than 2 400 A and a typical bushing is shown in detail in Fig. 20.57. Each set of bushings (upper or lower) can be rotated through 180° using an appropriate (normally locked) handle at the side of the main-contact connections, an operation requiring the withdrawal of the circuit-breaker from its housing. Thus, if it is required to earth the cable, the lower set of bushings will be rotated

Figure 20.57.   Cranked circuit-breaker bushing in epoxy resin as used in Figure 20.56 for cable and busbar earthing (courtesy A. Reyrolle & Co. Ltd.)

so that when the circuit-breaker is plugged-in again, contact will be made via these bushings with the star earth-bar seen in Figs. 14.20 and 20.56 lying between the upper and lower fixed contacts. For busbar earthing, the upper set of bushings are rotated, and in either operation the final connection to earth is made when the circuit-breaker is closed.

When rotatable bushings cannot be used, a system shown in Fig. 20.58 is used, noting that the blades *A* and *B* in the upper illustration are hinged, and, through an interlocked linkage, are brought out to an external operating mechanism which can, with the breaker withdrawn, be rotated through 90° so that when the breaker is plugged-in the blades so rotated make contact with earthing contacts mounted on an earth bar. By this means, cable or busbar earthing is achieved, again through the circuit-breaker.

The blade position for the condition of busbar earthing is seen in Fig. 20.58(b), blade *A* being in a vertical position and in contact at *E* with the earth bar. A rear view of a circuit-breaker fitted with hinged blades is seen in Fig. 20.59 with the blades in position for busbar earthing.

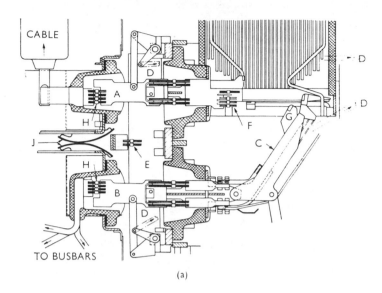

(a)

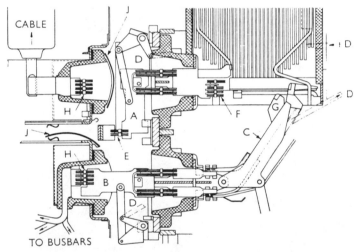

(b)

LEGEND

A	HINGED BLADE CONTACT FOR BUSBAR EARTHING
B	HINGED BLADE CONTACT FOR CIRCUIT EARTHING
C	CIRCUIT-BREAKER (IN OPEN POSITION BUT PLUGGED-IN)
D	OPERATING RODS FOR *A* AND *B*

E EARTH CONTACTS AND BAR
F FIXED MAIN AND ARCING CONTACTS
G MOVING MAIN AND ARCING CONTACTS
H ISOLATING CONTACTS
J LOCKING-OFF DOORS

Figure 20.58. Schematic diagram showing a part section of an air-break circuit-breaker unit with hinged blades for busbar or cable earthing. (a) Hinged blade contacts in service positions and (b) hinged blade contacts in position for busbar earthing; the cable isolating orifice is closed by the locking-off door. Note that to earth the circuit cable, the hinged blade B will be raised through 90° to the vertical position and hinged blade A will revert to its service position. For this operation the busbar isolating orifice will be closed by its locking-off door (courtesy A. Reyrolle & Co. Ltd.)

SECONDARY CONTACTS

LOCKING-OFF
DOOR DRIVE
INOPERABLE

HINGED
BLADES

Figure 20.59.   Rear view of 3·3/6·6 kV air-break circuit-breaker with isolating contacts set for busbar earthing (courtesy A. Reyrolle & Co. Ltd.)

With earthing through rotatable bushings or hinged blades, operation of these automatically immobilises the drive to the appropriate shutters and disconnects the circuit-breaker trip coil. Suitable interlocks prevent mal-operation, and to restore the bushings or the blades to the service position, the circuit-breaker must be opened and withdrawn.

An interesting detail concerning the unit shown in Figs. 14.20 and 20.56 is that the voltage transformer, encapsulated in epoxy resin, is carried on a turntable as seen in Fig. 20.60. This shows the transformer in the isolated position at which it can be turned to give access to the primary fuses which plug-in within the bushings forming part of the encapsulation. This is further illustrated in Chapter 23 in our discussion on voltage transformers.

Figure 20.60. Horizontally-withdrawable voltage transformer in isolated position. It rotates on the turntable to give access to fuses in bushings. The transformer is encapsulated in epoxy resin (courtesy A. Reyrolle & Co. Ltd.)

Switchgear units of the foregoing type have current ratings ranging from 800 to 3 000 A with interrupting capacities up to 500 MVA at 6·6 kV and 750 MVA at 11 kV.

As mentioned earlier, a unit employing vertical isolation has been shown in Fig. 14.25 in the course of discussing air-break circuit-breaker designs. This unit has rather lower ratings than noted above, the current range being 400–1 200 A with interrupting capacities of 75 MVA at 3·3 kV, 150 MVA at 6·6 kV and 250 MVA at 11 kV. A typical unit, with the circuit-breaker isolated and withdrawn, is shown in Fig. 20.61, and apart from the method of isolation and the use of the transfer-breaker method of earthing, most of the features previously described are applicable, epoxy resin again being used to a considerable extent.

Figure 20.62 shows a sectional arrangement of a 3·3 kV 2 000 A metal-clad

unit in which means are provided to isolate the circuit-breaker without movement of the latter on its truck. This is achieved by simply withdrawing the
isolating-bridge contacts which slide horizontally along the main stalks at the
rear of the circuit-breaker truck. This action is effected by the movement of a
detachable lever at the front of the unit, which through linkages slides the isolating bridge contacts in and out of contact with the busbar and cable connections.
Each set of bridging contacts can be independently operated, a feature which

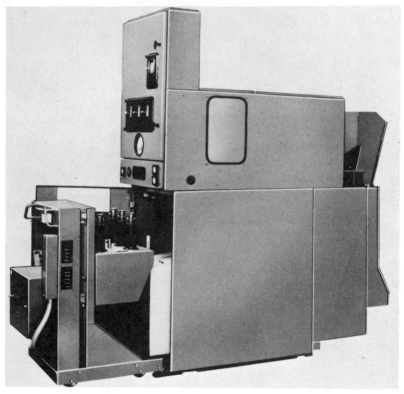

*Figure 20.61. Vertically isolated 11 kV switchgear unit with air-break circuit-breaker (shown
withdrawn). See also Figure 19.25 (courtesy A. Reyrolle & Co. Ltd.)*

simplifies the method of earthing adopted in this design and at the same time
provides a ready means of busbar selection when units are of a duplicate busbar
type. Figure 20.62 does in fact show the latter, with a duplicate set of bridging
contacts for the busbars and one set on the cable side; for single busbar units,
the lower set of busbars and bridging contacts are omitted. On duplicate busbar
units, selection can be made on-load provided the switchboard includes a
bus-coupling unit and it is ensured that this is closed before a changeover is
made at other units.

Figures 20.63 and 20.64 show a typical set of isolating contacts of the type
described, the system being designated *Isolector** (meaning to isolate and/or
select). It is applied to a wide range of air-break switchgear extending to 11 kV

* An English Electric patent and registered trade mark.

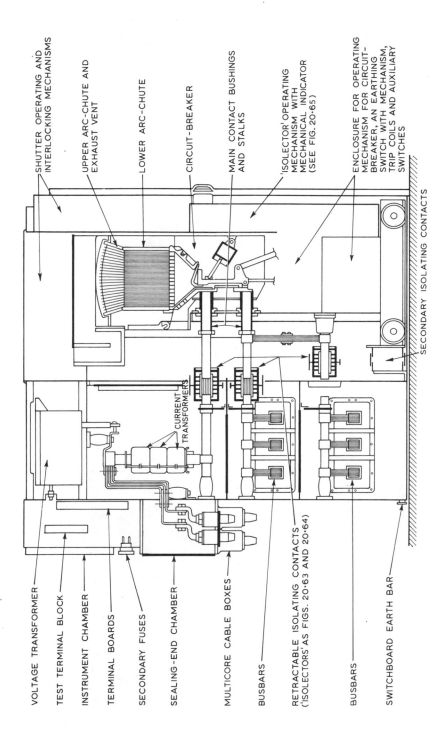

SHUTTER OPERATING AND
INTERLOCKING MECHANISMS

UPPER ARC-CHUTE AND
EXHAUST VENT

LOWER ARC-CHUTE

CIRCUIT-BREAKER

MAIN CONTACT BUSHINGS
AND STALKS

'ISOLATOR' OPERATING
MECHANISM WITH
MECHANICAL INDICATOR
(SEE FIG. 20·65)

ENCLOSURE FOR OPERATING
MECHANISM FOR CIRCUIT-
BREAKER, AN EARTHING
SWITCH WITH MECHANISM,
TRIP COILS AND AUXILIARY
SWITCHES

SECONDARY ISOLATING CONTACTS

VOLTAGE TRANSFORMER

TEST TERMINAL BLOCK

INSTRUMENT CHAMBER

TERMINAL BOARDS

SECONDARY FUSES

SEALING-END CHAMBER

MULTICORE CABLE BOXES

BUSBARS

RETRACTABLE ISOLATING CONTACTS
('ISOLECTORS' AS FIGS. 20·63 AND 20·64)

BUSBARS

SWITCHBOARD EARTH BAR

CURRENT
TRANSFORMERS

Figure 20.62. Sectional arrangement of English Electric 2 000A 3·3 kV duplicate-busbar horizontal draw-out switchgear unit with E3 air-break circuit-breaker. On single busbar units the lower set of busbars and retractable isolating contacts are omitted (based on an original, courtesy G.E.C. Switchgear Ltd.)

649

Figure 20.63. Close-up of English Electric 'Isolector' contacts at rear of circuit-breaker. Both sets in 'made' position (courtesy G.E.C. Switchgear Ltd.)

Figure 20.64. Close-up of English Electric 'Isolector' contacts at rear of circuit-breaker. Cable contacts in 'made' position and busbar contacts in 'isolated' position (courtesy G.E.C. Switchgear Ltd.)

650

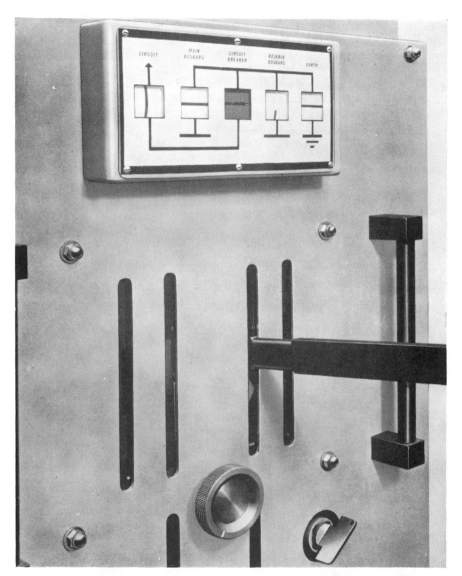

Figure 20.65.   Interlock gate on English Electric double-busbar unit showing operating lever inserted and isolating the reserve busbars (courtesy G.E.C. Switchgear Ltd.)

500 MVA, and in each design operation takes place through an interlocking gate on the circuit-breaker truck. This gate varies depending on the facilities required, i.e. isolation plus busbar selection, cable or busbar earthing, a typical gate shown in Fig. 20.65 covering isolation, busbar selection and cable earthing. The functions are achieved by pushing in and rotating the trip knob below the gate, firstly to ensure that the circuit-breaker is tripped and cannot be closed until the selected operation is complete, and secondly to move a slotted plate which slides to uncover the socket of the facility required to allow the operating lever to be inserted. It is seen that a mechanically-operated mimic diagram appears above the gate to show the state of the unit at any time.

For cable and busbar earthing, separate integral earthing switches can be provided, that for cable earthing on each unit and that for busbar earthing on

Figure 20.66.   Partial front view of an English Electric E7 switchboard of 11 kV units with air-break circuit-breakers. The breaker in the open cubicle is in the service position (courtesy G.E.C. Switchgear Ltd.)

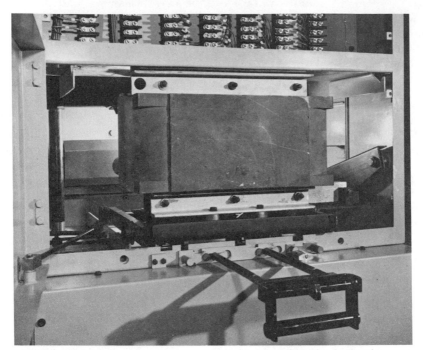

Figure 20.67.   Horizontally isolated voltage transformer in the English Electric E7 unit, transformer in the isolated position on the turntable (courtesy G.E.C. Switchgear Ltd.)

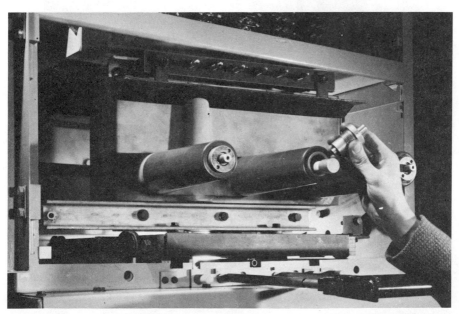

Figure 20.68.   Voltage transformer as shown in Figure 20.67 rotated in the isolated position to give access to fuses in the bushings (courtesy G.E.C. Switchgear Ltd.)

two selected units on each section of busbar. These switches are operated in conjunction with the 'isolector' interlock gate and an indication that a switch is closed is given on the mimic diagram. For example, in Fig. 20.65, the right-hand end slot would be used to close the cable earthing switch and the condition indicated at the right-hand indicator. In either earthing operation, the final connection with earth is made by closing the circuit-breaker.

In Chapter 14, note has been taken of a very-heavy-duty air-break circuit-breaker with current ratings of 2 000/3 000 A and interrupting capacities of 500/750 MVA at 11 kV, a design illustrated in Figs. 14.27, 14.28 and 14.29. Figure 20.66 shows a switchgear unit incorporating this breaker. It should be noted that here isolation is by the conventional method of withdrawing the complete circuit-breaker from the service to the isolated positions. The weight of the moving element and the necessary grip between the fixed and moving isolating contacts for heavy, normal and fault current ratings make it necessary to assist the operation of disengagement or re-engagement, and for this purpose

Figure 20.69.   Horizontally isolated 11 kV air-break circuit-breaker with breaker partly withdrawn and front cover removed (courtesy Brown Boveri & Co. Ltd.)

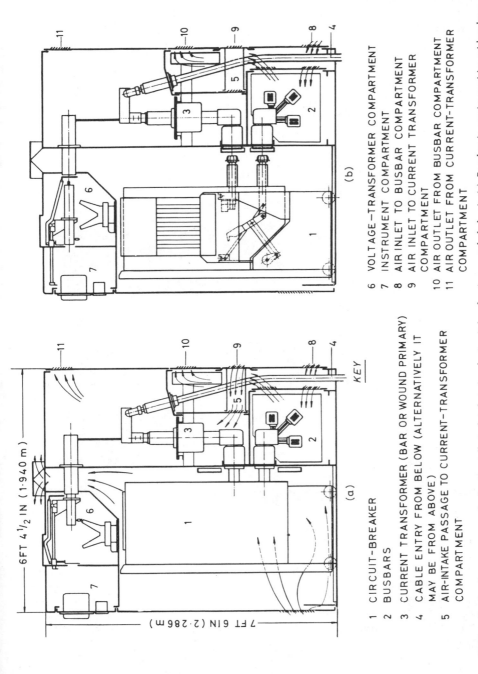

1 CIRCUIT-BREAKER
2 BUSBARS
3 CURRENT TRANSFORMER (BAR OR WOUND PRIMARY)
4 CABLE ENTRY FROM BELOW (ALTERNATIVELY IT
   MAY BE FROM ABOVE)
5 AIR-INTAKE PASSAGE TO CURRENT-TRANSFORMER
   COMPARTMENT

6 VOLTAGE-TRANSFORMER COMPARTMENT
7 INSTRUMENT COMPARTMENT
8 AIR INLET TO BUSBAR COMPARTMENT
9 AIR INLET TO CURRENT TRANSFORMER
   COMPARTMENT
10 AIR OUTLET FROM BUSBAR COMPARTMENT
11 AIR OUTLET FROM CURRENT-TRANSFORMER
   COMPARTMENT

KEY

Figure 20.70. Sectional arrangement of a horizontally-isolated air-break circuit-breaker in a metal-clad unit. (a) Breaker in service position with voltage transformer connected and (b) breaker in isolated position with voltage transformer disconnected (courtesy Brown Boveri & Co. Ltd.)

655

a racking gear is provided. The racking handle, seen in its 'parked' position in Fig. 20.66, is integral with the racking gear and is used as a steering handle when moving the truck.

The two indicators seen on the front panel give, on the left, the on/off condition of the circuit-breaker and the charged or discharged state of the motor-wound spring-closing device, and on the right, the service-earth-test indication, both being observable through the windows in the front door.

In this unit, as in one noted earlier, the voltage transformer which is encapsulated in epoxy resin is mounted on a withdrawable turntable. Figure 20.67 shows this in the isolated position with a safety cover protecting the fixed (live) contacts. Release of a bolt allows the transformer to be swivelled through 180° to bring the high-voltage fuses to an accessible position as seen in Fig. 20.68,

Figure 20.71.   Power station switchboard of 3·3 kV air-break circuit-breaker units (courtesy A. Reyrolle & Co. Ltd.)

noting that the fuses are contained within the transformer bushings, the latter forming a part of the encapsulation.

Integral features for cable and busbar earthing can be included using a system of extensible stalks stored normally within the main cable or busbar stalks on the circuit-breaker, and a hinged earthing beam which can be moved up or down depending on the required operation. The setting of the beam and the withdrawal of the appropriate extensible stalks is made with the breaker fully withdrawn from its housing, and a system of key and other interlocks ensures that a correct procedure is followed. Subject to this, the breaker is then moved back into its housing to the selected earthing position where the extended stalks make contact with the earthing beam and closure of the circuit-breaker now completes the connection to earth. The interlocks ensure that at this point the electrical

Figure 20.72. *English Electric switchboard of air-break circuit-breaker units* (E7/8) *at the C.E.G.B. Eggborough (Yorks) Power Station (courtesy G.E.C. Switchgear Ltd.)*

Figure 20.73. *27-unit switchboard with Brown Boveri air-break circuit-breakers for Romania (courtesy Simon Engineering Ltd. and the former Belmos Peebles Switchgear Ltd.)*

trip is disconnected during the earthing operation while the mechanical trip is rendered inoperative by the removal of a safety key. To trip the breaker at the end of the period of earthing, this safety key must first be reinserted.

Among the air-break circuit-breakers noted in Chapter 14, one example of a continental design has been included, a breaker suitable for the voltage range of 3·6 kV to 17·5 kV and with interrupting capacities ranging from 150/250 MVA at 3·6 kV to 500 MVA at 17·5 kV. The metal-clad unit incorporating this type of circuit-breaker is seen in Fig. 20.69 and basically this is similar to and has the features of British designs we have noted. Shown in section in Fig. 20.70 it is seen however that here the voltage transformer is a fixed unit connected to, or disconnected from, the high-voltage supply via retractable bushings moving into or out of spout insulators. The primary fuses are contained in these bushings and are accessible for renewal in the fully withdrawn position as in the sectional view in Fig. 20.70(b), a safety shutter covering spout orifices.

Integral earthing facilities are not a feature of this design, the preferred method being the use of an earthing truck which can be used in any unit for cable earthing, or in a busbar extension unit for busbar earthing, a unit which can be also used for a busbar voltage transformer, metering equipment, etc.

Typical examples of switchboards built of units such as the ones that have been described are shown in Figs. 20.71, 20.72 and 20.73.

REFERENCES

1. ANON., 'Packaged Substation with Low-oil 132 kV Circuit-breakers', *Elect. Rev.*, 18 Aug. (1967)
2. ROTHWELL, K., 'Cast Resin in High-voltage Switchgear', *Elect. Rev.*, 16 July (1965)
3. MANLEY, T.R., ROTHWELL, K. and GRAY, W., *The Application of Low-pressure Resins to some High-voltage Switchgear Designs*, available from A. Reyrolle & Co. Ltd. as Reprint No. RR 176/98
4. KNAPP, F., 'Epoxy Casting Resins', *Brown Boveri Rev.*, **52** No. 8, Aug. (1965)

BIBLIOGRAPHY

BAUMANN, J., 'Simplified Draw-out Units for Low-oil-volume Circuit-breakers Type SB', *Brown Boveri Rev.*, **52** No. 4, April (1965)
BLOWER, W., 'Modern Trends in Distribution Switchgear Design', *Proc. I.E.E.T.E.*, May (1967)
FREIDRICH, E., *et al.*, 'New Totally-enclosed and Metal-clad Cubicles for Low Voltage Switchgear', *Brown Boveri Rev.*, **58**, June (1971). *Note:* This article covers 3·8–13·8 kV units with air-blast circuit breakers
GARRARD, C.J.O., 'High-voltage Distribution Switchgear—A Review of Progress', *Proc. I.E.E.*, **116** No. 6, June (1969)
GARRARD, C.J.O., 'High-voltage Switchgear—A Review of Progress', *Proc. I.E.E.*, **113** No. 9 (1966)
GARRARD, C.J.O., 'Trends in Switchgear Design', *Elect. Rev.*, 26 Sept. (1969)
GARRARD, C.J.O., 'Scope for Cooperation in Switchgear Design and Manufacture', *Elect. Rev.*, 1 April (1966)
GARRARD, C.J.O., 'A Return to Generator Switching', *Elect. Rev.*, 9 Jan. (1970)
LATZKO, J., 'Metal-clad Switchgear with Magnetic Circuit-breakers for 3·6 and 7·2 kV', *Brown Boveri Rev.*, **46** No. 9, Sept. (1959)
LATZKO, J. and MUNZINGER, K., 'Draw-out Metal-clad Units for Low-oil-volume Circuit-breakers Rated at 12, 24 and 36 kV', *Brown Boveri Rev.*, **52** No. 4, April (1965)
LIGHTLE, D. and ARMSTRONG, T.V., 'Switchgear for Supply—Designs Adapted to Match Overseas Practice', *Elect. Times*, 16 May (1968)
LLOYD, L.J., 'Switchgear for Auxiliaries in Power Stations', *Elect. Times*, 12 June (1969)
MOSELE, J. and ROHR, R., 'Indoor Air-blast Circuit-breakers Type DB, and Switchgear Cubicles for Very-high Capacities, *Brown Boveri Rev.*, **54** No. 12, Dec. (1967)
MUNZINGER, K., 'Factory-assembled Switchgear Installations with Low-oil-volume Circuit-breakers Type SB for 12–36 kV', *Brown Boveri Rev.*, **54** No. 12, Dec. (1967)
MUNZINGER, K. and ZIMMERMANN, W., 'Standard Switchgear Cubicles with Minimum-oil Circuit-breakers for 12–36 kV', *Brown Boveri Rev.*, **58**, June (1971)
ROHR, R. and RUCKSTUHL, H., 'Metal-clad Heavy-current Switchgear', *Brown Boveri Rev.*, **51** No. 4, April (1964)

Chapter 21

High-voltage outdoor switchgear

There is a wide range of high-voltage switchgear which can be used in the open without the need for conventional buildings, i.e. from the relatively simple installation of fuses that are extensively used on rural distribution networks for the control and protection of small power transformers or spur feeders, to the gear found in major switching centres and substations on transmission systems operating up to today's highest voltage, i.e. 750 kV. Between these extremes, the switchgear takes on a variety of forms depending on the service sought and the facilities required, as for example auto-reclosers, individual metal-clad fuse switches and oil switches, ring main units, packaged switchgear and substations, and some indoor types of switchgear modified to make it suitable for outdoor use.

HIGH-VOLTAGE FUSES

Three classes of high-voltage fuse are in general use, i.e. the expulsion, liquid and h.r.c. cartridge types. The most common application is on distribution systems up to 33 kV, but noting that in the liquid and cartridge types, fuses are available for use on systems up to 132 kV which are used largely for protecting voltage transformers.

Up to 33 kV, the expulsion and cartridge types are frequently used in drop-out mountings, forming a fuse switch so designed that when the fuse element melts, the fuse-carrier or link is free to fall away from the upper contact to hang suspended from the lower hinge contact, typically as shown in Fig. 21.1. In this position, a 'blown' fuse gives an unmistakable indication of the condition and can be detected at some distance by a linesman seeking to locate a fault position. Using a specially designed operating pole, typically as shown in Fig. 21.2, the fuse-carrier or link can be lifted clear at the hinge point and lowered to ground level for attention. A rewired fuse carrier or a new h.r.c. fuse link can be relocated at the hinge point using the same pole and then reclosed to restore the service, as shown in Fig. 21.3. A further feature is that it can be used as a normal isolating switch, the latch mechanism being released manually by the operating pole.

For applications where the drop-out feature is not required or is physically impossible because of the size of the fuse, i.e. at the higher voltages, both the expulsion and cartridge types can be carried in fixed mounts for vertical or horizontal installation.

With the liquid fuse, fixed mounts at all voltages are common, but for designs up to 33 kV an alternative method is to provide a pull-down feature which enables the fuse to be pulled out of or pushed into the fixed contacts, again using a specially designed operating pole.

Faults occurring on overhead lines are very frequently of a transient nature, the cause of the fault being self-clearing, e.g. a branch of a tree blown across the

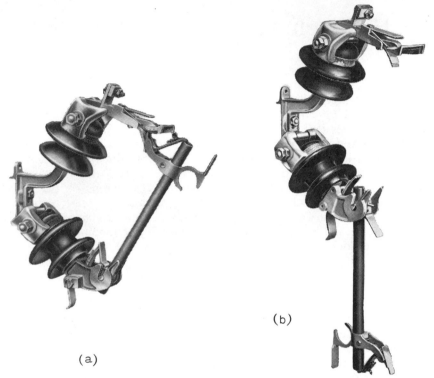

(b)

(a)

Figure 21.1. 11 kV type D *drop-out type expulsion fuse switch.* (a) *in closed position and* (b) *in isolated position (courtesy English Electric Fusegear Ltd.)*

lines will drop away. If this results in fuse operation, the outage time may be unnecessarily long, being dependent on the time it takes a linesman to locate and reach the position. To reduce the outage time, a single-shot repeater arrangement can be employed, using two fuses in parallel per phase as shown in Fig. 21.4. With both fuses in the closed position, only one fuse is in circuit, the second being isolated at a normally-open shunt contact, the condition being shown diagrammatically in Fig. 21.5. When a fault causes the fuse in circuit to operate, it drops out in the manner described so that the assembly now appears as in Fig. 21.6. In dropping down, the 'blown' fuse carrier automatically causes the shunt contact to close to place the second fuse in circuit. If the fault is still present, this will operate to finally isolate the circuit, but if the fault has cleared itself, service is at once restored via the second fuse. The restoration time will be of the order of 0·5 s, this being the time it takes the first fuse carrier to swing

Figure 21.2. The operating pole (left) in use to remove or replace a fuse carrier from its hinges. The complete pole assembled for carrying is on the right; note the torch for night use (courtesy English Electric Fusegear Ltd.)

down and close the shunt contact. By adding an adjustable delay device, closure of the contact can be delayed, e.g. for up to 60 s.

After the 'blown' fuse has been rewired or replaced, it is reclosed in the normal manner and the shunt contact is reset so that the combination is restored to the original condition ready for subsequent operation.

Single or three-phase arrangements of the drop-out fuse-switch are normally pole-mounted, the fuses being carried on a channel or other base, typical arrangements being shown in Figs. 21.7 and 21.8.

EXPULSION FUSES

In this type, the fuse carrier is an insulating tube with an inner lining of horn fibre or some other gas-producing substance. The fuse element may comprise a fusible section held between either two strain wires or fuse wires in parallel

Figure 21.3. Fuse-carrier tube being reclosed after renewal of the fuse element

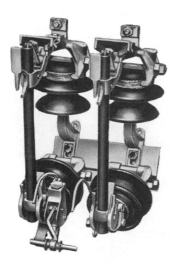

Figure 21.4. Repeater-switch arrangement for automatic circuit restoration, using two expulsion-type fuse switches per phase. Shown in original state with both fuse elements sound (courtesy English Electric Fusegear Ltd.)

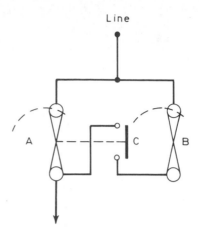

Line

A C B

Figure 21.5. Schematic diagram of drop-out fuse repeater switch. When fuse A blows and drops out it automatically closes contact C to put fuse B into service. Contact C is reset to open on reclosing A

Figure 21.6. Repeater-switch arrangement showing one fuse 'blown' to leave second fuse in circuit (courtesy Switchgear & Equipment Ltd.)

663

Figure 21.7. Type D expulsion fuse switches installed at a single-phase pole-mounted transformer substation (courtesy English Electric Fusegear Ltd.)

Figure 21.8. Typical mounting on an 'H'-pole for three-phase assembly of drop-out fuse switches (courtesy Switchgear & Equipment Ltd.)

664

with strain wires, and is threaded through the tube with its ends attached to metal fittings at each end.

When the fuse wire melts and an arc is formed, the heat of the latter produces a de-ionising gas from the horn fibre or other liner, the gas being expelled at the open ends of the tube. This tends to force the tails of the now ruptured element towards the ends of the tube thus lengthening the break to further assist the interrupting process. In the design illustrated in Figs. 21.6 and 21.8, the lower tail of the fuse element is in fact automatically pulled down the tube as the carrier falls away to the isolated position.

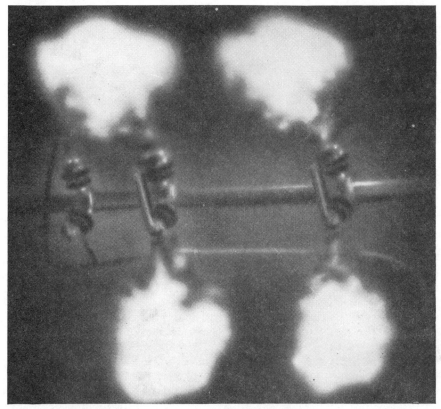

Figure 21.9. Expulsion-type fuses clearing a three-phase fault of 150 MVA at 11 kV during short-circuit tests. From a high-speed ciné film at 3 000 frames per second

Some idea of the outward expulsion of gas at both ends of a set of fuses clearing a three-phase fault of 150 MVA at 11 kV is noted in Fig. 21.9, noting that in the left-hand phase a solid link has been substituted for the fuse element thus ensuring that the recovery voltage across the fuses in the other phases is not less than line-to-line voltage.

With the fuse-carrier tube open at both ends, as in Fig. 21.9, trouble may arise due to the ingress of rain and dust at the upper end. To deal with relatively low fault power, single venting at the lower end may be adequate, but for high fault powers, double venting increases the interrupting ability. In the design shown in Figs. 21.6 and 21.8, a sealing diaphragm is fitted at the upper end of

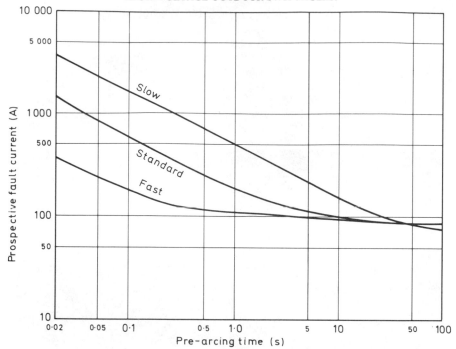

Figure 21.10. Approximate time/current characteristics of 40A expulsion fuses to illustrate differences between fast, standard and slow acting (courtesy Switchgear & Equipment Ltd.)

the tube which, while effectively sealing this while the fuse is intact, will blow out under pressure to give double venting. The ballooning of the hot gases as seen in Fig. 21.9 indicates that ample phase clearances between fuses are required.

It is normal practice with expulsion fuses to provide a choice of fuse elements having different time/current characteristics and designated as fast, standard or slow acting. By way of example, the characteristics of a 40 A fuse element in each category are shown in Fig. 21.10 and a study of this shows that while the pre-arcing times are only slightly different at low values of prospective fault current, the differences at high values are quite marked. Later in this chapter we shall note a design of automatic circuit recloser which has been developed to work in conjunction with fuses, the recloser being in the main feeder and the fuses in consumer circuits teed-off the main feed. The fuses chosen for this application need to be carefully selected in so far as time/current characteristics are concerned and in general it is found that those with a slow-acting characteristic are most suitable.

LIQUID FUSES

In very simple terms, this type comprises a relatively short fuse link contained in the upper end of an insulating tube, generally of heat-resisting glass, which is fitted with metal contacting ferrules at each end and filled with an arc-extinguishing liquid. Originally, oil was used for the purpose, hence the fuses were designated as *oil-blast*, but present-day fuses are filled with an inert liquid, e.g. carbon tetrachloride.

The fuse link has its upper end in contact with the upper ferrule while the lower end is attached to a spring whose opposite end is registered at the lower ferrule. This spring is not relied on to carry current. For this purpose a flexible conductor is used, contained within the coils of the spring and in parallel with it. The design is such that under normal conditions, the spring maintains the fuse link in tension, but when the link melts the spring causes rapid separation at the break. A conical liquid director, moving with the spring and the retracting fuse-link terminal, forces a stream of liquid into the arcing zone where the liquid volatilises so that the arc is burning in an atmosphere of vapour with

Figure 21.11. Three-phase assembly of liquid-type rewirable fuses (courtesy Switchgear & Equipment Ltd.)

de-ionisation taking place in the gaseous arc column. This process is very similar to that which takes place in an arc-controlled oil circuit-breaker.

In present day designs, considerable thought has been given to making re-wiring a simple and reliable process. In the fuse seen in Fig. 21.11, the fuse elements are contained in a cartridge, using silver and nickel-chromium wires in parallel, the silver being mainly current carrying with the nichrome relieving it of mechanical stress. The elements are shrouded in an arc-control sleeve of de-ionising material, and the lower contact carries the liquid director with facilities for connection to the spring.

After operation the fuse cartridge can readily be removed using a specially designed tool. First remove the end fittings, and then with the reverse end of the tool, engage the cartridge, release it from a contact socket on the spring and then lift out the cartridge, which is discarded. A new cartridge may then be fitted to the tool, inserted in the tube and engaged with the contact socket on the spring. Tension is then applied by pulling back the cartridge and spring until a top contact ring can be slipped into place; finally, the end fittings are replaced. All this is achieved without the use of screws or washers.

Carbon tetrachloride is highly volatile and will evaporate through the smallest aperture. In the presence of air and moisture it becomes highly corrosive, an action which can be accelerated by the heat generated during fault clearance. For these reasons, perfect sealing is essential, and when replacing a cartridge, precautions must be taken to keep the carbon tetrachloride free of water or moisture, particularly if topping-up is found necessary.

Figure 21.12. 11 kV pull-down fuse isolator with liquid-type fuse (courtesy Switchgear & Equipment Ltd.)

A pressure-relief diaphragm is trapped between the conical surface of the upper contact ferrule and a conical self-aligning ring in the fuse cap. This diaphragm is made of pure tin, and this gives a metal-to-metal joint which up to the bursting pressure of the diaphragm, is a perfect seal. The pressure at which the diaphragm will vent is related, with a good margin of safety, to the bursting strength of the glass tube, thus protecting the latter. Normally the pressure generated will be insufficient to cause the diaphragm to vent, but if it does, there will be a loss of liquid which must be topped up or preferably changed in case contamination has occurred due to the loss of the seal. Here, as with the expulsion fuse, fuse elements with fast or slow time/current characteristics may be used, the latter mainly when in association with automatic reclosers.

Liquid fuses of the type described are used in what are known as *pull-down* fuse isolators, examples being those shown in Figs. 21.12 and 21.13. To remove

Figure 21.13. 33 kV pull-down fuse isolator with liquid-type fuse (courtesy Switchgear & Equipment Ltd.)

a blown fuse, the head of an operating pole is inserted in the bell mouth and engaged with the fuse at a bayonet-socket arrangement. The fuse can then be released from a locking device at the bottom contact and pulled down out of contact with the top contacts. The latter comprise spring-loaded rollers which grip the top ferrule on the fuse but allow for easy withdrawal or re-entry.

Replacing a fuse is a reverse process, and after making full contact at the top, a twist of the operating pole engages a bayonet catch in the bell mouth, thus locking the fuse in position and at the same time disengaging the operating pole.

H.R.C. CARTRIDGE FUSES

These fuses are of the current-limiting type and have many applications, e.g. (*a*) where the interrupting capacity of other types is inadequate for the system fault level, (*b*) for applications beyond the voltage range of the expulsion types, (*c*) where the advantages of high-speed clearance and cut-off are sought, or a combination of these. The many advantages of this type of fuse have already been discussed in Chapter 10 and some details of their construction noted.

The interrupting capacity of the high-voltage h.r.c. fuse is very high, typical ratings being noted in Table 21.1 for a part of the available E.M.P. Electric Ltd. range.

It should be noted that the MVA ratings are related to the nominal voltage rating of the fuse cartridge (first column) and that they are those applicable to fuses of the *maximum* normal-current rating (third column) in each physical size of fuse. Fuses of lower normal-current ratings will have higher interrupting ability, as here, for the same prospective fault current, cut-off will occur at much lower values, as indicated in Fig. 21.14. As noted in Chapter 10, cut-off is not exhibited at all values of fault current, there being a minimum value for each rating of fuse. What this minimum is will vary between different makes of

Table 21.1

TYPICAL RATINGS OF THE HIGH-VOLTAGE h.r.c. FUSE

Nominal rating (kV)		Maximum continuous current ratings (A)	Interrupting capacity	
Fuse	System		R.M.S. symmetrical (A)	Three-phase symmetrical (MVA)
3·3	3·0 3·3 3·7	400	60 000	350
6·6	6·0 6·6 7·2	250	40 000	450
11·0	10·0 11·0 12·1	200	40 000	750
13·8	13·2 13·8 14·4	200	40 000	950
14·4	14·4 15·0 15·5	200	40 000	1 000
22·0	20·0 22·0 24·0	125	26 000	1 000
33·0	33·0 34·5 35·0	125	22 000	1 250
66·0	60·0 66·0 69·0	60	13 100	1 500
132·0	130·0 132·0 138·0	30	8 800	2 000

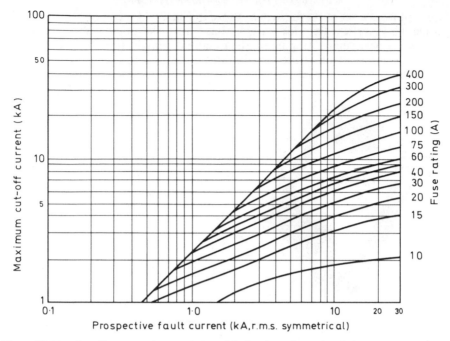

Figure 21.14. Cut-off current characteristics of high-voltage h.r.c. fuse-links (courtesy E.M.P. Electric Ltd.)

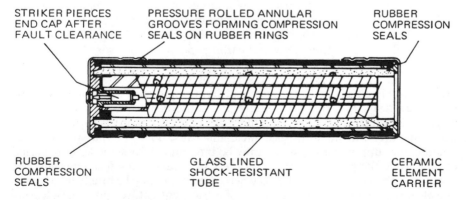

STRIKER PIERCES END CAP AFTER FAULT CLEARANCE

PRESSURE ROLLED ANNULAR GROOVES FORMING COMPRESSION SEALS ON RUBBER RINGS

RUBBER COMPRESSION SEALS

RUBBER COMPRESSION SEALS

GLASS LINED SHOCK-RESISTANT TUBE

CERAMIC ELEMENT CARRIER

Figure 21.15. Typical h.r.c. high-voltage fuse-link with striker pin (courtesy E.M.P. Electric Ltd.)

671

fuse, and from a set of curves such as those in Fig. 21.14 it can be determined by projecting a vertical line down to the base from the point where the cut-off curve for a particular rating meets the diagonal straight line. Thus a 40 A fuse starts to exhibit cut-off at prospective fault currents (r.m.s. symmetrical) above 1 kA, while a 200 A fuse requires the fault current to be 5 kA or more. It should

Figure 21.16. High-voltage fuse switch employing cartridge-type fuse link with striker pin

also be noted that cut-off curves are usually based on a fully asymmetrical fault condition, i.e. where the peak value in the first half-cycle of fault (first major loop of current) approximates to 2·55 times the r.m.s. symmetrical value.

Fitted with a striker pin as shown in Fig. 21.15 (a feature discussed in more detail in Chapter 10) this type of fuse link can generally be used in a drop-out mount as with expulsion fuses. Here the striker pin is used to upset a latching mechanism at the top contact to allow the fuse link to fall down to a vertical position suspended at the hinge, a typical drop-out unit being noted in Fig. 21.16.

AUTOMATIC RECLOSERS FOR RURAL DISTRIBUTION

Rural distribution consists largely of an extensive system of overhead radial feeders, each of which is controlled by a circuit-breaker at a main substation and supplies numerous spur lines protected by fuses of the types discussed. At 11 or 22 kV, conductor spacings will be relatively close and the network is prone to flash-overs caused by such things as straw or twigs being blown across the lines, large birds spanning the lines as a result of their large wing spans, or in high winds by the clashing of conductors. More particularly, these lines will be prone to the effects of lightning disturbances, and all these things can result in a transient failure, the cause being quickly eliminated. It has been estimated that something like 90% of all faults on overhead distribution lines are transitory. If such incidents cause fuses in the spur lines to operate, the supply to a consumer may be interrupted for some lengthy period of time while the point of fuse operation is located and the fuse replaced. The problem is then to find some means whereby a circuit may be briefly interrupted and then restored so that if the fault is of a transient nature and is self-clearing the supply is only interrupted temporarily.

We have seen on page 660 how this objective has been achieved by the use of repeater fuses. Here we shall note the availability of specially-designed automatic circuit reclosers which have been developed to operate in conjunction with fuses having suitable time/current characteristics or with an automatic sectionaliser.

The recloser is a circuit-breaker with an assigned breaking and making capacity while the sectionaliser is an oil-switch capable only of interrupting currents up to about twice its rated normal current, but it can make on to a fault of short-circuit magnitude.

Figure 21.17 may be regarded as being typical of recloser application, the recloser being inserted in the main overload line with slow-acting fuses to protect the consumer circuits. It will be fitted with a sequence timing mechanism

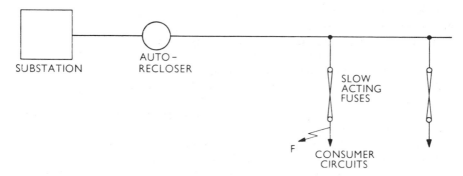

Figure 21.17.   Application of automatic recloser and fuses

to provide, for example, an operating sequence of two instantaneous trips to be followed by two time-delayed trips and then lock-out.

Thus, if a fault occurs at point F as shown, the recloser will open to interrupt the short circuit before the fuse link can operate and the recloser remains open for approximately 1 s. During this time the fault path de-ionises and as noted earlier, in the majority of cases the cause of the fault will have disappeared. After the 1 s period the recloser will automatically reclose, and if the fault has disappeared supply is restored, but if it has not, the recloser will open again instantaneously and remains open for 1 s before reclosing. If the fault still persists it may now be presumed to be permanent and the next trip is purposely delayed to permit the fuse link to operate and isolate the fault. The recloser now closes to restore supply to remaining (healthy) circuits leaving only the faulty circuit isolated.

If the fault current is insufficient to cause the fuse link to operate during this first delayed tripping operation, the equipment recloses and is followed by a second delayed tripping operation to give the fuse link a second chance to clear the fault. Should the fault persist, the recloser will lock-out and the operating mechanism must then be reset manually.

This sequence is best illustrated by the operating cycle diagram given in Fig. 21.18, but it may be noted that the sequence can be varied to suit operational requirements, e.g. the total of four tripping operations can be in any combination of instantaneous or delayed such as one instantaneous and three delayed or three instantaneous and one delayed.

673

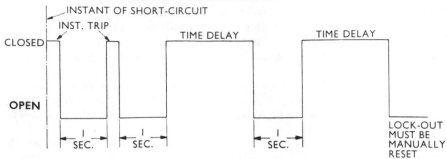

Figure 21.18. Operating cycle for auto-recloser

If the fault is cleared at any time during a sequence *before* lock-out, the mechanism of the recloser will reset so that it will be ready to commence the entire sequence again on the occurrence of any further fault.

The satisfactory operation of a recloser in association with fuses depends on the degree of co-ordination obtained, requiring that the time/current characteristic of the recloser be graded with that of the fuse to give optimum discrimination. Thus the selection to give this must ensure:

(*a*) That the recloser will perform the first two operations without causing the fuse link to deteriorate, and

(*b*) That the opening of the recloser will be sufficiently delayed on the third and fourth operations to permit the fuse link to operate.

Circumstances may be such that the necessary discrimination between a recloser and the spur-line fuses cannot be obtained, or there may be objections to the use of fuses. In such cases, an automatic sectionaliser should be used in the spur lines instead of fuses, as indicated in Fig. 21.19. With this arrangement, and if the fault *F* is permanent, the recloser will commence its selected sequence of four tripping operations, and during the third trip (when no current is flowing into the fault) the sectionaliser tripping device (overcurrent or earth fault) will operate to open the sectionaliser to isolate the faulty spur line. The recloser will then close and remain closed to maintain the supply to the remainder of the system. When the fault on the spur has been repaired, the sectionaliser can be reclosed to restore supply.

If the fault is transient, it should clear after the first or second tripping operation of the recloser so that the sectionaliser will not complete the sequence and

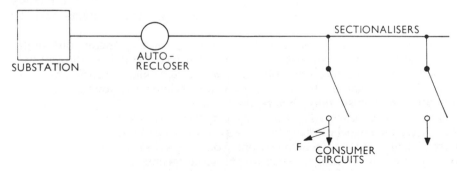

Figure 21.19. Application of auto-recloser and sectionalisers

will return to the normal condition in readiness for a full sequence on the occurrence of a subsequent fault, the sectionaliser having remained closed throughout.

Figure 21.20 shows diagrammatically a particular sequence arrangement of tripping and closing for a recloser/sectionaliser combination. This shows that if, after the three instantaneous trips on the recloser, the fault has not cleared, the sectionaliser will time itself out to open and clear the fault, but breaking no current as the recloser at that instant is open. With this arrangement, it is usual to arrange to set the recloser for instantaneous trips only.

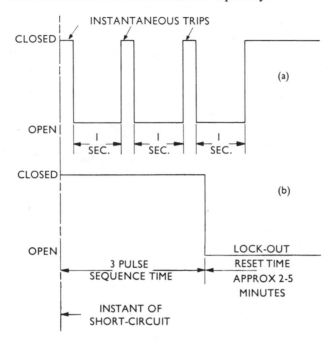

Figure 21.20. Operating cycles for (a) *auto-recloser and* (b) *sectionaliser*

Figure 21.21 shows a typical three-phase automatic recloser installed in the run of a mains feeder. If, as a result of a permanent fault, the recloser completes its operating sequence and locks-out it must be reclosed manually, using an operating pole to actuate an external lever. It can, using the pole-operated lever, be tripped manually and remains open until reset. An on/off indicator, visible at ground level, shows the state of the recloser.

Figure 21.22 shows the recloser in cross-section. The unit is closed by means of an electromagnetically charged spring mechanism and is held by a roller toggle against the action of a kick-off spring. Passage of fault current through self-resetting series-overcurrent coils causes the recloser to open, whereupon the sequence of reclosing and opening operations as described earlier proceed automatically, locking-out should the full sequence be completed.

The energy for closing is derived from what is described as a *multistroke electromagnet*, the coil of which is connected across two lines of the incoming supply through a pair of auxiliary contacts as shown in Fig. 21.23. These contacts close as the recloser contacts open, thus energising the magnet, the armature of which moves downwards to start the charging process of the closing spring via a clutch mechanism. When the armature is almost fully home, the auxiliary contacts separate, de-energising the magnet so that the armature returns to the open position under spring action. In this position the auxiliary contacts reclose and the magnet is re-energised to give a further charge to the closing spring. The sequence is repeated until the latter is fully charged, approximately seven strokes being required for the purpose and taking less than 1 s to complete.

While this charging of the closing spring is taking place a rotating cam is being moved into a position where, after the last charging stroke is completed, the spring is discharged thus closing the recloser contacts and opening the auxiliary contacts to de-energise the electromagnet. If, as a result of a permanent fault, the recloser completes its operating sequence, the auxiliary contacts are held open thus preventing any further charging of the closing spring and the recloser is locked open until reclosed manually by means of an external lever.

Figure 21.21. Automatic reclosure pole mounted in the run of a main feeder (courtesy A. Reyrolle & Co. Ltd.)

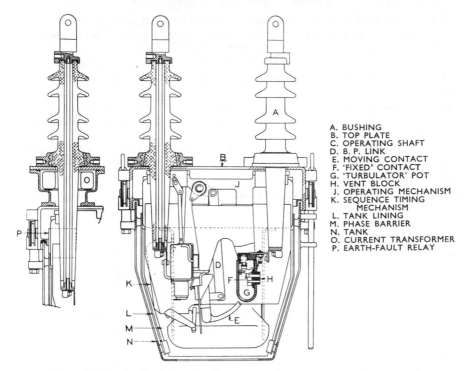

A. BUSHING
B. TOP PLATE
C. OPERATING SHAFT
D. B. P. LINK
E. MOVING CONTACT
F. 'FIXED' CONTACT
G. 'TURBULATOR' POT
H. VENT BLOCK
J. OPERATING MECHANISM
K. SEQUENCE TIMING
    MECHANISM
L. TANK LINING
M. PHASE BARRIER
N. TANK
O. CURRENT TRANSFORMER
P. EARTH-FAULT RELAY

Figure 21.22. Sectional view of recloser interior (courtesy A. Reyrolle & Co. Ltd.)

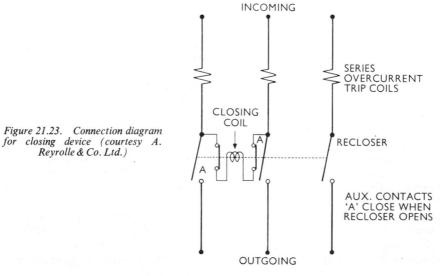

Figure 21.23. Connection diagram for closing device (courtesy A. Reyrolle & Co. Ltd.)

INCOMING

SERIES
OVERCURRENT
TRIP COILS

CLOSING
COIL

RECLOSER

AUX. CONTACTS
'A' CLOSE WHEN
RECLOSER OPENS

OUTGOING

Sequence timing is by means of an oil dashpot, which, for the instantaneous operations, is by-passed due to the opening of a piston valve. Thus the position of this valve determines whether the operation shall be instantaneous or time-delayed and its position is controlled by a sequence cam which moves whenever the recloser opens. The sequence cam indexes every opening operation and another cam on the same shaft operates a pull-rod controlling the position of the piston valve. Thus, by adjusting the position of these cams relative to each other, the required number of instantaneous and/or delayed operations can be selected.

It will be seen from the part sectional view in Fig. 21.22 that ring-type current transformers can be fitted over the recloser bushings and thus enable earth-fault protection to be included if required. This operates on the core-balance principle and employs a rectifier-operated moving-coil relay which is also

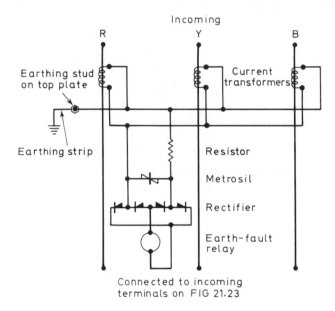

Figure 21.24. Connection diagram for earth-fault protection on auto-recloser (courtesy A. Reyrolle & Co. Ltd.)

accommodated within the recloser. When operating on earth fault, the recloser opens instantaneously throughout the predetermined number of operations to lock-out, i.e. no delayed tripping is allowed for.

A connection diagram for this protection is shown in Fig. 21.24, provision being made for it to be put out of action during live-line working in order to avoid mal-operation. This protection gives a fixed-minimum tripping value of 20 A so that when a recloser is fitted with series overcurrent coils of lesser current rating, e.g. 5 or 10 A, the fitting of earth-fault protection is unnecessary. Some difficulty can arise in co-ordination with phase-protection devices such as fuse links, but this can be overcome by fitting a transistorised time-delay device arranged to inhibit operation of the earth-fault relay for a period to allow other devices to operate. Where earth-fault currents less than 20 A obtain, it is possible, by introducing d.c. tripping, to provide *external* sensitive relays

678

operated from the current transformers in the unit to give settings down to 5 A primary current.

The recloser described is available in two sizes, one for operation on systems up to 14·4 kV with a maximum normal-current rating of 250 A, and another for systems up to 25·8 kV with a maximum normal current rating of 400 A. The making capacity of the two sizes is 13 400 A and 16 700 A respectively, both being peak values. The breaking capacity ratings are 100 MVA at 11 kV for the lower voltage unit and 250 MVA at 20/25·8 kV, 150 MVA at 14·4 kV and 125 MVA at 11 kV for the other. Care is necessary to site the recloser so that the available fault current does not exceed these ratings. Thus, if the fault level at the main substation is say 250 MVA at 11 kV, the recloser must be installed

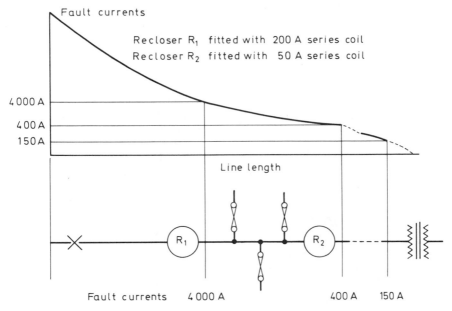

Figure 21.25. Discrimination obtainable with reclosers sited along the line, with different ratings (courtesy A. Reyrolle & Co. Ltd.)

some distance from the substation such that the impedance of the line between the substation and the recloser has reduced the fault level to 100 MVA for one size or 125 MVA for the other. This distance may need to be of the order of 2 miles (3·2 km).

The normal breaking capacities noted are independent of the current rating, i.e. no de-rating is necessary for a wide range of overcurrent coils. The rating of these however must be chosen to match the estimated load current as this will decide the *minimum* overcurrent which the recloser will detect which is 200% of the coil rating. This in turn determines the extent of the network protected by the recloser.

At the extremities of a system a careful check on the value of fault current is necessary. If it is not below the minimum of 200% of the chosen coil rating, then a single recloser will suffice. On the other hand, if it is less than this setting, full coverage can only be obtained by siting other recloser units further out on the system and fitting them with lower-rated series coils, as demonstrated in Fig. 21.25.

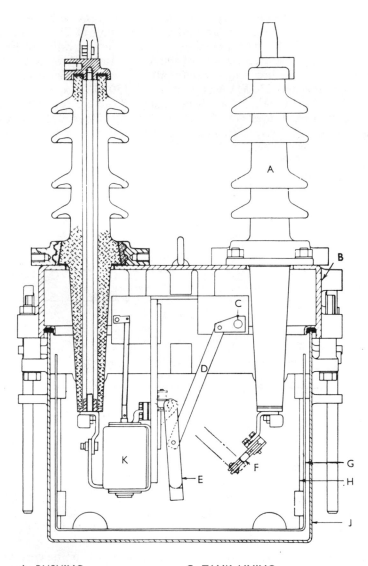

A. BUSHING
B. TOP PLATE
C. OPERATING SHAFT
D. B.P. LINK
E. MOVING CONTACT
F. FIXED CONTACT

G. TANK LINING
H. PHASE BARRIER
J. TANK
K. SERIES COIL TIMING DEVICE
   (SEE FIG. 21.27)

Figure 21.26.   Sectional view of automatic sectionaliser (courtesy A. Reyrolle & Co. Ltd.)

Figure 21.26 shows a sectional view of the type of sectionaliser discussed earlier. The switch is of the single-break type in oil and is manually closed by means of an external lever suitable for pole operation. It is prepared for opening by registering the passage of fault current through a tripping device which will operate with the associated protecting recloser. The mechanism is of the manually-operated spring-assisted type, the switch being held in the closed position by means of a roller latch arrangement against the action of the spring. The switch is opened when this latch is released either manually, by movement of the series-coil trip rods, or by the action of the spring-operated latch of an earth-fault tripping device.

The series-coil (overcurrent) tripping device comprises three series trip coils which will be given a setting of approximately 20% *less* than that of the series

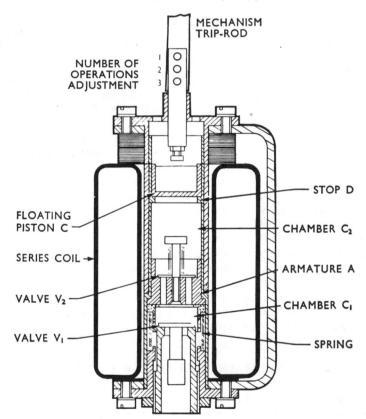

Figure 21.27. Sectional view illustrating operation of the overcurrent tripping device in an automatic sectionaliser (courtesy A. Reyrolle & Co. Ltd.)

coils in the co-operating recloser, irrespective of the normal current level of the spur feeder in which the sectionaliser is connected.

This device, shown in Fig. 21.27, allows a predetermined number of fault-current pulses to flow through the coils before actual tripping takes place. It consists of an armature A which, when the series coil is energised by fault current, is attracted downwards against a spring. This downward movement pumps oil from C_1 to C_2 through valve V_2. When the fault current is interrupted, i.e. when the recloser trips, the armature resets, raises the column of oil and the floating piston C and at the same time opens valve V_1 to recharge chamber C_1 with oil.

This operation is repeated each time the recloser trips and closes with the result that after a predetermined number of operations the piston C is raised sufficiently to operate the trip rod, the tripping action being arranged, as noted earlier, to take place during an open-circuit period of the recloser. If the fault is transient and is cleared by the recloser, the fault current pulses will cease and piston C will reset by gravity on to the stop D.

The number of pulse operations (maximum 3) to trip can be varied by altering the position of an adjustable link attached to the trip rod by a pin which can be located in any of the three holes seen in Fig. 21.27.

If required, instantaneous earth-fault protection can be added by installing three current transformers in the bushings and a relay in the sectionaliser. This relay will register fault-current pulses as in the overcurrent devices up to a maximum of three, and again tripping is initiated during the open-circuit period of the recloser. The normal earth-fault setting is 16 A.

On some spur lines it may be necessary to have sectionalisers in series, one at the beginning of the spur and another farther along. Discrimination between them can be obtained by setting the one nearer to the source to open after three pulses and the farther one after two pulses.

Two designs of sectionaliser of the type described are available, one for nominal service voltages up to 11 kV and having a normal current rating of 200 A maximum, the other for 12/14·4 kV with a maximum current rating of 100 A. Both are capable of making on to peak currents of 10 100 A.

As the sectionaliser does not have to interrupt short-circuit currents, it is not given a breaking-capacity rating in the sense applied to a recloser, but each can interrupt load currents up to 220% of rated full-load current, i.e. 440 and 220 A respectively.

Because they remain closed during the sequence of operations at the recloser, the sectionaliser must have a short-time current rating, and as the unit has series coils this rating will be related to that of the selected coils. For the unit described, the 1 s rating ranges from 200 A (r.m.s. symmetrical) with 5 A series coils to 4 000 A when 200 A coils are fitted, while a 10 s rating reduces these values to 60 and 2 600 A respectively*.

RING-MAIN AND OTHER UNITS

Chapter 17 has been devoted to a discussion on the technical and construction features of oil switches, fuse switches and ring-main units, the latter comprising the two former assembled in switchboard form when an *extensible* arrangement is required, but also being available in a composite form which is *non-extensible*,

---

* The description and illustrations relating to automatic reclosers and their application are based on designs (current at the time of writing) which rely on a combination of electromechanical and hydraulic devices for the protection and control functions. In complex schemes, difficulties of adjustment in the field coupled with variation of operating time due to variation of oil viscosity, have limited their use.

A. Reyrolle & Co. Ltd. have since overcome these problems with the perfection of a compatible solid-state reclosing scheme in which static protection and control circuits are used, providing considerable versatility of application, accuracy and virtual temperature independence. This scheme has been described in an article by Evans (see Reference 1 and manufacturers' literature).

i.e. without busbars. In that chapter it has been noted that, in the case of non-extensible ring-main units, most are suitable for both indoor and outdoor use.

Here it is convenient to note briefly some further units, both individual and composite and including switch and fuse units in which the fuses are air-insulated along with an oil switch.

Considering first the individual types, Fig. 21.28 shows a unit in which the fuses are oil-immersed and are an integral part of the switch. They are carriage mounted in a similar manner to that previously shown in Fig. 17.11, access to

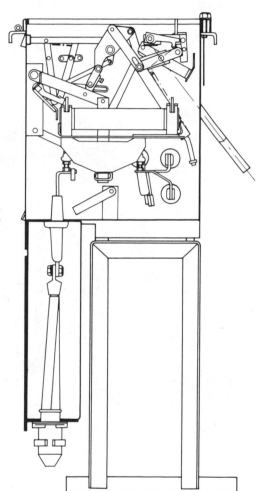

Figure 21.28. Cross-section of oil-insulated fuse switch with integral busbars and earthing switch (courtesy Long & Crawford Ltd.)

them being via a top cover which when opened gives visual indication that they are isolated. This unit, having busbars can be lined-up with other similar units or with the oil-switch unit seen in Fig. 17.8, a typical switchboard of this type being shown in Fig. 21.29. The fuse switch and the separate circuit-earthing switch (seen in Fig. 21.28 beside the outgoing bushing) are independently operated via spring-assisted mechanisms, interlocked to prevent simultaneous operation of both switches to the 'on' position.

Also designed to line up with the oil switch unit in Fig. 17.8 is a switch and fuse unit seen in the centre of the switchboard shown in Fig. 21.30. In this, air-insulated fuses are mounted in the chamber in front of the switch chamber, access to them being gained by opening two doors, the outer one opening upwards to afford a measure of protection against rain when inspecting or changing fuses. These doors are interlocked so that access to the fuses can only be obtained after the fuse terminals have been isolated and earthed. The fuses are of the striker-pin type so arranged that operation of any fuse automatically opens the oil switch. The inclusion of a tripping mechanism for this purpose makes it possible to add earth-fault protection, the release being operated from a core-balance current transformer.

A feature of this unit is that current and voltage transformers can be added for connection by pilot cable to separately mounted metering equipment, the

Figure 21.29. Switchboard comprising fuse switches as in Figure 21.28 and oil switches (courtesy Long & Crawford Ltd.)

current transformers being accommodated in an oil-filled chamber in unit with the cable box while the voltage transformer, encapsulated in epoxy resin, is housed in a chamber below the main fuse chamber.

Both of the foregoing units can be used singly, e.g. as might be required for controlling a transformer at the end of a spur line. For such a purpose, an incoming cable box will be fitted to one end of the busbar chamber, the other end being blanked-off. Both can also be a built-in unit with a transformer, a metal trunk between the terminal flanges enclosing copper conductors and thereby eliminating a short cable connection and associated boxes and joints.

684

In the fuse switch shown in Fig. 21.31, busbars can either be included (as in the illustration) for use in extensible arrangements, or they can be omitted, a cast-resin adaptor taking the place of the busbar chamber. An incoming cable box can then be fitted to the adaptor so that the fuse switch can be used as a single unit. Also bearing in mind the now extensive use of cast resin in switchgear design, it is of interest to note that the three-phase busbars are embedded in such insulation forming a self-contained assembly but protected from external damage by a metal shroud.

This fuse switch is of a type using oil-immersed fuses as seen in Figs. 21.32 and 21.33 and here again they are of the type which automatically trip open the

Figure 21.30. Ring-main equipment comprising two oil switches with tee-off switch and fuse unit (centre); the latter with air-insulated fuses (courtesy Long & Crawford Ltd.)

three-phase switch when any or all fuse links operate. Access for fuse replacement is obtained by raising a front cover (as shown in Fig. 21.33) after the fuse switch has been put in the 'off' position. The action of lifting the cover raises the fuses to the position shown, so that it is now *completely* isolated, and at the same time earth shields are moved to cover the fixed contacts on the busbar side. Each fuse is carriage mounted and can be removed through the aperture without the use of tools. Each carriage must be returned to the unit to reset the mechanism. With all fuses in position, the lowering of the cover lowers them to the 'off' position and moves the earth shields to expose the busbar fixed contacts ready for a closing operation.

Figures 21.32 and 21.33 are of a unit without cable earthing facilities. When these are required, a separate earthing switch is contained in the main chamber and may be one of two types, i.e. (*a*) a switch capable of making the fault current that can occur in the event of a back-feed from the medium-voltage network through a power transformer, or (*b*) one capable of handling any rating up to 250 MVA at 11 kV.

Figure 21.31. Oil-immersed fuse-switch unit with cartridge fuse links (courtesy A. Reyrolle & Co. Ltd.)

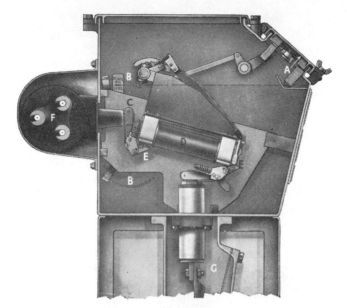

LEGEND

A ACCESS COVER FOR FUSE
     REPLACEMENT
B EARTH SHIELD
C INSULATING BARRIER
D FUSE LINK

E FUSE-SWITCH BUTT-TYPE
     CONTACTS
F BUSBAR CHAMBER
G OUTGOING CABLE BOX

*Figure 21.32.   Cross-section through fuse-switch unit with fuse switch closed (courtesy A. Reyrolle
& Co. Ltd.)*

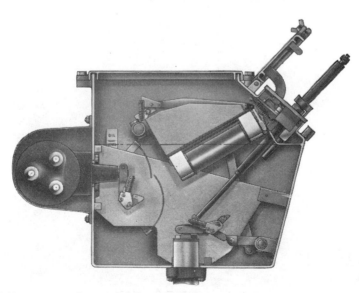

*Figure 21.33.   Fuse switch in 'isolated' position with earth shield over fixed (live) contacts. Also
shown are the cable test plugs which are inserted (courtesy A. Reyrolle & Co. Ltd.)*

Separate operating mechanisms are provided for the fuse switch and the earthing switch, the two operating shafts being brought out to the side as seen in Fig. 21.31 and a single removable handle is used for either the one or the other switch, the two mechanisms being interlocked with each other and with the access cover, etc. to prevent mal-operation. Both mechanisms are of the spring-assisted type on closing and so is that for the fuse switch on opening. Figure 21.33 shows cable test plugs in position for carrying-out insulation resistance or high-voltage tests, the procedure being generally as described earlier.

A ring-main unit of the non-extensible type with air-insulated fuses is shown in Fig. 21.34. This is a unit complying with the British Electricity Board's specification No. S.16 (1968). This unit has an oil-filled chamber above the fuse compartment which houses the two ring-main oil switches and a double-break tee-off oil switch, each switch having a spring-assisted operating mechanism.

Figure 21.34. Non-extensible ring-main unit with air-insulated fuses in the tee-off (courtesy Brush Switchgear Ltd.)

The fuses are of the striker-pin type to provide three-phase tripping of the tee-off switch when any one fuse operates. A connection diagram is given in Fig. 21.35, from which it is seen that earthing facilities are included on each circuit, and in addition, a double-pole switch is provided to earth the fuse terminals, access to the fuse chamber being only possible when the main switch is off *and* the fuse earth-switch is closed. Provision is also made for cable testing through test spikes inserted to make contact with the ring-main cables.

It is appropriate here to refer back to Chapter 20 where, in Fig. 20.23, an outdoor ring-main unit (extensible) is illustrated in which metal-clad units are employed and where a bulk-oil circuit-breaker with vertical isolation is used in the tee-off.

It is of interest at this point to note an analysis of the trends in the U.K. in the use of equipment such as that described here and in Chapter 17. This analysis by Lloyd[2] shows that of all types purchased (extensible and non-extensible), the vast majority were for outdoor use, probably about 96%. It

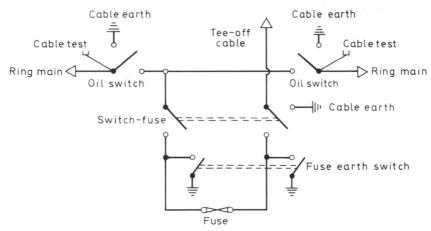

Figure 21.35. Circuit diagram for the ring-main unit shown in Figure 21.34 (courtesy Brush Switchgear Ltd.)

also shows a growing use of the non-extensible types at the expense of extensible units, the former being about 13% of the total ordered in 1966 and rising to about 34% in 1968.

As we have noted earlier, it is possible to eliminate the high-voltage cable, with its two joints, between the tee-off switch or fuse switch and the primary terminals of the power transformer, by making the connections with copper conductors contained in a metal trunk fixed to suitable flanges on the switch and the transformer. This results in some economy but the necessity remains to provide separate medium-voltage distribution equipment, with appropriate cabling back to the secondary terminals of the transformer. If this latter equipment could be incorporated in a self-contained substation, further economies are obviously possible, particularly if the substation can be completely assembled in the factory and transported to site in that state, thus eliminating the task and cost of erecting and connecting-up separate items of equipment.

This reasoning has led to the development of a number of types of substation arrangements on the lines indicated. Some are housed in kiosks of glass fibre, which is a design particularly suitable for locations demanding the preservation of amenities. There are other types which can be installed without amenity cover but with a simple surrounding fence to prevent unauthorised access and vandalism. Both concepts are based on the acceptance of non-extensible ring-main switchgear on the high-voltage side and on the use of a transformer of predetermined rating which cannot be changed to meet expanding demand, the latter condition being met by introducing a second identical substation.

In one particular type of kiosk* one standard design accepts a 500 or 750 kVA transformer and another takes a 1 000 kVA unit, the transformers being for 11 000/415–250 V service. In an open-type substation like the one shown in Fig. 21.36, the design is based on a transformer rated at 750 kVA.

Figure 21.36. English Electric design of outdoor-unit type of transformer substation. The covers are removed to show high voltage and medium-voltage switchgear (courtesy G.E.C. Switchgear Ltd.)

The high-voltage switchgear may or may not include fuses in the tee-off circuit to the transformer. The unit in Fig. 21.36 has no fuses at this point, the omission being based on the accepted reliability of the modern power transformer coupled with the fact that the relatively vulnerable cable and cable joints between the switch and the transformer have been eliminated. In the rare event of a fault, clearance will be achieved by the circuit-breakers at the origin of the ring main interrupting the supply to other substations on the ring main temporarily.

Figure 21.37 shows the main connections for this self-contained substation, the notes on the diagram indicating the extent of the secondary equipment

* South Wales Switchgear Ltd., pocket substations.

690

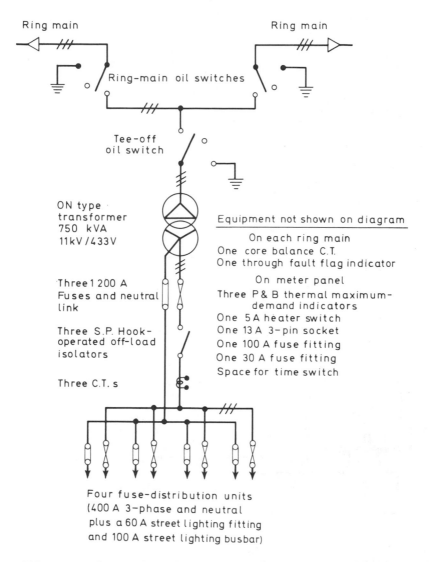

Ring main   Ring main

Ring-main oil switches

Tee-off
oil switch

ON type
transformer
750 kVA
11kV/433V

Equipment not shown on diagram

On each ring main
One core balance C.T.
One through fault flag indicator

On meter panel
Three P&B thermal maximum-
demand indicators
One 5A heater switch
One 13A 3-pin socket
One 100A fuse fitting
One 30A fuse fitting
Space for time switch

Three 1 200 A
Fuses and neutral
link

Three S.P. Hook-
operated off-load
isolators

Three C.T.s

Four fuse-distribution units
(400 A 3-phase and neutral
plus a 60 A street lighting fitting
and 100 A street lighting busbar)

*Figure 21.37.   Circuit diagram of English Electric designed outdoor-unit type of transformer sub-
station (courtesy G.E.C. Switchgear Ltd.)*

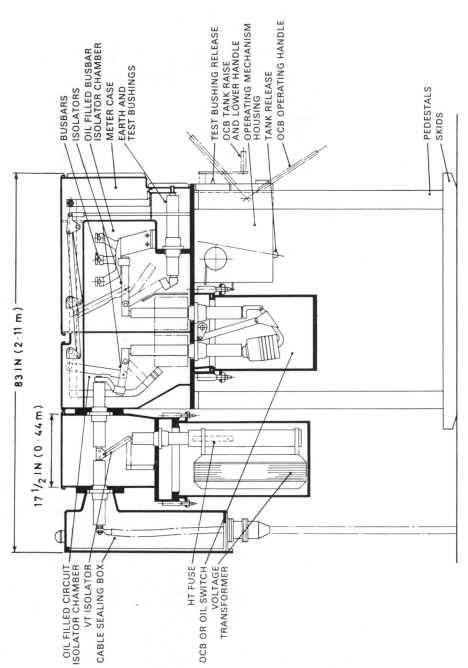

BUSBARS
ISOLATORS
OIL FILLED BUSBAR
ISOLATOR CHAMBER
METER CASE
EARTH AND
TEST BUSHINGS

TEST BUSHING RELEASE
OCB TANK RAISE
AND LOWER HANDLE
OPERATING MECHANISM
HOUSING
TANK RELEASE
OCB OPERATING HANDLE

PEDESTALS
SKIDS

83 IN (2·11 m)

17 1/2 IN (0·44 m)

OIL FILLED CIRCUIT
ISOLATOR CHAMBER
VT ISOLATOR
CABLE SEALING BOX

HT FUSE
OCB OR OIL SWITCH
VOLTAGE
TRANSFORMER

Figure 21.38.   22 kV unit as used in the Switchgear & Cowans ring-main equipment shown in Figure 21.39 (courtesy G.E.C. Switchgear Ltd.)

692

Figure 21.39. Switchgear & Cowans type GA/GS *22 kV 500 MVA outdoor ring-main unit incorporating switchgear as shown in Figure 21.38 (courtesy G.E.C. Switchgear Ltd.)*

693

included but not depicted. Much of this can be seen in Fig. 21.36, the core-balance current transformers and through-fault flag indicators for the ring main in the high-voltage compartment and the remainder in the medium-voltage distribution cabinet.

Generally similar secondary equipment will be provided in other forms of unit substation, e.g. pocket (kiosk) types, while variations will be noted in the number and rating of the distribution circuits.

The discussion on ring-main switchgear has so far been concerned with that for use on systems not exceeding 11 kV. In a design for 22 kV where the system fault level may be 500 MVA, the switchgear used is basically an indoor-type with weather-proofing covers, the gear comprising oil circuit-breakers and oil switches, both being of the fixed-type with separate isolating switches. The general design is as shown in Fig. 21.38, the difference between a circuit-breaker and an oil switch being that in the latter, the arc-control device is a simplified design as the current to be interrupted is limited to that of the load.

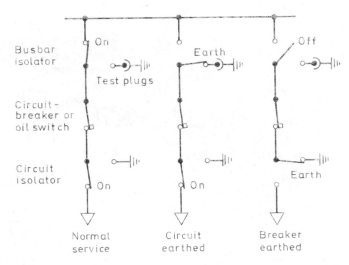

Figure 21.40. Facilities provided in the Switchgear and Cowans ring-main switchgear shown in Figures 21.38 and 21.39 (courtesy G.E.C. Switchgear Ltd.)

These units may be used in any combination comprising, for a ring-main unit, three oil switches or two oil switches and a circuit-breaker, and when used as an indoor assembly, any arrangement is extensible. As an outdoor unit however, the arrangement is nominally non-extensible in that the weather-proofing covers, seen in Fig. 21.39, determine its extent. As this illustration shows, a hinged cover, pivotted at two points is used in an outdoor application. This cover can take up three positions, (a) to enclose completely the front and top, (b) to give sheltered access to the internal mechanisms and the circuit isolators (after removing the normal top covers) and (c) to give shelter to an operator at the closing mechanisms (front), i.e. the top fully closed with the overhang projecting horizontally forward. Figure 21.39 shows the cover in position (b).

Earthing and cable test facilities are provided at the busbar and circuit isolators as indicated in Fig. 21.40.

METAL-CLAD AND METAL-ENCLOSED SWITCHGEAR

Much of the switchgear noted in the preceding section could be said to come within these categories. In that section however, the emphasis was on the application of oil switches in ring-main switchgear and unit-distribution sub-stations, and in this section a look will be taken at switchgear in which the bulk-oil circuit-breaker is the important element. As we have noted, such units can form a part of a ring-main substation but, in what follows, the types discussed will be assumed to be those which can form main switchboards for outdoor installation without the need for a conventional brick building.

In Chapter 20, an indoor-type of switchgear in which a fixed circuit-breaker with separate isolating switches are used, was noted. Figures 20.10 and 20.11 show for example a single-phase design especially for use in connection with railway

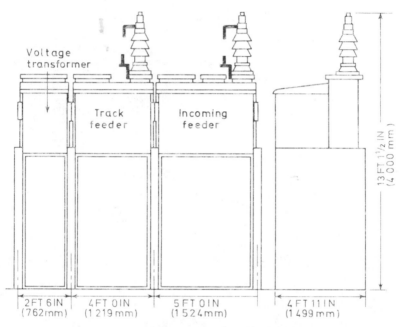

Figure 21.41. Switchgear & Cowans 25 kV single-phase switchgear for direct connection—see Figure 21.42 (courtesy G.E.C. Switchgear Ltd.)

electrification at 6·25 and 25 kV a.c. To eliminate costly buildings and yet afford weather protection, to eliminate cable connections and terminations by providing direct connection facilities to overhead lines and to permit installation on restricted space adjacent to the permanent way, a modified positioning of the circuit-breaker and other components along with open-type terminals, bushings and weather-proof cladding has resulted in an arrangement shown typically in Fig. 21.41. A fibreglass building alongside contains such items as control panels, battery and auxiliary supplies, etc. Figure 21.42 illustrates a typical track-side installation.

For use on systems up to 11 kV three-phase, another design employing the fixed circuit-breaker principle is noted in Fig. 21.43. In this, the busbar and cable isolating switches, busbars and current transformers are accommodated in an oil-filled chamber above the circuit-breaker, the isolating switches having independent operating mechanisms with 'on' and 'earth' positions only. Before these can be moved from 'on' to 'earth', the circuit-breaker must be open so that there is no possibility of breaking or making load current on the isolating switches or to making on to a fault. Before the oil tank can be lowered for contact inspection, not only must the breaker be open but *both* isolating switches must be in the earth position. An interlocked access cover in the roof of the unit allows for the insertion of test bushings for cable test purposes. Figure 21.44 illustrates the external appearance of this unit.

With a design using a fixed circuit-breaker, there are no electrical clearances in air as the need for air-insulated isolating spouts has been eliminated, thus

Figure 21.42. Switchgear & Cowans 25 kV single-phase switchgear in track-side substation, as Figure 21.41. A fibre-glass building houses the control panels, battery and auxiliary supplies (courtesy G.E.C. Switchgear Ltd.)

ensuring freedom from discharge which can occur in such spouts when associated with switchgear of high impulse level.

In outdoor substations, wide variations of temperature and humidity can be experienced, and under such circumstances the elimination of creepage surfaces in air is a distinct advantage. This has been achieved in another design using a fixed circuit-breaker. It is shown in Fig. 21.45. In this, the current transformers and the busbars have been encapsulated in epoxy resin as three-phase units, the encapsulation in both cases forming the insulation of the terminals as an integral part of the units. The circuit-breaker contact-fixing blocks have been embedded within the ends of the circuit-breaker bushings, which are also in epoxy resin cast with integral mounting flanges. Because the bushings must withstand lateral forces when short circuits occur, a glass-reinforced resin moulding is embedded in the flange of each bushing. The operating links for the circuit-breaker and the isolating switch are made of glass-fibre-reinforced resin.

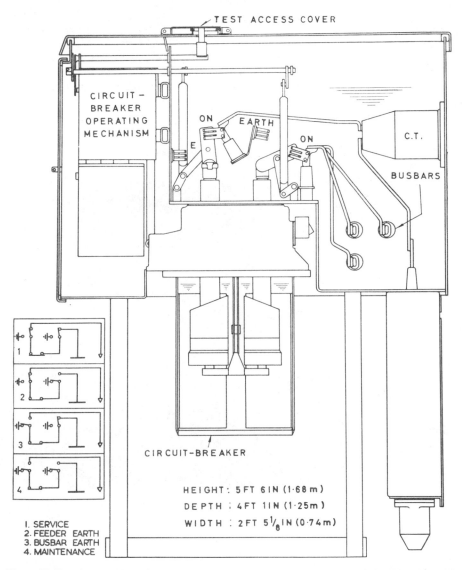

TEST ACCESS COVER

CIRCUIT –
BREAKER
OPERATING
MECHANISM

ON

EARTH

E

ON

C.T.

BUSBARS

CIRCUIT-BREAKER

HEIGHT : 5FT 6IN (1·68 m)

DEPTH : 4FT 1IN (1·25 m)

WIDTH : 2FT 5⅛IN (0·74 m)

1. SERVICE
2. FEEDER EARTH
3. BUSBAR EARTH
4. MAINTENANCE

Figure 21.43. Cross-section of 11 kV metal-clad unit for outdoor service, with fixed breaker and separate isolating switch (courtesy Long & Crawford Ltd.)

An example of outdoor metal-clad switchgear is shown in Figs. 21.46 and 21.47, the type being that based on the principle of 'inverted vertical isolation', a design available for voltages up to 22 kV and which has been noted previously in Chapter 20, Figs. 20.22 and 20.23. A weather-proof cabinet behind the switchboard in Fig. 21.46 houses relays, meters, telephone, etc.

In another design, shown typically in Fig. 21.48, all the features of an indoor vertical-isolation metal-clad unit, including integral earthing by the transfer-breaker method, are provided in an outdoor assembly, the cubicle being specially designed to make the unit completely weather-proof. This design is described as 'low-silhouette', its maximum height being only 5 ft 6 in (1·676 m), making it particularly suitable for installation in rural surroundings without intruding on the landscape. Matching units can accommodate oil switches and low-type power transformers, and these along with circuit-breaker units can be combined in a variety of arrangements to form main switchboards, ring-main units and packaged substations.

Figure 21.44. 11 kV outdoor metal-clad unit as shown in Figure 21.43 (courtesy Long & Crawford Ltd.)

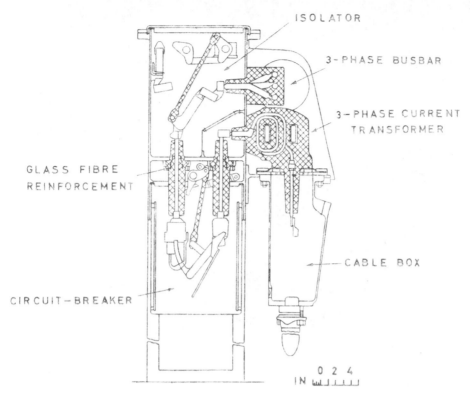

ISOLATOR

3-PHASE BUSBAR

3-PHASE CURRENT
TRANSFORMER

GLASS FIBRE
REINFORCEMENT

CABLE BOX

CIRCUIT-BREAKER

0 2 4
IN

Figure 21.45. 11 kV outdoor oil-break switchgear unit showing (hatched) cast-resin parts (courtesy A. Reyrolle & Co. Ltd.)

Figure 21.46. A typical four-panel 11 kV outdoor metal-clad switchboard (courtesy Yorkshire Switchgear & Engineering Co. Ltd.)

699

Figure 21.47. Weatherhood raised to permit inspection of outdoor metal-clad unit (courtesy Yorkshire Switchgear & Engineering Co. Ltd.)

Figure 21.48. Low-type packaged substation housing an oil circuit-breaker unit and an oil switch for voltages up to 11 kV (courtesy South Wales Switchgear Ltd.)

As part of our discussion on indoor high-voltage switchgear in Chapter 20, two illustrations (Figs. 20.2 and 20.3) were included to show a design of package switchgear for use on 33 kV systems. In these the switchgear is effectively 'indoors' in that it is under cover, but the complete assembly is primarily an outdoor substation.

The factory-built metal-enclosed units have air-insulated busbar and circuit chambers located under the roof, as shown in a typical cross-sectional view in Fig. 21.49. The compartments here are completely segregated and independently ventilated, air entering through gauze-protected apertures in the compartment floor and leaving through weather-protected outlets in the roof space.

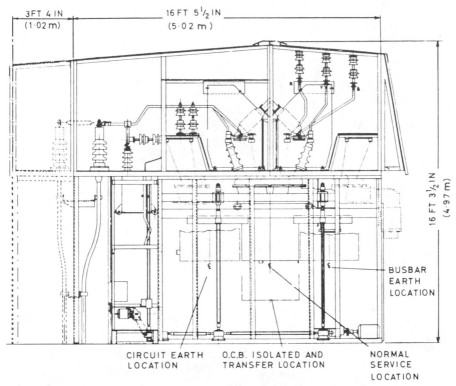

Figure 21.49.   33 kV outdoor packaged substation. Sectional view of single busbar arrangement with integral earthing (courtesy South Wales Switchgear Ltd.)

The principle of vertical isolation with horizontal withdrawal is adopted for both the circuit-breaker and the voltage transformer, the former being raised and lowered by a built-in electric motor with emergency hand-winding facilities, the latter either by hand or motor. Integral earthing for the busbars or the cable is provided using the transfer-breaker method discussed in Chapter 20.

The circuit-breaker can be fitted with spring or solenoid-closing mechanisms, and, as in designs of circuit-breaker noted in Chapter 12, provision for current transformers of the ring type is available on the bushings.

Main cable terminations may be at single-core sealing ends or three-core cable boxes, but if the substation is associated with an overhead-line system, bushings can be built into the side walls, as noted earlier in Fig. 20.3.

Structurally, the sides and rear of the units are clad in aluminium trough sheeting, while the roof comprises flat aluminium sheet. Doors are provided at the front for access to the operating mechanisms, the circuit-breaker and the voltage transformer, and may be either hinged or roller-shutter types. Aluminium flashings ensure that the structure is weather-proof and at the same time these enhance the general appearance. It is a feature of the design that a built-in control room can be located either at a central point or as an annexe at either end, a typical control room being shown in Fig. 21.50.

It is of interest to note that a packaged substation of generally similar design for 66 kV service has been developed by the same manufacturer.

Figure 21.50. Self-contained control room forming part of a six-unit 33 kV packaged substation (courtesy South Wales Switchgear Ltd.)

OPEN-TYPE OUTDOOR SUBSTATIONS AND SWITCHING CENTRES

For voltages up to 11/15 kV, outdoor switchgear or fusegear will comprise equipment of the types described in earlier sections, but there is one item of equipment we have not noted, viz. an outdoor isolator such as the one that might be required on rural distribution networks for the purpose of isolating sections of overhead line, small transformer substations, etc. A single pole of two such isolating switches is noted in Figs. 21.51 and 21.52, both rated 400 A and of the rocking-pedestal type. With the two-insulator type, the connection from the line to the moving contact must be a flexible conductor to allow for the movement of the rocking pedestal between the open and closed positions.

Manual operation may be either by a handle fixed near the base of the supporting structure or by a mechanism located at a high level and reached only by means of a hook stick. The isolators may or may not be fitted with arcing horns. When these are fitted they may be a fixed or quick-break type, making the isolators suitable for low-current switching duties.

For 33 kV and above, the open-type substation is an organised assembly of many individual items of equipment, i.e. circuit-breakers, main isolators (and

Figure 21.51. 11 kV racking-type isolator using two insulators (courtesy Switchgear & Equipment Ltd.)

probably by-pass isolators), current transformers (when these are not built into the circuit-breaker), voltage transformers, and in some circumstances, surge diverters. The layout may need to include one or more power transformers, and the form it takes will be dependent on voltage, whether a single or double busbar scheme is under consideration and on the switching scheme to be adopted (see Chapter 9).

To accept the insulator strings for the conductors from the overhead lines and to support the busbars, portal frames and other structures must be designed in steel or concrete; for the lower end of the voltage range, the isolators will also be mounted on the structure. At higher voltages, concrete plinths will be required on which to erect circuit-breakers, isolators, current and voltage transformers.

Provision has to be made for secondary and other cabling, often using a marshalling kiosk into which such wiring is brought from individual pieces of apparatus so that multicore cables can then be laid from the kiosk to a remote

Figure 21.52.   11 kV racking-type isolator using three insulators (courtesy Switchgear & Equipment Ltd.)

control room. In large installations, relays and meters can, with advantage, be installed in housings in the locality of the circuits, thus avoiding long cable runs and reducing the burden on current and voltage transformers. Provision may also be necessary for auxiliary supplies, e.g. compressed-air plant with a main storage tank and a feed system to individual receivers at circuit-breakers, etc. At the highest voltages, isolators will also be power operated and the supply for this purpose must be catered for.

In the open-type substation the circuit-breakers will be one of the types discussed in earlier chapters with the added possibility of the vacuum circuit-breaker. At 33 and 66 kV, British practice is largely based on the use of the bulk-oil circuit-breaker, but elsewhere the preference is for the small-oil-volume or air-blast types, particularly in continental Europe where the bulk-oil circuit-breaker does not figure.

As we have noted in Chapter 12, bulk-oil circuit-breakers are available for system voltages up to 330 kV, but in the majority of installations for the voltage range of 110–275 kV, the small-oil-volume, air-blast or SF_6 types will be found, noting in passing an installation at 132 kV in the U.K. where the vacuum circuit-breaker has been used. At 400 and 750 kV, the choice is, as yet, between the air-blast and SF_6 types, with the former predominating in existing installations.

Isolating switches for use on 33 and 66 kV systems may have either vertical or horizontal break, the former having the advantage that closer spacing between poles is possible. Both are operated through a rotating centre-post insulator,

Figure 21.53.   Rotating-stack vertical-break isolator for use on 33/66 kV systems (courtesy Switch-gear & Equipment Ltd.)

driven by a suitable hand or power operating mechanism. In the vertical-break type, an example being that shown in Fig. 21.53, the blade, on opening, is initially rotated on its own axis to change the horizontal position of the beaver-tail inserts to an angular one in preparation for a free exit movement of the moving contact out of the fixed contacts. The blade is then lifted through an arc of 80° to the fully open position, the blade turning further on its own axis.

When using isolators with a horizontal break, the blade rotates in the same plane as the centre-post insulator to give two breaks in series, the basic features being clear from Fig. 21.54. In some layouts, e.g. where circuits are connected to a busbar back-to-back, economy in space can be achieved by the use of five-post isolators. These are, in essence, two isolators arranged back-to-back on a common base with the centre-post insulator carrying two fixed contacts. Such isolators are shown in Figs. 21.55 and 21.56, but for many layouts this arrangement will not be convenient and separate units must be used. These can be in

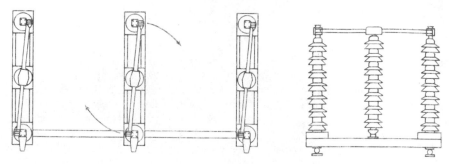

Figure 21.54. *Plan and end elevation of a 275 kV rotating centre-pillar isolator (courtesy Switchgear & Equipment Ltd.)*

Figure 21.55. *33 kV double rotating-pillar isolator using five insulator posts (courtesy A. Reyrolle & Co. Ltd.)*

two types, one with three post insulators as noted earlier in Fig. 21.54 and as the three-pole assembly in Fig. 21.57 giving a double break, and the other using only two post insulators as shown in Fig. 21.58. In the latter, a single centre break is provided, *both* post insulators rotating to open the separate elements of the switch blade at the central contact system. As in other types of gear, the contact system must have adequate current-carrying ability, both for the continuous rating and for the short-time rating.

In an outdoor-type the contacts will, under severe weather conditions, become iced-up and it is therefore essential that the design should have good ice-breaking

Figure 21.56. ' *275 kV back-to-back rotating centre-post isolator using five insulators. 2 000A rating (courtesy Switchgear & Equipment Ltd.)*

qualities. In the isolators shown in Figs. 21.55 and 21.57, a design known as a *bird-cage* contact is used, its elements being shown in Fig. 21.59. The moving contact here consists of a large number of silver-plated copper fingers arranged in the form of a cylindrical cage, surrounded by garter springs. One finger is extended with a silver-nickel-elkonite tip to form an arcing finger, so that any arcing which may occur when isolators are used to transfer the load current is localised and kept from the main current-carrying surfaces. A shroud protects the moving contact to minimise the accumulation of ice and snow on the contact surfaces. The fixed contact carried on the outer insulator posts is a solid copper rod, silver-plated and tapered for easy lead-in. During short-circuit conditions, the contact pressure is increased by the magnetising effect of the current through the parallel paths in the wires of the bird cage.

In the isolators shown in Figs. 21.54 and 21.56, self-cleaning multi-finger pattern fixed contacts are employed as seen in Fig. 21.60. These are made of

Figure 21.57. 132 kV three-phase rotating centre-pillar isolator (courtesy A. Reyrolle & Co. Ltd.)

silver-plated copper with insulated stainless-steel backing springs to provide adequate pressure. The tubular blade is made either in copper or aluminium. When it is made in the former the contact faces are tipped with solid-silver inserts, and when in aluminium, copper end contacts with silver inserts are fitted. To ensure a good wiping action as the contacts make or break and to break through ice or snow formation, an actuator mechanism at the top of the rotating

Figure 21.58.   275 kV centre-break rotating-type heavy-duty isolator using two post isolators both of which rotate (courtesy Switchgear & Equipment Ltd.)

centre-post causes the tube to rotate on its own axis when leaving or entering the fixed contacts.

Apart from icing at the contacts, this will occur elsewhere and it is important that this should not interfere with the functioning of any moving parts, e.g. in the operating mechanism and the linkages between the single-pole units forming the three-phase assembly. Operating mechanisms may be hand or power types, the latter being either motor-operated or electrohydraulic which are essential for all except the smaller isolators at the lower voltages.

Figure 21.59.   Bird-cage type assembly of fixed and moving contacts used on rotating post isolators (courtesy A. Reyrolle & Co. Ltd.)

There is a notable difference between British and European practice with regard to isolator designs. Instead of the rotating-post types that have been described, continental designs have been concentrated on the pantograph (single-column vertical reach) types. These have several advantages, the major one being that they require only a very small area of ground space coupled with the fact that the three single poles do not necessarily need to be in line as with rotating-post types. Other advantages are that down-dropper connections are eliminated and the foundations and supports are lighter and cheaper. The higher the voltage, the greater these advantages become, and while there may be little to choose between types below 275 kV, at least one continental manufacturer has a range down to 110 kV and extending to 765 kV.

The principle of this type of isolator is indicated schematically in Fig. 21.61, from which it is seen that a pantograph is mounted at the top of an insulator column and that in the closed position it grasps a contact bar suspended on and in contact with the line conductor(s), by a scissors action. In the open position the pantograph collapses to take up the position indicated by dotted lines.

Figure 21.60. Self-aligning finger-pattern fixed contacts with tubular moving contact used in rotating post isolators (courtesy Switchgear & Equipment Ltd.)

With the isolator open, the suspended contact bar will move in sympathy with the line conductor due to wind, changes in temperature or snow and ice, so that the distance between the bar and the conductor and the horizontal length of the bar must both be such that the reach of the pantograph will be more than sufficient to grasp the contact bar regardless of its position vertically or horizontally. Operation of the pantograph will normally be via a power-operated mechanism, e.g. by a motor or pneumatically, but a manual mechanism will be provided for use in emergency or when checking.

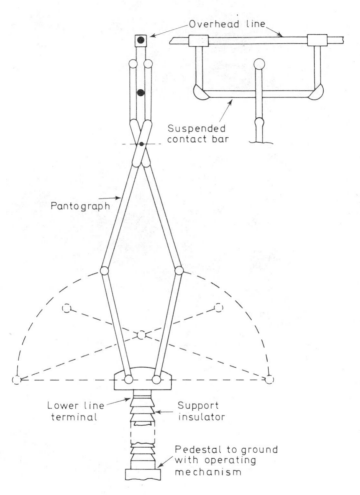

Figure 21.61. Schematic outline of a pantograph (vertical reach) isolator

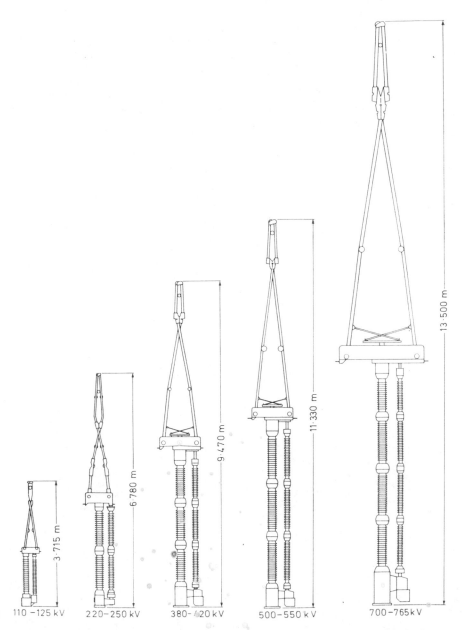

Figure 21.62.   Range of high-voltage pantograph isolators (courtesy Siemens (UK) Ltd.)

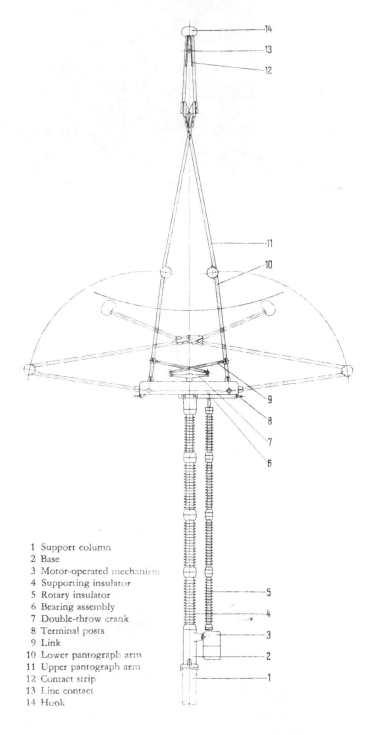

1 Support column
2 Base
3 Motor-operated mechanism
4 Supporting insulator
5 Rotary insulator
6 Bearing assembly
7 Double-throw crank
8 Terminal posts
9 Link
10 Lower pantograph arm
11 Upper pantograph arm
12 Contact strip
13 Line contact
14 Hook

Figure 21.63. Pantograph-type isolator for 700–765 kV (courtesy Siemens (UK) Ltd.)

714

Figure 21.62 shows a representative range of pantograph isolators for the voltage range 110–765 kV, an illustration which gives an indication of the overall height of the different isolators. Figure 21.63 is a more explanatory illustration of the constructional details comprising the 700/765 kV design, noting here that the pantograph is carried on a single insulator column whereas in another design it is supported on a tripod assembly of insulators. The operating mechanism is mounted at the base of the isolator and the pantograph is driven via a rotating insulator (5 in Fig. 21.63) which converts the linear motion of the

Figure 21.64. Typical outdoor substation with pantograph isolators with single post insulator support (courtesy Brown Boveri & Co. Ltd.)

mechanism to a rotary one. As with other isolators, the problem of icing has to be dealt with and comprehensive and severe icing tests are an essential feature in the development of the design.

To prevent any tendency for the pantograph contact arms to open, accidentally or otherwise, the mechanism moves to a position beyond the dead centre of the linkage travel.

Figures 21.64 and 21.65 show typical installations using pantograph isolators, the former showing isolators with single insulator columns and the latter showing the tripod type. Both illustrations show the suspended contact bar connected to double line conductors.

715

Figure 21.65. Typical outdoor substation with pantograph isolators having tripod support insulators (courtesy Brown Boveri & Co. Ltd.)

Figure 21.66. 33 kV outdoor substation with bulk-oil circuit-breakers at Flat Lane substation, Blackburn of The North Western Electricity Board (courtesy A. Reyrolle & Co. Ltd.)

Figure 21.67. 22 kV A.E.I. outdoor substation with bulk-oil circuit-breakers in an installation of the Perak River Hydro-electric Power Station Co., Malaya (courtesy G.E.C. Switchgear Ltd.)

Figure 21.68. 66 kV outdoor substation with small-oil-volume circuit-breakers, back-to-back isolators (see Figure 21.55) and prop-type busbars (eliminating busbar supporting structures and insulators) at Polemedhia substation, Electricity Authority of Cyprus (courtesy A. Reyrolle & Co. Ltd.)

Figure 21.69.   66 kV outdoor substation with air-blast circuit-breakers at Malton substation, North Eastern Electricity Board (courtesy A. Reyrolle & Co. Ltd.)

Figure 21.70.   132 kV outdoor substation with air-blast circuit-breakers at Grimsby West substation, Yorkshire Electricity Board (courtesy A. Reyrolle & Co. Ltd.)

To illustrate the general discussion on open-type outdoor substation layouts, a selection of site photographs are shown in Figs. 21.66 to 21.77. The selection covers installations from 33 kV through to 400 kV by British manufacturers and it has been made to include circuit-breakers of different types.

The Reyrolle system of 'Busbar Props' noted in Fig. 21.69 is covered by British Patent No. 1 071 814 and is seen in more detail in Fig. 21.77. This scheme eliminates the busbar supporting insulators and structures usually provided between bays in a substation, increases the security of the busbar zone and saves space.

The 'prop' is a conducting member that supports the busbar from the insulator of an isolator, the design taking into account the increased bending moment imposed on the insulator and its mounting by wind and short-circuit forces.

Figure 21.71. 132 kV outdoor substation with A.E.I. vacuum circuit-breakers at West Ham substation, C.E.G.B. (courtesy G.E.C. Switchgear Ltd.)

Figure 21.72.   132 kV small-oil-volume circuit-breakers at the Coalbrook substation of the South African Railways (courtesy A. Reyrolle & Co. Ltd.)

Figure 21.73.   132 kV outdoor substation with G.E.C. SF₆ circuit-breakers at Chadderton substation, C.E.G.B. (courtesy G.E.C. Switchgear Ltd.)

Figure 21.74.   275 kV outdoor substation with G.E.C. SF₆ circuit-breakers at Chadderton substation, C.E.G.B. (courtesy G.E.C. Switchgear Ltd.)

Figure 21.75. 220 kV outdoor substation with A.E.I. bulk-oil circuit-breakers at State Electricity Commission, Victoria, Australia (courtesy G.E.C. Switchgear Ltd.)

Figure 21.76. 400 kV substation with air-blast circuit-breakers at Pelham substation. C.E.G.B. (courtesy A. Reyrolle & Co. Ltd.)

Figure 21.77. Close-up view of the Reyrolle busbar-prop system used on a 132 kV duplicate-busbar indoor-substation at the China Light and Power Company's Hohn Un power station, Hong Kong (courtesy A. Reyrolle & Co. Ltd.)

REFERENCES
1. EVANS, J.W., 'Solid State Protection and Control for Automatic Reclosers', *Elect. Rev.*, 10 April (1970)
2. LLOYD, L.J., 'Fuse-switches for 11/0·4 kV Unit Substations', *Elect. Times*, 31 July (1969)

BIBLIOGRAPHY
ARMSTRONG, T.V., 'Portable Weatherproof Switchgear', *Elect. Rev.*, 3 April (1970)
CRANE, P.H.G., *Switchgear Principles*, Macmillan (1957)
GARRARD, C.J.O., 'Scope for Co-operation in Switchgear Design and Manufacture', *Elect. Rev.*, 1 April (1966)
GARRARD, C.J.O., 'Trends in Switchgear Design', *Elect. Rev.*, 26 Sept. (1969)
GARRARD, C.J.O., 'High-voltage Distribution Switchgear (1–100 kV)', *Proc. I.E.E.*, **116** No. 6 June (1969)
GARRARD, C.J.O., 'High-voltage Switchgear (above 100 kV)', *Proc. I.E.E.*, **113** No. 9, Sept. (1966)
GILES, R.L., 'E.H.V. Substation Designs with Busbar Props', *Reyrolle Parsons Rev.*, **1** No 1, Summer (1971)
LÄPPLE, H., *Electric Fuses*, Butterworths (1952)
LIGHTLE, D. and ARMSTRONG, T.V., 'Switchgear for Supply', *Elect. Times*, 16 May (1968)
PIERSON, G.F., POLLARD, A.H. and CARR, N., 'Automatic Circuit Reclosers', *Proc. I.E.E.*, **102**, Dec. (1954)
PIERSON, G.F., 'The Development of Rural Electrification', *Proc. I.E.E.*, **108**, April (1961)
PRATSCH, R. and GRAF, H., 'Isolators for Extra-high Transmission Voltages and Power Ratings', in a special issue on *Extra-high Voltage a.c. Transmission*, Siemens AG
REIMANN, R., 'The Further Development of the Brown Boveri Single-column Isolators for System Voltages up to 750 kV', *Brown Boveri Rev.*, **51** No. 1/2, Jan./Feb. (1964)
SCHNEIDER, J., 'Single-column Isolating Switches for 245 and 400 kV', *Brown Boveri Rev.*, **46** No. 9, Sept. (1959)
VARIOUS, 'Design Criteria and Equipment for Transmission at 400 kV and Higher Voltages', *I.E.E. Conf. Pub.* No. 15 (1965)
WEBER, P., 'Pantograph Isolators', *Elect. Rev.*, 3 March (1967)
Electrical Power Switchgear, BS 162 (1961)
Fuses for Alternating Current Circuits above 660 V, BS 2692 (1956)

Chapter 22

Control boards

The remote control of power switchgear requires the provision of suitable control panels located at a point removed from the immediate vicinity of the circuit-breakers and other apparatus. Preferably, the location should be a room set apart for the purpose and in a place of relative seclusion away from noise and other causes of distraction. Freedom from the latter is particularly important at times of emergency.

Not only will the remote control board carry the appropriate means whereby the circuit-breakers may be opened or closed, but also any necessary indicating, integrating or recording instruments, indicating lamps or semaphores to denote the open or closed state of circuit-breakers and isolating switches, protective relays, control circuit and other secondary fuses, and, in some instances, voltage regulating equipment.

In this chapter we shall be concerned only with remote control where the distance between the control board and the switchgear and other electrical apparatus is such as to permit direct wiring between the various items. Such conditions normally exist in power stations, most indoor and some outdoor substations and in large industrial undertakings. When remote control is required for an extensive distribution or transmission system where long distances are involved between the control point and the controlled switchgear, the centralised control equipment will be of a very different type in order to avoid the prohibitive cost of heavy control cables of long length. In these circumstances light-current engineering is called upon to provide remote control which employs supervisory equipment of the automatic telephone type.

In this respect, a large power network may be compared with a telephone communication system in that in the latter a coded signal initiated by a caller selects the remote subscriber to whom he wishes to speak, while in a power network the control engineer sends out a coded signal to select and operate a chosen circuit-breaker. There is, however, an important difference, namely the fact that whereas wrong coding or numbers when telephoning are simply inconvenient, any inaccuracy when controlling switching operations could have disastrous results, and therefore elaborate check-back precautions are necessary. How these are achieved and how many other problems associated with remote supervisory control are solved, are, however, beyond the scope of this chapter.

The layout of a particular control board and/or relay board will depend on the size of the system to be controlled, whether it is a power station or a simple switching centre, on operational requirements and on users preferences. When the number of circuits is large it is important that the control engineers should have clear indications of the operating conditions from a central point and it will often be necessary to incorporate a mimic diagram representing the primary circuits, with automatic semaphore indicators or hand-operated discrepancy switches to indicate at a glance the open or closed state of circuit-breakers, selector switches and isolating switches. In many cases, alarm indication equipment will be necessary which will give both visual and alarm indication to the

Figure 22.1. Corridor-type control cubicles (courtesy A. Reyrolle & Co. Ltd.)

control engineer of any change not initiated by him, e.g. the operation of protective devices, where a fault lies and which circuit-breakers have tripped.

If the system is such as to include a large number of protective relays, metering equipment and other items not under constant watch, it will be preferable to place such apparatus on separate relay or metering panels. An arrangement frequently adopted is to arrange the main control board and the relay board back-to-back to give a corridor formation, the corridor being roofed-in to provide a common trough running the full length of both boards and in which interconnecting wiring will be housed. A typical arrangement of this type is illustrated in Fig. 22.1. In power stations, it is often convenient to include the control equipment for the generators and perhaps the main step-up trans-formers, on a separate control desk located in front of the control board for the rest of the system.

The latter will, in the majority of installations, be built up of self-contained sheet-steel cubicles with hinged or removable back covers to give access to wiring, cable terminations, etc. typically as shown in Fig. 22.2. Each cubicle may be fitted with an interior light fitting which will normally be hand switched, or, if required, can be switched automatically when the door is opened. In corridor formations, the rear access doors may be replaced by wire-mesh screens and a door will then enclose each end of the corridor, the latter being illuminated automatically when either door is opened.

Most control or relay boards are enhanced in appearance by using flush or semi-flush instruments, and where possible by the use of the modern edgewise

Figure 22.2. Rear interior view of a typical cubicle with double doors (courtesy A. Reyrolle & Co. Ltd.)

instruments such as the ones noted in Chapter 23. There are many possible arrangements for the accommodation of synchronising instruments as required for generator circuits. These include hinged panels mounted in the run of the control board, hinged box panels at the end of the board, separately-mounted floor pedestals or a portable trolley with a flexible lead for plugging into sockets on the control board. Examples are shown in Figs. 22.3 to 22.6.

When the size of an installation is large enough to warrant a mimic diagram showing the main connections, this can be displayed directly on the control panels or on separate diagram panels surmounting the control panels. Such diagrams may include a number of automatic semaphores of the type shown in Fig. 22.7 to represent circuit-breakers and isolating or selector switches. The disc of the semaphore rotates so that the stripe on its face gives an immediate

Figure 22.3. Hinged synchronising panel inset into a cubicle (courtesy A. Reyrolle & Co. Ltd.)

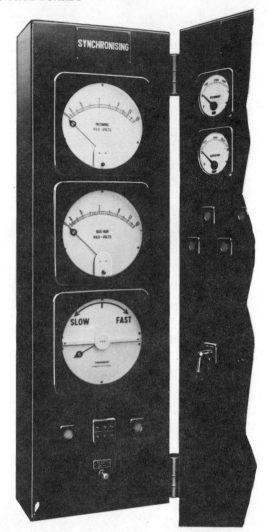

*Figure 22.4.   Hinged synchronising panel
mounted at the end of a control board*

indication of the state (open or closed) of the piece of apparatus it represents. Thus in Fig. 22.8, the semaphore indicators show that the selector switch connected to the main busbar, the circuit-breaker, the transformer isolator and the auxiliary-transformer earthing switch are all closed, the reserve busbar selector switch and the busbar earthing isolator being open, i.e. the semaphore discs are at right angles to the circuit connection mimic. Semaphore indicators may have discs of varying diameters, that for a circuit-breaker usually being larger than all the others. The stripe across the face may also vary in width, e.g. narrower for secondary parts of the circuit.

Electrically-operated semaphores derive an operating impulse from a separate a.c. or d.c. source of supply via auxiliary contacts on the associated circuit-breaker or isolating switch. Alternatively, for electrically-operated apparatus, the control switch itself may be mounted in the mimic diagram in place of the

Figure 22.5. Swivelling synchronising panel on pedestal

Figure 22.6. Portable synchronising trolley for
plugging into the circuit being synchronised
(courtesy A. Reyrolle & Co. Ltd.)

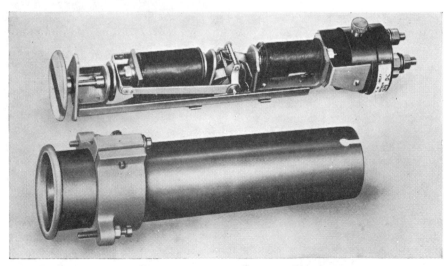

Figure 22.7. Automatic semaphore indicator for use in mimic diagrams. Cover removed (courtesy
G.E.C. Switchgear Ltd.)

730

semaphores. In this arrangement, the operating 'handle' substitutes the semaphore stripe and its position indicates the state of the controlled apparatus.
Being hand operated, a false indication can arise, e.g. when a circuit-breaker
has opened due to the protective gear functioning, leaving the control switch
giving a false indication, i.e. 'breaker closed'. Conversely, with the control
switch indicating 'breaker open' circumstances can arise when the breaker has
in fact been closed locally at the breaker. To overcome the dangers inherent
with such false indications, a discrepancy lamp built into the control switch is

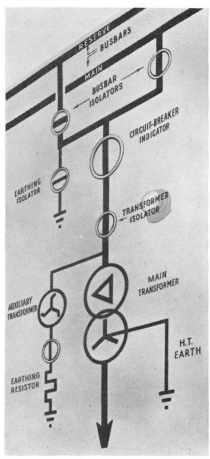

*Figure 22.8.   Example of a mimic circuit diagram
panel using automatic semaphore indicators (courtesy English Electric/G.E.C. Switchgear Ltd.)*

arranged so that it lights up automatically whenever there is a discrepancy
between the control switch indication and the actual condition. A typical switch
of this type is illustrated in Fig. 22.9.

Circuit-breaker control switches other than the discrepancy type will have a
pistol-grip handle generally as shown in Fig. 22.10. The switch will be so
designed that when released by the operator it will return automatically to a
neutral position and provision will normally be made for padlocking it in this
position.

For other types of circuit-breaker control switch, movement in a clockwise
direction will initiate a closing operation, and in an anticlockwise direction an

opening operation. This convention is generally applied for other rotary-type switches, e.g. clockwise for 'on' or 'raise' and anticlockwise for 'off' or 'lower'.

The pistol-grip handle is normally reserved for circuit-breaker control and other forms should be used for other purposes, so that an operator can identify its purpose by sight or touch. In so far as the British Electricity Boards are concerned, they have produced a standard (B.E.B.S. S11) giving the basic shapes of control handles for various purposes, e.g. horizontal-tee (remote controlled isolators), lozenge (governor control) three-point star (automatic voltage-regulator setting-motor operated), four-point star (motor-operated field rheostats) and pyramid (general purpose selector switch, e.g. local/remote).

Figure 22.9. Discrepancy-type control switch (courtesy A. Reyrolle & Co. Ltd.)

Ammeter and voltmeter switches will be very similar in construction, a typical voltmeter switch being shown in Fig. 22.11. This and those shown earlier are enclosed in moulded Diakon which excludes dust but permits the contacts to be seen.

Indicating lamps may be used for a variety of purposes and these follow a standard colour code:

Colour	Meaning
Red	Circuit-breaker or switch closed
Green	Circuit-breaker or switch open
White	Trip supply healthy (lamp normally illuminated)
Amber	Alarm indication, e.g. circuit-breaker tripped on fault.

Figure 22.10.   Circuit-breaker control switch with pistol-grip handle (courtesy A. Reyrolle & Co. Ltd.)

Figure 22.11.   Voltmeter switch to give readings between phases and each phase to neutral (courtesy A. Reyrolle & Co. Ltd.)

Figure 22.12. Control-board indicating lamp with built-in step-down transformer (courtesy Edgcumbe Peebles Ltd.)

Figure 22.13. Rear view of busbar-protection relay panels showing small wiring and terminal blocks

734

The source of supply for these lamps is usually the normal supply for control room general lighting, using 15 W pigmy lamps, as only sufficient illumination is required to give a positive indication. In an enclosed and relatively small fitting, even this may generate sufficient heat to be troublesome and to overcome this and at the same time reduce the panel space required, indicating lamps which have a small single-phase step-down transformer built in to the assembly can be used, a typical lamp being shown in Fig. 22.12. In this, the output voltage to the lamp is 12 V with a consumption of 2·2 W and an extremely long life.

Fuse holders or links mounted on control boards should also be coloured for identification. An accepted standard is black for 5 A fuses, green for 15 A fuses and white for links.

To facilitate checking, in the event of trouble, small wiring must be assembled in an orderly fashion and should carry numbered ferrules corresponding to the

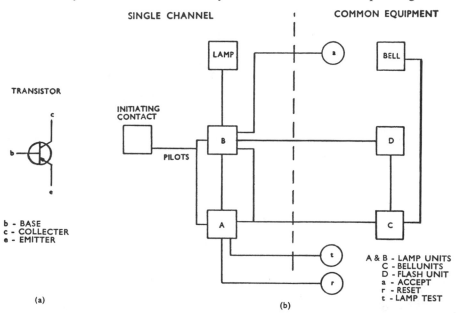

Figure 22.14. Transistor alarm annunciator scheme (courtesy A. Reyrolle & Co. Ltd.)

numbers given on the circuit connection diagrams. Terminal boards are not always easy for access but they can be made so in many cases by mounting them at an angle of 45°. A rear view of relay panels in Fig. 22.13 serves to illustrate these points.

When alarm indication is required, an annunciator scheme using illuminated facias with engraved legends may be used. Such equipment is of considerable value to control engineers in quickly assessing a problem and to minimise delay in taking remedial action. Initiation of the alarm and the visual indication is normally through contacts on protective relays or a moving element of the equipment under supervision. On initiation the sequence of events may be:

1. An alarm bell or klaxon will sound and the appropriate facia lamp flashes on and off to attract attention.

2. The control engineer 'accepts' the signal by pressing a button to silence the alarm and cause the lamp to show a steady light.

3. After taking remedial action and logging the event, the alarm circuit can be reset which extinguishes the lamp.

Static circuitry is used in present day annunciators, transistors superseding the telephone-type relays of old. A block schematic diagram is given in Fig. 22.14, the transistorised switching unit being indicated at A, B, C and D.

The transistors may be compared to the contacts on a relay, i.e. when the transistor is conducting ('on') it is equal to a pair of closed contacts, and when not conducting ('off') to a pair of open contacts. The transistor is basically a three terminal device (see Fig. 22.14(a)) switched on or off by the polarity appearing at the base relative to that at the emitter. In the arrangement shown, a negative potential applied to the base relative to the emitter will switch the

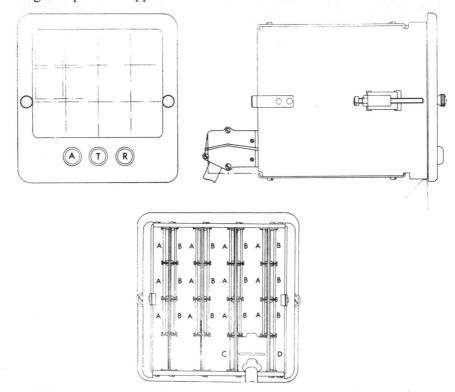

Figure 22.15. Typical 12-way alarm assembly (courtesy A. Reyrolle & Co. Ltd.)

transistor on, i.e. the collector-emitter path will have a low impedance. Conversely, a positive potential applied to the base relative to the emitter will switch the transistor off, i.e. the collector-emitter path will become one of very high impedance.

In the diagram shown in Fig. 22.14(b) the A and B transistor units control the lamp, the C unit the alarm bell and the D unit the lamp flashing sequence. The input to the A and B units are the initiating contact, lamp test and reset. The output from A is used to control the output from B, which in turn controls the lamp. When the fault initiating contacts are closed, the A and B units are switched over, which allows the C unit to operate the audible alarm and the D unit to control the lamp flashing sequence.

736

Figure 22.16. Part of a control board showing a transistorised alarm unit (courtesy A. Reyrolle & Co. Ltd.)

Figure 22.17. Cubicle-type control and relay board (courtesy A. Reyrolle & Co. Ltd.)

Figure 22.18. Power station control desk with mimic diagram on desk surface and transistorised alarm units

Figure 22.19. English Electric 400 kV control board at the 132/400 kV switching station at Legacy, C.E.G.B. North West Region (courtesy G.E.C. Switchgear Ltd.)

On pressing the 'accept' button a, the B unit is switched back to its quiescent state thereby switching off the audible alarm via the C unit and the flashing sequence via D, the lamp remaining on but now showing a steady light. Pressing the 'reset' button r switches the A unit to its quiescent state, thereby extinguishing the lamp by switching off the output from the B unit. From the diagram it is seen that the C and D units and the push buttons are common to a number of channels and can cover up to twenty-four. Provision is made whereby the lamps can be tested at any time by pressing button t.

The alarm assembly comprises a flush mounting housing which carries the appropriate number of lens boxes. On each of the latter is engraved the required

Figure 22.20.   Control cubicles and desk board at Grimethorpe power station, N.C.B. North East Div. No. 4 Area (courtesy A Reyrolle & Co. Ltd.)

legend and each lens box is illuminated from behind by its own lamp, the legend being seen through a translucent glass panel. Behind each lamp housing are sockets which receive the printed-circuit transistor switching units A and B, while the common transistor units C and D are accommodated behind the three push buttons at the base of the assembly (Fig. 22.15).

Annunciators of this type can be made to accommodate a large number of alarms, that shown in Fig. 22.16 having 48 facias.

In concluding this chapter, a selection of control board installations is given in Figs. 22.17 to 22.23. It may be noted that when designing a control board which incorporates a mimic diagram, the panels should be arranged so that they match the positioning of the individual circuits along the busbar, a point of particular importance when the latter is sectionalised, as in Figs. 22.20 and 22.22. When no mimic diagram is provided, the order of panels need not be

*Figure 22.21.   Control board and supervisor's desk at Hinkley Point Nuclear Power Station
(courtesy C.E.G.B.)*

Figure 22.22. Control room at Elstree 132 kV substation, C.E.G.B. Eastern Div. (courtesy A. Reyrolle & Co. Ltd.)

Figure 22.23. Part of the main control room at the Ferrybridge C Power Station, North-Eastern Region (courtesy C.E.G.B.)

related to that of the circuits controlled, providing each is clearly labelled. But, if with this arrangement there is a bus sectioning circuit, its control circuit should be located on the control board in a position such that the circuits to either side of it are those so located at the switchgear itself.

When protective and other relays are mounted on a separate relay board, those for each primary circuit should preferably be in a sequence following that of the switchgear, but providing there is adequate distinction between circuits (by labelling and spacing) this is not essential. When, in a corridor-type control board, the rear section carries the relays associated with the front section, then automatically it follows that the order of relay panels will be that of the circuit control panels.

Chapter 23

Instruments and measuring transformers

In this chapter it will be our purpose to discuss (*a*) those indicating instruments most regularly used on switch and control boards and (*b*) the instrument transformers (current and voltage) which, in the majority of cases, are necessary for the operation of such instruments.

In considering the instruments themselves, no attempt will be made to go into design details, as these are more appropriately dealt with in specialist books on the subject, and here discussion will be confined mainly to application. When dealing with instrument transformers however, some details of design will be studied because they form a significant part of a switchgear unit, current transformers in particular being subject to the effects of short-circuit as discussed in other chapters.

INDICATING INSTRUMENTS*

The instruments usually required on switchgear installations are those which give an indication of current, voltage and power (active or reactive). Associated with these may be instruments which indicate frequency and power factor, and synchronising conditions. In general, they are in accordance with the requirements of BS 89 (indicating instruments).

Instruments may be supplied in a variety of types and sizes, e.g. round, square, sector and controller types, and curvilinear cases or bezels designed for either flush or projecting mounting, with open or protected dials and with differing scale lengths. Apart from the sector and controller types the majority of instrument cases are made of pressed steel, while the smaller sizes are moulded. Flame-proof or sealed instruments are made to suit onerous site conditions.

The overall appearance of a switchboard or control board is important, and this has led to greater attention being paid to the styling of instruments. Thus, the trend has been towards flush-mounted cases (to eliminate projecting parts) and to greatly simplified dials. 'Square' or 'rectangular' frontal formats are frequently achieved on flush-mounted instruments by the use of specially styled bezels.

---

* Based on information supplied by Nalder Bros. & Thompson Ltd., a member of the Reyrolle Parsons Group.

Concurrently, the use of smaller instrument sizes has become more common. Sizes above 6 in are now comparatively rare and cases of 4 in or less are now in general use on switchboards. Further miniaturisation is normal on control desks. A reduction in size without loss of scale length is obtained by the use of 'long scale' instruments, i.e. those in which the scale subtends an angle usually of the order of 240°, in place of the 'short scale' designs which have a subtended angle of the order of 110°. Improved scale aesthetics have also enhanced the scale clarity and the ease with which instruments can be read.

Two further case formats should be mentioned. The edgewise instrument has become increasingly popular for use on process control panels or control desks, etc. It has the advantage of permitting a high stacking density, since either of the instruments may be in close juxtaposition and be either stacked horizontally or vertically (depending on the type). Very recently, a variant of

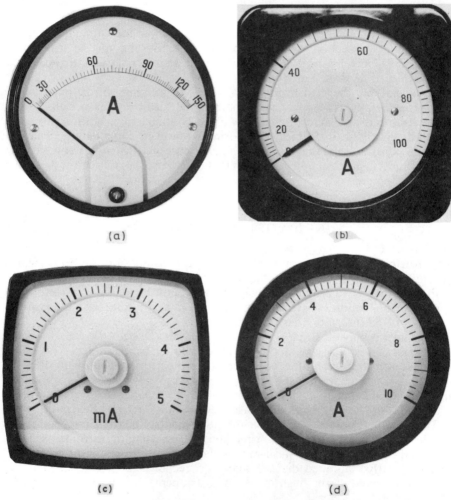

(a) (b)

(c) (d)

Figure 23.1. Typical indicating instrument cases. (a) 6in round and projecting, short scale, (b) 6in square and flush, long scale, (c) 3·5in curvilinear and flush, long scale and (d) 4in round and flush, long scale (courtesy Nalder Bros. & Thompson Ltd.)

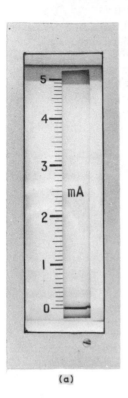

(a)

Figure 23.2. Typical edgewise and Edgeline cases. (a) 5in vertical edgewise, (b) 5in horizontal edgewise and (c) 5in horizontal Edgeline (courtesy Nalder Bros. & Thompson Ltd.)

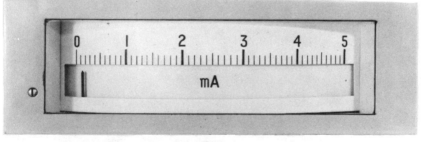

(b)

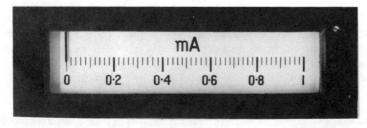

(c)

745

the edgewise instrument has become available, which while retaining the virtues of the edgewise type eliminates the disadvantages of the curved scale plate which is normally inherent in edgewise instruments; the scale, being flat, has a greater effective length than that of the equivalent edgewise instrument. The latter type is marketed under the trade name Edgeline and, at present, is fitted with moving coil movements only.

Examples of instrument cases typical of British practice are shown in Fig. 23.1 and 23.2 which also indicate typical modern scale plate markings. (These are in accordance with BS 89 and with I.E.C. 5.)

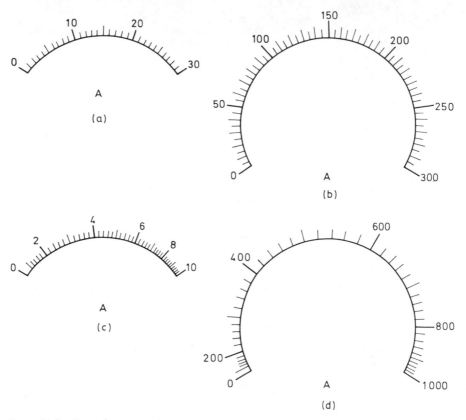

Figure 23.3.   Typical moving coil and moving iron scales. (a) *linear short scale, moving coil.* (b) *linear long scale, moving coil.* (c) *non-linear short scale, moving iron and* (d) *non-linear long scale, moving iron (courtesy Nalder Bros. & Thompson Ltd.)*

An indicating instrument should have a clear, openly-divided scale which is not over crowded with division marks. For most purposes, the scale range and scale shape should be so chosen as to ensure that the normal reading will be at a point beyond the middle and up to three-quarters of the scale length. For some special applications, the scaling is arranged so that all related instruments have similar pointer deflections under normal system conditions. A selection of scales are noted in Figs. 23.3 and 23.4.

In certain applications, scale suppression or compression is particularly useful. Thus, the zero and lower part of the scale may be suppressed on voltmeters where the only voltage values of interest are those near to the normal system voltage. Such scales are shown in Fig. 23.4(c) and (d).

Ammeters used on motor circuits usually have the upper part of their scales compressed; on such scales, the normal load current is at an open part of the scale, and the high starting currents may be indicated within the compressed upper part of the scale. The starting current of an induction motor may be up to six or eight times the normal full load current, and if a conventional scale shape were used, light load currents would hardly be indicated. In addition to improving the indication, the use of such compressed upper scales also buffers the movement and pointer during the transient surges arising from starting. Typical overload scales are shown in Fig. 23.4(a) and (b).

The damping of instruments and their resistance to shock and vibration has been the subject of much development during the past decade. Many modern movements now use a fluid damping system, which in addition to being highly effective, permits considerable reductions to be made in the weight of movements.

Voltage and current are usually measured using moving coil or moving iron instruments, each type having its own particular advantages as will be seen from the following descriptions.

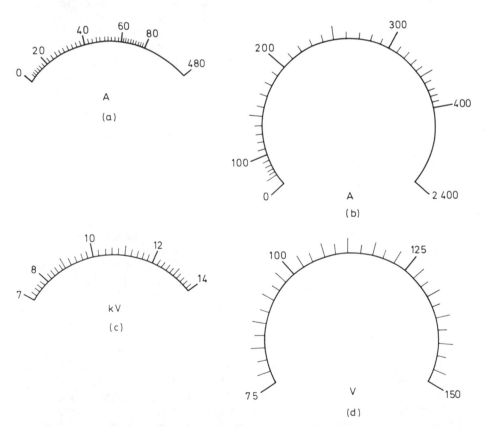

Figure 23.4. Typical moving iron purpose scales. (a) overload ammeter, short scale. (b) overload ammeter, long scale. (c) suppressed zero voltmeter, short scale and (d) suppressed zero voltmeter, long scale (courtesy Nalder Bros. & Thompson Ltd.)

Moving coil instruments are responsive to d.c. and normally have linear scaling (though other scale shapes can be obtained by special design). In their simplified forms they can measure d.c. voltage or current. With the addition of a rectifier, they become a.c. voltmeters or ammeters. In conjunction with transducers (which convert a quantity to an analogue voltage or current) they can be used to indicate other electrical quantities such as frequency or power, or non-electrical quantities such as temperature or pressure. The movement comprises a pivoted moving coil working in an air gap in a magnetic circuit containing a highly stable permanent magnet.

On d.c. circuits, ammeters are operated from shunts connected in the primary circuit. In most power system applications, a potential difference of 75 mV is produced across the voltage terminals of the shunt at currents corresponding to full scale deflection of the associated instrument, and the latter is calibrated with shunt leads having a resistance of 0·025 Ω. D.C. voltmeters are usually directly connected into systems up to 650 V (depending on the size of the instrument); for higher voltages, externally-mounted resistance boxes are used. Displaced zero scales, e.g. centre zero, are of course, readily obtainable.

On a.c. circuits, rectifier moving-coil instruments are becoming more popular because of their well defined scale shape, low VA consumption and small frequency errors. Although calibrated in r.m.s. values, they respond to average values and are therefore susceptible to bad waveform. As ammeters, they are usually energised from current transformers (which may be very small and are often self-contained within the instrument). Zero suppression or scale compression is usually achieved by some means external to the actual movement, but, as mentioned above, special scale shapes can be achieved by the use of a non-linear air gap.

Moving iron instruments are most commonly used on a.c. circuits for the measurement of voltage and current, and some may also be calibrated for use on d.c. circuits. The normal scale shape is non-linear and slightly compressed at both ends of the scale. The majority of such instruments operate on the principles of the repulsion and/or attraction between fixed and moving irons located in a magnetic field.

Since there are no electrical currents to the moving system, moving iron instruments may be used as directly-connected ammeters up to current levels which are limited only by the design of the fixed coil. However, in practice it is usually preferable to use instrument transformers, normally with 5 A or 1 A secondary ratings. Overload scales are readily obtainable by appropriate design of the fixed and/or moving irons, and the instruments have a high overload capacity.

Voltmeters may be directly connected into systems of up to approximately 650 V (depending on the size of the instrument case); for higher voltage, externally-mounted resistance boxes are used. Zero suppression, when required, is obtained by modification to the movement (i.e. to the springs and irons).

Active and reactive power may be measured using induction, electrodynamic or ferrodynamic instruments, or by a combination of transducer and moving coil instrument. Although the induction wattmeter was most common in the past, its inherent frequency, waveform and temperature errors and relatively high VA consumption have led to an increasing preference for the ferrodynamic instrument which is better with respect to each of these properties. The air-cored dynamometer movements are mainly used at higher frequencies than

748

(a)

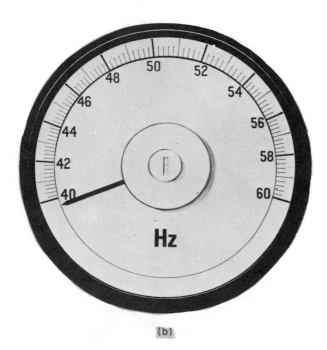

(b)

Figure 23.5. Typical indicating instruments. (a) *wattmeter and* (b) *frequency meter (courtesy Nalder Bros. & Thompson Ltd.)*

50 or 60 Hz, or where the instrument is to be used on either a.c. or d.c. Descriptions of the induction and electrodynamic movements have therefore not been included in this edition.

The ferrodynamic movement may be thought of as being similar to a moving-coil type in which the (fixed) permanent magnet is replaced by an electric magnet. On a single phase or d.c. instrument there are therefore two electrical circuits, respectively associated with and including the moving coil and the fixed coil. One of these is energised from the system voltage (via resistor boxes, if necessary) and the other from the system current (via current transformers or, more rarely, shunts). For the measurement of polyphase power, two or three elements are stacked together, the moving parts being assembled on a common spindle. The scale shape of ferrodynamic wattmeters is linear, and long-scale instruments are normally used, a typical instrument is shown in Fig. 23.5(a), while a number of connection diagrams are given at the end of the chapter.

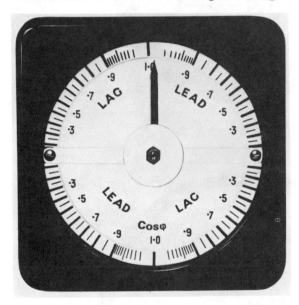

Figure 23.6. Typical power factor meter (courtesy Nalder Bros. & Thompson Ltd.)

The use of transducer-operated moving coil instruments for the measurement of power is a relatively recent development, but may well become more general as transducers are installed for other purposes (e.g. computer control).

Frequency has been measured by a variety of instruments. The once popular 'vibrating reed' or 'resonance' type was superseded by a deflectional type shown in Fig. 23.5(b) using a ratiometer movement. In its turn, the latter is being increasingly displaced by transducer-operated moving coil instruments. Both long scale and short scale designs are used.

Power factor is important to both power station engineers and to commercial and industrial users, the latter being particularly interested in view of the power factor clauses which appear in tariff agreements and the widespread use of techniques for power factor correction. The instrument shown in Fig. 23.6 is of the Lipman moving-iron type operating on what is described as the 'component field' theory. In this there is a fixed system comprising a set of field coils and a set of magnetising coils, the former energised by the current from the line either directly or from current transformer secondaries, and the latter energised from the pressure (voltage) circuit either directly or from the secondary of a voltage transformer. The moving system consists of a number of thin iron plates of special shape attached to a spindle which carries the pointer. This rotor system when magnetised rotates to take up a position related to the power factor of the system to which it is connected, the pointer showing whether the current is leading or lagging relative to the voltage. If the pointer takes up a position in the upper half of the scale it indicates forward power, e.g. generators to line, and if in the lower half, reverse power, i.e. lines to load.

As in the case of wattmeters, the number of current and voltage elements will depend on the nature of the system to which an instrument is to be connected, i.e. single of three phase, three of four wire, balanced or unbalanced loading, and here again a series of diagrams are shown at the end of the chapter to cover the various conditions.

MEASURING TRANSFORMERS

In this chapter our concern is with those transformers (current or voltage) which are intended for use with measuring instruments. These have to be distinguished from those used with protective gear because the requirements differ radically. In the case of current transformers, these differences are those concerned with accuracy, noting that for measuring current transformers they need to be accurate within the normal working range up to 125% of rated current. For overcurrent conditions beyond this, accuracy is unnecessary and indeed it is best that at higher values saturation should occur, since this tends to relieve the connected instruments of the stresses resulting from heavy overcurrent. A protective current transformer, on the other hand, is not normally required to be accurate at currents below the rated value, but it must be accurate within the limits specified in BS 3938 at all *higher* values of current up to a maximum primary current at which the transformer meets the accuracy in that specification. This means that it is extremely difficult to produce a current transformer capable of being used for both purposes, although in some instances with simple forms of protection and instrumentation, e.g. direct-acting overload and an ammeter, the dual purpose may be served by a common current transformer. For other cases, a decision as to whether a single current transformer can be used depends on factors such as design, space and cost, and particularly on the ability of the instruments to withstand short-time overcurrents.

In the case of voltage transformers, the prescribed accuracy is in general the same for both measurement and protective purposes, but in some cases the latter purpose requires that the voltage transformer shall comply with additional limits of accuracy depending on how small or large the permissible errors over an extended voltage range are. Apart from this a voltage transformer associated with certain forms of protection will require to have a residual voltage winding connected in broken delta for which special characteristics and limits of error are specified in BS 3941.

In the following discussion, only the requirements for measuring purposes will be noted, the supplementary requirements for protective purposes having been noted in Chapter 11. In advance of this discussion however, it will be appropriate to comment on some general aspects. It has been noted, for example, that up to certain current and voltage levels, moving-iron ammeters and volt-meters can be direct-connected, i.e. without the use of current or voltage transformers respectively. In the case of ammeters this means that the fixed coil in the instrument has not only to carry the normal full load current of the circuit but also (as it is now a series element of the primary circuit) the short-circuit current appropriate to the system fault level for the period of time taken by a circuit-breaker or fuse to interrupt the fault. Thus the coil and the terminal structure will be subjected to the electromagnetic forces and thermal conditions which have been discussed in relation to other apparatus.

To design a coil capable of withstanding these conditions when the fault level is high and the normal current is low, and within the limited space available in a commercial instrument, is not easy. The problem is solved by using current-transformer operated instruments, but this means of course that the current transformer primary winding has now to withstand the conditions. However, here the designer has greater freedom. As we shall note later, current trans-formers other than those with a bar primary, i.e. those with a wound primary winding, are given what is known as a *short-time factor*, which is the ratio of the rated short-time current to the rated primary current, so that a current trans-former suitable for the short-circuit conditions may be chosen.

In the case of moving-iron voltmeters, these, subject to limitations imposed by the size of the instrument case, can be direct-connected on systems where the voltage does not exceed about 650 V. Above this, but again with limitations, voltage-dropping resistors may be used. These are normally mounted external to the instrument.

For high-voltage systems (1·1 kV upwards) instrument transformers will be used as standard practice, the current transformers having secondary ratings of either 5 A or 1 A and voltage transformers having a secondary rating of 110 V (or $110/\sqrt{3}$ in the case of single-phase line-to-earth). These ratings are British standards and other ratings may be necessary to meet other standards.

CURRENT TRANSFORMERS

The choice of a current transformer for measurement purposes should be made by basing it on its rated output in relation to the burden connected to its second-ary winding and on the degree of accuracy required. To choose a transformer with a rated output considerably in excess of the required output can result in increased errors, so that it is desirable that the rated output should be near to (but not less than) the actual output at which the transformer is to operate. It is important to remember that the output required is not only that of the connected instruments but also that of the connecting leads. In some instances the distance between the current transformers and the instruments may be quite long, e.g. between a switchgear unit and a remote control board, such that the output at 5 A secondary current would be excessive. This is a case where a secondary current of 1 A will be of value.

With regard to accuracy, a choice of a class of accuracy higher than is necessary is not economical and can result in the transformer being excessively large, requiring considerable space in the switchgear for its accommodation. BS 3938 recommends that the accuracy class be selected in accordance with Table 23.1, the limits of current and phase errors for the six classes being those given in

752

Table 23.1
VARIOUS APPLICATIONS AND RECOMMENDED ACCURACY CLASSES

Application	Class of accuracy
Precision testing or as a standard for testing other current transformers	AL
Meters of precision grade in accordance with BS 37 (Electricity Meters)	AM
Meters of commercial grade in accordance with BS 37	BM or CM
Precision measurement (indicating instruments and recorders)	AL or AM
General industrial measurements (indicating instruments and recorders)	C
Approximate measurements	D

Table 23.2
LIMITS OF CURRENT AND PHASE ERRORS FOR MEASURING CURRENT TRANSFORMERS. MEASURED WITH RATED BURDEN, AT UNITY p.f. AND RATED FREQUENCY (BS 3938, TABLE 8)

	Absolute errors								Variation in error	
	From 125% to 20% of rated current		From 125% to 10% of rated current		Below 20% and up to 10% of rated current		Below 10% and up to 5% of rated current		From 125% to 5% of rated current	
Accuracy class	Current error	Phase error	Current error	Phase error	Current error	Phase error	Current error	Phase error	Current error	Phase error
	(%) + or −	(min) + or −	(%) + or −	(min) + or −	(%) + or −	(min) + or −	(%) + or −	(min) + or −	(%)	(min)
AL	—	—	0·1	5	—	—	0·2	10	—	—
AM	—	—	0·5	30	—	—	0·75	40	0·5	20
BM	—	—	1·0	40	—	—	1·5	60	1·0	30
CM	—	—	1·5	120	—	—	2	150	1·5	75
C	1·0	120	—	—	2·0	180	—	—	—	—
D	5·0	—	—	—	—	—	—	—	—	—

Table 23.2. These errors are those measured at rated burden, unity power factor and rated frequency, noting that the current error (previously known as the *ratio error*) is the error in the magnitude of the secondary current expressed as a percentage, while the phase error is the displacement in phase between the primary and secondary current vectors, the direction of the phasors being so chosen that the angle is zero for a perfect transformer.

How the errors with which we are concerned arise can best be considered by a study of the phasor diagram for a current transformer, as shown in Fig. 23.7.

When drawing the phasor diagram for a current transformer it is usual to commence with the flux as reference phasor since this is common to both primary and secondary windings. The induced e.m.f.s E_S and E_P lag behind the flux by 90° and can be drawn in, the magnitude of the phasors E_S and E_P being proportional to the secondary and primary turns.

The excitation current I_O taken by the primary, is made up of two components I_M and I_W. I_M is the reactive magnetising component which produces the flux and I_W is the active component supplying the hysteresis and eddy current losses in the core; this is in phase with the primary induced e.m.f. E_P.

The secondary current I_S lags behind the secondary induced e.m.f. by an angle θ_S. θ_S is made up of δ the angle produced by the secondary winding resistance and reactance, and γ the angle produced by the burden connected to the secondary winding. In practice, for a bar primary current transformer the secondary winding reactance is usually negligible and δ is zero. The secondary current is now transferred to the primary side by reversing I'_S and multiplying by the turns ratio K_T. The resultant current flowing in the primary winding I_P is then the vector sum of $K_T I_S$ and I_O.

It should be noted that the flux Φ and exciting current I_O are determined by the secondary voltage required, which is in turn determined by the burden

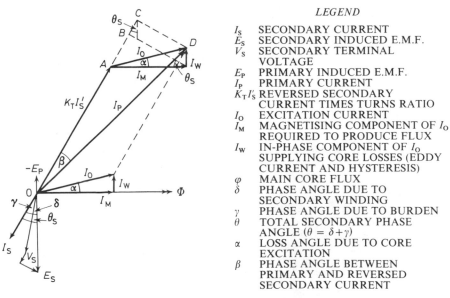

LEGEND

I_S	SECONDARY CURRENT
E_S	SECONDARY INDUCED E.M.F.
V_S	SECONDARY TERMINAL VOLTAGE
E_P	PRIMARY INDUCED E.M.F.
I_P	PRIMARY CURRENT
$K_T I_S$	REVERSED SECONDARY CURRENT TIMES TURNS RATIO
I_O	EXCITATION CURRENT
I_M	MAGNETISING COMPONENT OF I_O REQUIRED TO PRODUCE FLUX
I_W	IN-PHASE COMPONENT OF I_O SUPPLYING CORE LOSSES (EDDY CURRENT AND HYSTERESIS)
φ	MAIN CORE FLUX
δ	PHASE ANGLE DUE TO SECONDARY WINDING
γ	PHASE ANGLE DUE TO BURDEN
θ	TOTAL SECONDARY PHASE ANGLE ($\theta = \delta + \gamma$)
α	LOSS ANGLE DUE TO CORE EXCITATION
β	PHASE ANGLE BETWEEN PRIMARY AND REVERSED SECONDARY CURRENT

Figure 23.7. Phasor diagram for a current transformer (not to scale)

connected to the secondary winding, or for a given burden by the current flowing in the secondary and primary windings. Hence with a current transformer the flux density in the core is not constant but varies with the primary current, this being the basic difference between a current and voltage (or power) transformer where the voltage and flux density remains constant and the current varies with the load.

There are two main errors introduced into a circuit by a current transformer. These are (a) the current error and (b) the phase error.

The current error

Since the primary current has to contribute to the magnetising and iron loss components, the ratio of primary to secondary current is not exactly equal to the turns ratio. The error introduced is known as the *current error* and is defined in BS 3938:1965 as:

$$\text{Percentage current error} = \frac{K_N (I_S - I_P)}{I_P} \times 100$$

Where K_N = Nominal ratio, i.e. $\dfrac{\text{Rated primary current}}{\text{Rated secondary current}}$

There are two other ratios which are of importance in a current transformer, these are:

$$K_T = \text{Turns ratio} = \frac{\text{Secondary turns}}{\text{Primary turns}}$$

$$K_C = \text{Actual current ratio} = \frac{\text{Actual primary current}}{\text{Actual secondary current}}$$

By studying the phasor diagram it is possible to derive an expression for the current error in terms of other known components.

If the reversed secondary current phasor OA is produced to a point OC where CD is a perpendicular dropped from the primary current vector OD, then since in practice the angle β is small the length OC is very nearly equal to the length of OD, and all components can be resolved along the OC axis.

Now, actual ratio $K_C = \dfrac{I_P}{I_S}$

$$\simeq \frac{\text{length } OC}{I_S}$$

$$= \frac{OA + AB + BC}{I_S}$$

$$= \frac{K_T I_S' + I_M \sin \theta_S + I_W \cos \theta_S}{I_S}$$

$$= K_T + \frac{I_M \sin \theta_S + I_W \cos \theta_S}{I_S}$$

but $I_M = I_O \cos \alpha$ and $I_W = I_O \sin \alpha$ and if θ_S is very small then the expression can be reduced further:

$$K_C = K_T + \frac{I_O \cos \alpha \sin \theta_S + I_O \sin \alpha \cos \theta_S}{I_S}$$

$$= K_T + \frac{I_O}{I_S} \sin (\theta_S + \alpha)$$

If θ_S is very small then:

$$K_C - K_T + \frac{I_O \sin \alpha}{I_S}$$

but $I_O \sin \alpha = I_W$

$$\therefore K_C = K_T + \frac{I_W}{I_S}$$

From this expression it can be seen that for a small secondary phase angle the current error is mainly due to the iron loss component of the excitation current.

Another point that emerges from the above expression is that since the actual current ratio is equal to the turns ratio plus I_W/I_S then the magnitude of I_W/I_S determines the amount of turns compensation necessary to reduce the errors to a minimum.

The phase error

The phase error is also introduced by the fact that the primary current has to supply the components of the exciting current, and the reversed secondary current is not exactly in phase with the primary current. The angle between the two phasors is known as the phase difference of the current transformer.

This error can easily be derived from again studying the phasor diagram. Now, since β is very small, in practice $\tan \beta \simeq \beta$

$$\therefore \beta = \frac{I_M \cos \theta_S - I_W \sin \theta_S}{K_T I_S + I_M \sin \theta_S + I_W \cos \theta_S}$$

$$= \frac{I_M \cos \theta_S - I_W \sin \theta_S}{K_T I_S + I_O \cos \alpha \sin \theta_S + I_O \sin \alpha \cos \theta_S}$$

$$= \frac{I_M \cos \theta_S - I_W \sin \theta_S}{K_T I_S + I_O \sin (\theta_S + \alpha)}$$

In practice $I_O \sin (\theta_S + \alpha)$ is very small compared with $K_T I_S$ and can be neglected.

$$\therefore \beta = \frac{I_M \cos \theta_S - I_W \sin \theta_S}{K_T I_S}$$

$$= \frac{I_O \cos \theta_S \cos \alpha - I_O \sin \theta_S \sin \alpha}{K_T I_S}$$

$$= \frac{I_O \cos (\theta_S + \alpha)}{K_T I_S}$$

756

If the secondary phase angle is very small

$$\beta = \frac{I_0 \cos \alpha}{K_T I_S}$$

$$\therefore \beta = \frac{I_M}{K_T I_S}$$

From this expression it can be seen that if θ_S is small the phase error is mainly due to the magnetising component of the exciting current.

The phase error is usually expressed in minutes.

An improvement in the current and phase errors can be obtained by a combination of methods:

(a) By the use of high permeability and low loss magnetic material for the core, e.g. spirally-wound cold-rolled grain-oriented silicon steel.

(b) By reducing the length of the flux path in the core and increasing the area of the path, with all joints reduced to a minimum or avoided altogether.

(c) By increasing the primary ampere turns, using a 'wound-type' coil where the short-circuit current permits such a coil structure.

(d) By reducing the internal secondary burden as far as possible, which includes its reactance as well as its resistance. Sometimes it may be necessary to use two secondary windings connected in parallel with each other.

(e) By keeping the connected burden on the secondary as small as is possible. This may entail the reduction of the secondary current from 5 A to 1 A in cases where the connected burden is remote from the transformer. The use of 1 A secondaries is not, however, recommended in high ratios, because of the increased induced voltage upon open-circuit under load, which may destroy the interturn and interlayer insulation and may also prove to be dangerous to life.

(f) By specifying the rated burden as near to the actual burden as is possible, because the correction of current error by turns compensation will be made for the rated burden and may not necessarily be so close for a lower burden.

Mention has been made earlier of the problems arising in the design of current transformers in relation to the ability they must have to withstand the electromagnetic forces and thermal effects when the primary winding is called upon to carry high values of short-circuit current for a short time. Thus a current transformer will be given a short-time current rating related to the design and giving an indication of the magnitude of short-circuit current which the primary winding can carry without (a) mechanical damage to the primary winding due to the electromagnetic forces set up by the peak value of current in the first half-cycle of short circuit, and (b) the period of time during which the symmetrical r.m.s. value of the short-circuit current can be carried without overheating the windings and possibly damaging the insulation.

In both these respects, no problem arises when a current transformer of the bar-primary type as shown in Fig. 23.8 can be used, but when the primary winding is of the wound-type, and most likely of relatively small cross section with a large number of turns, the problems are or can be significant, particularly if the fault level is high, the normal primary current is low, the output and accuracy required is high and the clearance time of an associated circuit-breaker is relatively long.

The 'short-time factor' assigned to a current transformer therefore provides an indication of its ability in these matters, and in BS 3938 a table is given

Figure 23.8. Typical bar-primary type current transformer

Table 23.3
MAXIMUM SHORT-TIME FACTORS OBTAINABLE
ECONOMICALLY WITH WOUND PRIMARY
CTs (BS 3938, TABLE 12)

Accuracy class	Rated output (VA)	STF obtainable corresponding to the rated duration		
		0·5 s	1·0 s	3·0 s
AM	5	350	250	150
	7·5	300	200	125
	10	275	190	115
	15	250	175	100
BM	5	400	275	175
	7·5	350	250	150
	10	325	225	140
	15	300	200	125
CM	1·5	600	425	250
	5	450	325	200
	7·5	425	300	190
	10	400	275	175
	15	350	250	150
C	5	600	425	250
	7·5	525	400	225
	10	475	350	200
	15	400	275	175
D	5	1 000	700	400
	7·5	925	650	375
	10	850	600	350
	15	750	525	300

showing the maximum short-time factors which can be obtained economically for wound-primary current transformers related to accuracy, output and time. This table is reproduced here as Table 23.3.

By way of example, let it be assumed that we are concerned with a set of measuring current transformers for use on an 11 kV system with a fault level of 350 MVA, which corresponds to a symmetrical breaking current (r.m.s.) of 18 400 A. If it is further assumed that the current transformers must have a ratio of 60/5 A, then, by the definition given earlier, the 'short-time factor' (STF) will be given by:

$$STF = \frac{18\ 400}{60} = 306 \text{ approximately.}$$

Reference to Table 23.3 shows that for the alternative rated times the rated output for the various classes of accuracy can be any one of those given in Table 23.4. From this and a study of Table 23.3 it is seen that the lower the class of accuracy the higher is the rated output for a given short-time, and conversely the lower the output and rated time the greater the short-time factor. It is obvious that the duration of the short-circuit current is important, and for many applications the preferred time of 0·5 s is adequate, but in other cases higher times cannot be avoided, e.g. when circuit-breakers in series have time-graded protection. This time has an important bearing on the permissible current density in the primary winding at the rated short-time current, so that the longer the time, so the cross-sectional area of the primary winding conductor must be increased. This is demonstrated in Table 23.5.

If the secondary winding of a current transformer is open-circuited while normal current is flowing in the primary winding, a very high and dangerous

Table 23.4
RATED OUTPUT (VA) FOR VARIOUS CLASSES
OF ACCURACY

Accuracy class	Rated time (s)		
	0·5	1·0	3·0
AM	5	—	—
BM	7·5	—	—
CM	15	5	—
C	15	10	—
D	15	15	10

Table 23.5
PERMISSIBLE CURRENT DENSITIES

Rated time (s)	Permissible current density	
	(A/in²)	(A/cm²)
0·25	212 000	32 860
0·5	150 000	23 250
1·0	106 000	16 430
2·0	75 000	11 625
3·0	61 000	9 455

759

overvoltage may be induced in the secondary winding and the core may over-heat. It is also possible that the magnetic characteristics of the core will be modified such as to affect the transformer accuracy.

In service, open-circuiting should be a rare occurrence but it can arise if the secondary burden is removed inadvertently, e.g. an instrument. This may put personnel in danger or it can lead to the breakdown of small wiring connected to the secondary winding.

The waveform of the open-circuit voltage is a series of sharp peaks alternating about zero, the peaks occurring as the sinusoidal primary current passes through zero. The magnitude of these peaks is dependent on several factors such as the number of secondary turns, the sectional area of the core and the magnitude of the primary current. Investigators have found that the use of superior core materials leads to the peak voltages being higher. In a recent article, Seeley[1] quotes 10 kV as being commonplace, an article which, incidentally, also discusses various methods which can be adopted to afford protection against this hazard. Of these devices, one which is simple and robust is that comprising a high resistance winding incorporated in the transformer in the form of a tertiary winding. This problem is also discussed in a paper by Gray and Wright[2].

Even without open-circuiting the secondary winding, over-voltages can arise due to switching an unloaded cable. We have noted in Chapter 2 that this operation can give rise to high frequency current transients of some magnitude. If the burden connected to the secondaries of current transformers in the circuit being switched is inductive, it will, at the high frequency involved, be of high impedance and voltages of several kilovolts may be induced in the secondary windings. They are, however, of very short duration, and a current transformer designed to withstand the open circuit peak voltages for 1 min should be in no difficulty withstanding the likely switching overvoltages. The ability of the secondary wiring to withstand these voltages depends largely on the type and grade of insulation, and in this respect it has to be borne in mind that mineral-insulated cables have a much lower instantaneous breakdown voltage than rubber or paper-insulated types, and here the use of voltage protective devices at the current transformers may well be justified. The problem is most important when multicore cables are used between a switchgear installation and a remote control board as a breakdown in such a cable can be expensive, not easily replaced and far-reaching in its effects.

One problem associated with some types of current transformer is that of insulating the primary winding from the iron core and secondary coils. This rarely arises in the case of bar primary (single-turn) types where the insulation over the primary conductor may be any of the conventional bushing materials such as porcelain, synthetic-resin-bonded paper or epoxy resin. Unfortunately, as discussed elsewhere in this chapter, this type cannot always be used, and when a high accuracy combined with a low ratio is involved, it is necessary to use a wound primary (multi-turn) type. Here the problem is much more difficult and in the past various methods have been tried, the most common being to wrap insulation in tape form round the winding (see Fig. 23.12 for example). Because of the shape of the winding, with its projecting terminations, the tape has to be applied by hand which is a slow and costly process requiring skilled labour to ensure a satisfactory quality of insulation on the finished product.

It was not until materials were found which could be poured round the winding in a suitable mould and which would set into an impervious insulator that a more satisfactory solution was achieved. Two such materials are in wide use today, viz. epoxy resin and butyl rubber. The former was introduced as an insulant on current transformers in Switzerland in 1947, and the latter was introduced in the U.K. by A.E.I. (now part of G.E.C. Switchgear Ltd.) in 1958. Both materials are superior to other insulants in their ability to withstand the bursting forces under short-circuit conditions, give protection against damage from external causes and are impervious to moisture. The techniques associated with the application of these materials call for separate study, but the present state of the art coupled with experience in service is such that their use is firmly established.

When moulded resin is employed, the resin is of the 'low pressure' epoxy or polyester types which can be 'cast' in shapes and configurations and can also be transformed into a hard infusible material by the addition of hardeners or

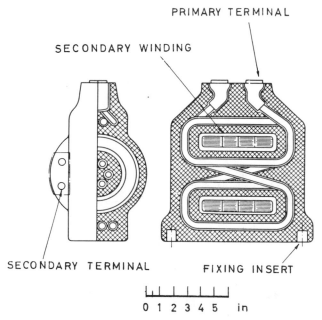

PRIMARY TERMINAL

SECONDARY WINDING

SECONDARY TERMINAL   FIXING INSERT

0 1 2 3 4 5   in

Figure 23.9.   Cast-resin insulated wound primary current transformer (courtesy A. Reyrolle & Co. Ltd.)

catalysts in a process known as *curing*. Most present-day designs use the epoxy resins because they have a higher viscosity than the polyester types, shrink less during curing and have better electrical and mechanical properties.

Figure 23.9 shows in section an 11 kV wound-primary design, the core being of high-permeability wound strip, and this together with the primary and secondary windings, is hermetically sealed by the resin. Another example is that shown in Fig. 23.10 which is again 11 kV.

Not all designs include the core in the encapsulation. In a Brown Boveri range for example, current transformers for use on systems up to 17·5 kV, and of the wound-primary type, have the core outside the encapsulation, these being the transformers shown in the middle row of Fig. 23.11. Those on the top row are fully encapsulated and are for voltages of 24 kV to 72·5 kV, while the bottom

Figure 23.10. 11 kV epoxy-resin-encapsulated current transformer (courtesy A. Reyrolle & Co. Ltd.)

Figure 23.11. Moulded-resin current transformers for maximum service voltages of 1·1 kV to 72·5 kV. The bottom row shows the busbar-type for (from left to right) 1·1, 7·2 and 24 kV*. The middle row shows the wound-type with the core outside the frame for (from left to right) 7·2, 12, 12*, 12 and 17·5 kV. The top row shows the fully-encapsulated type for (from left to right) 24, 36, 52 and 72·5 kV*. The transformers marked with an asterisk (*) have two cores and secondary windings for separate purposes and require different classes of accuracy and output rating (courtesy Brown Boveri & Co. Ltd.)

762

row shows busbar types. The reasoning behind this encapsulation is discussed in an article by Tanner[3].

Butyl is one of four types of synthetic rubber which emerged as a result of intense research which was given great impetus due to the 1939/45 war. It is a rubber obtained from oil products and oil refiners. The process involved in manufacturing transformers insulated with butyl are beyond the scope of this chapter, and reference should be made to the article by Blower[4]. Suffice it here to say that the raw material is first reduced to a form which will flow more readily round the primary winding to prevent the inclusion of air. The primary winding is suitably supported in a steel mould, the assembly preheated and the butyl forced-in under high pressure. When full, the mould is placed in an oven for the butyl compound to cure into a homogenous, tough rubber dielectric.

Figure 23.12.   Current transformer (A.E.I.) with tape-insulated primary (courtesy G.E.C. Switchgear Ltd.)

After this is complete and after cooling, the steel mould is opened for the completed primary to be removed and assembled with its core and secondary coil, so that the latter are outside the encapsulation. Although total encapsulation is possible it is not a preferred method as it involves a loss of flexibility obtained from the ability to assemble quickly any ratio of current transformer from a reasonably limited range of standard primary and secondary coils.

We have noted earlier the problems associated with tape-insulated wound primary windings of irregular shape, an example of such a transformer being shown in Fig. 23.12. Figure 23.13 on the other hand, shows this same transformer with its primary winding encapsulated in butyl, a neater and much more satisfactory final product.

Later developments have led to an alternative arrangement in which the primary winding completely surrounds the secondary coil, the resulting transformer appearing as in Fig. 23.14, and which may have a single secondary or a tapped secondary. An alternative to this is a transformer as shown in Fig. 23.15 which has an extended primary to allow two completely separate secondary windings each with its own core to be mounted on the common primary. This

Figure 23.13.   Butyl rubber used as a substitute for the tape insulation shown in Figure 23.12 (courtesy G.E.C. Switchgear Ltd.)

Figure 23.14.   Butyl-rubber current transformer (A.E.I.) in which the primary completely surrounds the secondary coil (courtesy G.E.C. Switchgear Ltd.)

enables the transformer to combine the dual purposes of measuring and protection, and meeting the different requirements as noted earlier and in Chapter
11.

We have seen in Chapter 12 how, in h.v. bulk-oil circuit-breakers for outdoor
use, ring-type current transformers can be accommodated over the breaker
bushings, the latter acting as the primary insulation and the through stem as
the primary winding. Similar arrangements are possible with the more recent
sulphur hexafluoride (SF_6) circuit-breaker, but unfortunately not with the
small-oil-volume and air-blast types. With these, separate current transformers
must therefore be used, either oil filled or gas insulated and of the post type.

*Figure 23.15.   Transformer of the type shown in Figure 23.14, but with a longer primary enclosing
two secondary windings (courtesy G.E.C. Switchgear Ltd.)*

Typical of an oil-filled type for the voltage range of 33 kV to 132 kV is the
unit shown in Figs. 23.16 and 23.17. As the latter shows, the cores and primary
and secondary windings are situated at the upper (live) end of the unit, the
primary winding normally being of the bar-type (as shown) or, for low primary
currents, it may be of the wound type. The top fabricated housing is at line
potential and is supported on a shedded porcelain appropriate to the system
voltage.

At the base, to which the secondary leads are taken, provision is made to
accommodate expansion bellows. The major insulation is oil impregnated paper
(OIP) wrapped around the core and secondary windings and the assembly is
filled with oil, completely sealed from the atmosphere. The major insulation is
dried-out under a high degree of vacuum and is filled with oil without breaking
the vacuum.

Figure 23.16. English Electric outdoor oil-filled current transformer. Range 33–132 kV (courtesy G.E.C. Switchgear Ltd.)

For use on high-voltage systems from 110 kV to 500 kV, oil-filled units of the so-called 'hairpin' type are in general use, a cross-section of a typical unit being shown in Fig. 23.18. The description 'hairpin' arises out of the fact that the high-voltage primary winding is of that shape, comprising a tube having graded insulation of oil-impregnated paper in which metal foils are interposed at suitable intervals. The outermost of these foils is connected to earth via an insulated terminal and link enabling dielectric loss-angle measurements to be taken to check the quality of insulation. This foil further acts as an earth shield between the primary and secondary windings. The latter, each with their own cores, are mounted over the legs of the hairpin as shown in Fig. 23.18. In this

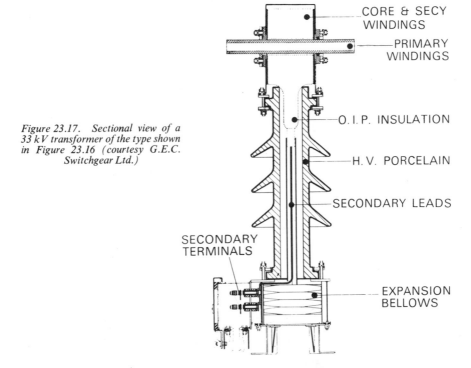

Figure 23.17. Sectional view of a 33 kV transformer of the type shown in Figure 23.16 (courtesy G.E.C. Switchgear Ltd.)

CORE & SECY WINDINGS

PRIMARY WINDINGS

O. I. P. INSULATION

H. V. PORCELAIN

SECONDARY LEADS

SECONDARY TERMINALS

EXPANSION BELLOWS

design, up to four such secondary assemblies can be accommodated, an alternative design allowing accommodation for five secondaries.

Each unit is completely oil-filled and sealed to ensure that the oil cannot come into contact with the atmosphere or any gas. In Fig. 23.18, the flexible oil reservoir in the top housing above the high-voltage terminal chamber ensures this by preventing the creation of undue pressures or depressions due to oil expansion or contraction. In the alternative form which has a larger volume of oil, the latter is sealed under pressure, oil expansion and contraction being catered for by metal bellows externally housed in cylinders at the transformer base.

If required, a tapping can be brought out from a suitable foil in the major insulation which can be used to energise an electromagnetic unit and thus provide a voltage output at 63·5 V, the arrangement operating in a similar manner to a capacitor voltage transformer, to be noted later.

For services on a 700 kV system an oil-filled design known as a 'two-stage cascade current transformer' is used. This is shown in Fig. 23.19. From the sectional view on the left it is seen that it consists of two transformers (head-type) arranged in vertical formation, each with its own capacitively-controlled bushing. Each assembly is accommodated in a shedded porcelain and each top casing (7 and 8) contains a bellows to compensate for the temperature-dependent change of volume of the insulating oil. The schematic diagram on the right shows the magnetic circuit for the transformer from which it is seen that the bar primary conductor (11) passes through a driving core (12). This core has a single secondary winding (13) which feeds into the primary winding (14) on the lower cores (15, 16 and 17), and each of these has its own secondary winding (18, 19 and 20) the leads from which are taken to terminals in the base for connection to the external burden.

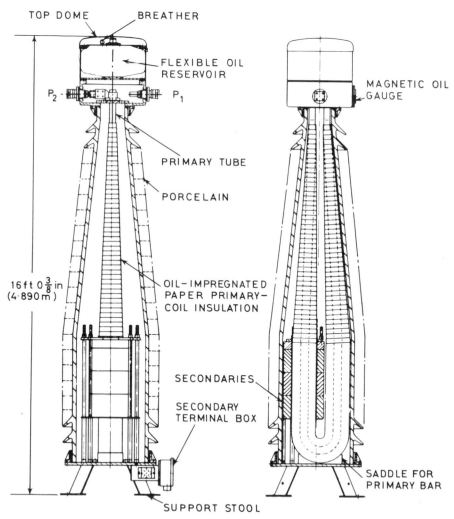

Figure 23.18. Sectional view of a 400 kV English Electric oil-filled current transformer with hairpin-type primary, insulated with oil-impregnated paper (courtesy G.E.C. Switchgear Ltd.)

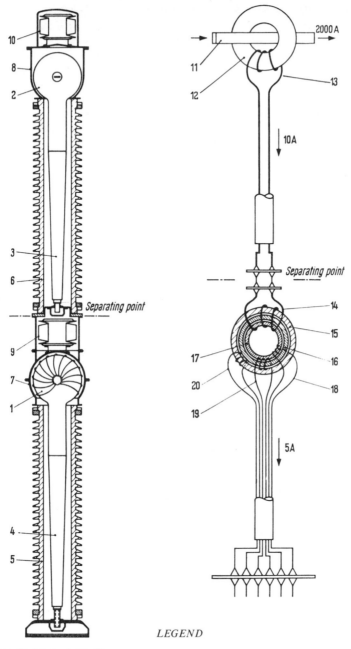

LEGEND

1, 2	HEAD-TYPE CURRENT TRANSFORMER	11	BAR-TYPE PRIMARY CONDUCTOR
3, 4	CAPACITIVE CONTROLLED BUSHINGS	12	DRIVING CORE
5, 6	INSULATORS	13	SECONDARY WINDING
7, 8	TOP HOUSINGS	14	PRIMARY WINDING
9, 10	BELLOWS	15, 16, 17	CORES
		18, 19, 20	SECONDARY WINDING

Figure 23.19.   700 kV two-stage cascade-type current transformer, sectional view (left) and magnetic circuit arrangement (right) (courtesy Siemens (UK) Ltd.)

769

A major problem with oil-filled current transformers at very-high voltages is the large bulk of oil-impregnated paper necessary for the major insulation which must also be brought to a high state of dryness and be fully impregnated. At the highest voltages, the two-stage cascade design results in a simplification of this problem and in an article[5] discussing the design shown in Fig. 23.19, it was noted that the paper volume is only 5 times that of a 220 kV transformer, whereas a single-stage 700 kV design would require 17 times the volume.

It is for these reasons that the high-voltage current transformer in which the insulant is an electronegative gas, i.e. sulphur hexafluoride (SF_6), has been developed. This inert gas does not burn and has a dielectric strength of the order of 2 or 3 times that of air, but against this it has a low impulse ratio, so that a problem can arise in relation to securing a high impulse level. Here, advantage is taken of the fact that the electric strength increases linearly with pressure so that by maintaining the gas under pressure at say two or three atmospheres, the required impulse level can be obtained.

Figure 23.20 illustrates in section an SF_6-filled current transformer for 132 kV service. It comprises a steel pressure chamber, which is live at line voltage, supported on a porcelain insulator which stands on an earthed steel base, the complete structure being gas filled. The primary conductor is a copper tube,

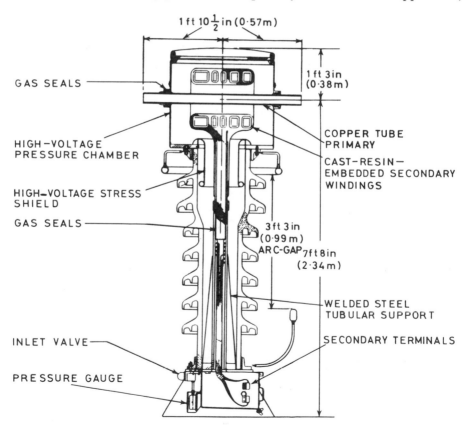

Figure 23.20. Sectional view of a 132 kV SF_6-filled current transformer (courtesy A. Reyrolle & Co. Ltd.)

Figure 23.21. 132 kV SF₆ –filled current transformer as shown in Figure 23.20 (courtesy A. Reyrolle & Co. Ltd.)

Figure 23.22. 400 kV SF₆–filled current transformer (courtesy A. Reyrolle & Co. Ltd.)

Figure 23.23. 3-phase bank of English Electric 400 kV gas-insulated SF$_6$ current transformers installed at the Waltham Cross 275/400 kV transformer station of the C.E.G.B. (courtesy G.E.C. Switchgear Ltd.)

lightly insulated from the pressure chamber at one end and with pressure seals at both entries to the chamber. The core and secondary windings are embedded in a cylindrical cast-resin block, the secondary leads being brought through the tubular centre of the pedestal support to terminals at the base. The complete transformer is shown in Fig. 23.21.

Current transformers of this type are in service in the U.K. on systems up to 400 kV, and designs exist for 750 kV. A typical 400 kV unit is seen in Fig. 23.22, and its size can be judged by comparison with the man, while Fig. 23.23 illustrates a bank of three such transformers installed at a transforming station.

VOLTAGE TRANSFORMERS

It is obviously not possible to energise the voltage elements of indicating or integrating instruments at the system voltage when this is in excess of about 650 V and some suitably scaled-down voltage must be made available either by voltage-dropping resistors (when applicable) or, as is more usual, from a voltage transformer, the secondary voltage of which is substantially proportional to the voltage in the primary winding. Circumstances can arise where, even at 650 V or less, the use of voltage transformers stepping down to say 110 V may be desirable, and in these cases an air-insulated design which is typically as shown in Fig. 23.24, is economical and satisfactory.

For indoor switchgear of up to 33 kV, an oil-filled electromagnetic-type will often be used which is fundamentally similar in principle to a power transformer,

772

but having a rated output in VA instead of kVA. The final form taken by the transformer will be dictated in many instances by the type of switchgear with which it will be associated. For example, the transformer shown in Fig. 23.25 is one intended for use in cubicle or cellular switchgear in which no draw-out features are included. For metal-clad gear incorporating withdrawal features for the circuit-breaker, it is usual to provide similar features for the voltage transformer when it would be of the form shown in Fig. 23.26. When this type of metal-clad switchgear is used at 33 kV, it will often be arranged for vertical rather than horizontal isolation, and in this case it is convenient to design the transformer on the same basis. An example of this is given in Fig. 23.27, where the transformer, after having been isolated within the switchgear unit, has been removed on a handling bogey.

As in the case of current transformers, cast-resin encapsulation is extensively used, again either in part or in full, the former generally being applicable to transformers for use on the lower system voltages. A fully encapsulated 11 kV

Figure 23.24. *Air-insulated voltage transformer for use up to 660 V*

Figure 23.25. *Typical 3-phase stationary-type oil-immersed voltage transformer*

Figure 23.26. *Typical 3-phase draw-out type oil-immersed voltage transformer*

unit is shown in Fig. 23.28, which is a design in which the high-voltage fuses are located in, but are withdrawable from, the cast-resin bushings. This transformer, used in a metal-clad switchgear unit, is carried on a swivel base so that after it has been withdrawn and thereby isolated, it can be turned to give access to the fuses, one of which is shown partly withdrawn in the illustration. The general design of this transformer is seen in the sectional view of Fig. 23.29. It employs layer-type primary windings, and although these are larger than those in a comparable oil-impregnated paper-type, the overall dimensions are in fact less.

Figure 23.27. Oil-filled electromagnetic voltage transformer arranged for vertical isolation in 33 kV metal-clad switchgear, shown removed on bogey (courtesy A. Reyrolle & Co. Ltd.)

In the illustration shown in Fig. 23.30 a group of moulded-resin voltage transformers forming part of the Brown Boveri range is shown. This range includes units for use on service voltages up to 72·5 kV. Those for the higher voltages of 52 and 72·5 kV are the two pillar-type units and are designed for connection between phase and earth.

In the electromagnetic transformer, the accuracy depends on the leakage reactance and the winding resistances, these determining how the phase error and the voltage error vary as the burden on the secondary increases. The permeability and power dissipation of the core material affect the exciting current and thus the errors at zero burden. The core material used will affect the physical

Figure 23.28. 11 kV epoxy-resin encapsulated voltage transformer, withdrawable-type with h.v. fuses in bushings and secondary fuses on the right (courtesy A. Reyrolle & Co. Ltd.)

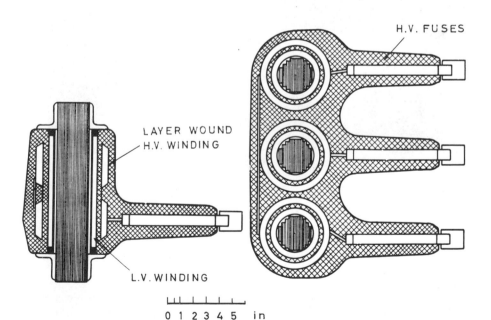

H.V. FUSES

LAYER WOUND
H.V. WINDING

L.V. WINDING

0 1 2 3 4 5 in

Figure 23.29. Sections of cast-resin insulated 11 kV voltage transformer as shown in Figure 23.28 (courtesy A. Reyrolle & Co. Ltd.)

size of the transformer, a smaller unit being possible if cold-rolled grain-oriented silicon-iron alloys are used instead of hot-rolled silicon-iron. This reduction in size can be achieved without reduction in output or accuracy but the construction of the core with the grain-oriented alloys is somewhat complicated since the flux path must follow the direction of rolling.

For measurement purposes, BS 3941 :1965 recognises five classes of accuracy as noted in Table 23.6, which also indicates their application. The limits of voltage and phase errors at rated frequency and at the prescribed percentage of rated primary voltage and rated output for these classes of accuracy are also established in BS 3941, and these, scheduled here in Table 23.7, must not be exceeded.

In passing, it may be noted that when a voltage transformer is used for the dual purpose of measurement and protection, it has to meet additional limits of

Figure 23.30. Group of moulded-resin insulated voltage transformers for 3·6 kV to 72·5 kV. The two small units in the centre at the bottom are only partially encapsulated and are for 3·6 kV and 12/17·5 kV respectively. The pillar types are for 52 and 72·5 kV maximum service voltage (courtesy Brown Boveri & Co. Ltd.)

error, details of which have been noted in Chapter 11. Similarly, if a three-phase transformer has a residual winding, usually required for protective purposes, there are further limits of error which must be met.

As noted earlier, the general principles of power-transformer design also apply to the voltage transformer, but there are certain considerations of performance which are of particular importance. To comply with the requirements of BS 3941, the voltage and phase errors at unity power factor of the connected burdens (on the secondary side) are limited according to the grade of accuracy

Table 23.6
TYPICAL APPLICATIONS OF VOLTAGE TRANSFORMERS FOR THE
VARIOUS ACCURACY CLASSES (BS 3941, TABLE 13)

Accuracy class	Application
AL	Precision testing or where a standard is required for testing industrial voltage transformers
A	Precision instruments in accordance with BS 89
B	Meters of precision or commercial grade in accordance with BS 37 Industrial switchboard and portable voltmeters and wattmeters in accordance with BS 89 Graphic voltmeters and wattmeters in accordance with BS 90
C	Where accuracy is of less importance than in the above applications (e.g. for the operation of certain indicating and graphic voltmeters and for synchronising)
D	Where ratio is relatively unimportant (e.g. polarity-reversing transformers for synchronising)

Table 23.7
LIMITS OF VOLTAGE AND PHASE ERRORS FOR VOLTAGE TRANSFORMERS
(BS 3941, TABLE 6)

Accuracy class	0·9 to 1·1 times rated primary voltage 0·25 to 1·0 times rated output at unity power factor		0·8 to 1·2 times rated primary voltage and at any output not exceeding rated output and at unity power factor	
	Voltage error ± (%)	Phase error ± (minutes of arc)	Voltage error ± (%)	Phase error ± (minutes of arc)
AL*	—	—	0·25	10
A	0·5	20	—	—
B	1·0	30	—	—
C	2·0	60	—	—
D	5·0	—	—	—

* Not capacitor types

777

specified, and these limitations will largely determine the permissible watt-loss and magnetising currents. The general effect of these requirements is that the normal flux density permissible in the core is lower than the value generally used in power transformers. This leads to an increase in the dimensions of the core and windings. The turns ratio and voltage drop due to the resistance and reactance of these windings must be carefully determined, in order that the permissible errors will not be exceeded.

It will be of interest to consider the phasor diagram of a voltage transformer operating upon a secondary burden with a lagging power factor. Referring to Fig. 23.31, the secondary terminal voltage V_S is produced from the induced secondary e.m.f. E_S after subtracting, vectorially, the resistive and reactive drops

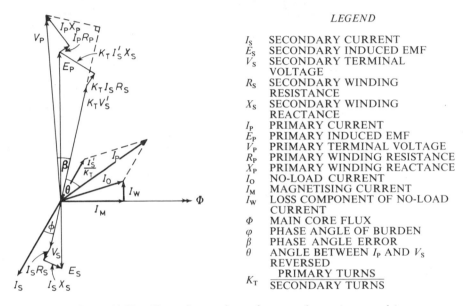

LEGEND

I_S	SECONDARY CURRENT
E_S	SECONDARY INDUCED EMF
V_S	SECONDARY TERMINAL VOLTAGE
R_S	SECONDARY WINDING RESISTANCE
X_S	SECONDARY WINDING REACTANCE
I_P	PRIMARY CURRENT
E_P	PRIMARY INDUCED EMF
V_P	PRIMARY TERMINAL VOLTAGE
R_P	PRIMARY WINDING RESISTANCE
X_P	PRIMARY WINDING REACTANCE
I_O	NO-LOAD CURRENT
I_M	MAGNETISING CURRENT
I_W	LOSS COMPONENT OF NO-LOAD CURRENT
Φ	MAIN CORE FLUX
φ	PHASE ANGLE OF BURDEN
β	PHASE ANGLE ERROR
θ	ANGLE BETWEEN I_P AND V_S REVERSED
K_T	$\dfrac{\text{PRIMARY TURNS}}{\text{SECONDARY TURNS}}$

Figure 23.31. Phasor diagram for a voltage transformer (not to scale)

($I_S R_S$ and $I_S X_S$) occurring in the secondary winding, I_S lagging V_S by the phase angle of the burden ϕ.

The primary induced e.m.f. E_P, which is in opposition to the secondary induced e.m.f. E_S, is derived from the applied voltage V_P after supplying resistive and reactive drops caused by both load and excitation currents. The phase angle of the transformer is the angle β between the reversed secondary voltage $K_T V'_S$ and the primary voltage V_P, and is regarded as having a positive sign when the reversed secondary voltage phasor is in advance of the primary voltage phasor (anticlockwise rotation of phasors).

In order to derive equations for the errors of the voltage transformer, it is necessary to refer all the quantities to one side, usually the primary. The secondary drops can be transferred to the primary by multiplying by the turns ratio (K_T) and adding vectorially to the reversed secondary voltage, and an expression for the errors can be derived by resolving all quantities along the $K_T V_S$ axis.

The voltage error

The voltage error is defined in BS 3941 as:

$$\text{Percentage voltage error} = \frac{K_N(V_S - V_P)}{V_P} \times 100$$

where $K_N = $ Nominal ratio $= \dfrac{\text{Rated primary voltage}}{\text{Rated secondary voltage}}$

Resolving along the $K_T V_S$ axis gives:

$$V_P \cos \beta = K_T V_S + K_T I_S R_S \cos \phi + K_T I_S X_S \sin \phi + I_P R_P \cos \theta + I_P X_P \sin \theta \dots \tag{23.1}$$

Now, in practice β is very small and $\cos \beta \simeq 1$, and hence $K_T V_S$ is very nearly in phase with E_P

$$\therefore \ I_P \cos \theta \simeq I_W + \frac{I_S}{K_T} \cos \phi, \text{ and } I_P \sin \theta \simeq I_M + \frac{I_S}{K_T} \sin \phi.$$

Substituting in expression (23.1):

$$V_P \simeq K_T V_S + K_T I_S R_S \cos \phi + K_T I_S X_S \sin \phi + \frac{I_S}{K_T} R_P \cos \phi + \frac{I_S}{K_T} X_P \sin \phi$$

$$+ I_W R_P + I_M X_P$$

$$= K_T V_S + \frac{I_S}{K_T} \cos \phi \, (R_P + K_T^2 R_S) + \frac{I_S}{K_T} \sin \phi \, (X_P + K_T^2 X_S) + I_W R_P + I_M X_P$$

But $(R_P + K_T^2 R_S)$ is equal to the total resistance referred to the primary winding, i.e. $\overline{R_P}$ and $(X_P + K_T^2 X_S)$ is equal to the total reactance referred to the primary winding, i.e. $\overline{X_P}$.

$$\therefore \ V_P = K_T V_S + \frac{I_S}{K_T} (\overline{R_P} \cos \phi + \overline{X_P} \sin \phi) + I_W R_P + I_M X_P$$

$\therefore$ the actual ratio is

$$\frac{V_P}{V_S} = K_T + \frac{\dfrac{I_S}{K_T} (\overline{R_P} \cos \phi + \overline{X_P} \sin \phi) + I_W R_P + I_M X_P}{V_S}$$

The phase-angle error

An expression giving the phase error of the voltage transformer can also be derived quite readily by studying the phasor diagram:

$$\tan \beta = \frac{\text{Horizontal components of voltages}}{\text{Vertical components of voltages}}$$

$$= \frac{K_T I_S X_S \cos \phi - K_T I_S R_S \sin \phi + I_P X_P \cos \theta - I_P R_P \sin \theta}{K_T V_S + K_T I_S R_S \cos \phi + K_T I_S X_S \sin \phi + I_P R_P \cos \theta + I_P X_P \sin \theta}$$

$$\simeq \frac{K_T I_S X_S \cos \phi - K_T I_S R_S \sin \phi + I_P X_P \cos \theta - I_P R_P \sin \theta}{K_T V_S}$$

779

All other terms in the denominator are small compared with $K_T V_S$ and can be neglected. Also, since β is small, $\tan \beta \simeq \beta$.

Substituting for $I_P \cos \theta$ and $I_P \sin \theta$, as before, gives:

$$\beta = \frac{K_T I_S X_S \cos \phi - K_T I_S R_S \sin \phi + I_W X_P + \dfrac{I_S X_P}{K_T} \cos \phi - I_M R_P - \dfrac{I_S R_P}{K_T} \sin \phi}{K_T V_S}$$

$$= \frac{\dfrac{I_S}{K_T} \cos \phi \,(X_P + K_T^2 X_S) - \dfrac{I_S}{K_T} \sin \phi \,(R_P + K_T^2 R_S) + I_W X_P - I_M R_P}{K_T V_S},$$

and

$$\beta = \frac{\dfrac{I_S}{K_T} (\overline{X_P} \cos \phi - \overline{R_P} \sin \phi) + I_W X_P - I_M R_P}{K_T V_S} \quad \text{rad}$$

By definition, β as calculated here will be negative, since in the phasor diagram, $K_T V_S$ is drawn lagging V_P. For β to be positive:

$$\beta = \frac{\dfrac{I_S}{K_T} (\overline{R_P} \sin \phi - \overline{X_P} \cos \phi) - I_W X_P + I_M R_P}{K_T V_S}$$

By careful design of the windings, the internal resistance and reactance can be kept to an appropriate magnitude, and the magnetising and loss components of the exciting current required by the core itself may be reduced, so that the overall errors are within the specified limits of accuracy.

The voltage and phase errors of a voltage transformer may readily be determined with fair accuracy from a circle diagram, such as that shown in Fig. 23.32.

If the load is maintained constant and only the power factor of the burden is varied between zero and unity, the locus of the resultant voltage will be a circle. The impedance drop remains constant in magnitude but alters in position according to the angle of lag of the current. Thus, in the diagram, the points OA, OA_1, OA_2, etc. lie on the circumference of a circle whose centre is at O and whose radius is equal (in scale) to the impedance drop of the transformer.

To construct the diagram, it is sufficient to calculate and plot the values of voltage error and phase error at no load and at 100% load at unity power factor. These give points O and A on the graph, the horizontal axis representing the percentage voltage error and the vertical axis representing the phase error, expressed either as a percentage or in centiradians to scale.

The line OA_6 may be drawn at right angles to OA to represent the position of the voltage drop at zero power factor. The locus is now drawn between OA and OA_6 and the errors at any other power factor may then be ascertained directly from the graph by choosing a point on the circle representing the power factor required. The errors for intermediate burdens may also be read from the graph by choosing a radius corresponding, in the scale used, to the magnitude of the burden, e.g. OD represents 25% burden, as it is drawn at 0·25 of full radius, OA.

It is common practice to provide fuse protection on both the primary and secondary sides of voltage transformers, but those on the primary side are of doubtful value. This is because they must be rated very high in relation to the normal primary current to ensure that they do not operate due to the magnetising current surge when switching in. They cannot therefore provide adequate protection against inter-turn faults which initially cause only a small increase in primary current, leaving the fault to develop dangerously but slowly. Such insulation failures are clearly undesirable, involving as they do local discharges and heating and giving rise to the production of dangerous gas by breaking down the oil. For this reason some large voltage transformers (33 kV and upwards) are provided with Buchholtz protection which detects the presence of gas, and when a prescribed quantity has been produced, causes an alarm to be given. This form of protection is in common use on power transformers and has been noted in more detail in this respect in Chapter 11.

Such protection on smaller voltage transformers is rarely if ever possible simply on account of space, and Gray and Wright[2] have suggested that when noninflammable insulating media is used, they could be omitted, placing the reliance on the main circuit protection to clear any serious fault in the transformer. They

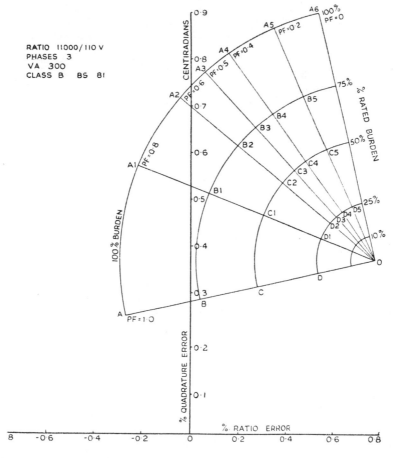

Figure 23.32. Locus diagram for a voltage transformer showing the effect of burden and power factor on voltage (ratio) and phase error

781

Figure 23.33. English Electric low-oil-volume 22/33 kV 3-phase voltage transformer (courtesy G.E.C. Switchgear Ltd.)

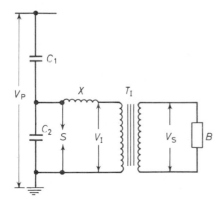

Figure 23.34. Circuit diagram for a capacitor voltage transformer

make the alternative suggestion that it may be possible to detect inter-turn faults more quickly by embedding temperature-responsive devices in the insulation. This would appear to be a good use for thermistors, which are solid state devices of exceedingly small dimensions and which are often used in electric motors to detect overheating due to overloads. Thus, in this application it is possible to dispense with the orthodox overload protection. When fuses are used however, they will be of the h.r.c. type having a low ohmic resistance so that they have no effect, or very little, on the phase and voltage errors.

Voltage transformers for outdoor use can be of the electromagnetic-type and oil filled. For system voltages of 22 kV and 33 kV, three-phase units of the type illustrated in Fig. 23.33 are available with the core and windings in the low-oil-volume tank at the base. The bushing is oil filled and this oil can freely mingle with that in the tank. The primary leads pass through the hollow bushing in an insulating tube, but as an alternative, the h.r.c. fuses can be fitted in the bushing. An expansion chamber surmounts each bushing and restricted breathing to the atmosphere is allowed via a breather under the dome of this chamber. For 66 kV and 88 kV, basically similar transformers are used but they are in single-phase construction for connection between line and earth, three such units being used to form a three-phase transformer.

With the higher voltages of 110 kV and upwards, the electromagnetic design is a costly item, and an economical alternative is found in the capacitor voltage transformer. This comprises a capacitor divider unit in which capacitors are connected in series between line and earth as shown diagrammatically in Fig. 23.34.

A tapping is made at a convenient voltage (known as the *intermediate* voltage) which is usually about 12 kV. The secondary burden is connected to this tapping via a reactor and intermediate transformer, the latter being of the electromagnetic type. In practice, the reactor and the intermediate transformer may be combined in one unit.

The inductive reactance of the combination is such as to balance the capacitive reactance of the coupler at rated frequency, i.e. there is a resonating circuit. Facilities can be provided through tappings on the intermediate transformer so that adjustment of the reactance of this unit is possible. A relief gap connected across the tapping point on the capacitor divider and earth may be provided to prevent the voltage rising to a dangerous level in the event of a short-circuit in the burden circuit, but in some designs a relief gap is unnecessary.

Transformers of this type can readily comply with the limits of accuracy listed earlier, but it should be noted that class AL is excluded although designs exist in which this accuracy is obtained with an output limited to about 50 VA. The output, however, for a given accuracy is dependent on the range of frequencies over which the transformer is to operate, as frequency variations cause detuning of the resonating circuit. BS 3941 requires that the given class of accuracy shall be maintained within the range 101–99% of rated frequency for classes A, B and C and within 103–97% for class D and the additional limits applicable to transformers used for protective purposes.

Figure 23.35 shows a typical voltage transformer of this type, the primary and intermediate voltage capacitors being housed in the ceramic insulators and sealed to prevent air and moisture coming into contact with the insulating oil. The intermediate voltage transformer is housed in the base compartment and is oil filled.

783

Figure 23.35.   400 kV capacitor-type voltage transformer (courtesy A. Reyrolle & Co. Ltd.)

Figure 23.36.   English Electric 400 kV capacitor voltage transformers with line traps and through-wall type current transformers installed at the West Burton 400 kV indoor substation of the C.E.G.B. (courtesy G.E.C. Switchgear Ltd.)

In Chapter 11, a brief description has been included of a carrier-current system of protection, and in Fig. 11.82 a schematic diagram has shown the line-coupling equipment essential to this protective system. In that diagram also it has been shown how the line-coupling equipment can form a part of the capacitor voltage transformer such as the one we are discussing. An illustration showing such a combination is shown in Fig. 23.36, the suspended details being the two line traps associated with the carrier protection. In this installation, the through bushings in the wall of the switch room are in fact current transformers.

INSTRUMENT CIRCUIT DIAGRAMS

The circuit connections for power-factor meters and indicating wattmeters are dependent on various load conditions, i.e. balanced or unbalanced and on the system. The latter may be single or three phase, and if three phase may be three or four wire. A selection of typical connection diagrams is given in Figs. 23.37

785

to 23.46, and when studying these it should be noted that for three-phase systems the phases are assumed to come up in the order A, B, C. Alternative voltage connections are shown, i.e. direct (X), via voltage transformers (Y) or via resistances (Z). In some circumstances a combination of Y and Z may be used as marked W in Figs. 23.44, 23.45 and 23.46. The primary and secondary terminal markings at current transformers have been modified by BS 3938 and should read P_1P_2 (primary) and S_1S_2 (secondary).

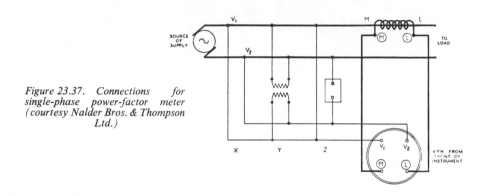

Figure 23.37. Connections   for single-phase   power-factor   meter (courtesy Nalder Bros. & Thompson Ltd.)

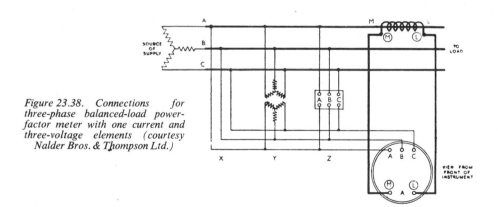

Figure 23.38. Connections   for three-phase balanced-load power-factor meter with one current and three-voltage elements (courtesy Nalder Bros. & Thompson Ltd.)

786

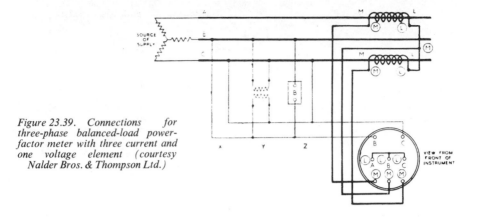

Figure 23.39. Connections for three-phase balanced-load power-factor meter with three current and one voltage element (courtesy Nalder Bros. & Thompson Ltd.)

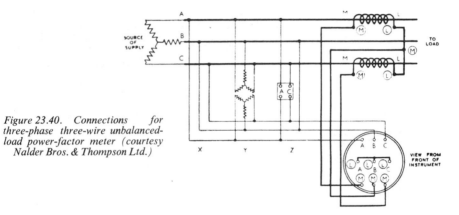

Figure 23.40. Connections for three-phase three-wire unbalanced-load power-factor meter (courtesy Nalder Bros. & Thompson Ltd.)

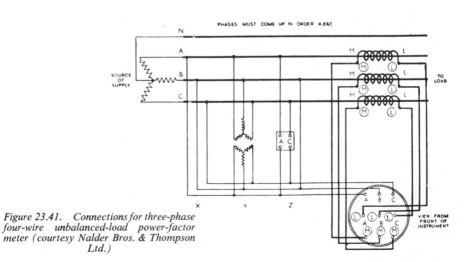

Figure 23.41. Connections for three-phase four-wire unbalanced-load power-factor meter (courtesy Nalder Bros. & Thompson Ltd.)

787

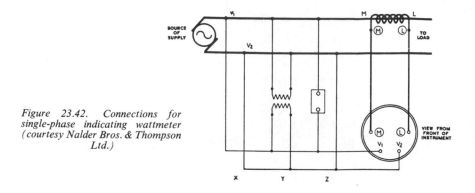

Figure 23.42. Connections for single-phase indicating wattmeter (courtesy Nalder Bros. & Thompson Ltd.)

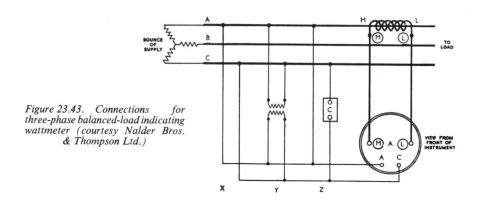

Figure 23.43. Connections for three-phase balanced-load indicating wattmeter (courtesy Nalder Bros. & Thompson Ltd.)

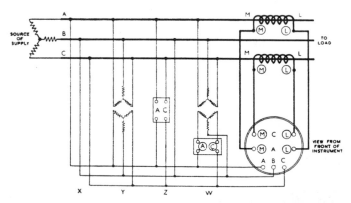

Figure 23.44. Connections for three-phase three-wire unbalanced-load indicating wattmeter (courtesy Nalder Bros. & Thompson Ltd.)

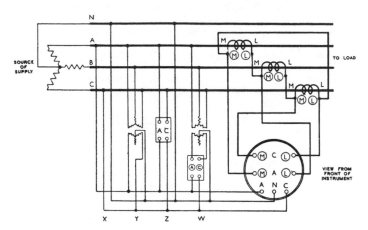

Figure 23.45. Connections for three-phase four-wire unbalanced-load indicating wattmeter of the two-element type (courtesy Nalder Bros. & Thompson Ltd.)

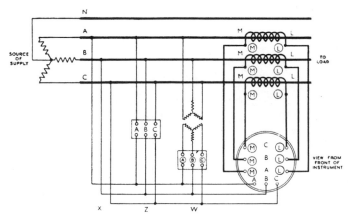

Figure 23.46. Connections for three-phase four-wire unbalanced-load indicating wattmeter of the three-element type (courtesy Nalder Bros. & Thompson Ltd.)

REFERENCES

1. SEELEY, S., 'Current Transformers on Open Circuit', *Elect. Rev.*, 18 April (1969)
2. GRAY, W. and WRIGHT, A., 'Voltage Transformers and Current Transformers Associated with Switchgear', *J.I.E.E.*, **100** Pt. 2, No. 75, June (1953)
3. TANNER, A., 'The Brown Boveri Range of Moulded Resin Instrument Transformers', *Brown Boveri Rev.*, **52** No. 8, Aug. (1965)
4. BLOWER, R.W., 'Butyl Rubber Insulated Current Transformers', *A.E.I. Engng.*, Nov./Dec. (1965). Available as a reprint No. 1486–71
5. HERMSTEIN, W. and KETTLER, H., 'Extra-high-voltage a.c. Transmission', Siemens AG, special issue

BIBLIOGRAPHY

ANON., 'Gases for e.h.v. Insulation', *Elect. Rev.*, 28 Jan. (1966)
CRANE, P.H.G., *Switchgear Principles*, Macmillan (1957)
Current Transformers, BS 3938 (1965)
Electrical Indicating Instruments, BS 89 (1970)
FLACK, T. and TODD, M., 'The Development of a Gas-insulated High-voltage Current Transformer', *Reyrolle Rev.*, **180**, July (1962). Available as reprint No. RR 105
GEE, R., 'Gas Insulation for h.v. Current Transformers', *Elect. Times*, 20 Aug. (1964)
HARTMANN, H., 'Landmarks in the Further Development of Moulded Resin Transformers', *Brown Boveri Rev.*, **55** No. 4/5, April/May (1968)
HARTMANN, H. and HUSY, C., 'The Use of Epoxy Resins in High-voltage Instrument Transformers', *Brown Boveri Rev.*, **52** No. 8, Aug. (1965)
HOBSON, A., 'Instrument Transformers', *J.I.E.E.*, **91** No. 20, Part 2, April (1944)
KNAPP, F., 'Epoxy Casting Resins', *Brown Boveri Rev.*, **52** No. 8, Aug. (1965)
KORPONAY, N., 'The Transient Behaviour and Uses of Current Transformers', *Brown Boveri Rev.*, **56** No. 11/12, Nov./Dec. (1969)
MUSY, C. and MICHELAKAKIS, P., 'Design Features and Discharge Capacity of Outdoor Oil-filled Transformers for 52–750 kV', *Brown Boveri Rev.*, **56** No. 11/12, Nov./Dec. (1969)
ROTHWELL, K., 'Cast Resin for High-voltage Switchgear', *Elect. Rev.*, 16 July (1965)
SEELY, S., 'Effect of Stray Flux on Current Transformers', *J. Sci & Tech.*, **37** No. 3, (1970)
Voltage Transformers, BS 3941 (1965)
WADDINGTON, F.B. and HEIGHES, J., 'Sulphur Hexafluoride Insulation for Current Transformers', *A.E.I. Engineering*, No. 4 (1967)

Appendix

Vacuum interrupters

Although the possibilities of current interruption in vacuum have been recognised for many years (investigations in the U.S.A. are recorded in the early 1920s), it is only within the last decade that renewed and intensive research has led to practical high-power interrupters becoming available if only, as yet, in a limited way.

Of the many problems with which this research has been concerned are those relating to (a) current chopping tendencies and the resulting high overvoltages (refer to the discussion in Chapter 2), (b) gross melting of contacts and the liability to weld when making or carrying high currents, (c) contamination of the vacuum due to gas produced by the action of the arc on contact metals with high gas content and (d) to ensure non-deterioration of the insulation due to condensing metal vapour on the inner surfaces of the insulating container.

The solutions to these problems have required many years of work on such matters as (a) the geometry of the contacts to ensure that the arc root rotates over a large area and thus prevents gross melting, (b) the processing techniques including de-gassing of contact materials and the surface cleanliness of components within the envelope, and (c) most fundamentally, on contact metallurgy to produce new contact materials of low gas content, good anti-weld properties and low current-chopping probabilities. Other work has been devoted to the selection of envelope materials capable of withstanding high processing temperatures and to the protection of the inner insulation by shielding.

The first applications of vacuum devices on a large scale were to load, line and capacitor switching duties. In the U.S.A., multibreak arrangements for use on systems up to 345 kV have been in operation for several years, the switches being capable of interrupting currents up to 2 000 A.

Practical vacuum interrupters for other duties have resulted and are now manufactured in several countries. In the U.K. they include an initial application in 1965 as a contactor* for motor switching duties at 3·3 kV, followed in 1967 by a 132 kV circuit-breaker† with a breaking capacity of 3 500 MVA (15·3 kA r.m.s. symmetrical) for transmission line duty and then in 1969 by an 11 kV 250 MVA (13·1 kA r.m.s. symmetrical) circuit-breaker‡ for distribution, recloser and industrial process control.

This latter unit is shown in Fig. A.1, from which it is seen that three single-phase vacuum interrupters (in a trefoil arrangement) are mounted on the carriage of a standard vertical-isolation metal-clad unit which is interchangeable with the corresponding part of an existing bulk-oil circuit-breaker equipment, i.e. that noted in Chapter 20, Fig. 20.19. The interrupters are air-insulated in a moulded-epoxy-resin tank (seen removed in Fig. A.1) with epoxy-resin phase barriers. A standard oil circuit-breaker operating mechanism has been

* A.E.I. (now G.E.C.-Elliott Industrial Controls Ltd.).
† A.E.I. (now part of G.E.C. Switchgear Ltd.).
‡ A. Reyrolle & Co. Ltd.

791

adapted to meet the requirements of the vacuum interrupters, notably the extremely short travel of the moving contacts and the necessity for a static loading to be applied to each moving contact in the closed position in order to minimise contact welding.

Design variations is vacuum interrupters between manufacturers are largely due to individual solutions to the problems noted earlier, but all are essentially similar in concept and are typically as shown in Fig. A.2. A cylindrical insulating body, normally of glass or ceramic, is fitted with ends of a low expansion alloy by brazed seals. A pair of butt contacts

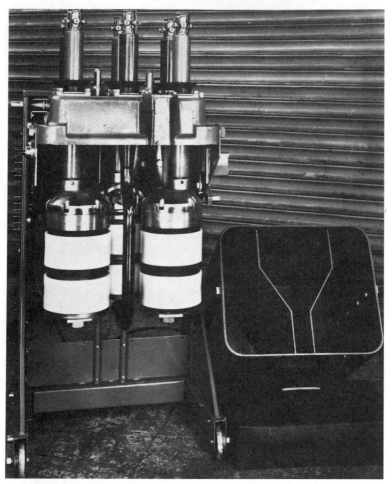

Figure A.1. Rear view of the carriage of a vertical-isolation metal-clad unit with three 11 kV 250 MVA vacuum interrupters mounted in trefoil and with the epoxy-resin tank removed (courtesy A. Reyrolle & Co. Ltd.)

are carried on stems, one of which is movable via a metal bellows. A metal shield surrounds the arcing region to prevent vaporised contact material being deposited on the insulating body, a further shield giving protection to the thin bellows.

The technique of a.c. interruption in vacuum consists of separating a pair of current carrying contacts in a high vacuum environment of 10^{-5} torr (1.333×10^{-3} N/m^2) or better*. Like all a.c. interrupting devices, the objective during the interrupting process is to remove continuously the arc plasma so that at the normal current zero the arc path has

* 1 torr is the pressure required to support a column of mercury 1 mm high.

a minimum memory of the arcing which has preceded the zero. The arc will then be extinguished if the input power from the circuit is less than that dissipated in the de-ionisation process, and it will remain extinguished if the dielectric strength between the contacts recovers sufficiently rapidly to withstand the restriking and recovery voltages.

Unlike other a.c. interrupters, the current carriers in the arc are mainly metal ions from the contacts, since a negligible amount of gas is present in the arc plasma. The memory of the arc is shortened by condensation of these metal ions and vapours on to the contacts and shields, and the effectiveness of this determines the efficiency of the interrupting process at current zero.

The unique properties of the vacuum interrupter offer many advantages. These include (*a*) long life with minimum maintenance, (*b*) the completely enclosed and sealed construction, (*c*) maximum arc-durations being of the order of 1–1·5 loops at *all* current levels whereas up to 4 loops may result when interrupting currents below 1 kA in a similarly-rated bulk-oil circuit-breaker), (*d*) extremely short and consistent arcing and total break times, (*e*) its suitability for very-fast automatic reclosure, (*f*) no fire risk and (*g*) no noise and no emission of gas or air during operation. At the end of its life, a 'bottle' can be quickly

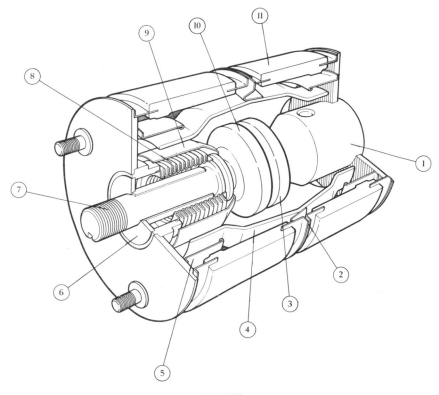

LEGEND

1. FIXED-CONTACT STEM
2. SPUTTER-SHIELD MOUNTING
3. FIXED CONTACT
4. SPUTTER SHIELD
5. GRADING SHIELD
6. MOVING-CONTACT GUIDE

7. MOVING-CONTACT STEM
8. BELLOWS
9. SPUTTER SHIELD FOR BELLOWS
10. MOVING CONTACT
11. GLASS-CERAMIC BODY

Figure A.2. Constructional features of the 11 kV vacuum interrupters shown in Figure A.1 (courtesy A. Reyrolle & Co. Ltd.)

removed, discarded and replaced by another, spare 'bottles' having an extremely long shelf life.

For voltages above 33 kV, a number of interrupters per pole can be connected in series as in air-blast or small-oil-volume types, the same precautions being necessary to ensure correct voltage distribution between the series breaks. An example of interrupters in series is the 132 kV vacuum breaker, mentioned earlier and noted in Fig. 21.71.

The present relatively high cost of vacuum interrupters is an obstacle to their widespread use, but new designs of switchgear specifically tailored to match the unique features of the bottles may increase the demand. Wider usage of vacuum interrupters enabling mass production techniques to be employed in their manufacture will undoubtedly reduce costs, and within the next decade vacuum circuit-breakers could become a viable alternative to the existing oil or air-break designs over a wide range, particularly in the voltage range of 3·3 kV to 11 or 33 kV.

BIBLIOGRAPHY

ANON., 'Competitive Vacuum-power Interrupters', *Elect. Rev.*, 12 April (1968)
ANON., 'Vacuum Interruption, Key to Future High-power Switchgear', *Elect. Rev.*, 15 Jan. (1971)
ANON., 'World's First e.h.v. Vacuum Circuit-breaker', *Elect. Rev.*, 2 June (1967)
ANON., 'MANWEB to Field-test Vacuum Interrupters', *Elect. Rev.*, 29 Aug. (1969)
GARRARD, C.J.O., 'High-voltage Distribution Switchgear—Review of Progress', *Proc. I.E.E.*, **116** No. 6, June (1969)
GARRARD, C.J.O., 'Trends in Switchgear Design', *Elect. Rev.*, 26 Sept. (1969)
HORE, C.M., 'Vacuum Contactor Starters for High-voltage Motors', *Elect. Rev.*, 3 April (1970)
REECE, M.P. and ELLIS, N.S., 'Good Prospects for Vacuum Interrupters in Circuit-breakers', *Elect. Rev. Sup.*, 18 June (1971)
RIEDER, W., 'Vacuum and SF$_6$ Circuit-breakers', *Elect. Rev.*, 10 June (1966)

Additional Bibliography

Chapter 2   Circuit Breaking
RAGALLER, K., 'Plasma Physics Applied in Circuit-Breaker Design', *Brown Boveri Rev.* 59 No. 4, Apr. (1972)
URBANCK, J., 'Stresses in High-voltage Circuit-breakers when Interrupting Currents', *Brown Boveri Rev.* 61 No. 4, Apr. (1974)
HERMANN, W. *et. al.*, 'Interaction Between an Electric Arc and the Flow of Gaseous Quenching Medium', *Brown Boveri Rev.* 61 No. 4, Apr. (1974)
CANAY, M. and KLEIN, H., 'Asymmetric Short-circuit Currents from Generators and the Effect of the Breaking Arc', *Brown Boveri Rev.* 61 No. 5, May (1974)
ANON., 'Examining Arc Behaviour', *Elect. Rev.*, 20 Sept. (1974)

Chapter 5   Short-circuit Testing
BRAUN, A. and HUBER, H., 'Testing Circuit-breakers by Synthetic Methods', *Brown Boveri Rev.* 60 No. 4, Apr. (1973)
ADDISON, J. and STEBBING, G. C., 'ASTA – The widening horizon', *Elect. Rev.*, 6 June (1975)
STOKES, A. D. and ROVELLI, S., 'Balanced Synthetic Circuits: New Circuit for High-power Testing with Low-frequency Transient Recovery Voltage', *Proc. I.E.E.*, 121 No. 3, March (1974)

Chapter 6   Surge Protection and Impulse Levels
BURGER, U., 'The Brown Boveri Range of Lighting Arresters – Design and Application', *Brown Boveri Rev.* 59 No. 4, Apr. (1972)
BURGER, U. and GREUTER, R., 'High-performance Lightning Arresters Types HM and HMM', *Brown Boveri Rev.* 60 No. 4, Apr. (1973)
BURGER, U. 'The HMM Lightning Arrester, an Efficient Addition to the HM Arrester Family', *Brown Boveri Rev.* 63 No. 4, Apr. (1976)
BALASUBRAMANIAN, R. and GUPTA, S., 'Calculation of Transient Due to Fault Initiation on a Double-circuit Transmission Line', *Proc. I.E.E.*, 123 No. 6, June (1976)

Chapter 10   H.R.C. Fuses
JACKS, E., *High Rupturing Capacity Fuses*, E. & F. N. Spon Ltd. (1975)
FEENAN, J., 'British Practice Influences Fusegear Standards', *Elect. Rev.*, 11 May (1973)
ANON., 'Better Protection by Combining Fuses', *Elect. Rev.*, 29 March (1974)
WILKINS, R. and MCEWAN, P. M., 'A.C. Short-circuit Performance of Uniform Section Fuse Elements', *Proc. I.E.E.*, 122 No. 3, March (1975)
WILKINS, R. and MCEWAN, P. M., 'A.C. Short-circuit Performance of Notched Fuse-elements', *Proc. I.E.E.*, 122 No. 3, March (1975)
TONIOL, S. B. and CANTARELLA, G., 'Simulation of Fuse Performance for Co-ordination and Testing Purposes', *Proc. I.E.E.*, 122 No. 5, May (1975)
WILKINS, R., 'Generalised Short-circuit Characteristics for H.R.C. Fuses', *Proc. I.E.E.*, 122 No. 11, November (1975)
NEWBERY, P. G., 'Fuse Technology – Progress to Date', *Electronics and Power*, February (1976)
WRIGHT, A. and BEAUMONT, K. J., 'Analysis of High-breaking-capacity Fuse-link Arcing Phenomena', *Proc. I.E.E.* 123 No. 3, March (1976)

795

ADDITIONAL BIBLIOGRAPHY

Chapter 11   Protective Gear

MILNE, A. G., 'Distribution of Electricity', *Proc. I.E.E.* 121 No. 1, January (1974)

JACKSON, L., 'Distance-protection Comparator with Signal-dependent Phase-angle Criterion', *Proc. I.E.E.*, 121 No. 8, August (1974)

HUGHES, M. A., 'Distance Relay Performance as Affected by Capacitor Voltage-transformers', *Proc. I.E.E.*, 121 No. 12, Dec. (1974)

COOK, V., 'Generalised Method of Assessing Polarising Signals for the Polarised-mho Relay', *Proc. I.E.E.*, 122 No. 5, May (1975)

FIELDING, G., 'Improved System Protection with Static Relays', *Elect. Rev.*, 22 August (1975)

GANTNER, J. *et al.*, 'Protection for Large Generators', *Brown Boveri Rev.* 62 No. 9, Sept. (1975)

ROBERTSON, M. A., 'Solid State Systems for Generator Protection', *Elect. Rev.*, 10 Oct. (1975)

Chapter 13   Small-oil-volume Circuit-breakers

LATAL, W. and BOISSIN, C., 'Minimum-oil Circuit-breakers in Power Transmission and Distribution', *Brown Boveri Rev.* 59 No. 4, April (1972)

LATAL, W., 'Minimum-oil Circuit-breakers Type T for General Applications up to 170 kV', *Brown Boveri Rev.* 60 No. 4, April (1973)

LARSSON, P. and WEHRLI, R., 'Switching Capacitive Currents with Minimum-oil Circuit-breakers', *Brown Boveri Rev.* 61 No. 4, April (1974)

LATAL, W. and PEDRINI, G., 'Type F and T Minimum-oil Circuit-breakers', *Brown Boveri Rev.* 62 No. 4, April (1975)

MAYER, A. and ZIMMERMANN, W., 'Minimum-oil Circuit-breakers for Medium-high Voltage Installations', *Brown Boveri Rev.* 62 No. 4, April (1975)

GANZ, A., 'Interruption Tests on Minimum-oil Circuit-breakers for $16^2/3$ Hz Railway Supply Systems', *Brown Boveri Rev.* 63 No. 4, April (1976)

Chapter 14   Air-break Circuit-breakers

ANON., 'Experience with New Distribution Techniques Improves System Design Flexibility', *Elect. Rev.*, 11 May (1973)

Chapter 15   Airblast Circuit-breakers

BOEHLE, B. *et al.*, 'Trends in the Application and Further Development of Type DLF Outdoor Airblast Circuit-breakers', *Brown Boveri Rev.* 39 No. 4, April (1972)

SLAMECZKA, O., 'Type DR36 Generator Breakers throughout the World', *Brown Boveri Rev.* 60 No. 4, April (1973)

SCHUBERT, H. and CUK, N., 'The DLF Range of Highly Adaptable Airblast Circuit-breakers for Voltages up to 1100 kV and Low, Medium and Very High Powers', *Brown Boveri Rev.* 60 No. 4, April (1973)

ERDINGER, A. and SANDERS, M., 'Increasing the Breaking Capacity of Type DLF Airblast Circuit-breakers by Maintaining Constant Pressure during Extinction', *Brown Boveri Rev.* 60 No. 4, April (1973)

ANON., 'Compressed Air Increases Breaker Capacity', *Elect. Rev.*, 25 May (1973)

BURCKHARDT, P., 'Generator Breakers for Large Power Stations', *Brown Boveri Rev.* 60 No. 10/11, Oct./Nov. (1973)

CUK, N. *et. al.*, 'DLF Airblast Circuit-breakers, Continued Development Yields Results', *Brown Boveri Rev.* 61 No. 4, April (1974)

KÖPPL, G. *et. al.*, 'DLF Airblast Circuit-breakers Proving and Progress', *Brown Boveri Rev.* 62 No. 4, April (1975)

BURCKHARDT, P. *et. al.*, 'DR Generator Breakers for Extremely High Service and Short-circuit Currents', *Brown Boveri Rev.* 62 No. 4, April (1975)

MCANANY, G. and LUPTON, W. T., 'Development of a New Range of E.H.V. Heavy-duty Airblast Circuit-breakers', *Proc. I.E.E.* 122 No. 5, May (1975)

BROSS, E., 'DLF Airblast Circuit-breakers for Rated Voltages of 72·5 kV to 765 kV', *Brown Boveri Rev.* 63 No. 4, April (1976)

Chapter 16   SF6 Circuit-breakers and Metal-clad Switchgear

MEIER, A. *et. al.*, 'High-voltage SF6 Insulated Switchgear: Gas Monitoring, Maintenance and Servicing', *Brown Boveri Rev.* 59 No. 4, April (1972)

SPENDAL, E. and MENON, K. V., 'Germany's First 245 kV Metalclad SF6 Switchgear Installation', *Brown Boveri Rev.* 60 No. 2/3, Feb./March (1973)

MAUTHE, G. *et. al.*, 'SF6 Switchgear Type ELK for 145 to 525 kV', *Brown Boveri Rev.* 60 No. 4, April (1973)

ADDITIONAL BIBLIOGRAPHY

ANON., 'Development Trends in High Fault-level Circuit-breakers Point to SF6 Liquid', *Elect. Rev.*, 9 Nov. (1973)

KRENICKY, A. *et. al.*, 'Arcing Faults in SF6 Insulated Metalclad H.V. Switchgear', *Brown Boveri Rev.* 61 No. 4, April (1974)

MAUTHE, G. *et. al.*, 'Type ELK Circuit-breakers for Metal-enclosed SF6 Insulated Switchgear Installations', *Brown Boveri Rev.* 61 No. 4, April (1974)

ANON., 'Rapid Increase in SF6 Metalclad Switchgear Applications', *Elect. Rev.*, 13 Sept. (1974)

ANON., 'Metalclad SF6 Substations Challenge Air Insulated Designs', *Elect. Rev.*, 7 Feb. (1975)

SZENTE-VARGA, H. P., 'High-voltage SF6 Switchgear Installations – Applications and Performance', *Brown Boveri Rev.* 62 No. 4, April (1975)

RAPPANGE, A., 'SF6 High-voltage Circuit-breaker Type ELF for Installations Outdoors', *Brown Boveri Rev.* 63 No. 4, April (1976)

HERRMANN, G. and STOLARZ, W., 'Extension of a 245 kV SF6 Switchgear Installation Without Interruption of Service', *Brown Boveri Rev.* 63 No. 4, April (1976)

Author's Note: *The Electrical Review* of 7 February 1975 includes a survey of SF6 metal-clad switchgear by 13 manufacturers throughout the world.

Chapter 20   High-voltage Indoor Switchgear

VAN DER WAL, A. and MUNZINGER, K., '11/16 kV Switchgear in the Engehalde Substation of the City of Berne Electricity Authority', *Brown Boveri Rev.* 59 No. 4, April (1972)

KÖNIGER, L., '72·5 kV Indoor Switchgear Installations with Truck-mounted Circuit-breakers', *Brown Boveri Rev.* 59 No. 4, April (1972)

CATON, P. S., 'H.V. Distribution Circuit-breakers Designed for Infrequent Operation', *Elect. Rev.*, 13 July (1973)

DORN, H. *et. al.*, 'Compact Indoor Switchgear for 72·5 kV', *Brown Boveri Rev.* 62 No. 4, April (1975)

POOLE, D. and MUNZINGER, K., 'Medium-voltage Switchgear Installations Using Airblast and Magneblast Circuit-breakers', *Brown Boveri Rev.* 62 No. 4, April (1975)

Chapter 21   High-voltage Outdoor Switchgear

STEPINSKI, B. and DRGANC, I., '330 kV Outdoor Switchgear Installations in Central Africa', *Brown Boveri Rev.* 59 No. 4, April (1972)

GILES, R. L., 'Reducing the Cost of E.H.V. Substations While Increasing their Reliability', *Elect. Rev.*, 22 June (1973)

Chapter 23   Instrument and Measuring Transformers

VAN DER WAL, A. and KORPONAY, N., 'Designing Current Transformers for Generators', *Brown Boveri Rev.* 62 No. 6, June (1975)

TOMIC, B., 'New Moulded Resin Instrument Transformers', *Brown Boveri Rev.* 63 No. 4, April (1976)

Appendix   Vacuum Interrupters

ANON., 'Vacuum Circuit-breakers for 25 kV Trackside Supply', *Elect. Rev.*, 13 April (1973)

GRIERSON, R. A., 'Vacuum Circuit-breaker Design', *Elect. Rev.*, 11 May (1973)

ANON., 'Preparing for Expansion in Vacuum Switchgear', *Elect. Rev.*, 1 June (1973)

ANON., 'British Rail Electrification Uses Vacuum Circuit-breakers', *Elect. Equip.*, June (1973)

TILBROOK, G. H., 'Major Benefits from Using Vacuum Circuit-breakers in Distribution Networks', *Elect. Rev.*, 15 June (1973)

ANON., 'GEC Offers Two-tier 11 kV Vacuum Switchboards', *Elect. Rev.*, 16 Nov. (1973)

ARMSTRONG, T. V. and HEADLEY, P., 'Vacuum Techniques in Modern Circuit-breakers', *Electronics and Power*, 21 March (1974)

ANON., 'Are Vacuum Breakers Justified?', *Elect. Rev.*, 11 April (1975)

ANON., 'British Companies Demonstrate Vacuum Techniques for Control and Switchgear', *Elect. Rev.*, 11 April (1975)

ROWLAND, F. G., 'The Ins and Outs of Vacuum Circuit-breakers', *Electronics and Power*, 1 May (1975)

AUTON, G., 'Progress in Design and Application of Vacuum Switchgear', *Elect. Rev.*, 9 May (1975)

FORRESTER, J. T., 'The Benefits of Vacuum Switchgear', *Elect Rev.*, 14 Nov. (1975)

HUGHES, J. L., 'The Rural Application of Vacuum Breakers', *Elect. Rev.*, 14 Nov. (1975)

FLURSCHEIM, C. H., 'Switchgear Designs for Future Power Systems', *Elect. Rev.*, 14 May (1976)

ADDITIONAL BIBLIOGRAPHY

General

The following publications are recommended for further reading, each dealing in depth with many aspects of the subject denoted in its title.

Power Circuit-breaker Design and Theory. Ed C. H. Flurscheim. I.E.E. Monograph Series 17. Peter Peregrinus Ltd. (1975)

Metalclad Switchgear. I.E.E. Conference Publication No. 82. Institution of Electrical Engineers (1972)

Developments in Power System Protection. I.E.E. Conference Publication No. 125. Institution of Electrical Engineers (1975)

Layout of E.H.V. Substations. R. L. Giles. I.E.E. Monograph Series 5. Peter Peregrinus Ltd. (1970)

Switchgear. G. J. O. Garrard. A bound reprint of 17 articles which appeared in the journal *Electrical Equipment* between April 1972 and August 1973.

Protection Relays Application Guide. Various authors. GEC Measurements Ltd. (1975). This new edition supersedes that noted under reference 3 on page 373.

Electrical Indicating Instruments. G. F. Tagg. Butterworths (1974)

Index

Index